Fourth Grade

Everyday Mathematics®

Teacher's Lesson Guide
Volume 2

The University of Chicago
School Mathematics Project

The McGraw-Hill Companies

UCSMP Elementary Materials Component

Max Bell, Director

Authors

Max Bell
John Bretzlauf
Amy Dillard
Robert Hartfield
Andy Isaacs
James McBride, Director
Kathleen Pitvorec
Peter Saecker
Robert Balfanz*
William Carroll*
Sheila Sconiers*

Technical Art

Diana Barrie

*First Edition only

Photo Credits

Phil Martin/Photography; Mark Gibson/Visuals Unlimited, p. 10; Dan Casper/ Chicago Tribune, p. 74; Wally McNamee/CORBIS, p. 231; Paolo Negri/Stone, p. 653; Cover: Bill Burlingham/Photography; Photo Collage: Herman Adler Design Group

Permissions

The Wall Street Journal, June 29, 2000, p. 74

Contributors

Martha Ayala, Virginia J. Bates, Randee Blair, Donna R. Clay, Vanessa Day, Jean Faszholz, James Flanders, Patti Haney, Margaret Phillips Holm, Nancy Kay Hubert, Sybil Johnson, Judith Kiehm, Carla L. LaRochelle, Deborah Arron Leslie, Laura Ann Luczak, Mary O'Boyle, William D. Pattison, Beverly Pilchman, Denise Porter, Judith Ann Robb, Mary Seymour, Laura A. Sunseri

This material is based upon work supported by the National Science Foundation under Grant No. ESI-9252984. Any opinions, findings, and conclusions or recommendations expressed in this material are those of the authors and do not necessarily reflect the views of the National Science Foundation.

Printed in the United States of America.

Send all inquiries to:
Wright Group/McGraw-Hill
P.O. Box 812960
Chicago, IL 60681

ISBN 0-07-600015-X

7 8 9 10 11 QPD 09 08 07 06 05

The McGraw·Hill Companies

Contents

Volume 1

Welcome xxiv

Unit 1 Naming and Constructing Geometric Figures 2

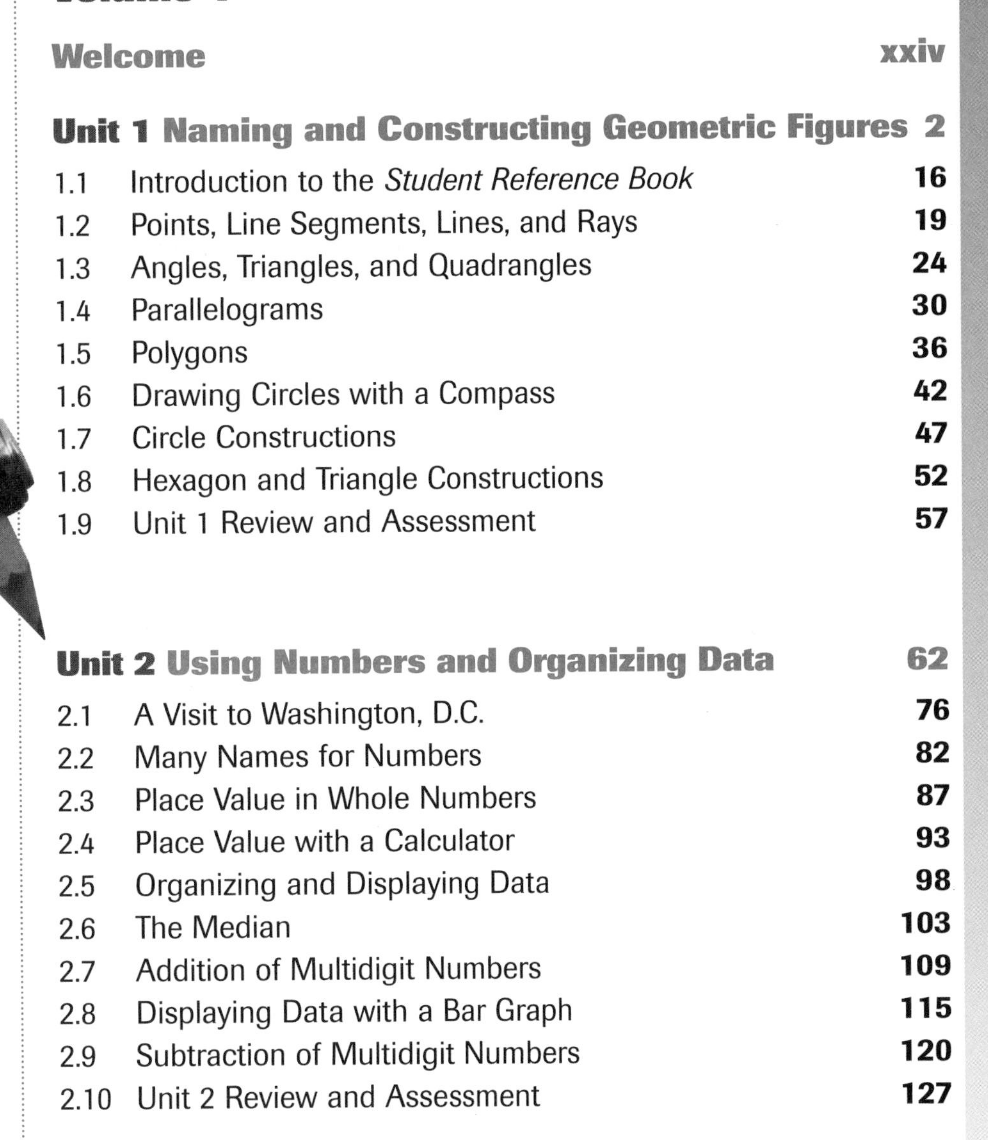

1.1	Introduction to the *Student Reference Book*	16
1.2	Points, Line Segments, Lines, and Rays	19
1.3	Angles, Triangles, and Quadrangles	24
1.4	Parallelograms	30
1.5	Polygons	36
1.6	Drawing Circles with a Compass	42
1.7	Circle Constructions	47
1.8	Hexagon and Triangle Constructions	52
1.9	Unit 1 Review and Assessment	57

Unit 2 Using Numbers and Organizing Data 62

2.1	A Visit to Washington, D.C.	76
2.2	Many Names for Numbers	82
2.3	Place Value in Whole Numbers	87
2.4	Place Value with a Calculator	93
2.5	Organizing and Displaying Data	98
2.6	The Median	103
2.7	Addition of Multidigit Numbers	109
2.8	Displaying Data with a Bar Graph	115
2.9	Subtraction of Multidigit Numbers	120
2.10	Unit 2 Review and Assessment	127

Unit 3 Multiplication and Division; Number Sentences and Algebra **132**

3.1	Multiplication Facts	146
3.2	Multiplication Facts Practice	152
3.3	More Multiplication Facts Practice	157
3.4	Multiplication, Division, and Fractions	162
3.5	World Tour: Flying to Africa	166
3.6	Finding Air Distances	171
3.7	A Guide for Solving Number Stories	175
3.8	True or False Number Sentences	179
3.9	Parentheses in Number Sentences	184
3.10	Open Sentences	189
3.11	Logic Problems	194
3.12	Unit 3 Review and Assessment	198

Unit 4 Decimals and Their Uses **202**

4.1	Decimals: Review of Basic Concepts	214
4.2	Comparing and Ordering Decimals	219
4.3	Estimating with Decimals	223
4.4	Decimal Addition and Subtraction	227
4.5	Decimals in Money	232
4.6	Thousandths	237
4.7	Metric Units of Length	242
4.8	Personal References for Metric Length	247
4.9	Measuring in Millimeters	252
4.10	Decimal Place Value	256
4.11	Unit 4 Review and Assessment	261

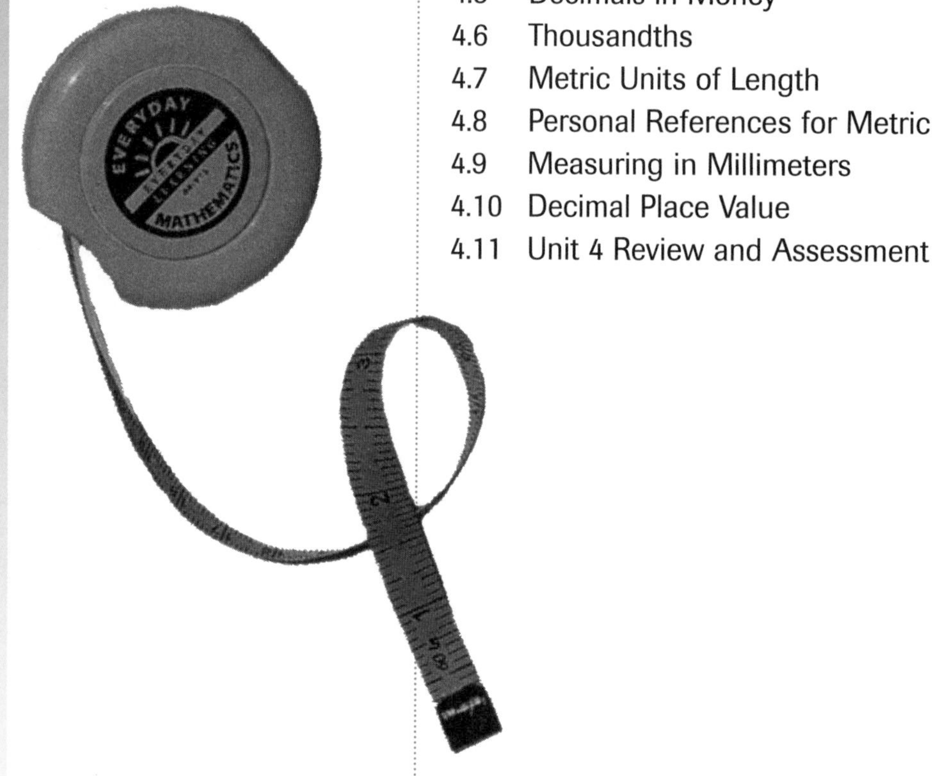

Unit 5 Big Numbers, Estimation, and Computation **266**

5.1	Extended Multiplication Facts	280
5.2	*Multiplication Wrestling*	286
5.3	Estimating Sums	291
5.4	Estimating Products	297
5.5	The Partial-Products Algorithm for Multiplication (Part 1)	303
5.6	The Partial-Products Algorithm for Multiplication (Part 2)	309
5.7	Lattice Multiplication	315
5.8	Big Numbers	322
5.9	Powers of 10	328
5.10	Rounding and Reporting Large Numbers	334
5.11	World Tour: Traveling to Europe	340
5.12	Unit 5 Review and Assessment	345

Unit 6 Division; Map Reference Frames; Measures of Angles **350**

6.1	A Multiples Strategy for Division	366
6.2	The Partial-Quotients Division Algorithm	372
6.3	Multiplication and Division Number Stories	377
6.4	Expressing and Interpreting Remainders	382
6.5	Rectangular Coordinate Grids for Maps	387
6.6	Rotations and Angles	392
6.7	Using a Circle Protractor	397
6.8	The Half-Circle Protractor	402
6.9	The Global Grid System	407
6.10	Latitude and Longitude	412
6.11	Unit 6 Review and Assessment	417

Appendices **423**

Projects	424
Fourth Grade Key Vocabulary	457
Scope and Sequence	469
Index	489

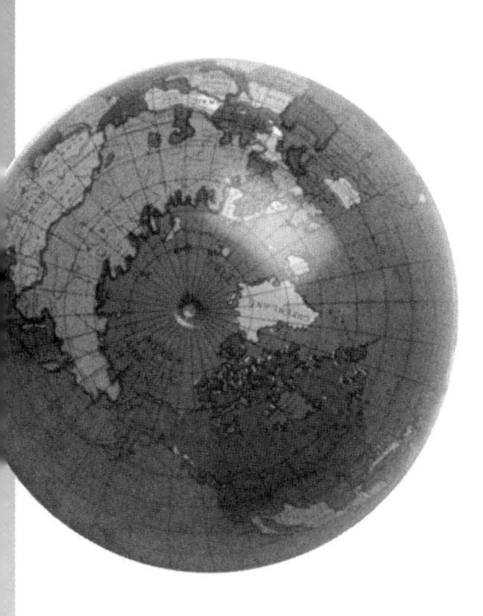

Volume 2

Unit 7 Fractions and Their Uses; Chance and Probability **498**

7.1 Review of Basic Fraction Concepts **512**
7.2 Fractions of Sets **518**
7.3 Pattern-Block Fractions **523**
7.4 Fraction Addition and Subtraction **528**
7.5 Clock Fractions **535**
7.6 Many Names for Fractions **541**
7.7 Equivalent Fractions **545**
7.8 Fractions and Decimals **549**
7.9 Comparing Fractions **554**
7.10 The ONE for Fractions **559**
7.11 Probability, Fractions, and Spinners **564**
7.12 A Cube-Drop Experiment **570**
7.13 Unit 7 Review and Assessment **576**

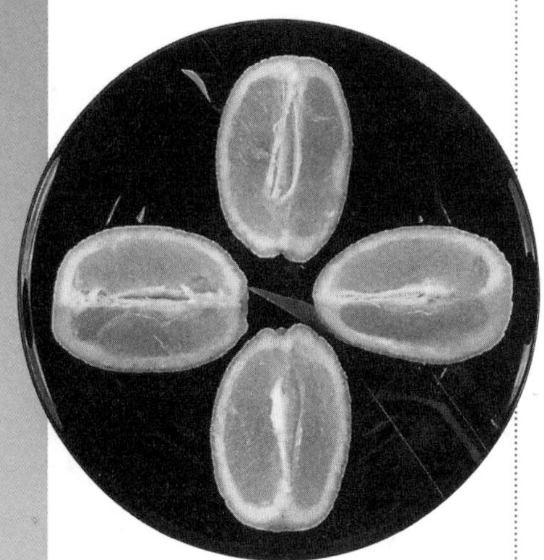

Unit 8 Perimeter and Area **582**

8.1 Kitchen Layouts and Perimeter **596**
8.2 Scale Drawings **601**
8.3 Area **607**
8.4 What Is the Area of My Skin? **611**
8.5 Formula for the Area of a Rectangle **616**
8.6 Formula for the Area of a Parallelogram **621**
8.7 Formula for the Area of a Triangle **627**
8.8 Geographical Area Measurements **632**
8.9 Unit 8 Review and Assessment **637**

Unit 9 Percents **644**

9.1 Fractions, Decimals, and Percents **656**
9.2 Converting "Easy" Fractions to Decimals and Percents **662**
9.3 Using a Calculator to Convert Fractions to Decimals **668**
9.4 Using a Calculator to Convert Fractions to Percents **674**
9.5 Conversions among Fractions, Decimals, and Percents **680**
9.6 Comparing the Results of a Survey **686**
9.7 Comparing Population Data **692**
9.8 Multiplication of Decimals **698**
9.9 Division of Decimals **704**
9.10 Unit 9 Review and Assessment **710**

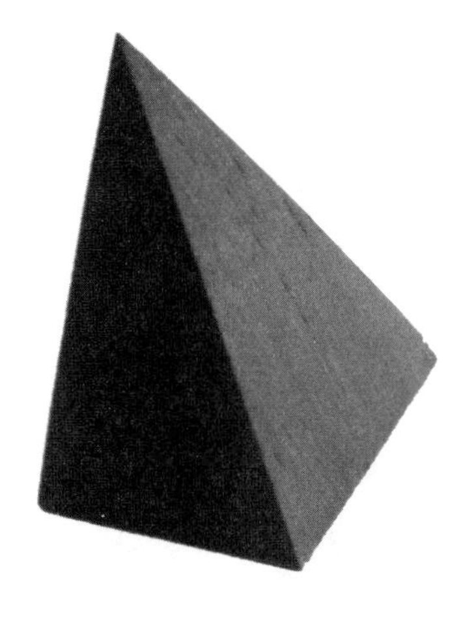

Unit 10 Reflections and Symmetry **716**

10.1 Explorations with a Transparent Mirror **730**
10.2 Finding Lines of Reflection **735**
10.3 Properties of Reflections **741**
10.4 Line Symmetry **746**
10.5 Frieze Patterns **752**
10.6 Positive and Negative Numbers **757**
10.7 Unit 10 Review and Assessment **763**

Unit 11 3-D Shapes, Weight, Volume, and Capacity **768**

11.1 Weight **782**
11.2 Geometric Solids **788**
11.3 Constructing Geometric Solids **794**
11.4 A Volume Exploration **801**
11.5 A Formula for the Volume of Rectangular Prisms **807**
11.6 Subtraction of Positive and Negative Numbers **813**
11.7 Capacity and Weight **819**
11.8 Unit 11 Review and Assessment **825**

Unit 12 Rates **830**

12.1 Introducing Rates **842**
12.2 Solving Rate Problems **848**
12.3 Converting between Rates **854**
12.4 Comparison Shopping: Part 1 **860**
12.5 Comparison Shopping: Part 2 **865**
12.6 World Tour Wrap-Up **870**
12.7 Unit 12 Review and Assessment **874**

Appendices **881**

Projects **882**
Fourth Grade Key Vocabulary **915**
Scope and Sequence **927**
Index **947**

Unit 7
Fractions and Their Uses; Chance and Probability

overview

Unit 7 has three main objectives:

1. To provide reminders, review, and practice of fraction ideas introduced earlier

2. To develop a good understanding of equivalent fractions

3. To provide informal activities related to chance and probability

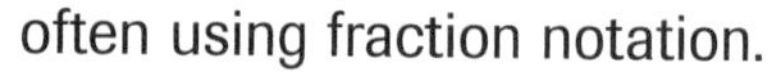

The probability activities in Lessons 7.11 and 7.12 illustrate a new use of fractions for most students. Fractions, along with decimals and percents, may be used to express probabilities. In these lessons, however, probabilities are expressed most often using fraction notation.

UNIT 7

contents

Lesson	Objective	Page
7.1	**Review of Basic Fraction Concepts** *To review fractions as parts of a whole (ONE), fractions on number lines, and uses of fractions.*	512
7.2	**Fractions of Sets** *To find fractional parts of sets.*	518
7.3	**Pattern-Block Fractions** *To find fractional parts of polygonal regions.*	523
7.4	**Fraction Addition and Subtraction** *To use pattern blocks to help add and subtract fractions.*	528
7.5	**Clock Fractions** *To model fractions on a clock face; and to use a clock face to help add and subtract fractions.*	535
7.6	**Many Names for Fractions** *To identify equivalent fractions.*	541
7.7	**Equivalent Fractions** *To develop and use a rule for generating equivalent fractions.*	545
7.8	**Fractions and Decimals** *To rename fractions as decimals and decimals as fractions; and to explore the relationship between fractions and division.*	549
7.9	**Comparing Fractions** *To order sets of fractions.*	554
7.10	**The ONE for Fractions** *To find the whole, or ONE, for given fractions.*	559
7.11	**Probability, Fractions, and Spinners** *To review basic ideas of probability, including fairness and expected results; and to apply knowledge of fractions to spinners.*	564
7.12	**A Cube-Drop Experiment** *To compare predicted and actual results from an experiment with random outcomes.*	570
7.13	**Unit 7 Review and Assessment** *To review and assess students' progress on the material covered in Unit 7.*	576

learning goals in perspective

	learning goals	links to the past	links to the future
7a	**Beginning Goal** Add and subtract fractions. **(Lessons 7.4 and 7.5)**	Grade 3: Review basic fraction concepts and notation. Make a number-line poster for fractions.	Grade 5: Use a slide rule to add and subtract fractions. Use common denominators to add and subtract fractions with unlike denominators. Add and subtract mixed numbers. Grade 6: Add, subtract, multiply, and divide fractions and mixed numbers with like or unlike denominators.
7b	**Developing Goal** Rename fractions with denominators of 10 and 100 as decimals. **(Lesson 7.8)**	Grades 1 and 2: Model decimals through hundredths with base-10 blocks, 10 by 10 grids, money, and on rulers and number lines. Grade 3: Make and use place-value tools to display decimals through thousandths.	Grade 5: Rename fractions as decimals. Find decimal equivalents by using a Fraction-Stick Chart and by dividing with a calculator. Develop reflex recognition of "easy" fraction-decimal equivalents. Grade 6: Rename numbers expressed by fractions, mixed numbers, decimals, and percents.
7c	**Developing Goal** Apply basic vocabulary and concepts associated with chance events. **(Lessons 7.11 and 7.12)**	Grade 3: Introduce the vocabulary of chance events. Conduct probability experiments: predict outcomes; test predictions; make frequency tables and bar graphs.	Grade 5: Perform experiments to estimate the probability of a chance event; record results on a Probability Meter. Grade 6: Review the basic vocabulary and concepts of probability. Calculate probabilities for situations with equally likely outcomes. Use random numbers; compare actual to expected outcomes. Use tree diagrams.
7d	**Developing Goal** Compare and order fractions. **(Lesson 7.9)**	Grades 2 and 3: Sort fractions by size (relative to $\frac{1}{2}$). Play *Fraction Top-It* to compare fractions.	Grade 5: Compare fractions by renaming them with a common denominator. Grade 6: Compare fractions by renaming them as decimals. Compare ratios by renaming them as *n*-to-1 ratios.
7e	**Developing Goal** Find equivalent fractions for given fractions. **(Lessons 7.6 and 7.7)**	Grade 2: Identify equivalent fractions with Fraction Cards. Play *Equivalent Fractions.* Grade 3: Create name-collection boxes for fractions. Find equivalent fractions using fraction cards and on a fraction number line.	Grade 5: Rename fractions and mixed numbers in simplest form. Grade 6: Applications and maintenance.
7f	**Secure Goal** Identify the whole for fractions. **(Lessons 7.1, 7.3, and 7.10)**	Grades 1–3: Name parts of a whole as fractions.	Grade 5: Find the whole, given a fraction or percent of the whole.
7g	**Secure Goal** Identify fractional parts of a collection of objects. **(Lesson 7.2)**	Grade 3: Name numbers of fractional parts of collections and regions as fractions and mixed numbers.	Grade 5: Solve parts and whole problems. Review concept of whole or ONE.
7h	**Secure Goal** Identify fractional parts of regions. **(Lessons 7.1–7.3, 7.5, and 7.9)**	See Goal 7g.	See Goal 7g.

assessment

ongoing • product • periodic

Informal Assessment

Math Boxes These *Math Journal* pages provide opportunities for cumulative review or assessment of concepts and skills.

Ongoing Assessment: Kid Watching Use the Ongoing Assessment suggestions in the following lessons to make quick, on-the-spot observations about students' understanding of:

- Numeration **(Lesson 7.1, Part 1; Lesson 7.3, Part 1; Lesson 7.6, Part 1; and Lesson 7.7, Part 1)**
- Operations and Computation **(Lesson 7.4, Part 1 and Lesson 7.12, Part 1)**
- Geometry **(Lesson 7.3, Part 1)**

Portfolio Ideas Samples of students' work may be obtained from the following assignments:

- Constructing an Equilateral Triangle **(Lesson 7.1)**
- Writing and Solving "Fraction-of" Number Stories **(Lesson 7.2)**
- Drawing and Comparing Line Segments **(Lesson 7.4)**
- Naming Fractional Parts of a Region **(Lesson 7.10)**
- Comparing Actual and Expected Results of 1,000 Cube Drops **(Lesson 7.12)**
- Describe a Fraction Addition or Subtraction Strategy **(Lesson 7.13)**

Unit 7 Review and Assessment

Math Message Use the Time to Reflect questions in Lesson 7.13 to assess students' progress toward the following learning goals: **Goals 7c and 7f–7h**

Oral and Slate Assessments Use oral or slate assessments during Lesson 7.13 to assess students' progress toward the following learning goals: **Goals 7a, 7b, 7d, 7e, 7g, and 7h**

Written Assessment Use a written review during Lesson 7.13 to assess students' progress toward the following learning goals: **Goals 7a and 7c–7h**

Alternative Assessment Options Use independent alternative assessments in Lesson 7.13 to assess students' progress toward the following learning goals: **Goals 7a and 7e**

assessmenthandbook

For more information on how to use different types of assessment in Unit 7, see the Assessment Overview on pages 57–59 in the *Assessment Handbook.* The following Assessment Masters can be found in the *Math Masters* book:

- Unit 7 Checking Progress, pp. 402 and 403
- Unit 7 Class Checklist, p. 438
- Unit 7 Individual Profile of Progress, p. 439
- Class Progress Indicator, p. 467
- Interest Inventories, pp. 468 and 469
- Math Logs, pp. 470–472
- Self-Assessment Forms, pp. 473 and 474

problemsolving

A process of modeling everyday situations using tools from mathematics

Encourage students to use a variety of strategies when attacking a given problem—and to explain those strategies. *Strategies students might use in this unit:*

- Acting out the problem
- Using and drawing a picture
- Using computation
- Using and making a table
- Using estimation

Four Problem-Solving **REPRESENTATIONS**

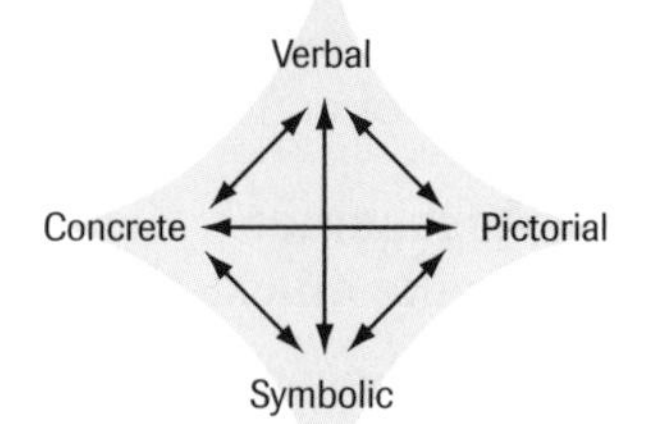

Lessons that teach *through* problem solving, not just *about* problem solving

Lesson	Activity	Lesson	Activity
7.2	Solving "fraction-of" problems with pennies	**7.7**	Solving hiking number stories involving distance and time
7.3	Finding fractional parts of regions with pattern blocks	**7.10**	Solving "What Is the ONE?" problems
7.4, 7.5	Solving number stories involving fractions	**7.11**	Designing spinners to meet given conditions
7.6, 7.8	Making a collection of equivalent names for fractions	**7.12**	Conducting a cube-drop experiment: making predictions

For more information about problem solving in *Everyday Mathematics,* see the *Teacher's Reference Manual.*

cross-curricularlinks

literature

- Students discuss fractions by reading *Gator Pie* by Louise Mathews and *Eating Fractions* by Bruce McMillan. **(Lesson 7.1)**
- Students explore tangram arrangements in *Grandfather Tang's Story* by Ann Tompert. **(Lesson 7.3)**
- Students discuss probability by reading *Do You Wanna Bet? Your Chance to Find Out about Probability* by Jean Cushman. **(Lesson 7.11)**

social studies

- Students continue the World Tour by going to Brasília, Brazil. **(Lesson 7.2)**

language arts

- Students use the book *Only One* by Marc Harshman to help them understand "collection" words. **(Lesson 7.2)**
- Students think of words and phrases that express the likelihood of events occurring. **(Lesson 7.11)**

art

- Students create circle designs based on those in *Ed Emberley's Picture Pie: A Circle Drawing Book* by Ed Emberley. **(Lesson 7.1)**
- Students draw and color a geometric shape to explore the relationship between fractions and ONE. **(Lesson 7.10)**

technology

- Students look up information about tangram puzzles on the Internet. **(Lesson 7.3)**

meeting INDIVIDUAL needs

UNIVERSAL ACCESS

✦ RETEACHING

The following features provide some additional instructional support:

Adjusting the Activity

- **Lesson 7.1, Part 1**
- **Lesson 7.2, Part 1**
- **Lesson 7.9, Part 1**
- **Lesson 7.10, Part 1**
- **Lesson 7.12, Part 1**

Options for Individualizing

- **Lesson 7.1** Dividing Shapes into Equal Parts
- **Lesson 7.6** Playing *Name That Number*
- **Lesson 7.8** Creating Base-10 Block Designs
- **Lesson 7.11** Judging the Likelihood of Events

✦ ENRICHMENT

The following features suggest some enrichment and extension activities found in this unit:

Adjusting the Activity

- **Lesson 7.6, Part 1**
- **Lesson 7.7, Part 1**

Options for Individualizing

- **Lesson 7.1** Constructing an Equilateral Triangle
- **Lesson 7.1** Creating Fraction Art
- **Lesson 7.2** Writing and Solving "Fraction-of" Number Stories
- **Lesson 7.3** Exploring Tangrams
- **Lesson 7.5** Modeling Fractions with Other Denominators on a Clock Face
- **Lesson 7.9** Using Digits to Create Fractions
- **Lesson 7.10** Naming Fractional Parts of a Region
- **Lesson 7.11** Reading about Chance Events
- **Lesson 7.12** Comparing Actual and Expected Results of 1,000 Cube Drops

✦ LANGUAGE DIVERSITY

The following features suggest some ways to support students who are acquiring proficiency in English:

Adjusting the Activity

- **Lesson 7.3, Part 1**

Options for Individualizing

- **Lesson 7.2** Matching "Collection" Words with Names of Things
- **Lesson 7.11** Building Background for Mathematics Words

✦ MULTIAGE CLASSROOM

The following chart lists related lessons from Grades 3 and 5 that can help you meet your instructional needs:

Grade 3	8.1 8.2	8.1	11.2			8.4		8.5	8.6		11.5	1.3 11.4
Grade 4	7.1	7.2	7.3	7.4	7.5	7.6	7.7	7.8	7.9	7.10	7.11	7.12
Grade 5	5.1			6.8	6.9	6.10	5.4	5.5– 5.7	5.3			

materials

lesson	math masters pages	manipulative kit items	other items
7.1	Study Link Master, p. 311 Teaching Master, p. 102	pattern blocks ***See* Advance Preparation, p. 512**	pattern blocks for overhead (optional) straightedge *Gator Pie; Eating Fractions* *Ed Emberley's Picture Pie: A Circle Drawing Book*
7.2	Study Link Master, p. 312 Teaching Masters, pp. 36–38 (optional); and p. 103	straws or twist-ties (optional) ***See* Advance Preparation, p. 518**	20 pennies or other counters *Only One* dictionary (optional)
7.3	Study Link Master, p. 313 Teaching Masters, pp. 104 and 105 transparency of Teaching Master, p. 104 (optional) ***See* Advance Preparation, p. 523**	pattern blocks	pattern blocks for overhead (optional) straightedge; envelopes dictionary (optional) *Grandfather Tang's Story*
7.4	Study Link Master, p. 314 Teaching Master, p. 106	pattern blocks	rubber band pattern blocks for overhead (optional)
7.5	Study Link Master, p. 315 Teaching Master, p. 108 transparency of Teaching Master, p. 107 (optional) ***See* Advance Preparation, p. 535**		semipermanent chalk (optional) slate
7.6	Study Link Master, p. 316 Assessment Master, p. 471 or 475 (optional)		Fraction Cards (see Lesson 7.4)
7.7	Study Link Master, p. 317	pattern blocks	pattern blocks for overhead (optional) butcher paper (or large paper) radio, tape recorder, or CD player
7.8	Study Link Master, p. 318 Teaching Master, p. 110 transparency of Teaching Master, p. 109 (optional)	base-10 blocks ***See* Advance Preparation, p. 549**	slate semipermanent chalk (optional)
7.9	Study Link Master, p. 319		Fraction Cards (see Lesson 7.4)
7.10	Study Link Master, p. 320	pattern blocks	pattern blocks and counters for overhead (optional) beans, pennies, or other counters slate; Geometry Template
7.11	Study Link Masters, pp. 321–323 Teaching Master, p. 111		coloring pencils, markers, or crayons straightedge; slate 1 large (2") paper clip 2 pieces of removable tape data pad or chart paper (optional) *Do You Wanna Bet? Your Chance to Find Out about Probability* ***See* Advance Preparation, p. 564**
7.12	Study Link Master, p. 324 Teaching Masters, pp. 112–114 ***See* Advance Preparation, p. 570**		coloring pencils, markers, or crayons cm cube; slate
7.13	Study Link Masters, pp. 325–328 Teaching Masters, pp. 115 and 116 Assessment Masters, pp. 402 and 403		slate large paper clip straightedge

planningtips

Pacing

Pacing depends on a number of factors, such as students' individual needs and how long your school has been using *Everyday Mathematics.* At the beginning of Unit 7, review your Content by Strand Poster to help you set a monthly pace.

← MOST CLASSROOMS →

JANUARY	FEBRUARY	MARCH

Using the Projects

Use Project 3, A Carnival Game, after Unit 7 to help make a "quilt" out of the grids students colored in Lesson 7.12. In this project, students use their quilt as a target mat for a cube-tossing game. The Projects can be found at the back of this book.

Home Communication

Share Study Links 7.1–7.12 with families to help them understand the content and procedures in this unit. At the end of the unit, use Study Link 7.13 to introduce Unit 8. Supplemental information can be found in the *Home Connection Handbook.*

NCTM Standards

Standard	1	2	3	4	5	6	7	8	9	10
Unit 7 Lessons	1–12	4, 9, 10	1, 3, 4		11, 12	1–13	1–13	1–13	1–13	1–13

Content Standards
1 Number and Operations
2 Algebra
3 Geometry
4 Measurement
5 Data Analysis and Probability

Process Standards
6 Problem Solving
7 Reasoning and Proof
8 Communication
9 Connections
10 Representation

PRACTICE *through* Games

Everyday Mathematics uses games to help students develop good fact power and other math skills.

- *Name That Number* reinforces skills used in all four operations **(Lesson 7.6)**
- *Musical Name-Collection Boxes* to practice naming fractions equivalent to a given fraction **(Lesson 7.7)**
- *Fraction Top-It* to practice comparing fractions **(Lesson 7.10)**

unit 7 content highlights

The discussion below highlights the major content ideas presented in Unit 7 and may help you establish instructional priorities.

Fraction Concepts, Notation, and Uses
(Lessons 7.1–7.3 and 7.10)

In today's world, people seldom add, subtract, or divide using fractional notation. But very often, they do use fractional notation to express and convey information such as the following:

- fractions of sets or collections of discrete things (things difficult to partition or break into parts)
  Examples: half-dozen eggs; $\frac{1}{4}$ of the cars in the parking lot
- fractions as parts of continuous things
  Examples: A recipe calls for $\frac{2}{3}$ cup of milk, $\frac{1}{2}$ cup of sugar, and $\frac{1}{4}$ pound of butter.
- fractions to name points between whole numbers on rulers, other measurement scales, and number lines
  Examples: rulers marked in inches and sixteenths of inches; scale on a measuring cup
- fractions to express rates
  Example: 24 miles per gallon, perhaps set up originally as the rate $\frac{240 \text{ miles}}{10 \text{ gallons}}$
- fractions to set up ratio comparisons or express scales on architectural plans, maps, or pictures
  Examples: Johannes got $\frac{1}{4}$ of the vote ($\frac{53 \text{ votes}}{212 \text{ votes}}$); the scale of the encyclopedia picture of the aardvark is $\frac{1}{12}$, or 1 to 12.
- fraction notation for division
  Example: As indicated above, information in a rate or ratio comparison is often expressed first as a fraction before being divided.

Everyday Mathematics uses a device called the "whole" box to remind students that a fraction is a part of a whole thing ($\frac{1}{4}$ of an orange is a fraction of a whole orange). A box, pictured next to a problem or at the top of a page, contains a word or phrase that describes the whole, such as "quart of milk" or "1 hour."

NOTE: Except for those cases in which fractions are used to express comparisons in rates or ratios, a fraction will be a fraction of something. *Everyday Mathematics* refers to this "something" as the "whole," or the "ONE." It is important to emphasize that fractions can be meaningless unless one thinks of them in reference to the whole. Half a glass of milk is different from half a quart; and half a second is very different from half an hour.

In Lesson 7.2, students solve a variety of "fraction-of" problems, in which the whole is a collection of objects. There are many words in the English language that name collections, such as *team, litter, crew,* and *flock*. Students use these collection words to make up and solve fraction-of stories.

Pattern blocks are used in Lesson 7.3 to partition various 2-dimensional shapes. They also provide students with practice in naming fractional parts of a region. These activities reinforce the idea that fractions should always be viewed in relation to the whole, unless they are used to indicate rates or ratios.

In Lesson 7.10, Students use pattern blocks and counters to find the whole for given fractions.

Continuing the World Tour (Lesson 7.2)

Students continue the World Tour by flying from Budapest, Hungary, to Brasília, Brazil. They follow the established World Tour routine to update the Route Map and begin gathering information about countries in South America.

Fraction Addition and Subtraction (Lessons 7.4 and 7.5)

In Lesson 7.4, fractional relationships between pattern blocks are applied to solve simple fraction addition and subtraction problems, such as $\frac{2}{3} + \frac{1}{6}$ and $\frac{5}{6} - \frac{2}{3}$. The focus is not on using common denominators to add and subtract fractions, but on gaining hands-on experience with these kinds of problems. Paper-and-pencil methods for fraction addition and subtraction are treated in detail in *Fifth Grade Everyday Mathematics.*

In Lesson 7.5, fractions are modeled as shaded sectors on a clock face. This work is then extended to modeling fraction addition and subtraction on a clock face. There is a brief discussion of why fractions and multiples of 60 are used in time and angle measurements.

Equivalent Fractions (Lessons 7.6, 7.7, and 7.9)

NOTE: Understanding equivalent fractions is the key ingredient needed to compare and compute with fractions. By placing special emphasis on equivalent fractions, the authors hope to avoid difficulties faced by many students and even adults when working with fractions.

By now, students should be very familiar with the idea of equivalent names for numbers. They have been filling in name-collection boxes, usually with names for whole numbers, since the beginning of second grade. And in third grade, students began collecting names for equivalent fractions. However, the application of this idea to fractions will require careful teaching, time, and practice.

There is an unlimited choice of names for any fraction. For example, the number "one-half" can be written as $\frac{1}{2}$ or as $\frac{2}{4}, \frac{3}{6}, \frac{4}{8}, \frac{5}{10}, \frac{6}{12}, \ldots, \frac{100}{200}, \ldots, \frac{1{,}000}{5{,}000}, \ldots$, and so on. It can also be written in non-fraction notation, such as 0.5 and 50%. The ability to change the name or form of a number in countless ways is a very powerful tool in mathematics.

In this unit, ideas of equivalent fractions are developed with decks of Fraction Cards, which students cut out from pages in the journal. (You may want students to cut out these cards prior to their mathematics class time.) The cards show fraction symbols on one side and shaded pictures for the fractions on the other side.

In Lesson 7.6, students use their Fraction Cards to identify equivalent fractions by matching cards that have equal amounts of shading. They begin a collection of fraction names in the journal and add names to this table throughout the school year.

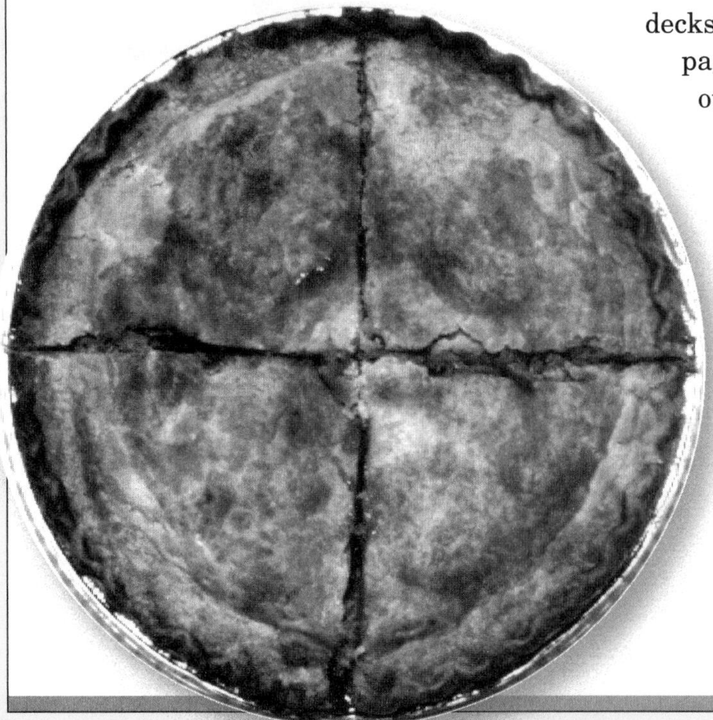

In Lesson 7.7, students learn that they can rename a fraction by multiplying both its numerator and denominator by the same number. Students will expand their collection of fraction names with the help of this rule.

Fraction Cards play an important role in Lesson 7.9, in which students use them to determine whether a fraction is greater or less than another fraction; to order sets of fractions from the smallest fraction to the largest fraction; and to compare fractions to $\frac{1}{2}$.

Fraction Cards are used again in Lesson 7.10 to play a game called *Fraction Top-It,* which is an adaptation of the card game *War*. Equivalent names for fractions are used to compare pairs of fractions. Players can check who has the larger fraction by comparing the amounts shaded. Eventually, students who play this game frequently will not need to rely on visual confirmation as much.

Fractions and Decimals (Lesson 7.8)

Equivalent fractions and shaded grid squares are used to rename fractions as decimals. Students add these decimal versions to their collections of fraction names.

Advantages and Disadvantages of Fractions and Decimals

Both fractions and decimals are used to represent numbers that are between whole numbers. Each form has its advantages and disadvantages. Relative size is easy to determine with decimals (for example, $0.45 > 0.095$), but sometimes difficult with fractions (for example, is $\frac{7}{9}$ greater than or less than $\frac{5}{6}$?). Decimals are much easier to use in most calculations, because the place-value structure and algorithms for decimals are closely linked to those of whole numbers. Decimals also appear in scientific notation for very large and very small numbers. Hence, decimals are universally used in science and industry. But people often want to refer to a part of something or compare one thing with another, and, for that reason, they find fractions very useful.

Chance and Probability (Lessons 7.11 and 7.12)

NOTE: The authors believe that most students should be exposed to concepts and skills many times and in many different ways, often only briefly, before they can master them. The probability activities in *Everyday Mathematics* are good examples.

The authors want students to feel comfortable talking about chance events. Therefore, one focus in Lessons 7.11 and 7.12 is on vocabulary development. While many expressions are suggested (for example, *chance, unlikely, more likely, probably, certain*), they should not be taught formally. Students will gradually make these words part of their vocabulary through repeated use. Choose expressions that are meaningful to the class. Students are familiar with *expect* and *predict,* but *probability* is a difficult word which does not need to be used at this time.

Most of the probability activities follow a similar pattern: Students make predictions about the likelihood of a particular outcome and then check their predictions by performing an experiment. The authors want students to become aware of the fact that the more often they repeat an experiment, the more reliable their predictions will be. In these activities, some individual results may be very close to the expected results, but others may be far off. However, when the class data are combined, the results should be very close to the predicted results.

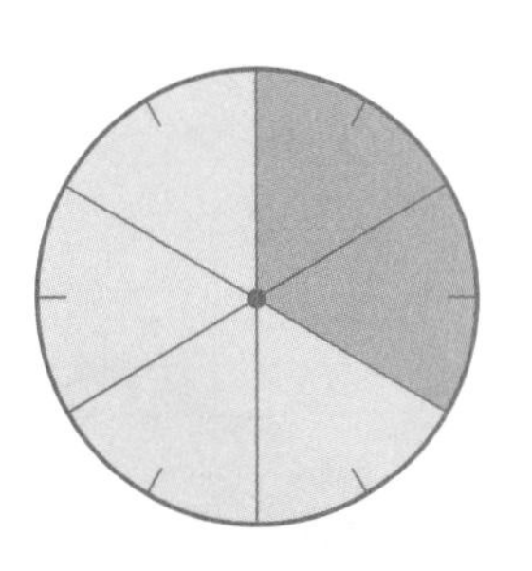

The probability of a spinner landing on the darker area is $\frac{1}{3}$.

Review and Assessment (Lesson 7.13)

Lesson 7.13 includes oral, slate, and written assessments of the following concepts and skills:

- identifying the whole for fractions
- adding and subtracting fractions
- finding fractions and decimals equivalent to given fractions
- comparing and ordering fractions
- identifying fractional parts of sets and regions
- finding equivalent names for fractions
- applying concepts of chance

For additional information on the following topics, see the *Teacher's Reference Manual:*

- data and chance
- fraction and decimal notation
- numeration and order
- pattern blocks
- semipermanent chalk

7.1 Review of Basic Fraction Concepts

OBJECTIVE **To review fractions as parts of a whole (ONE), fractions on number lines, and uses of fractions.**

summaries	materials
1 Teaching the Lesson	
Students review the meaning and uses of fractions. They draw various pattern-block shapes and color a fractional part of each shape, as specified. [Numeration]	☐ *Math Journal 2,* pp. 189–191 ☐ *Student Reference Book,* p. 41 ☐ pattern blocks ☐ pattern blocks for overhead (optional) ☐ straightedge ***See* Advance Preparation**
2 Ongoing Learning & Practice	
Students practice and maintain skills through Math Boxes and Study Link activities.	☐ *Math Journal 2,* p. 192 ☐ Study Link Master (*Math Masters,* p. 311)
3 Options for Individualizing	
Reteaching Students read books about dividing shapes into equal parts. [Geometry] **Enrichment** Students construct equilateral triangles. [Geometry] **Enrichment** Students create fraction art with circles. [Numeration]	☐ Teaching Master (*Math Masters,* p. 102) ☐ *Gator Pie* ☐ *Eating Fractions* ☐ *Ed Emberley's Picture Pie: A Circle Drawing Book* ***See* Advance Preparation**

Additional Information

Advance Preparation For Mental Math and Reflexes, you will need a hexagon pattern block and some trapezoid pattern blocks. You may prefer to use ones that are made for an overhead projector.

For the optional Reteaching activity in Part 3, obtain the books *Gator Pie* by Louise Mathews (Sundance, 1995) and *Eating Fractions* by Bruce McMillan (Scholastic, 1991). For the second optional Enrichment activity in Part 3, obtain the book *Ed Emberley's Picture Pie: A Circle Drawing Book* by Ed Emberley (Little, Brown, 1984).

Vocabulary • **whole (or ONE or unit)** • **denominator** • **numerator** • **"whole" box** • **mixed number** • **equilateral triangle**

Getting Started

Mental Math and Reflexes

Display a hexagon pattern block on the overhead projector or hold up one for the class to see. Tell students that this is ONE. Next, display 1 trapezoid and ask what it is worth, or what fractional part of the hexagon it is. $\frac{1}{2}$ Display 2 trapezoids and ask what they are worth. $\frac{2}{2}$, or 1 Continue adding trapezoids while students count aloud. $\frac{3}{2}$, $\frac{4}{2}$, and so on

Math Message

List three ways that fractions are used outside of your math class.

1 Teaching the Lesson

✦ Math Message Follow-Up (*Student Reference Book,* p. 41)

WHOLE-CLASS DISCUSSION

Ask students to share their examples, and record them on the board.

Page 41 of the *Student Reference Book* describes some uses of fractions from books and newspapers. If students had difficulty thinking of examples, consider reading through some of these examples with the class.

ONGOING ASSESSMENT

Fractions that indicate parts of wholes and measures and counts have been taught and reinforced throughout *Everyday Mathematics,* Grades 1 through 3. Students should be familiar and proficient with these concepts. The use of fractions in rate and ratio comparisons will be addressed in Unit 12.

✦ Reviewing Fraction Ideas and Notation

WHOLE-CLASS DISCUSSION

Write several fractions on the board and remind students of these basic aspects of fraction notation:

▷ A fraction is always a fraction of something—for example, $\frac{1}{2}$ of an orange, $\frac{2}{3}$ of a rectangular region, $\frac{3}{5}$ of a mile, $\frac{1}{4}$ of the marbles in a bag. We refer to this "something" as the **whole,** or **ONE;** for measures and counts, it is considered the **unit.**

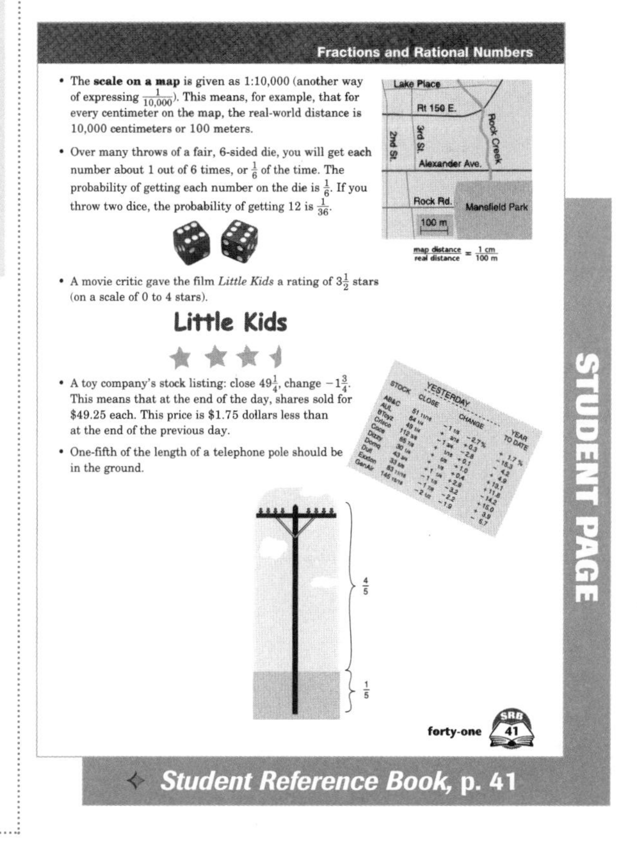

Fractions and Rational Numbers

- The **scale on a map** is given as 1:10,000 (another way of expressing $\frac{1}{10{,}000}$). This means, for example, that for every centimeter on the map, the real-world distance is 10,000 centimeters or 100 meters.
- Over many throws of a fair, 6-sided die, you will get each number about 1 out of 6 times, or $\frac{1}{6}$ of the time. The probability of getting each number on the die is $\frac{1}{6}$. If you throw two dice, the probability of getting 12 is $\frac{1}{36}$.
- A movie critic gave the film *Little Kids* a rating of $3\frac{1}{2}$ stars (on a scale of 0 to 4 stars).
- A toy company's stock listing: close $49\frac{1}{4}$, change $-1\frac{3}{4}$. This means that at the end of the day, shares sold for $49.25 each. This price is $1.75 dollars less than at the end of the previous day.
- One-fifth of the length of a telephone pole should be in the ground.

forty-one 41

✦ *Student Reference Book,* p. 41

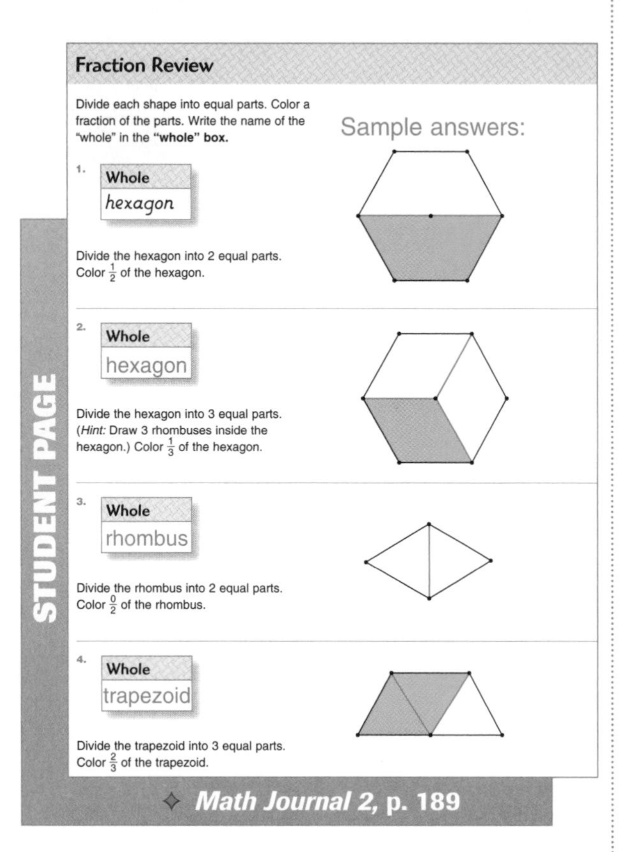
STUDENT PAGE

Fraction Review

Divide each shape into equal parts. Color a fraction of the parts. Write the name of the "whole" in the **"whole" box.**

Sample answers:

1. Whole: *hexagon*

Divide the hexagon into 2 equal parts. Color $\frac{1}{2}$ of the hexagon.

2. Whole: hexagon

Divide the hexagon into 3 equal parts. (*Hint:* Draw 3 rhombuses inside the hexagon.) Color $\frac{1}{3}$ of the hexagon.

3. Whole: rhombus

Divide the rhombus into 2 equal parts. Color $\frac{0}{2}$ of the rhombus.

4. Whole: trapezoid

Divide the trapezoid into 3 equal parts. Color $\frac{2}{3}$ of the trapezoid.

Math Journal 2, p. 189

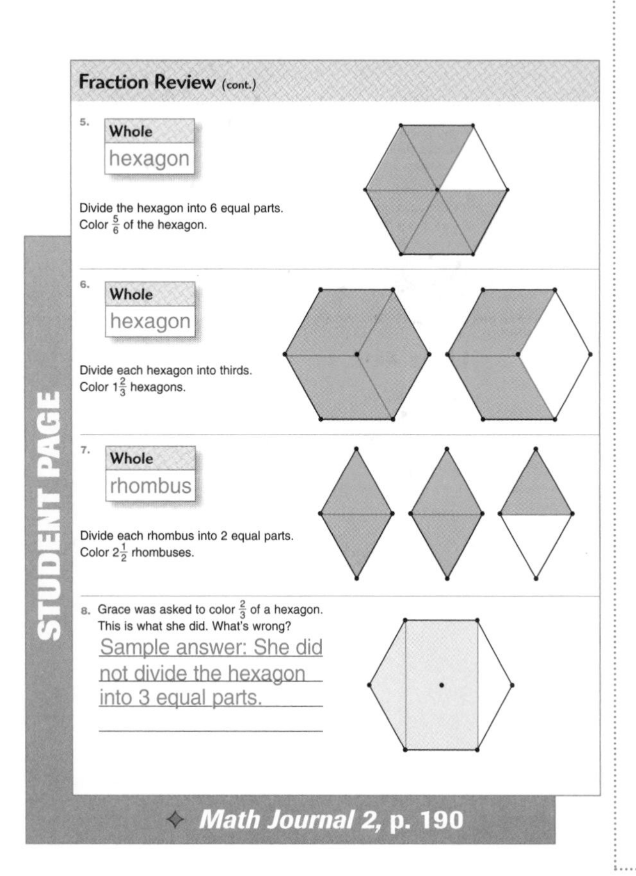
STUDENT PAGE

Fraction Review (cont.)

5. Whole: hexagon

Divide the hexagon into 6 equal parts. Color $\frac{5}{6}$ of the hexagon.

6. Whole: hexagon

Divide each hexagon into thirds. Color $1\frac{2}{3}$ hexagons.

7. Whole: rhombus

Divide each rhombus into 2 equal parts. Color $2\frac{1}{2}$ rhombuses.

8. Grace was asked to color $\frac{2}{3}$ of a hexagon. This is what she did. What's wrong?

Sample answer: She did not divide the hexagon into 3 equal parts.

Math Journal 2, p. 190

- The parts into which the whole is divided must be the same size—"fair shares."
- Students are familiar with the fraction notation $\frac{a}{b}$. Mention that fractions can also be written with a slash: a/b.
- The number below the fraction bar is called the **denominator** of the fraction. The denominator names the number of equal parts into which the whole is divided.
- The number above the fraction bar is called the **numerator** of the fraction. The numerator names the number of parts under consideration. For example, in the statement "Sue ate $\frac{2}{3}$ of the pizza," the pizza is the "whole." The fraction $\frac{2}{3}$ tells us that the pizza was probably divided into three equal parts, and Sue ate 2 of them.

✦ Identifying Fractional Parts of Pattern-Block Shapes (*Math Journal 2,* pp. 189 and 190)

WHOLE-CLASS ACTIVITY 

Students divide each shape on journal pages 189 and 190 into a specified number of equal parts and color a fraction of the shape.

Do Problem 1 with the class. Remind students that the whole (or ONE) is the hexagon. Call students' attention to the **"whole" box,** which is used to write the name of the whole. As they work on Problems 2–7, students record the name of each item in the "whole" box.

Adjusting the Activity Students who are having difficulty may benefit from modeling these problems with pattern blocks.

Identifying Fractional Parts of Number Lines
(*Math Journal 2,* p. 191)

WHOLE-CLASS ACTIVITY

In Problems 9–14 on journal page 191, students write fractions and mixed numbers for points on number lines. Students have had plenty of experience with this kind of problem—using whole numbers and decimals. Number-line problems reinforce the concept that both fractions and decimals can be used to name numbers between whole numbers.

After students have completed journal pages 189–191, bring the class together to go over the answers. Mention that numbers such as $2\frac{1}{2}$ and $1\frac{3}{5}$ are called **mixed numbers.**

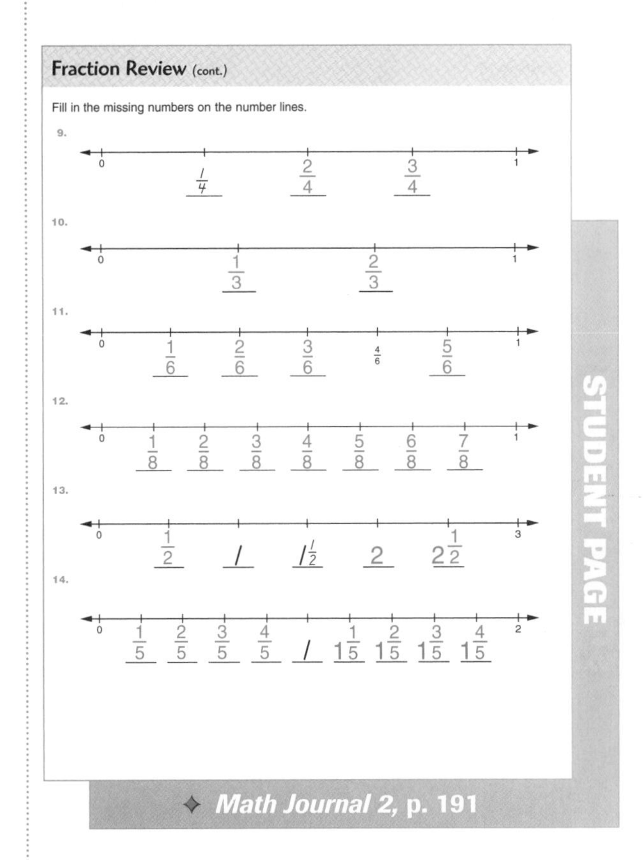
Fraction Review (cont.)

Fill in the missing numbers on the number lines.

9. 0, $\frac{1}{4}$, $\frac{2}{4}$, $\frac{3}{4}$, 1

10. 0, $\frac{1}{3}$, $\frac{2}{3}$, 1

11. 0, $\frac{1}{6}$, $\frac{2}{6}$, $\frac{3}{6}$, $\frac{4}{6}$, $\frac{5}{6}$, 1

12. 0, $\frac{1}{8}$, $\frac{2}{8}$, $\frac{3}{8}$, $\frac{4}{8}$, $\frac{5}{8}$, $\frac{6}{8}$, $\frac{7}{8}$, 1

13. 0, $\frac{1}{2}$, 1, $1\frac{1}{2}$, 2, $2\frac{1}{2}$, 3

14. 0, $\frac{1}{5}$, $\frac{2}{5}$, $\frac{3}{5}$, $\frac{4}{5}$, 1, $1\frac{1}{5}$, $1\frac{2}{5}$, $1\frac{3}{5}$, $1\frac{4}{5}$, 2

Math Journal 2, p. 191

Ongoing Learning & Practice

Math Boxes 7.1 (*Math Journal 2,* p. 192)

INDEPENDENT ACTIVITY 

Mixed Review Math Boxes in this lesson are paired with Math Boxes in Lesson 7.3. The skill in Problem 1 is a prerequisite for Unit 8.

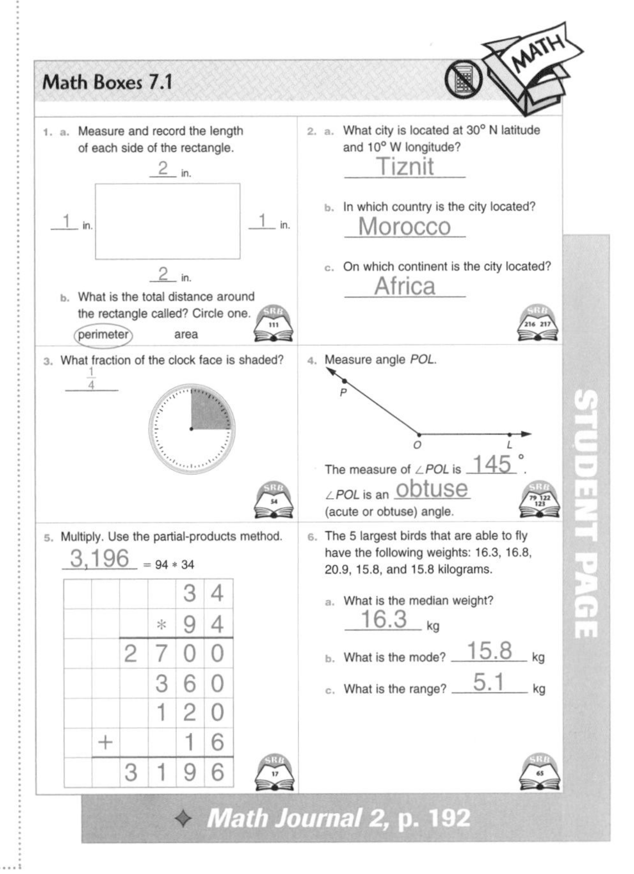
Math Boxes 7.1

1. a. Measure and record the length of each side of the rectangle. 2 in., 1 in., 1 in., 2 in.
   b. What is the total distance around the rectangle called? Circle one. (perimeter) area

2. a. What city is located at 30° N latitude and 10° W longitude? Tiznit
   b. In which country is the city located? Morocco
   c. On which continent is the city located? Africa

3. What fraction of the clock face is shaded? $\frac{1}{4}$

4. Measure angle *POL*.
   The measure of $\angle POL$ is 145°.
   $\angle POL$ is an obtuse (acute or obtuse) angle.

5. Multiply. Use the partial-products method.
   3,196 = 94 ∗ 34
   34 ∗ 94: 2700 + 360 + 120 + 16 = 3196

6. The 5 largest birds that are able to fly have the following weights: 16.3, 16.8, 20.9, 15.8, and 15.8 kilograms.
   a. What is the median weight? 16.3 kg
   b. What is the mode? 15.8 kg
   c. What is the range? 5.1 kg

Math Journal 2, p. 192

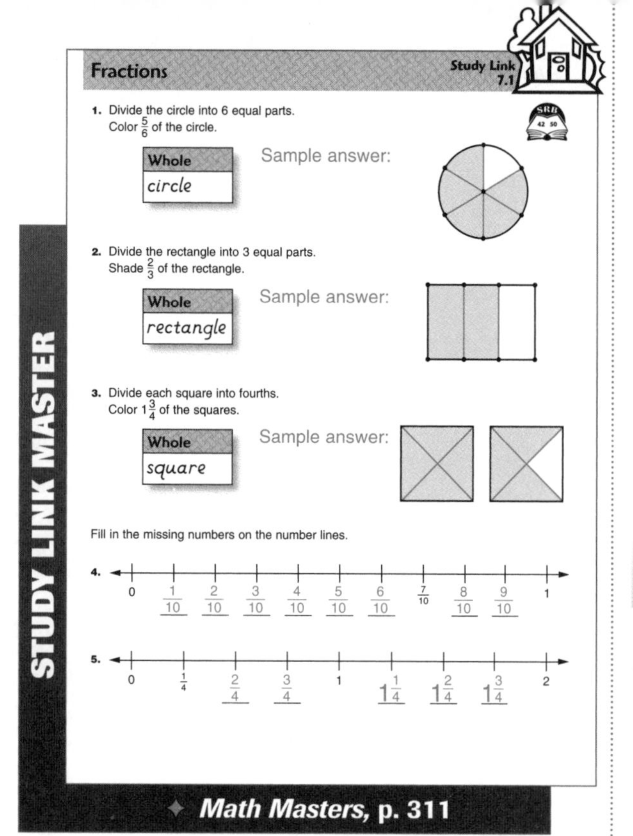

✦ *Math Masters,* p. 311

✦ Study Link 7.1 (*Math Masters,* p. 311)

Home Connection Students identify fractional parts of shapes and number lines. For the number-line problems, you may wish to remind students that they should look for the 1 (or the whole) on each number line and count the number of parts into which the whole is divided.

3 Options for Individualizing

✦ RETEACHING Dividing Shapes into Equal Parts

SMALL-GROUP ACTIVITY  **15–30 min** 

Literature Link A basic fraction concept is that all the parts into which the whole (or ONE) is divided must be the same size. Read the following books with students to reinforce this concept:

Gator Pie

Summary: Three alligators decide to share a pie. Before they can cut it, additional alligators arrive. They need to determine how to cut the pie into thirds, fourths, eighths, and finally, hundredths.

Eating Fractions

Summary: Wholes, halves, thirds, and fourths are reviewed through color photographs of food, such as bananas and muffins.

✦ ENRICHMENT Constructing an Equilateral Triangle (*Math Masters,* p. 102)

INDEPENDENT ACTIVITY  **15–30 min** 

Students construct an **equilateral triangle** using a compass and straightedge. Then they cut out the triangle and divide it into six equal parts by folding it in half through each pair of opposite vertices.

✦ ENRICHMENT Creating Fraction Art

INDEPENDENT ACTIVITY  **15–30 min** 

Art Link Circles cut into halves, fourths, or eighths are the basis for the artwork in the book *Ed Emberley's Picture Pie: A Circle Drawing Book* by Ed Emberley (Little, Brown, 1984). The circles are of various colors and form elaborate designs. Students may wish to create their own circle designs based on those in the book and discuss the number of circles and fractional parts of circles they used in their designs.

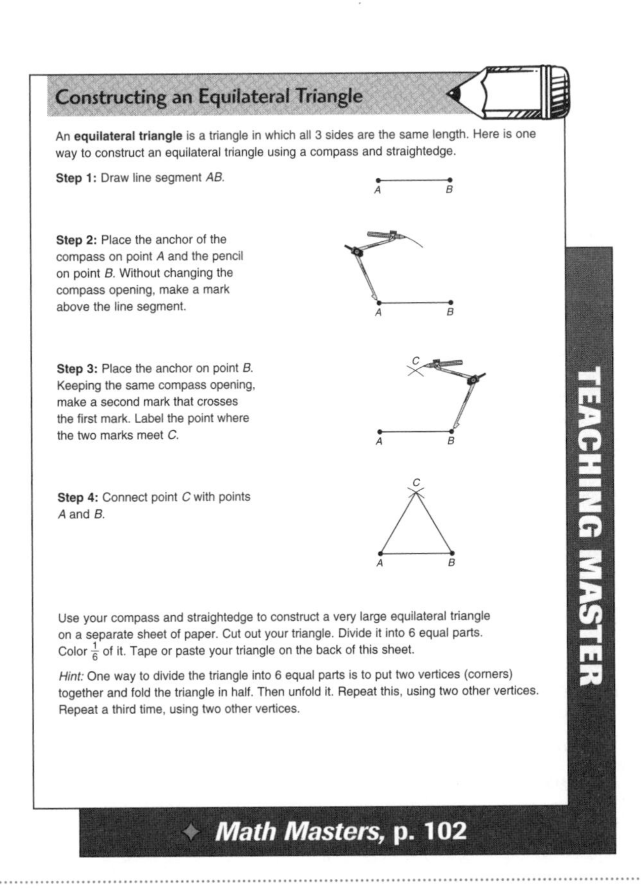

Constructing an Equilateral Triangle

An **equilateral triangle** is a triangle in which all 3 sides are the same length. Here is one way to construct an equilateral triangle using a compass and straightedge.

Step 1: Draw line segment *AB*.

Step 2: Place the anchor of the compass on point *A* and the pencil on point *B*. Without changing the compass opening, make a mark above the line segment.

Step 3: Place the anchor on point *B*. Keeping the same compass opening, make a second mark that crosses the first mark. Label the point where the two marks meet *C*.

Step 4: Connect point *C* with points *A* and *B*.

Use your compass and straightedge to construct a very large equilateral triangle on a separate sheet of paper. Cut out your triangle. Divide it into 6 equal parts. Color $\frac{1}{6}$ of it. Tape or paste your triangle on the back of this sheet.

Hint: One way to divide the triangle into 6 equal parts is to put two vertices (corners) together and fold the triangle in half. Then unfold it. Repeat this, using two other vertices. Repeat a third time, using two other vertices.

✦ *Math Masters,* p. 102

7.2 Fractions of Sets

OBJECTIVE **To find fractional parts of sets.**

summaries	materials
1 Teaching the Lesson	
Students find fractions of a whole, when the whole is a collection of objects. [Numeration]	☐ *Math Journal 2,* pp. 193 and 194 ☐ Study Link 7.1 ☐ 20 pennies or other counters ☐ straws or twist-ties (optional) ***See* Advance Preparation**
2 Ongoing Learning & Practice	
Students continue the World Tour. [Measurement and Reference Frames; Operations and Computation] Students practice and maintain skills through Math Boxes and Study Link activities.	☐ *Math Journal 2,* pp. 195 and 345–349 ☐ *Student Reference Book* ☐ Teaching Masters (*Math Masters,* pp. 36–38; optional) ☐ Study Link Master (*Math Masters,* p. 312)
3 Options for Individualizing	
Language Diversity Students match "collection" words with names of things in the collection. **Enrichment** Students write and solve "fraction-of" number stories. [Operations and Computation]	☐ Teaching Master (*Math Masters,* p. 103) ☐ *Only One* ☐ dictionary (optional) ***See* Advance Preparation**

Additional Information

Advance Preparation For Part 1, put a supply of pennies (or other counters) next to the Math Message (at least 20 per student).

For the optional Language Diversity activity in Part 3, obtain the book *Only One* by Marc Harshman (Cobblehill, 1993).

Getting Started

Mental Math and Reflexes

Draw a shape on the board. Divide the shape into parts. Shade a fraction of the shape. Students write the fraction of the shape that is shaded. *Suggestions:*

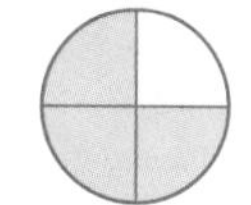

$\frac{3}{4}$

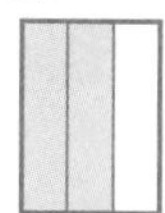

$\frac{2}{3}$

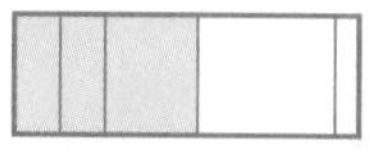

Unable to tell; the shape is not divided into equal parts.

Math Message

Take 20 pennies. What is $\frac{1}{2}$ of 20?

Study Link 7.1 Follow-Up

Review answers.

1 Teaching the Lesson

Math Message Follow-Up

WHOLE-CLASS DISCUSSION

Go over the answer to the problem. 10 Have students share their thinking or strategies for finding the answer.

Modeling "Fraction-of" Problems with Pennies

PARTNER ACTIVITY

Divide the class into partnerships. Ask each partnership to place 24 pennies on the desk or table and to count out $\frac{2}{3}$ of them. Emphasize that the whole is 24 pennies, or 24 cents, not 1 penny. Stress the importance of identifying the whole in any problem involving fractions.

Have students share solution strategies. If no one suggests it, model the following strategy with drawings on the board or overhead projector.

Divide the 24 pennies into 3 equal groups. Separate the groups from one another with straws, twist-ties, or pencils. Say that you want to make 3 "fair shares."

- How much is the whole? 24 pennies, or 24¢
- The pennies in each group represent what fraction of all the pennies? $\frac{1}{3}$
- How many pennies are in each group (or share)? 8 pennies
- How much is $\frac{2}{3}$ of 24 pennies? 16 pennies, or 16¢

Whole
24 pennies

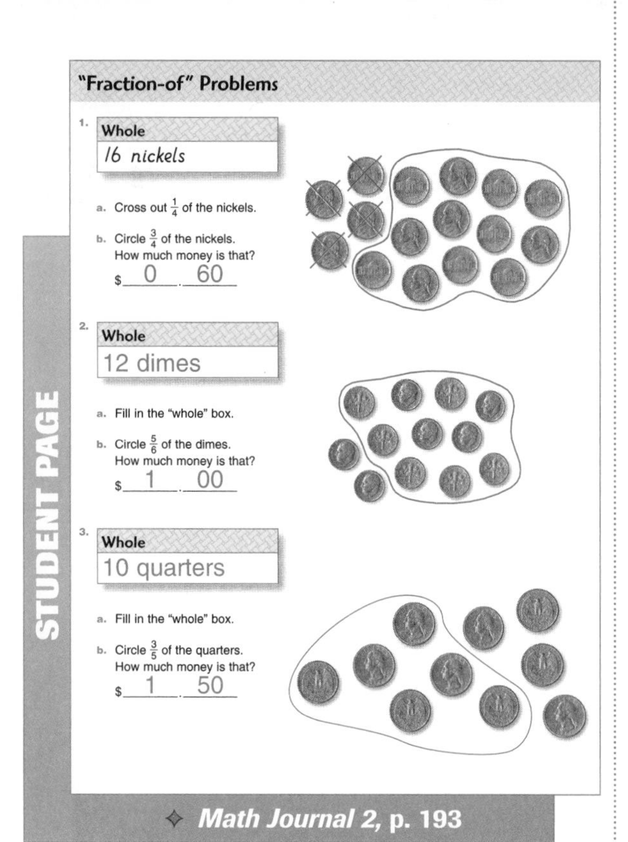
"Fraction-of" Problems

1. Whole: *16 nickels*

a. Cross out $\frac{1}{4}$ of the nickels.

b. Circle $\frac{3}{4}$ of the nickels. How much money is that? $ 0 . 60

2. Whole: 12 dimes

a. Fill in the "whole" box.

b. Circle $\frac{5}{6}$ of the dimes. How much money is that? $ 1 . 00

3. Whole: 10 quarters

a. Fill in the "whole" box.

b. Circle $\frac{3}{5}$ of the quarters. How much money is that? $ 1 . 50

STUDENT PAGE

✦ *Math Journal 2,* p. 193

Summary: One way to find $\frac{2}{3}$ of 24 is to first find $\frac{1}{3}$ of 24. 8 Since $\frac{1}{3}$ of 24 is 8, $\frac{2}{3}$ of 24 must be twice as much. 16

$\frac{1}{3}$ of 24 = 8

$\frac{2}{3}$ of 24 = 16

Pose similar problems and have students model the solutions with pennies. *Suggestions:*

- How much is $\frac{1}{4}$ of 32¢? 8¢ $\frac{2}{4}$ of 32¢? 16¢ $\frac{3}{4}$ of 32¢? 24¢
- How much is $\frac{2}{5}$ of 30¢? 12¢ $\frac{4}{5}$ of 20¢? 16¢
- How much is $\frac{2}{3}$ of 27¢? 18¢ $\frac{5}{6}$ of 30¢? 25¢ $\frac{3}{8}$ of 40¢? 15¢

✦ Solving "Fraction-of" Problems
(*Math Journal 2,* pp. 193 and 194)

PARTNER ACTIVITY

Suggest that students use pennies to model the "fraction-of" problems on journal pages 193 and 194.

Adjusting the Activity For Problem 13, point out that $\frac{2}{4}$ is another name for $\frac{1}{2}$. Renaming $\frac{2}{4}$ as $\frac{1}{2}$ makes it easier to solve the problem.

"Fraction-of" Problems (cont.)

4. Michael had 20 baseball cards. He gave $\frac{1}{5}$ of them to his friend, Alana, and $\frac{2}{5}$ to his brother, Dean.

a. How many baseball cards did he give to Alana? 4 cards

b. How many did he give to Dean? 8 cards

c. How many did he keep for himself? 8 cards

Solve.

5. $\frac{1}{3}$ of 12 = 4　6. $\frac{2}{3}$ of 12 = 8　7. $\frac{3}{5}$ of 15 = 9

8. $\frac{3}{4}$ of 36 = 27　9. $\frac{5}{8}$ of 32 = 20　10. $\frac{4}{6}$ of 24 = 16

11. $\frac{2}{5}$ of 30 = 12　12. $\frac{5}{6}$ of 30 = 25　13. $\frac{2}{4}$ of 14 = 7

14. What is $\frac{1}{2}$ of 25? $12\frac{1}{2}$ Explain. Sample answer: 25 = 20 + 5. Half of 20 is 10. Half of 5 is $2\frac{1}{2}$. 10 + $2\frac{1}{2}$ = $12\frac{1}{2}$.

15. Maurice spent $\frac{1}{2}$ of his money on lunch. He had $2.50 left. How much money did he start with? $5.00

16. Erika spent $\frac{3}{4}$ of her money on lunch. She had $2.00 left. How much money did she start with? $8.00

STUDENT PAGE

✦ *Math Journal 2,* p. 194

2 Ongoing Learning & Practice

✦ Continuing the World Tour (*Math Journal 2,* pp. 345–349; *Student Reference Book; Math Masters,* pp. 36–38)

INDEPENDENT ACTIVITY 

Social Studies Link Students follow the established World Tour routine.

▷ They update the Route Map by drawing a line to connect Budapest, Hungary, and Brasília, Brazil.

▷ They use the World Tour section of the *Student Reference Book* to locate facts about Brazil and Brasília and then fill in the Country Notes pages for this country and capital.

▷ If they are keeping a Route Log, they update it.

Allow students a week or more to complete the Country Notes pages. The second page of Country Notes provides space for students to record interesting facts about the countries they are visiting. Discourage rote copying of facts. Encourage students to use classroom and library resources to collect facts they find interesting.

✦ Math Boxes 7.2 (*Math Journal 2,* p. 195)

INDEPENDENT ACTIVITY 

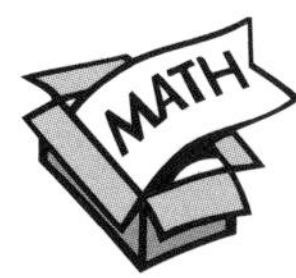

Mixed Review Math Boxes in this lesson are paired with Math Boxes in Lesson 7.4. The skill in Problem 1 is a prerequisite for Unit 8.

✦ Study Link 7.2 (*Math Masters,* p. 312)

Home Connection Students solve "fraction-of" problems. You may wish to ask students to underline the number that represents the "whole" in Problems 2–12.

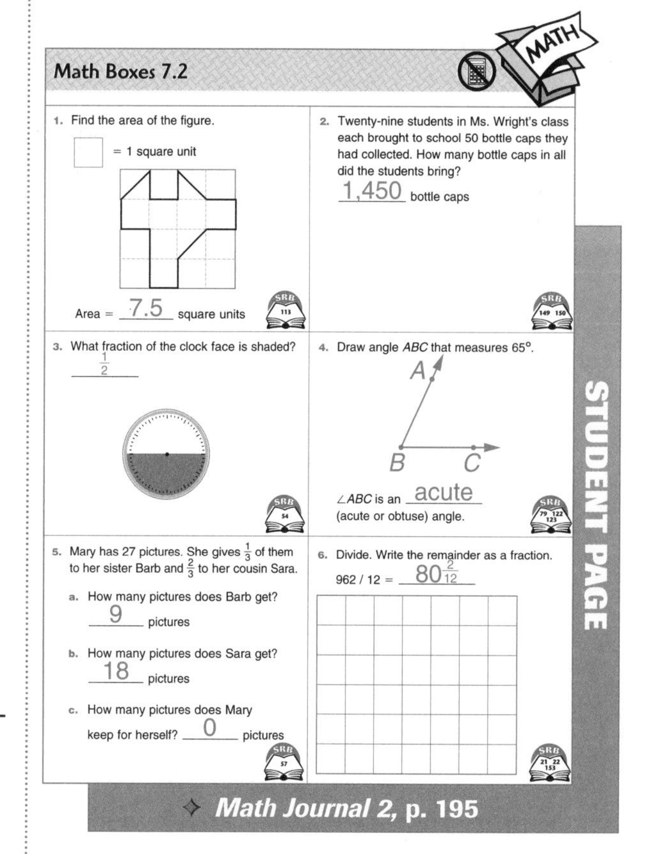

Math Boxes 7.2

1. Find the area of the figure.
   □ = 1 square unit
   Area = 7.5 square units
2. Twenty-nine students in Ms. Wright's class each brought to school 50 bottle caps they had collected. How many bottle caps in all did the students bring?
   1,450 bottle caps
3. What fraction of the clock face is shaded?
   $\frac{1}{2}$
4. Draw angle *ABC* that measures 65°.
   ∠*ABC* is an acute (acute or obtuse) angle.
5. Mary has 27 pictures. She gives $\frac{1}{3}$ of them to her sister Barb and $\frac{2}{3}$ to her cousin Sara.
   a. How many pictures does Barb get? 9 pictures
   b. How many pictures does Sara get? 18 pictures
   c. How many pictures does Mary keep for herself? 0 pictures
6. Divide. Write the remainder as a fraction.
   962 / 12 = $80\frac{2}{12}$

STUDENT PAGE

✦ *Math Journal 2,* p. 195

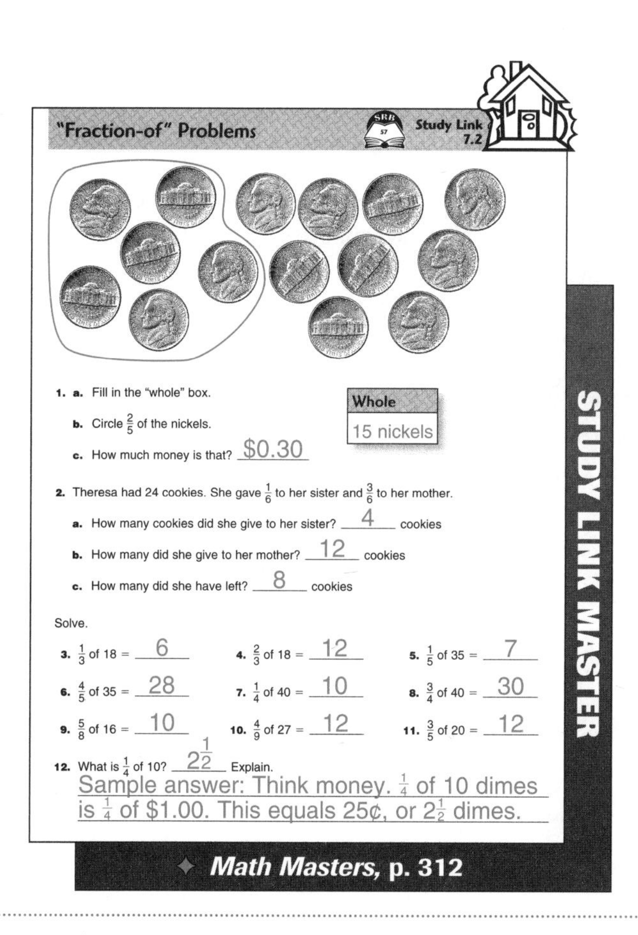

"Fraction-of" Problems — Study Link 7.2

1. a. Fill in the "whole" box.
   b. Circle $\frac{2}{5}$ of the nickels.
   c. How much money is that? $0.30

Whole
15 nickels

2. Theresa had 24 cookies. She gave $\frac{1}{6}$ to her sister and $\frac{3}{6}$ to her mother.
   a. How many cookies did she give to her sister? 4 cookies
   b. How many did she give to her mother? 12 cookies
   c. How many did she have left? 8 cookies

Solve.

3. $\frac{1}{3}$ of 18 = 6
4. $\frac{2}{3}$ of 18 = 12
5. $\frac{1}{5}$ of 35 = 7
6. $\frac{4}{5}$ of 35 = 28
7. $\frac{1}{4}$ of 40 = 10
8. $\frac{3}{4}$ of 40 = 30
9. $\frac{5}{8}$ of 16 = 10
10. $\frac{4}{9}$ of 27 = 12
11. $\frac{3}{5}$ of 20 = 12
12. What is $\frac{1}{4}$ of 10? $2\frac{1}{2}$ Explain.
    Sample answer: Think money. $\frac{1}{4}$ of 10 dimes is $\frac{1}{4}$ of $1.00. This equals 25¢, or $2\frac{1}{2}$ dimes.

STUDY LINK MASTER

✦ *Math Masters,* p. 312

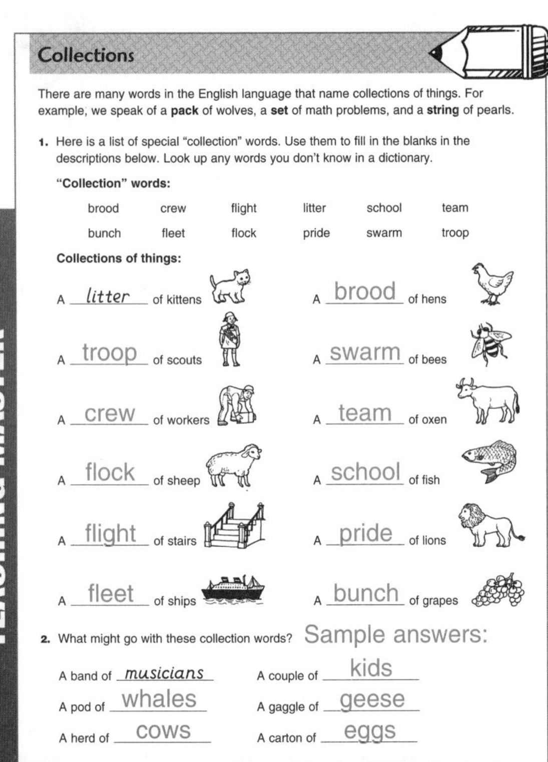
Collections

There are many words in the English language that name collections of things. For example, we speak of a **pack** of wolves, a **set** of math problems, and a **string** of pearls.

1. Here is a list of special "collection" words. Use them to fill in the blanks in the descriptions below. Look up any words you don't know in a dictionary.

"Collection" words:

brood	crew	flight	litter	school	team
bunch	fleet	flock	pride	swarm	troop

Collections of things:

A litter of kittens — A brood of hens

A troop of scouts — A swarm of bees

A crew of workers — A team of oxen

A flock of sheep — A school of fish

A flight of stairs — A pride of lions

A fleet of ships — A bunch of grapes

2. What might go with these collection words? Sample answers:

A band of musicians — A couple of kids

A pod of whales — A gaggle of geese

A herd of cows — A carton of eggs

TEACHING MASTER

✦ *Math Masters,* p. 103

3 Options for Individualizing

✦ LANGUAGE DIVERSITY Matching "Collection" Words with Names of Things (*Math Masters,* p. 103)

PARTNER ACTIVITY **15–30 min**

Language Arts Link There are many words in the English language that name sets or collections of things—a *bouquet* of flowers, a *slate* of candidates, a *ream* of paper, and so on.

Pair a student learning English with a proficient English speaker. Have students match "collection" words with the names of the things in the collections.

As an additional activity, read the following book or have students read it on their own:

Only One

Summary: The book identifies objects that make up a collection. For example, "There may be a million stars, but there is only one sky. There may be 11 cows, but there is only one herd."

✦ ENRICHMENT Writing and Solving "Fraction-of" Number Stories

PARTNER ACTIVITY  **15–30 min**

Students write "fraction-of" number stories. They exchange stories with a partner to solve and revise if necessary.

Example: A colony of 24 ants was marching up an anthill. $\frac{2}{3}$ of the ants each carried 2 blades of grass. The rest carried only 1 blade of grass. How many ants carried just 1 blade? 8 ants How many blades of grass did the whole colony carry? 40 blades

7.3 Pattern-Block Fractions

OBJECTIVE **To find fractional parts of polygonal regions.**

summaries	materials
1 Teaching the Lesson	
Students use pattern blocks to partition 2-dimensional shapes, and they name fractional parts of regions. [Geometry; Numeration]	□ *Math Journal 2,* pp. 196–198 □ Study Link 7.2 □ Teaching Master (*Math Masters,* p. 104) □ Transparency (*Math Masters,* p. 104; optional) □ pattern blocks □ pattern blocks for overhead (optional) □ straightedge □ dictionary (optional) ***See* Advance Preparation**
2 Ongoing Learning & Practice	
Students practice and maintain skills through Math Boxes and Study Link activities.	□ *Math Journal 2,* p. 199 □ Study Link Master (*Math Masters,* p. 313)
3 Options for Individualizing	
Enrichment Students explore tangrams. [Geometry]	□ Teaching Master (*Math Masters,* p. 105) □ *Grandfather Tang's Story* □ envelope ***See* Advance Preparation**

Additional Information

Advance Preparation This lesson may take two days. For Part 1, each partnership or small group will need at least 2 yellow, 4 red, 4 blue, and 6 green pattern blocks.

For the optional Enrichment activity in Part 3, make one copy per student of the tangram puzzle on *Math Masters,* page 105—on cardstock, if possible. Cut each copy in half along the dashed line. Cut apart the 7 tangram shapes on the top half and put them in an envelope. Provide the bottom half of *Math Masters,* page 105 as a template. Also, obtain the book *Grandfather Tang's Story* by Ann Tompert (Crown, 1990).

Getting Started

Mental Math and Reflexes

Pose "fraction-of" problems. *Suggestions:*

- $\frac{1}{4}$ of 20¢ 5¢
  $\frac{3}{4}$ of 20¢ 15¢
- $\frac{1}{6}$ of 24¢ 4¢
  $\frac{5}{6}$ of 24¢ 20¢
- $\frac{1}{5}$ of 45¢ 9¢
  $\frac{4}{5}$ of 45¢ 36¢

Math Message

$\frac{1}{2}$ *of the students in Mrs. Lopez's class went to the soccer game.*

$\frac{1}{2}$ *of the students in Mr. Williams's class also went to the game.*

Did the same number of students from each class go to the game?

Study Link 7.2 Follow-Up

Review answers. If students are having difficulty with Problem 12, suggest that they approach the problem in terms of money. Ask questions like the following:

- What is $\frac{1}{4}$ of \$1.00? 1 quarter, or 25¢
- If you have \$10.00, what is $\frac{1}{4}$ of that amount? 10 quarters, which is equal to \$2.50, or $2\frac{1}{2}$

1 Teaching the Lesson

✦ Math Message Follow-Up

WHOLE-CLASS DISCUSSION

As students share their ideas, help them understand that a fraction is not meaningful if one does not know what it is a fraction of—that is, what the "whole" is. For example, half of each class went to the game, but the classes may have different numbers of students.

✦ Exploring Fractional Parts of Regions with Pattern Blocks

WHOLE-CLASS ACTIVITY

Lesson 7.3 consists of three sets of problems. Each set requires the use of one of the three shapes on *Math Masters,* page 104 and a set of pattern blocks. Each shape is actual pattern-block size so that it can be completely covered by pattern blocks.

In each set of problems, students do the following:

1. Determine what fraction of the shape is covered by each pattern block.
2. Cover the shape on the master with a combination of pattern blocks, not all the same size and shape.
3. Record a partition of the shape on journal page 196, 197, or 198.
4. Label each fractional part of the shape with a fraction.

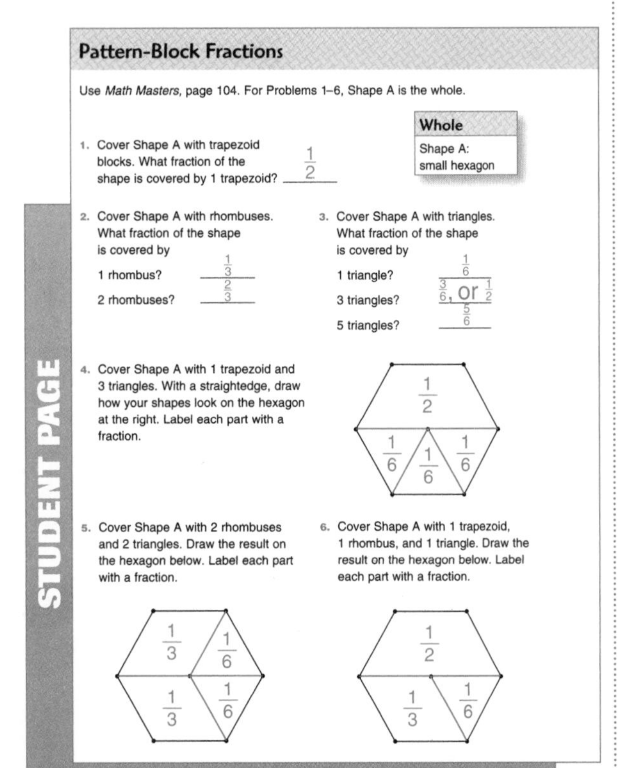

Pattern-Block Fractions

Use *Math Masters,* page 104. For Problems 1–6, Shape A is the whole.

Whole: Shape A: small hexagon

1. Cover Shape A with trapezoid blocks. What fraction of the shape is covered by 1 trapezoid? $\frac{1}{2}$
2. Cover Shape A with rhombuses. What fraction of the shape is covered by
   1 rhombus? $\frac{1}{3}$
   2 rhombuses? $\frac{2}{3}$
3. Cover Shape A with triangles. What fraction of the shape is covered by
   1 triangle? $\frac{1}{6}$
   3 triangles? $\frac{3}{6}$, or $\frac{1}{2}$
   5 triangles? $\frac{5}{6}$
4. Cover Shape A with 1 trapezoid and 3 triangles. With a straightedge, draw how your shapes look on the hexagon at the right. Label each part with a fraction.
5. Cover Shape A with 2 rhombuses and 2 triangles. Draw the result on the hexagon below. Label each part with a fraction.
6. Cover Shape A with 1 trapezoid, 1 rhombus, and 1 triangle. Draw the result on the hexagon below. Label each part with a fraction.

STUDENT PAGE

✦ *Math Journal 2,* p. 196

Adjusting the Activity For those students who are learning English, have them look up the word *pattern* in the dictionary. Help them identify or find examples of patterns inside or outside the classroom. Ask them to explain why they think the blocks they are using are called "pattern blocks."

Solving Problems about Shape A
(*Math Journal 2,* p. 196; *Math Masters,* p. 104)

WHOLE-CLASS ACTIVITY

Form partnerships or small groups and pass out pattern blocks, but work with the whole class on Problems 1–6 on journal page 196.

Students should use Shape A on *Math Masters,* page 104 for the problems on this journal page. Ask the questions on page 196, one at a time. Have students solve them using pattern blocks and then record their answers in the journal. You might want to use an overhead transparency of the master and overhead pattern blocks while you discuss the problems and answers.

Solving Problems about Shape B
(*Math Journal 2,* p. 197; *Math Masters,* p. 104)

PARTNER ACTIVITY

Before students begin Problems 7–12 on journal page 197, point out that Shape B is not the same size as Shape A, and therefore, each pattern block takes on a different fractional value. Let students work with their partners or small groups on this set of problems while you circulate. Then bring the class together and discuss solutions.

Solving Problems about Shape C
(*Math Journal 2,* p. 198; *Math Masters,* p. 104)

PARTNER ACTIVITY

Problems 13–16 on journal page 198 may prove to be quite challenging. Because it is not possible to completely cover Shape C with hexagon blocks, students will have to determine the fractional value of a hexagon block based on the fractional values of other pattern blocks. (For example, since two trapezoids make one hexagon and one trapezoid is $\frac{1}{8}$ of Shape C, a hexagon is $\frac{2}{8}$, or $\frac{1}{4}$, of Shape C.) Note that Problem 16 has a number of solutions.

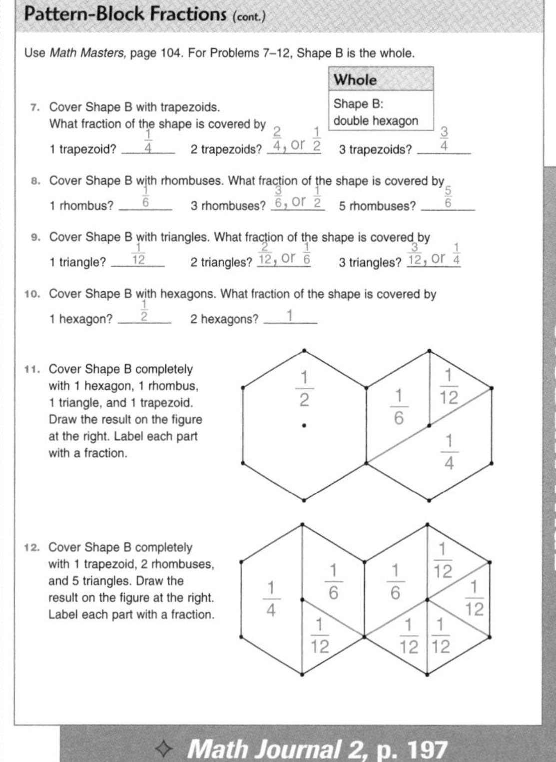

Pattern-Block Fractions (cont.)

Use *Math Masters,* page 104. For Problems 7–12, Shape B is the whole.

Whole
Shape B: double hexagon

7. Cover Shape B with trapezoids. What fraction of the shape is covered by 1 trapezoid? $\frac{1}{4}$ 2 trapezoids? $\frac{2}{4}$, or $\frac{1}{2}$ 3 trapezoids? $\frac{3}{4}$
8. Cover Shape B with rhombuses. What fraction of the shape is covered by 1 rhombus? $\frac{1}{6}$ 3 rhombuses? $\frac{3}{6}$, or $\frac{1}{2}$ 5 rhombuses? $\frac{5}{6}$
9. Cover Shape B with triangles. What fraction of the shape is covered by 1 triangle? $\frac{1}{12}$ 2 triangles? $\frac{2}{12}$, or $\frac{1}{6}$ 3 triangles? $\frac{3}{12}$, or $\frac{1}{4}$
10. Cover Shape B with hexagons. What fraction of the shape is covered by 1 hexagon? $\frac{1}{2}$ 2 hexagons? 1
11. Cover Shape B completely with 1 hexagon, 1 rhombus, 1 triangle, and 1 trapezoid. Draw the result on the figure at the right. Label each part with a fraction.
12. Cover Shape B completely with 1 trapezoid, 2 rhombuses, and 5 triangles. Draw the result on the figure at the right. Label each part with a fraction.

STUDENT PAGE

◆ *Math Journal 2,* p. 197

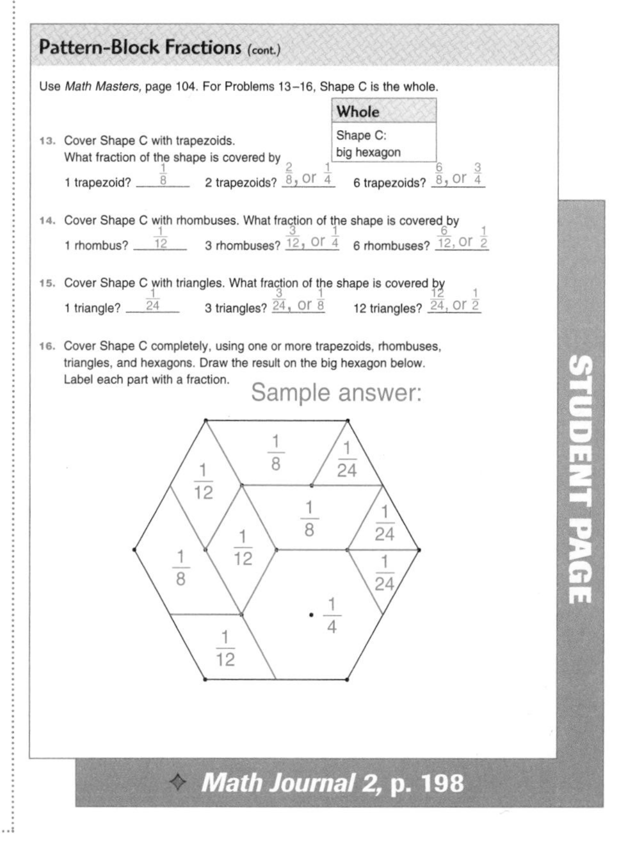

Pattern-Block Fractions (cont.)

Use *Math Masters,* page 104. For Problems 13–16, Shape C is the whole.

Whole
Shape C: big hexagon

13. Cover Shape C with trapezoids. What fraction of the shape is covered by 1 trapezoid? $\frac{1}{8}$ 2 trapezoids? $\frac{2}{8}$, or $\frac{1}{4}$ 6 trapezoids? $\frac{6}{8}$, or $\frac{3}{4}$
14. Cover Shape C with rhombuses. What fraction of the shape is covered by 1 rhombus? $\frac{1}{12}$ 3 rhombuses? $\frac{3}{12}$, or $\frac{1}{4}$ 6 rhombuses? $\frac{6}{12}$, or $\frac{1}{2}$
15. Cover Shape C with triangles. What fraction of the shape is covered by 1 triangle? $\frac{1}{24}$ 3 triangles? $\frac{3}{24}$, or $\frac{1}{8}$ 12 triangles? $\frac{12}{24}$, or $\frac{1}{2}$
16. Cover Shape C completely, using one or more trapezoids, rhombuses, triangles, and hexagons. Draw the result on the big hexagon below. Label each part with a fraction.

Sample answer:

STUDENT PAGE

◆ *Math Journal 2,* p. 198

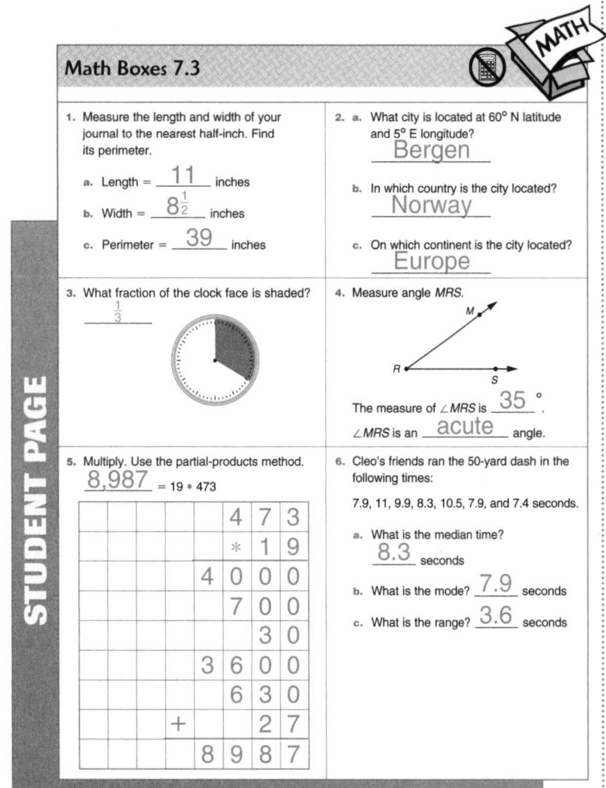
Math Boxes 7.3

1. Measure the length and width of your journal to the nearest half-inch. Find its perimeter.
   a. Length = 11 inches
   b. Width = $8\frac{1}{2}$ inches
   c. Perimeter = 39 inches

2. a. What city is located at 60° N latitude and 5° E longitude? Bergen
   b. In which country is the city located? Norway
   c. On which continent is the city located? Europe

3. What fraction of the clock face is shaded? $\frac{1}{3}$

4. Measure angle *MRS*.
   The measure of ∠*MRS* is 35 °.
   ∠*MRS* is an acute angle.

5. Multiply. Use the partial-products method.
   8,987 = 19 ∗ 473

			4	7	3
			∗	1	9
		4	0	0	0
			7	0	0
				3	0
		3	6	0	0
			6	3	0
	+			2	7
		8	9	8	7

6. Cleo's friends ran the 50-yard dash in the following times:
   7.9, 11, 9.9, 8.3, 10.5, 7.9, and 7.4 seconds.
   a. What is the median time? 8.3 seconds
   b. What is the mode? 7.9 seconds
   c. What is the range? 3.6 seconds

STUDENT PAGE

Math Journal 2, p. 199

ONGOING ASSESSMENT

Make sure that students understand why the same pattern blocks take on different fractional values for each of Shapes A, B, and C. The shapes represent different wholes.

Help students see the relationship between the size of Shape A and Shape B and how this relationship affects the fractional values of the pattern blocks: Shape B is twice the size of Shape A. Therefore, the fractional value of each pattern block for Shape B is half its fractional value for Shape A.

Ask: *Shape C is how many times the size of Shape A?* 4 times *How can you tell?* Possible response: It takes 8 trapezoids to cover Shape C and 2 trapezoids to cover Shape A.

2 Ongoing Learning & Practice

✦Math Boxes 7.3 (*Math Journal 2,* p. 199)

INDEPENDENT ACTIVITY 

Mixed Review Math Boxes in this lesson are paired with Math Boxes in Lesson 7.1. The skill in Problem 1 is a prerequisite for Unit 8.

✦Study Link 7.3 (*Math Masters,* p. 313)

Home Connection Students divide squares into fourths and eighths in different ways.

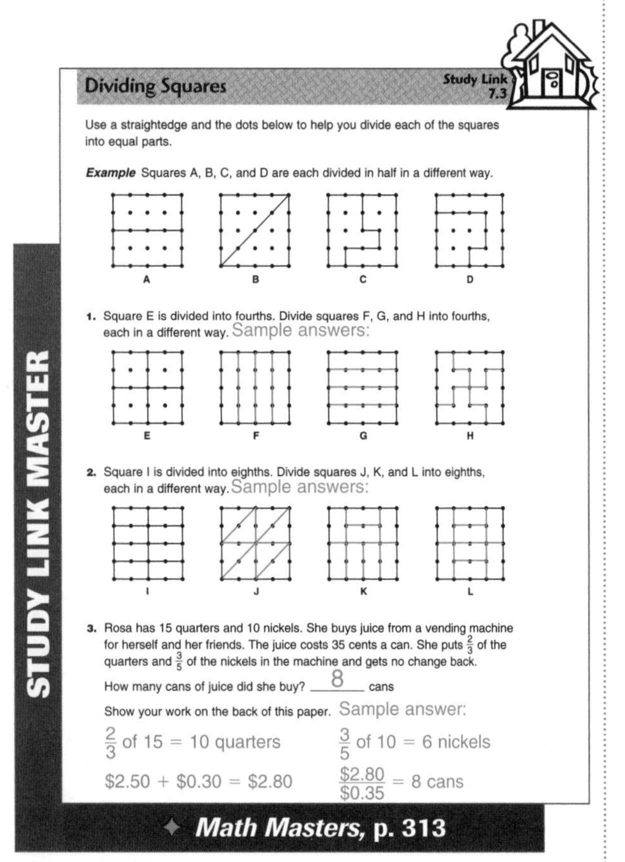
Dividing Squares — Study Link 7.3

Use a straightedge and the dots below to help you divide each of the squares into equal parts.

Example Squares A, B, C, and D are each divided in half in a different way.

A B C D

1. Square E is divided into fourths. Divide squares F, G, and H into fourths, each in a different way. Sample answers:

E F G H

2. Square I is divided into eighths. Divide squares J, K, and L into eighths, each in a different way. Sample answers:

I J K L

3. Rosa has 15 quarters and 10 nickels. She buys juice from a vending machine for herself and her friends. The juice costs 35 cents a can. She puts $\frac{2}{3}$ of the quarters and $\frac{3}{5}$ of the nickels in the machine and gets no change back.

How many cans of juice did she buy? 8 cans

Show your work on the back of this paper. Sample answer:

$\frac{2}{3}$ of 15 = 10 quarters $\frac{3}{5}$ of 10 = 6 nickels

\$2.50 + \$0.30 = \$2.80 $\frac{\$2.80}{\$0.35}$ = 8 cans

STUDY LINK MASTER

Math Masters, p. 313

Options for Individualizing

ENRICHMENT Exploring Tangrams
(*Math Masters,* p. 105)

INDEPENDENT ACTIVITY  **15–30 min** 

Literature Link If students enjoyed covering shapes, they may also enjoy working with tangrams, a popular geometric puzzle.

Provide the 7 tangram pieces and the template from *Math Masters,* page 105. Challenge students to put the 7 pieces together to form the template square.

If interest in this activity is high, challenge students to make other geometric shapes, such as a triangle or a trapezoid using all 7 pieces. You can find additional tangram puzzles in many commercially available books.

As a follow-up activity, read the following book aloud or have students read it on their own:

Grandfather Tang's Story

Summary: The book is about two foxes, Chou and Wu Ling, and their quest to outdo each other by changing themselves into different animals. Each fox is represented by a set of 7 tangram pieces. Each time a fox changes into a new animal, its set of tangram pieces is rearranged.

Technology Link For a possible research topic, have students use the Internet to find out information about tangram puzzles: find out from which country these puzzles originated and any interesting facts about these puzzles that could be shared with the class.

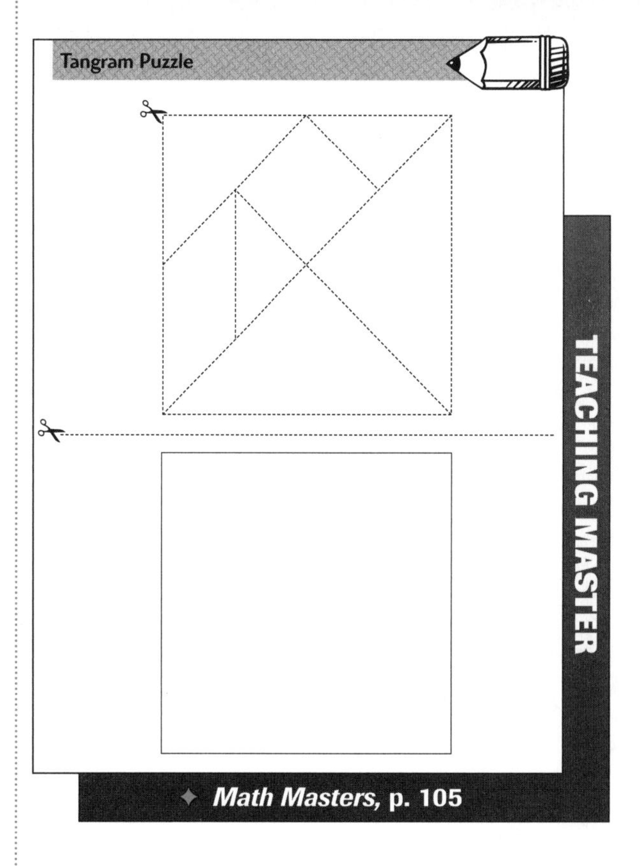

Math Masters, p. 105

7.4 Fraction Addition and Subtraction

OBJECTIVE **To use pattern blocks to help add and subtract fractions.**

summaries	materials
1 Teaching the Lesson	
Students model fraction sums and differences with pattern blocks. [Operations and Computation; Numeration]	☐ *Math Journal 2,* p. 200 ☐ Study Link 7.3 ☐ pattern blocks ☐ pattern blocks for overhead (optional)
2 Ongoing Learning & Practice	
Students prepare Fraction Cards for use in Lesson 7.6. Students practice and maintain skills through Math Boxes and Study Link activities.	☐ *Math Journal 2,* p. 201; Activity Sheets 5 and 6 ☐ Study Link Master (*Math Masters,* p. 314) ☐ rubber band
3 Options for Individualizing	
Extra Practice Students draw and compare line segments. [Geometry]	☐ Teaching Master (*Math Masters,* p. 106)

Getting Started

Mental Math and Reflexes

Write fractions like the following on the board. Students indicate whether each fraction is closest to 0, $\frac{1}{2}$, or 1 and give an explanation for their answer.

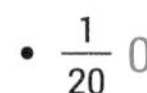

- $\frac{1}{20}$ 0
- $\frac{9}{10}$ 1
- $\frac{48}{50}$ 1
- $\frac{5}{8}$ $\frac{1}{2}$
- $\frac{3}{16}$ 0
- $\frac{8}{15}$ $\frac{1}{2}$

Math Message

If the hexagon pattern block is the whole, what fractions are represented by the trapezoid, the rhombus, and the triangle?

Study Link 7.3 Follow-Up

Ask students to share their solution strategies for Problem 3. Possible response: $\frac{2}{3}$ of 15 quarters = 10 quarters, or \$2.50; $\frac{3}{5}$ of 10 nickels = 6 nickels, or 30 cents. Therefore, Rosa spent \$2.50 + \$0.30 = \$2.80. Since each can costs 35 cents, she was able to buy 8 cans with the money.

Teaching the Lesson

Math Message Follow-Up

WHOLE-CLASS ACTIVITY

Go over the answers with the class. The trapezoid represents $\frac{1}{2}$, the rhombus represents $\frac{1}{3}$, and the triangle represents $\frac{1}{6}$.

Ask students to use a trapezoid, a rhombus, and a triangle to form a hexagon. Ask what number model describes what they just did. $\frac{1}{2} + \frac{1}{3} + \frac{1}{6} = 1$ Tell students that in this lesson they will use pattern blocks to model fraction addition and subtraction problems.

NOTE: For all of the activities in Part 1 of this lesson, the hexagon pattern block represents 1, the whole.

Modeling Fraction Sums with Pattern Blocks

WHOLE-CLASS ACTIVITY

Use pattern blocks on the overhead projector to work through one or two more fraction addition problems with the class. *Suggestions:*

- ▷ $\frac{2}{3} + \frac{1}{6} = ?$ $\frac{5}{6}$
- ▷ $\frac{1}{3} + \frac{1}{2} = ?$ $\frac{5}{6}$
- ▷ $\frac{5}{6} + \frac{1}{3} = ?$ $\frac{7}{6}$, or $1\frac{1}{6}$

You can either let students devise their own methods or demonstrate the following step-by-step procedure:

Step 1: Use pattern blocks to model the fractions to be added.

Step 2: Combine the blocks to show the sum.

Step 3: Trade the blocks in the sum for blocks of a single type.

Step 4: Name the fraction for the sum.

Example: $\frac{2}{3} + \frac{1}{6} = ?$

Step 1: Model the fractions to be added.

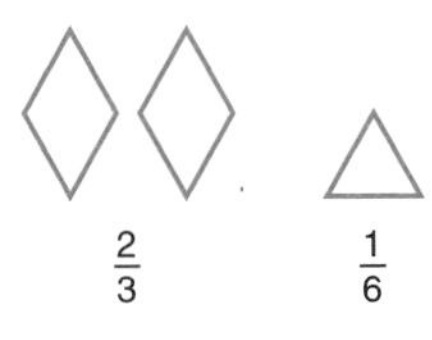

NOTE: If you have an overhead projector, you can use regular pattern blocks to illustrate the problem and its solution. Overhead pattern blocks are useful but not necessary.

Step 2: Combine the blocks to show the sum.

$\frac{2}{3} + \frac{1}{6}$

Step 3: Trade for one kind of block.

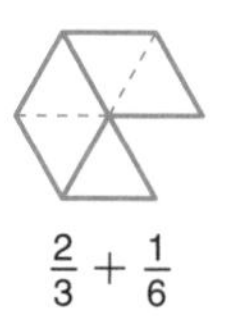

Step 4: Name the fraction for the sum.

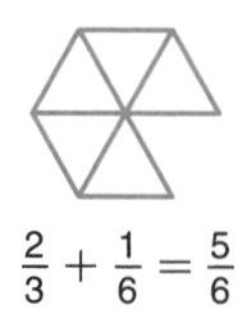

Modeling Fraction Differences with Pattern Blocks

WHOLE-CLASS ACTIVITY

Ask students how they could use pattern blocks to solve $\frac{5}{6} - \frac{2}{3}$. After a few minutes, ask students to share their approaches. Subtraction can be harder to model than addition, so students' methods may be awkward. Below are two approaches that work well.

Cover-Up Method

Model both fractions with pattern blocks. Then put the blocks representing the smaller fraction on top of the blocks representing the larger fraction. The part of the larger fraction that remains uncovered is the difference.

Example: $\frac{5}{6} - \frac{2}{3} = ?$

Step 1: Model the fractions with pattern blocks.

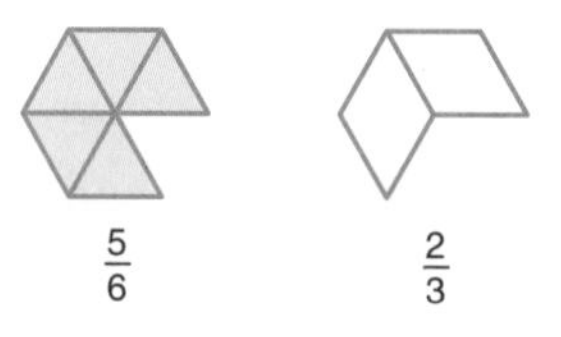

Step 2: Cover up the larger fraction with the smaller.

$\frac{5}{6} - \frac{2}{3}$

Step 3: The uncovered part of the larger fraction is the difference. The uncovered part is a triangle representing $\frac{1}{6}$. So, $\frac{5}{6} - \frac{2}{3} = \frac{1}{6}$.

Take-Away Method

Model the larger fraction with pattern blocks. Then take away blocks representing the smaller fraction, trading for blocks of the proper size if necessary. The remaining blocks represent the difference.

Example: $\frac{5}{6} - \frac{2}{3} = ?$

Step 1: Model the larger fraction with pattern blocks.

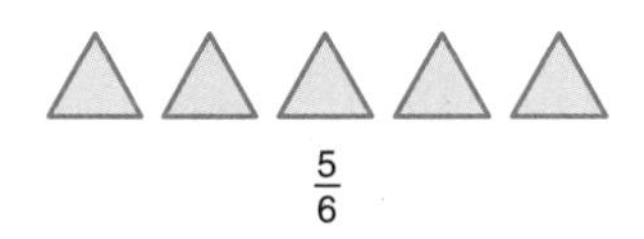

$\frac{5}{6}$

Step 2: Remove blocks representing the smaller fraction. The smaller number, $\frac{2}{3}$, can be represented by 2 rhombuses. Since there are no rhombuses, trade 4 triangles for 2 rhombuses. Then remove 2 rhombuses.

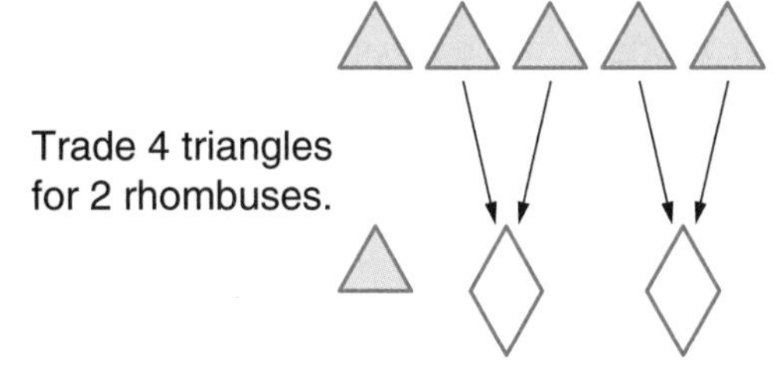
Trade 4 triangles
for 2 rhombuses.

Take away
2 rhombuses.

Step 3: The block(s) that are left represent the difference.

$\frac{5}{6} - \frac{2}{3} = \frac{1}{6}$

Pose fraction subtraction problems for students to solve with pattern blocks. *Suggestions:*

- $\frac{2}{3} - \frac{1}{2} = \frac{1}{6}$
- $\frac{1}{2} - \frac{1}{3} = \frac{1}{6}$
- $1\frac{1}{3} - \frac{5}{6} = \frac{3}{6}$, or $\frac{1}{2}$
- $\frac{2}{3} - \frac{1}{6} = \frac{3}{6}$, or $\frac{1}{2}$
- $1\frac{1}{2} - \frac{2}{3} = \frac{5}{6}$

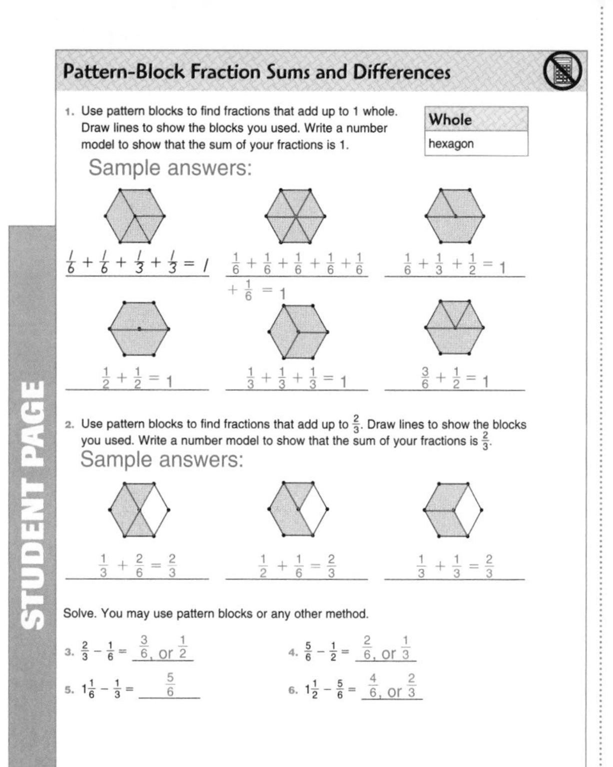

Pattern-Block Fraction Sums and Differences
1. Use pattern blocks to find fractions that add up to 1 whole. Draw lines to show the blocks you used. Write a number model to show that the sum of your fractions is 1.
Whole
hexagon
Sample answers:
2. Use pattern blocks to find fractions that add up to 2/3. Draw lines to show the blocks you used. Write a number model to show that the sum of your fractions is 2/3.
Sample answers:
Solve. You may use pattern blocks or any other method.
STUDENT PAGE

◆ *Math Journal 2*, p. 200

ONGOING ASSESSMENT

The purpose of these activities is not to teach students to add and subtract fractions with unlike denominators using common denominators, but to provide initial exposure to these kinds of problems using concrete models. Paper-and-pencil methods for fraction addition and subtraction are treated in *Fifth Grade Everyday Mathematics.*

To check students' understanding of adding and subtracting fractions, provide opportunities for them to verbally explain their answers using pattern blocks to model the problems.

◆ Solving Fraction Addition and Subtraction Problems (*Math Journal 2,* p. 200)

PARTNER ACTIVITY 

Students use pattern blocks to solve fraction addition problems. They use pattern blocks or any other method to solve fraction subtraction problems. When solutions are discussed for Problems 1 and 2, be sure to point out alternative number models for some of the problems. For example, $\frac{1}{3} + \frac{1}{3} + \frac{1}{6} + \frac{1}{6} = 1$ and $\frac{2}{3} + \frac{2}{6} = 1$ are two models that could be used for Problem 1.

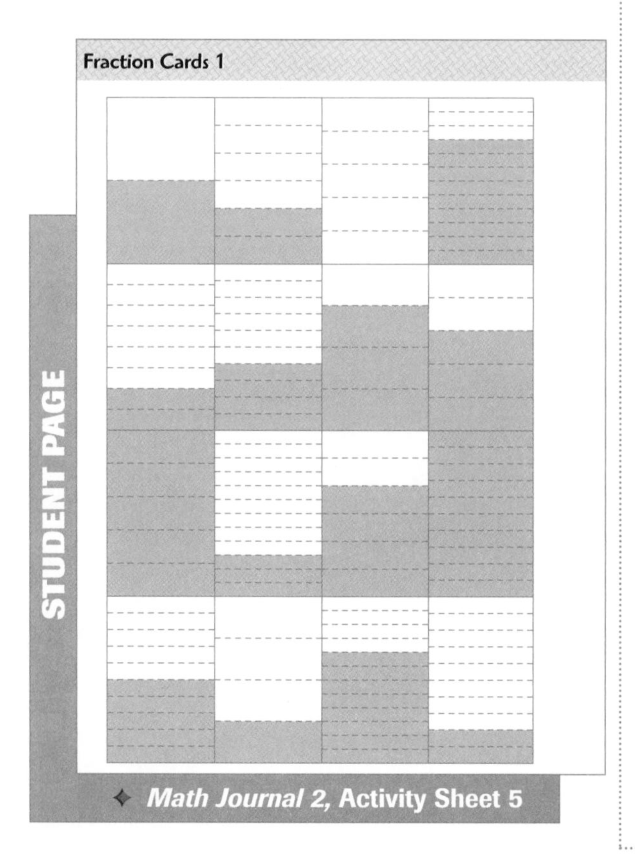

◆ *Math Journal 2*, Activity Sheet 5

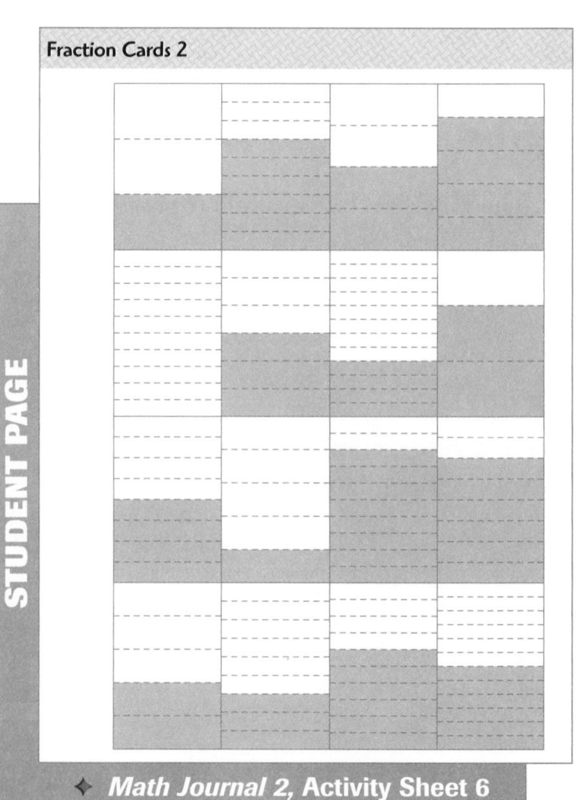

◆ *Math Journal 2*, Activity Sheet 6

2 Ongoing Learning & Practice

Preparing Fraction Cards for Lesson 7.6 (*Math Journal 2,* Activity Sheets 5 and 6)

INDEPENDENT ACTIVITY 

Direct students to carefully remove Activity Sheets 5 and 6 from the back of the journal. Have them cut the Fraction Cards apart along the solid lines and hold the cards together with a rubber band. You may wish to have students mark each of their cards with their initials for easy identification. The Fraction Cards will be used in Lesson 7.6.

NOTE: It is important that the cards are cut out carefully. You may wish to have a student or adult volunteer prepare the cards for those who are not dexterous.

Math Boxes 7.4 (*Math Journal 2,* p. 201)

INDEPENDENT ACTIVITY 

Mixed Review Math Boxes in this lesson are paired with Math Boxes in Lesson 7.2. The skill in Problem 1 is a prerequisite for Unit 8.

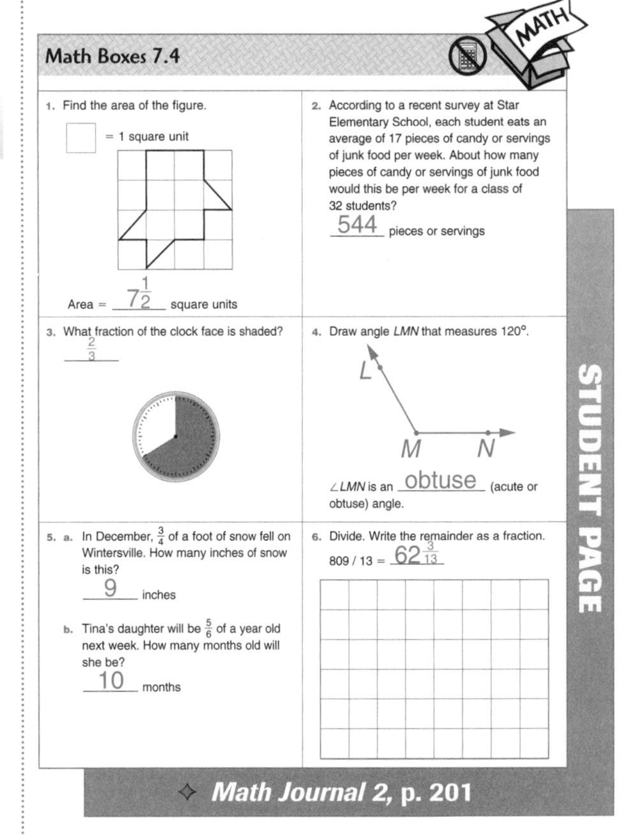

Math Boxes 7.4

1. Find the area of the figure.
   □ = 1 square unit
   Area = $7\frac{1}{2}$ square units
2. According to a recent survey at Star Elementary School, each student eats an average of 17 pieces of candy or servings of junk food per week. About how many pieces of candy or servings of junk food would this be per week for a class of 32 students?
   544 pieces or servings
3. What fraction of the clock face is shaded? $\frac{2}{3}$
4. Draw angle *LMN* that measures 120°.
   ∠*LMN* is an obtuse (acute or obtuse) angle.
5. a. In December, $\frac{3}{4}$ of a foot of snow fell on Wintersville. How many inches of snow is this?
   9 inches
   b. Tina's daughter will be $\frac{5}{6}$ of a year old next week. How many months old will she be?
   10 months
6. Divide. Write the remainder as a fraction.
   809 / 13 = $62\frac{3}{13}$

◆ *Math Journal 2,* p. 201

Study Link 7.4 (*Math Masters,* p. 314)

Home Connection Students solve fraction addition and subtraction problems.

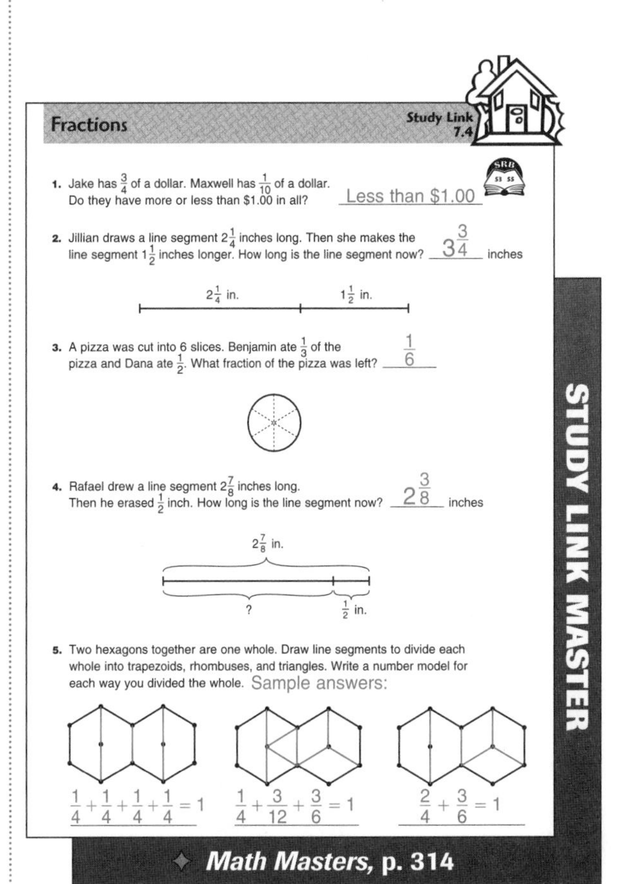

Fractions — Study Link 7.4

1. Jake has $\frac{3}{4}$ of a dollar. Maxwell has $\frac{1}{10}$ of a dollar. Do they have more or less than $1.00 in all? Less than $1.00
2. Jillian draws a line segment $2\frac{1}{4}$ inches long. Then she makes the line segment $1\frac{1}{2}$ inches longer. How long is the line segment now? $3\frac{3}{4}$ inches
   $2\frac{1}{4}$ in. $1\frac{1}{2}$ in.
3. A pizza was cut into 6 slices. Benjamin ate $\frac{1}{3}$ of the pizza and Dana ate $\frac{1}{2}$. What fraction of the pizza was left? $\frac{1}{6}$
4. Rafael drew a line segment $2\frac{7}{8}$ inches long. Then he erased $\frac{1}{2}$ inch. How long is the line segment now? $2\frac{3}{8}$ inches
   $2\frac{7}{8}$ in. ? $\frac{1}{2}$ in.
5. Two hexagons together are one whole. Draw line segments to divide each whole into trapezoids, rhombuses, and triangles. Write a number model for each way you divided the whole. Sample answers:
   $\frac{1}{4}+\frac{1}{4}+\frac{1}{4}+\frac{1}{4}=1$ $\frac{1}{4}+\frac{3}{12}+\frac{3}{6}=1$ $\frac{2}{4}+\frac{3}{6}=1$

◆ *Math Masters,* p. 314

Options for Individualizing

✦ EXTRA PRACTICE Drawing and Comparing Line Segments (*Math Masters,* p. 106)

INDEPENDENT ACTIVITY  **15–30 min** 

Portfolio Ideas

Students' understanding of fraction addition and subtraction is applied to the context of line segments. The problems require students to draw and compare different line segments using fraction notation.

TEACHING MASTER

Line Segments

1. Draw a line segment $4\frac{1}{2}$ inches long.

2. If you made this line segment $\frac{1}{4}$ inch longer **at each end,** how long would the new segment be? Use your ruler to figure this out. 5 inches

3. If you removed $\frac{1}{4}$ inch from one end of the original line segment, how long would the new segment be? $4\frac{1}{4}$ inches

4. Draw a line segment $2\frac{1}{8}$ inches long.

5. How much would you need to add to the segment to make it 3 inches long? $\frac{7}{8}$ inch

6. How much would you need to add to the segment to make it $2\frac{1}{2}$ inches long? $\frac{3}{8}$ inch

7. Which is longer—the first line segment you drew in Problem 1 or a line segment $4\frac{3}{8}$ inches long? Line segment in Problem 1
   It is longer by how much? $\frac{1}{8}$ inch

8. Which is longer—the line segment you drew in Problem 4 or a line segment $2\frac{3}{16}$ inches long? Line segment $2\frac{3}{16}$ inches long
   It is longer by how much? $\frac{1}{16}$ inch

✦ *Math Masters,* p. 106

7.5 Clock Fractions

OBJECTIVES **To model fractions on a clock face; and to use a clock face to help add and subtract fractions.**

summaries	materials
1 Teaching the Lesson	
Students model halves, thirds, fourths, sixths, and twelfths on a clock face. They use a clock face to help add and subtract fractions. [Numeration; Operations and Computation]	☐ *Math Journal 2,* pp. 202 and 203 ☐ Study Link 7.4 ☐ Transparency (*Math Masters,* p. 107; optional) ☐ semipermanent chalk (optional) ☐ slate ***See* Advance Preparation**
2 Ongoing Learning & Practice	
Students practice and maintain skills through Math Boxes and Study Link activities.	☐ *Math Journal 2,* p. 204 ☐ Study Link Master (*Math Masters,* p. 315)
3 Options for Individualizing	
Enrichment Students model other denominators on a clock face. [Numeration]	☐ Teaching Master (*Math Masters,* p. 108)

Additional Information

Background Information For additional information on semipermanent chalk, see the *Teacher's Reference Manual.*

Advance Preparation For Part 1, if you are using a transparency of *Math Masters,* page 107, tape the transparency under a blank transparency or under the roll of film on your overhead projector. This will make displaying different fractions easier. Or consider using semipermanent chalk to draw an unnumbered clock face on the chalkboard.

Getting Started

Mental Math and Reflexes

Pose "fraction-of" problems with 12 and 60. *Suggestions:*

- $\frac{1}{2}$ of 12 = 6
- $\frac{1}{3}$ of 12 = 4
- $\frac{1}{4}$ of 12 = 3
- $\frac{1}{6}$ of 12 = 2
- $\frac{1}{12}$ of 12 = 1
- $\frac{1}{2}$ of 60 = 30
- $\frac{1}{3}$ of 60 = 20
- $\frac{1}{4}$ of 60 = 15
- $\frac{1}{6}$ of 60 = 10

Encourage students to think of a clock face when solving these problems. The division of an hour into 60 minutes makes a clock face a convenient model for many fractions (halves, thirds, fourths, fifths, sixths, twelfths, twentieths, thirtieths, and sixtieths). Use of the clock model for fractions will continue in Lesson 7.6.

Math Message

Why do you think there are 60 minutes in 1 hour?

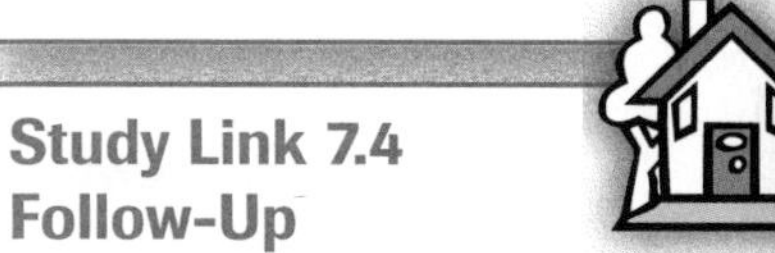

Study Link 7.4 Follow-Up

Review answers. For Problem 5, consider having students draw and discuss their solutions on the board or overhead projector.

1 Teaching the Lesson

✦ Math Message Follow-Up

WHOLE-CLASS DISCUSSION 

Briefly discuss students' ideas about why an hour is divided into 60 minutes.

Explain that the ancient Babylonians based their number system on 60. They were the first to divide the day into 24 hours, the hour into 60 minutes, and the minute into 60 seconds.

The Babylonians used 60 because it can be evenly divided by many numbers. Ask students to name whole numbers by which 60 can be divided with no remainder. Generate the following list on the board: 1, 2, 3, 4, 5, 6, 10, 12, 15, 20, 30, and 60. Compare this list with the list of whole numbers by which 10 can be evenly divided: 1, 2, 5, and 10. Since 60 can be evenly divided by so many numbers, many fractions are easy to handle in a base-sixty number system.

Although the number system commonly used today is based on 10, measures of angles are based on a multiple of 60 (360° in a circle), and measures of time are based on 60. This makes a clock face a convenient model for many fractions.

NOTE: An article about Babylonian mathematics can be found on the Internet at http://www-groups.dcs.st-and.ac.uk:80/~history/HistTopics/Babylonian_and_Egyptian.html.

This is part of an excellent resource on the history of mathematics at the University of St. Andrews, Scotland: http://www-groups.dcs.st-and.ac.uk:80/~history/.

✦ Representing Fractions on a Clock Face (*Math Masters,* p. 107)

WHOLE-CLASS ACTIVITY

Review fractions on a clock face. Use an overhead transparency of *Math Masters,* page 107 to display shaded sectors of a clock face, or use the clock face you have drawn on the board with semipermanent chalk to display these shaded sectors. Ask students to write the corresponding fraction on their slates. Include examples of sectors that do not begin at 12:00.

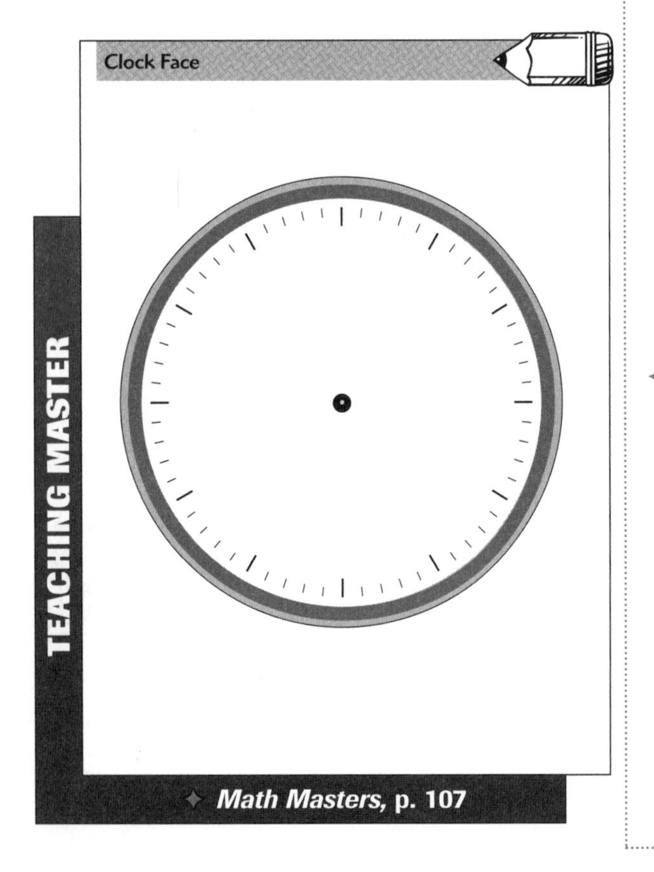

Math Masters, p. 107

Suggestions

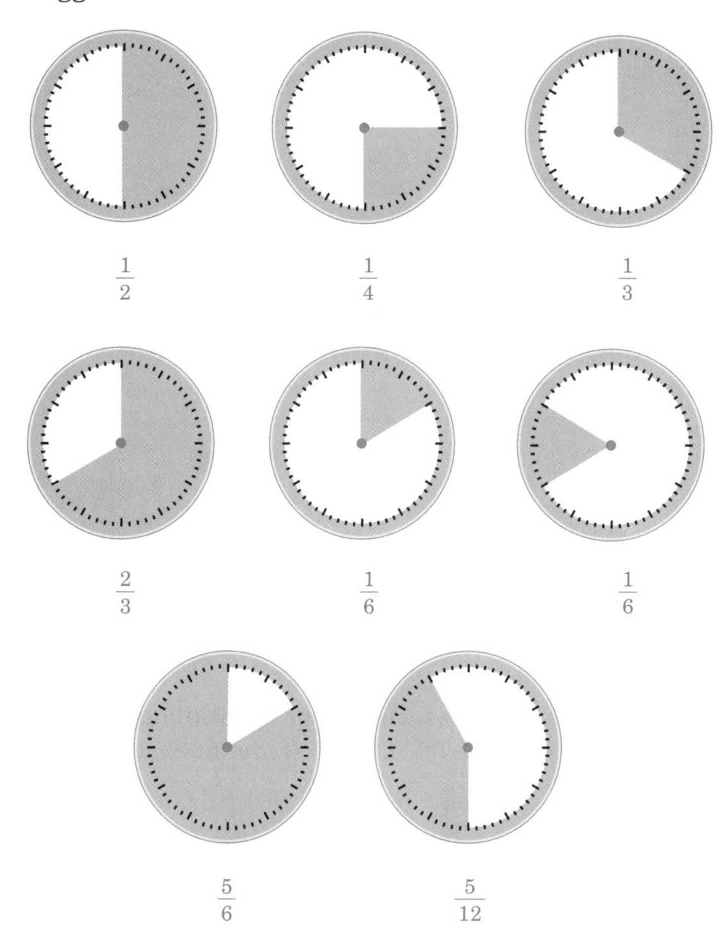

✦ Modeling Fraction Addition on a Clock Face (*Math Masters,* p. 107)

WHOLE-CLASS DISCUSSION

When students are comfortable modeling fractions on a clock face, write the following problem on the board and ask whether anyone can solve it using a clock face:

$$\frac{1}{3} + \frac{1}{6} = ?$$

Discuss students' ideas. In the unlikely event that no one suggests it, demonstrate how to find the answer by shading two sectors on the board or on the *Math Masters* transparency. See example below:

$$\frac{1}{3} + \frac{1}{6} = \frac{1}{2}$$

NOTE: A blank clock face is useful for modeling equivalencies between fractions with denominators of 2, 3, 4, 5, 6, 10, 12, 15, 20, 30, and 60. The sector below, for example, can be named as $\frac{1}{2}$, $\frac{2}{4}$, $\frac{3}{6}$, $\frac{5}{10}$, $\frac{6}{12}$, $\frac{10}{20}$, $\frac{15}{30}$, or $\frac{30}{60}$.

Equivalent fractions are addressed later in this unit. For now, simply note that a given sector can often have more than one fraction name, so many of these problems can have more than one correct answer.

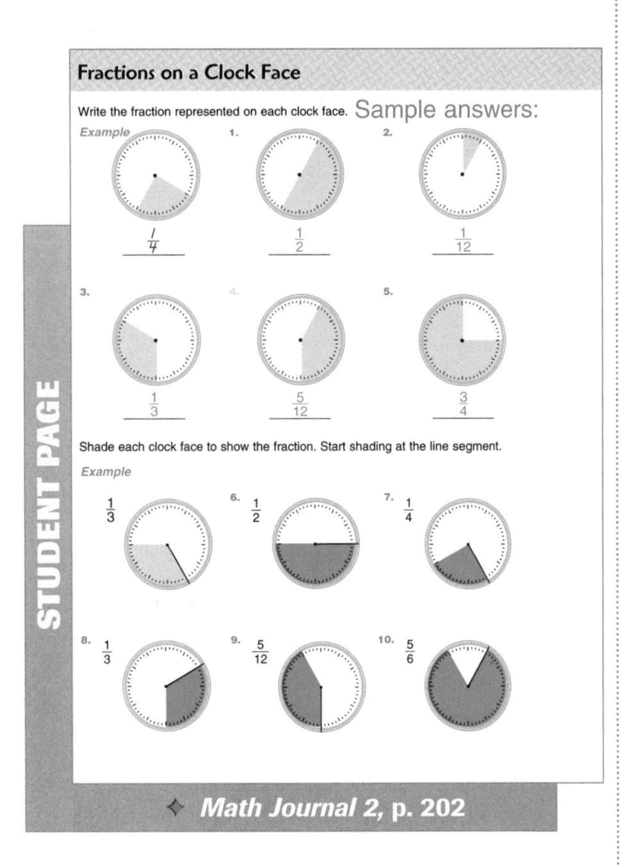

STUDENT PAGE

Fractions on a Clock Face

Write the fraction represented on each clock face. Sample answers:

Example $\frac{1}{4}$ 1. $\frac{1}{2}$ 2. $\frac{1}{12}$

3. $\frac{1}{3}$ 4. $\frac{5}{12}$ 5. $\frac{3}{4}$

Shade each clock face to show the fraction. Start shading at the line segment.

Example $\frac{1}{3}$ 6. $\frac{1}{2}$ 7. $\frac{1}{4}$

8. $\frac{1}{3}$ 9. $\frac{5}{12}$ 10. $\frac{5}{6}$

✦ *Math Journal 2*, p. 202

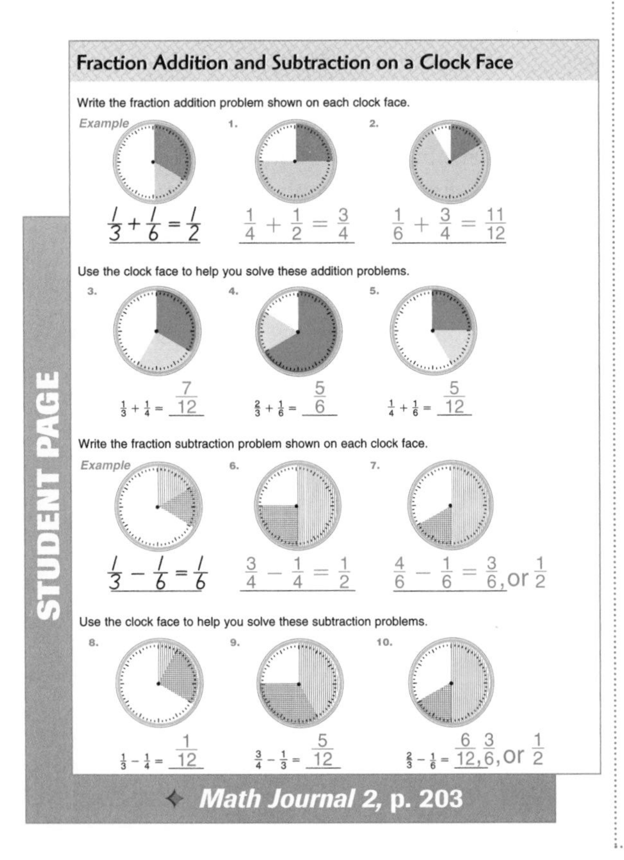

STUDENT PAGE

Fraction Addition and Subtraction on a Clock Face

Write the fraction addition problem shown on each clock face.

Example $\frac{1}{3} + \frac{1}{6} = \frac{1}{2}$ 1. $\frac{1}{4} + \frac{1}{2} = \frac{3}{4}$ 2. $\frac{1}{6} + \frac{3}{4} = \frac{11}{12}$

Use the clock face to help you solve these addition problems.

3. $\frac{1}{3} + \frac{1}{4} = \frac{7}{12}$ 4. $\frac{2}{3} + \frac{1}{6} = \frac{5}{6}$ 5. $\frac{1}{4} + \frac{1}{6} = \frac{5}{12}$

Write the fraction subtraction problem shown on each clock face.

Example $\frac{1}{3} - \frac{1}{6} = \frac{1}{6}$ 6. $\frac{3}{4} - \frac{1}{4} = \frac{1}{2}$ 7. $\frac{4}{6} - \frac{1}{6} = \frac{3}{6}$, or $\frac{1}{2}$

Use the clock face to help you solve these subtraction problems.

8. $\frac{1}{3} - \frac{1}{4} = \frac{1}{12}$ 9. $\frac{3}{4} - \frac{1}{3} = \frac{5}{12}$ 10. $\frac{2}{3} - \frac{1}{6} = \frac{6}{12}, \frac{3}{6}$, or $\frac{1}{2}$

✦ *Math Journal 2*, p. 203

Work through one or two more fraction addition problems, modeling each solution on a blank clock face. *Suggestions*

▷ $\frac{1}{6} + \frac{5}{12} = \frac{7}{12}$

▷ $\frac{1}{12} + \frac{2}{3} = \frac{9}{12}$, or $\frac{3}{4}$

▷ $\frac{1}{4} + \frac{1}{12} + \frac{1}{6} = \frac{6}{12}$, or $\frac{1}{2}$

✦ Modeling Fraction Subtraction on a Clock Face

WHOLE-CLASS DISCUSSION

Modeling fraction subtraction on a clock face may be a bit awkward at first, but it is manageable with a little practice. Begin by posing the problem below for students to solve on a clock face:

$$\frac{1}{2} - \frac{1}{6} = ?$$

Discuss students' ideas. Below are several approaches they may suggest.

▷ Convert the fractions into minutes, subtract the minutes, and then convert the answer back to a fraction:

$\frac{1}{2} \rightarrow 30$ minutes

$\frac{1}{6} \rightarrow 10$ minutes

30 minutes − 10 minutes = 20 minutes

20 minutes $\rightarrow \frac{1}{3}$

▷ Shade $\frac{1}{2}$, starting at 12:00. Shade $\frac{1}{6}$ differently, starting at 12:00. The sector that is shaded only once represents the difference. (See first illustration below.)

▷ Shade $\frac{1}{2}$, starting at 12:00. Shade $\frac{1}{6}$ differently, starting at 6:00 and going counterclockwise. The sector that is shaded only once represents the difference. (See second illustration below.)

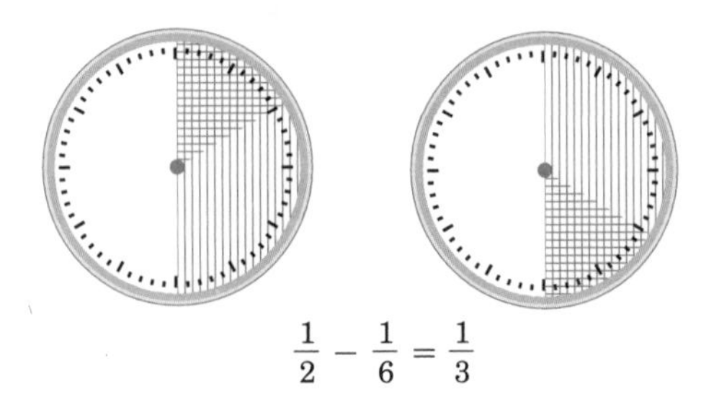

$\frac{1}{2} - \frac{1}{6} = \frac{1}{3}$

Work through one or two more fraction subtraction problems, modeling the solution on a blank clock face on the board or transparency of *Math Masters,* page 107. *Suggestions*

▷ $\frac{3}{4} - \frac{2}{3} = \frac{1}{12}$

▷ $\frac{7}{12} - \frac{1}{3} = \frac{3}{12}$, or $\frac{1}{4}$

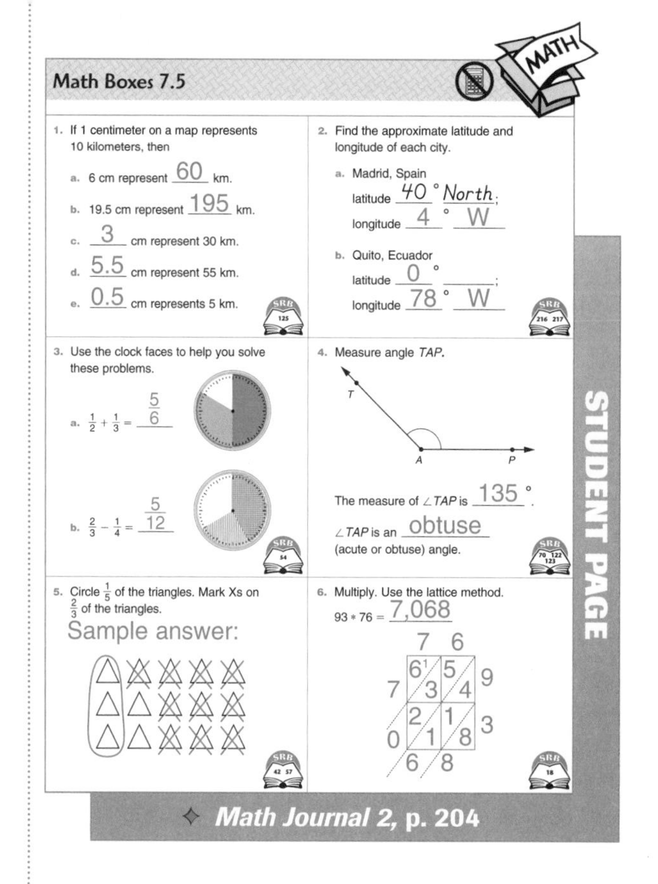

Math Boxes 7.5

1. If 1 centimeter on a map represents 10 kilometers, then
   a. 6 cm represent 60 km.
   b. 19.5 cm represent 195 km.
   c. 3 cm represent 30 km.
   d. 5.5 cm represent 55 km.
   e. 0.5 cm represents 5 km.

2. Find the approximate latitude and longitude of each city.
   a. Madrid, Spain
   latitude 40 ° North;
   longitude 4 ° W
   b. Quito, Ecuador
   latitude 0 ° ;
   longitude 78 ° W

3. Use the clock faces to help you solve these problems.
   a. $\frac{1}{2} + \frac{1}{3} = \frac{5}{6}$
   b. $\frac{2}{3} - \frac{1}{4} = \frac{5}{12}$

4. Measure angle *TAP*.
   The measure of ∠*TAP* is 135 °.
   ∠*TAP* is an obtuse (acute or obtuse) angle.

5. Circle $\frac{1}{5}$ of the triangles. Mark Xs on $\frac{2}{3}$ of the triangles.
   Sample answer:

6. Multiply. Use the lattice method.
   93 ∗ 76 = 7,068

STUDENT PAGE

◆ *Math Journal 2,* p. 204

◆ Representing, Adding, and Subtracting Fractions on a Clock Face (*Math Journal 2,* pp. 202 and 203)

PARTNER ACTIVITY

Have students work in pairs or independently as they solve the problems on journal pages 202 and 203. Circulate and assist as needed.

NOTE: The purpose of these exercises is not to teach students to add and subtract fractions with unlike denominators, but to provide initial exposure to these kinds of problems in a concrete context. Some students may prefer to think in terms of pattern blocks instead of clocks. Encourage students to solve problems using whichever method makes most sense to them.

2 Ongoing Learning & Practice

◆ Math Boxes 7.5 (*Math Journal 2,* p. 204)

INDEPENDENT ACTIVITY 

Mixed Review Math Boxes in this lesson are paired with Math Boxes in Lesson 7.7. The skill in Problem 1 is a prerequisite for Unit 8.

◆ Study Link 7.5 (*Math Masters,* p. 315)

Home Connection Students use a clock face to represent, add, and subtract fractions.

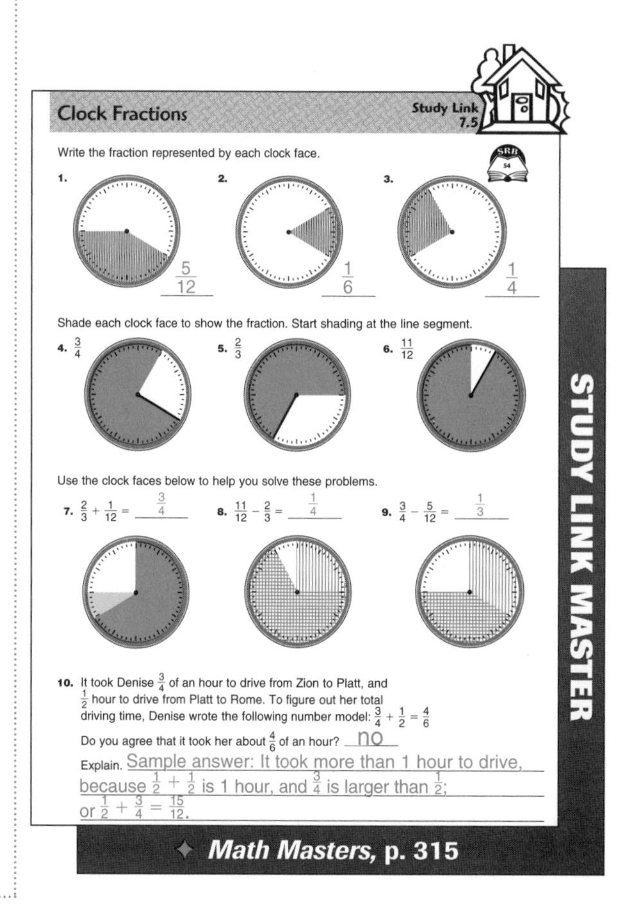

Clock Fractions Study Link 7.5

Write the fraction represented by each clock face.

1. $\frac{5}{12}$ 2. $\frac{1}{6}$ 3. $\frac{1}{4}$

Shade each clock face to show the fraction. Start shading at the line segment.

4. $\frac{3}{4}$ 5. $\frac{2}{3}$ 6. $\frac{11}{12}$

Use the clock faces below to help you solve these problems.

7. $\frac{2}{3} + \frac{1}{12} = \frac{3}{4}$ 8. $\frac{11}{12} - \frac{2}{3} = \frac{1}{4}$ 9. $\frac{3}{4} - \frac{5}{12} = \frac{1}{3}$

10. It took Denise $\frac{3}{4}$ of an hour to drive from Zion to Platt, and $\frac{1}{2}$ hour to drive from Platt to Rome. To figure out her total driving time, Denise wrote the following number model: $\frac{3}{4} + \frac{1}{2} = \frac{4}{6}$

Do you agree that it took her about $\frac{4}{6}$ of an hour? no

Explain. Sample answer: It took more than 1 hour to drive, because $\frac{1}{2} + \frac{1}{2}$ is 1 hour, and $\frac{3}{4}$ is larger than $\frac{1}{2}$; or $\frac{1}{2} + \frac{3}{4} = \frac{15}{12}$.

STUDY LINK MASTER

◆ *Math Masters,* p. 315

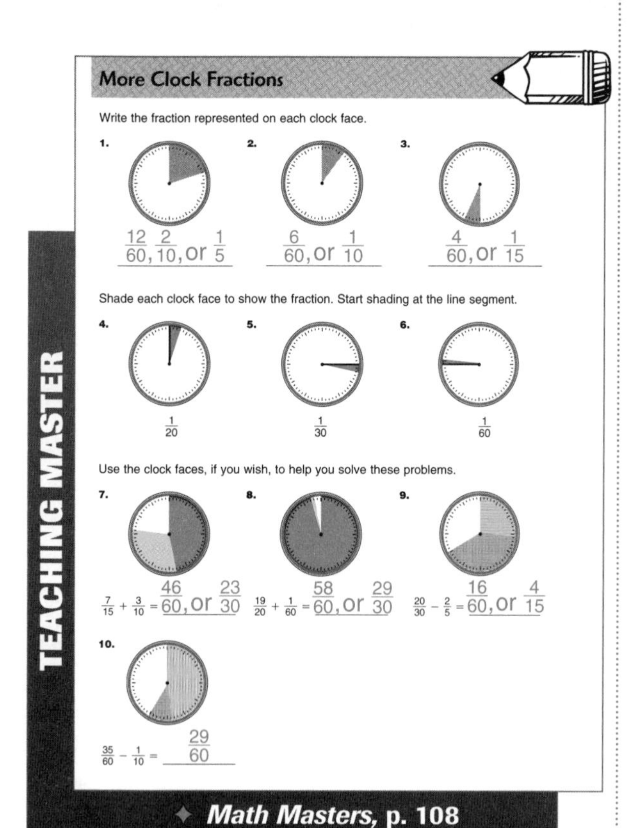
TEACHING MASTER

More Clock Fractions

Write the fraction represented on each clock face.

1. $\frac{12}{60}$, $\frac{2}{10}$, or $\frac{1}{5}$
2. $\frac{6}{60}$, or $\frac{1}{10}$
3. $\frac{4}{60}$, or $\frac{1}{15}$

Shade each clock face to show the fraction. Start shading at the line segment.

4. $\frac{1}{20}$
5. $\frac{1}{30}$
6. $\frac{1}{60}$

Use the clock faces, if you wish, to help you solve these problems.

7. $\frac{7}{15} + \frac{3}{10} = \frac{46}{60}$, or $\frac{23}{30}$
8. $\frac{19}{20} + \frac{1}{60} = \frac{58}{60}$, or $\frac{29}{30}$
9. $\frac{20}{30} - \frac{2}{5} = \frac{16}{60}$, or $\frac{4}{15}$
10. $\frac{35}{60} - \frac{1}{10} = \frac{29}{60}$

✦ *Math Masters,* p. 108

Options for Individualizing

✦ ENRICHMENT Modeling Fractions with Other Denominators on a Clock Face
(*Math Masters,* p. 108)

INDEPENDENT ACTIVITY  **15–30 min** 

In this lesson, students solve problems with halves, thirds, fourths, sixths, and twelfths. They can also use clock faces to help them solve problems involving fractions in fifths, tenths, fifteenths, twentieths, thirtieths, and sixtieths. One approach is to convert the fractions into minutes, carry out the computation using minutes, and then convert the answer back to a fraction.

Example: $\frac{2}{15} + \frac{7}{10} = ?$

Step 1

$\frac{2}{15} \rightarrow$ 8 minutes

$\frac{7}{10} \rightarrow$ 42 minutes

Step 2

8 minutes + 42 minutes = 50 minutes

Step 3

50 minutes $\rightarrow \frac{5}{6}$

7.6 Many Names for Fractions

OBJECTIVE To identify equivalent fractions.

summaries	materials
1 Teaching the Lesson	
Students use Fraction Cards to help them start a table of equivalent fractions. [Numeration]	□ *Math Journal 2,* pp. 356 and 357 □ Study Link 7.5 □ Assessment Master (*Math Masters,* p. 471 or 475; optional) □ Fraction Cards (see Lesson 7.4)
2 Ongoing Learning & Practice	
Students practice finding fractional parts of collections of objects and of regions. [Numeration] Students practice and maintain skills through Math Boxes and Study Link activities.	□ *Math Journal 2,* pp. 205 and 206 □ Study Link Master (*Math Masters,* p. 316)
3 Options for Individualizing	
Reteaching Students play *Name That Number* to reinforce the idea that numbers can have many names. [Numeration]	□ *Student Reference Book,* p. 203

Getting Started

Mental Math and Reflexes

Pose fraction addition and subtraction problems. Have students estimate whether the sum or difference is greater than or less than 1 and explain their answer. *Suggestions:*

- $\frac{9}{10} + \frac{7}{8}$ greater
- $\frac{1}{3} + \frac{1}{4}$ less
- $1\frac{1}{2} - \frac{15}{16}$ less
- $1\frac{5}{6} - \frac{1}{12}$ greater

Math Message

Take out your Fraction Cards. Write down two things that you notice about the cards.

Study Link 7.5 Follow-Up

Review answers. Have students share the strategies they used to solve Problem 10. The chances are that most students recognized immediately that Denise had made a mistake. Had students been asked to add $\frac{3}{4} + \frac{1}{2}$ without putting the problem in context, some might have assumed that Denise's answer was correct.

Equivalent Names for Fractions

Fraction	Equivalent Fractions	Decimal	Percent
$\frac{0}{2}$		0	0%
$\frac{1}{2}$	$\frac{2}{4}$, $\frac{3}{6}$		
$\frac{2}{2}$		1	100%
$\frac{1}{3}$			
$\frac{2}{3}$			
$\frac{1}{4}$			
$\frac{3}{4}$			
$\frac{1}{5}$			
$\frac{2}{5}$			
$\frac{3}{5}$			
$\frac{4}{5}$			
$\frac{1}{6}$			
$\frac{5}{6}$			
$\frac{1}{8}$			
$\frac{3}{8}$			
$\frac{5}{8}$			
$\frac{7}{8}$			

STUDENT PAGE

Math Journal 2, p. 356

NOTE: Students will add fractions to the Equivalent Names for Fractions table during the rest of the year. The column for decimals will be started in Lesson 7.8, and the column for percents in Unit 9.

Equivalent Names for Fractions (cont.)

Fraction	Equivalent Fractions	Decimal	Percent
$\frac{1}{9}$			
$\frac{2}{9}$			
$\frac{4}{9}$			
$\frac{5}{9}$			
$\frac{7}{9}$			
$\frac{8}{9}$			
$\frac{1}{10}$			
$\frac{3}{10}$			
$\frac{7}{10}$			
$\frac{9}{10}$			
$\frac{1}{12}$			
$\frac{5}{12}$			
$\frac{7}{12}$			
$\frac{11}{12}$			

STUDENT PAGE

Math Journal 2, p. 357

1 Teaching the Lesson

Math Message Follow-Up

WHOLE-CLASS DISCUSSION 

Students share their observations. Be sure to include the following points in the discussion:

- One side of each card is divided into equal parts, and some of the parts are shaded.
- A fraction with the numerator or denominator missing appears on the other side of each card.

On each card, ask students to write the missing numerator or denominator in order to name the fractional part of the card that is shaded. For example, if the rectangle is divided into 6 equal parts and 4 of them are shaded, the completed fraction on the back should be $\frac{4}{6}$.

Starting a Collection of Fraction Names
(*Math Journal 2,* pp. 356 and 357)

PARTNER ACTIVITY

Divide the class into partnerships. One student in each partnership puts his or her Fraction Cards away. Model the procedure for sorting the cards as follows:

1. Ask students to find the card with 1 out of 2 parts shaded and the card with 2 out of 4 parts shaded.

   Point out that although the fractions on the back of the cards ($\frac{1}{2}$ and $\frac{2}{4}$) are not the same, the same amount is shaded on each of these cards. It follows that $\frac{1}{2}$ and $\frac{2}{4}$ are names for the same fractional part of the card.

2. Ask students to find all of the other cards that are half-shaded. $\frac{3}{6}$, $\frac{4}{8}$, $\frac{5}{10}$, $\frac{6}{12}$

3. Ask students to turn to the Equivalent Names for Fractions table on page 356 at the back of the journal. Next to the fraction $\frac{1}{2}$ in the table, have them record all the fractions for the cards that are half-shaded. $\frac{2}{4}$, $\frac{3}{6}$, $\frac{4}{8}$, $\frac{5}{10}$, $\frac{6}{12}$

Continuing a Collection of Fraction Names
(*Math Journal 2,* pp. 356 and 357)

PARTNER ACTIVITY

Instruct partners to sort the remaining cards into groups that have the same amount shaded. Then have them turn over the cards in each group, fraction-side up, and record these fractions on the appropriate lines in the Equivalent Names for Fractions table.

Adjusting the Activity Challenge students to suggest other fraction names to add to the table, such as fraction names for 0 and 1.

ONGOING ASSESSMENT

Consider asking students to respond to the following question in a Math Log or on an Exit Slip:

> Suppose a classmate was absent. What would you tell the classmate about the most important thing that you learned in math class today?

When assessing students' responses, see whether they grasp the idea that it is possible to name a fractional part of something in many different ways.

Ongoing Learning & Practice

Picturing Fractions (*Math Journal 2,* p. 205)

INDEPENDENT ACTIVITY 

Students practice finding fractional parts of collections of objects and of regions. They also calculate the number of minutes that pass when the minute hand on a clock makes a specified fraction of a turn.

Picturing Fractions

1. Circle $\frac{1}{2}$ of the stars. Cross out $\frac{1}{3}$ of the stars that are not circled. Put a box around $\frac{1}{4}$ of the stars that are not circled or crossed out.

   How many stars are left? 6 stars

   Sample answer:

2. Circle $\frac{2}{3}$ of the squares below.

   Sample answer:

3. Shade $\frac{2}{3}$ of the circle below.

   Sample answer:

4. How many minutes pass when the minute hand on a clock makes
   a. $\frac{1}{2}$ of a turn? 30 minutes
   b. $\frac{3}{4}$ of a turn? 45 minutes
   c. $\frac{2}{3}$ of a turn? 40 minutes
   d. $\frac{1}{6}$ of a turn? 10 minutes

STUDENT PAGE

Math Journal 2, p. 205

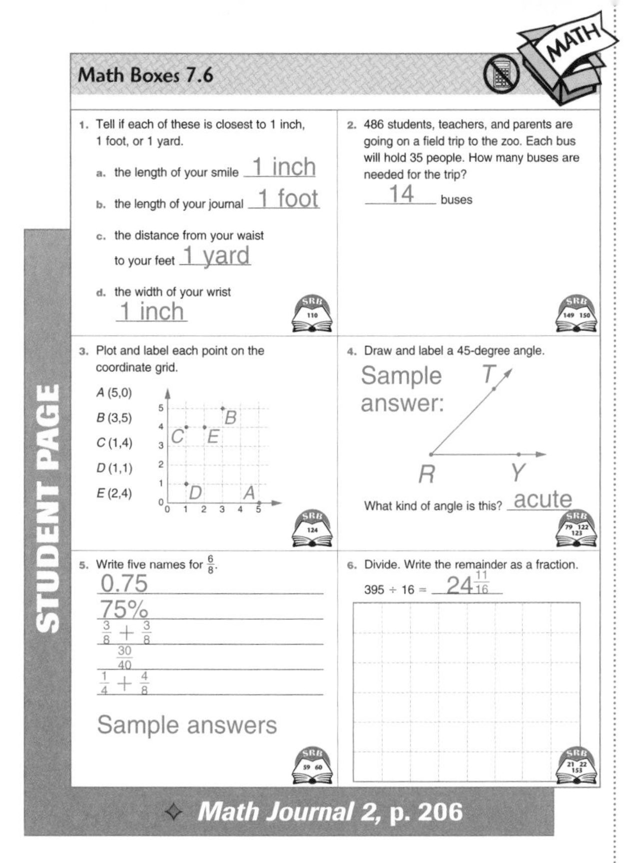

Math Boxes 7.6
1. Tell if each of these is closest to 1 inch, 1 foot, or 1 yard.
a. the length of your smile 1 inch
b. the length of your journal 1 foot
c. the distance from your waist to your feet 1 yard
d. the width of your wrist 1 inch
2. 486 students, teachers, and parents are going on a field trip to the zoo. Each bus will hold 35 people. How many buses are needed for the trip?
14 buses
3. Plot and label each point on the coordinate grid.
A (5,0)
B (3,5)
C (1,4)
D (1,1)
E (2,4)
4. Draw and label a 45-degree angle.
Sample answer:
What kind of angle is this? acute
5. Write five names for 6/8.
0.75
75%
Sample answers
6. Divide. Write the remainder as a fraction.
395 ÷ 16 = 24 11/16
STUDENT PAGE
Math Journal 2, p. 206

Math Boxes 7.6 (*Math Journal 2,* p. 206)

INDEPENDENT ACTIVITY 

Mixed Review Math Boxes in this lesson are paired with Math Boxes in Lesson 7.8. The skill in Problem 1 is a prerequisite for Unit 8.

Study Link 7.6 (*Math Masters,* p. 316)

Home Connection Students match fractions with pictures of shaded regions and collections of objects.

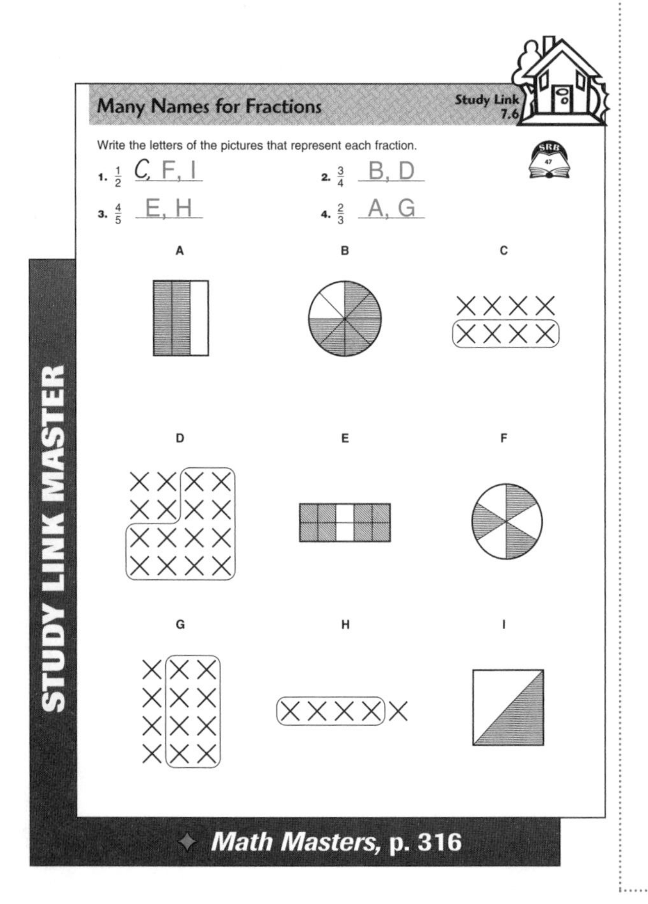

Many Names for Fractions
Study Link 7.6
Write the letters of the pictures that represent each fraction.
1. 1/2 C, F, I
2. 3/4 B, D
3. 4/5 E, H
4. 2/3 A, G
A
B
C
D
E
F
G
H
I
STUDY LINK MASTER
Math Masters, p. 316

3 Options for Individualizing

RETEACHING Playing *Name That Number* (*Student Reference Book,* p. 203)

PARTNER ACTIVITY  **15–30 min** 

Students play *Name That Number* to reinforce the idea that numbers can have many names.

7.7 Equivalent Fractions

OBJECTIVE **To develop and use a rule for generating equivalent fractions.**

summaries	materials
1 Teaching the Lesson	
Students use examples of equivalent fractions to develop a rule for finding equivalent fractions. [Numeration]	□ *Math Journal 2,* pp. 207 and 356 □ Study Link 7.6 □ pattern blocks □ pattern blocks for overhead (optional)
2 Ongoing Learning & Practice	
Students solve "fraction-of" problems. [Operations and Computation] Students practice and maintain skills through Math Boxes and Study Link activities.	□ *Math Journal 2,* pp. 208 and 209 □ Study Link Master (*Math Masters,* p. 317)
3 Options for Individualizing	
Extra Practice Students play *Musical Name-Collection Boxes.* [Numeration]	□ butcher paper (or large paper) □ radio, tape recorder, or CD player

Additional Information

Vocabulary • **equivalent fractions** • **Equivalent Fractions Rule**

Getting Started

Mental Math and Reflexes

Display a pattern-block triangle, rhombus, trapezoid, and hexagon on the overhead projector, or hold them up for the class to see. Pose problems like the following:

- If the triangle is $\frac{1}{3}$, what is the whole, or ONE? trapezoid
- If the triangle is $\frac{1}{2}$, what is ONE? rhombus
- If the rhombus is $\frac{2}{3}$, what is ONE? trapezoid
- If the rhombus is $\frac{1}{3}$, what is ONE? hexagon
- If the trapezoid is $\frac{1}{4}$, what is ONE? 2 hexagons

Math Message

Complete journal page 207.

Study Link 7.6 Follow-Up

Go over the answers with the class.

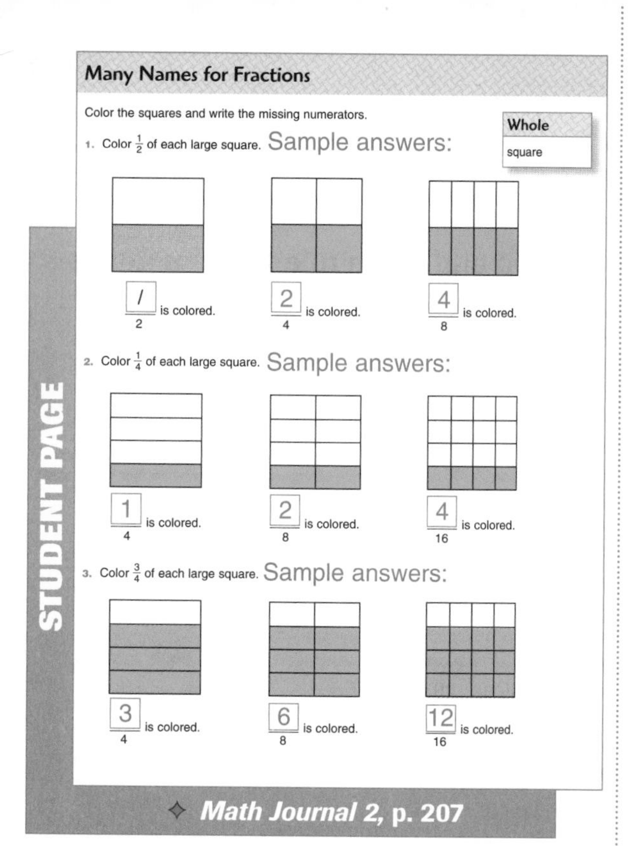
STUDENT PAGE

Many Names for Fractions

Color the squares and write the missing numerators.

Whole
square

1. Color $\frac{1}{2}$ of each large square. Sample answers:

$\frac{1}{2}$ is colored. $\frac{2}{4}$ is colored. $\frac{4}{8}$ is colored.

2. Color $\frac{1}{4}$ of each large square. Sample answers:

$\frac{1}{4}$ is colored. $\frac{2}{8}$ is colored. $\frac{4}{16}$ is colored.

3. Color $\frac{3}{4}$ of each large square. Sample answers:

$\frac{3}{4}$ is colored. $\frac{6}{8}$ is colored. $\frac{12}{16}$ is colored.

◆ *Math Journal 2,* p. 207

1 Teaching the Lesson

◆ Math Message Follow-Up
(*Math Journal 2,* p. 207)

WHOLE-CLASS DISCUSSION

Ask students to examine the squares they colored on journal page 207. Point out that the three fractions they wrote for each problem all name the same fractional part of the square. Such fractions are called **equivalent fractions.** Students should notice that whenever the total number of equal parts is doubled (or quadrupled), the number of colored parts is also doubled (or quadrupled), but the fractional part represented by the colored parts does not change.

◆ Developing a Rule for Finding Equivalent Fractions (*Math Journal 2,* p. 207)

WHOLE-CLASS DISCUSSION

In each problem on journal page 207, the numerator and denominator of the first fraction were each multiplied by 2 to obtain the second fraction. They were each multiplied by 4 to obtain the third fraction.

Problem 1:

$\frac{1 * \mathbf{2}}{2 * \mathbf{2}} = \frac{2}{4}$ $\qquad$ $\frac{1 * \mathbf{4}}{2 * \mathbf{4}} = \frac{4}{8}$

Problem 2:

$\frac{1 * \mathbf{2}}{4 * \mathbf{2}} = \frac{2}{8}$ $\qquad$ $\frac{1 * \mathbf{4}}{4 * \mathbf{4}} = \frac{4}{16}$

Problem 3:

$\frac{3 * \mathbf{2}}{4 * \mathbf{2}} = \frac{6}{8}$ $\qquad$ $\frac{3 * \mathbf{4}}{4 * \mathbf{4}} = \frac{12}{16}$

The following rule can be used to rename any fraction: The **Equivalent Fractions Rule** states that if both the numerator and denominator of a fraction are multiplied by the same non-zero number, the result is a fraction that is equivalent to the original fraction.

Adjusting the Activity You might want to present a more abstract rationale for this rule:

- ▷ If any number is multiplied by 1, the product is the number you started with.
- ▷ A fraction with the same numerator and denominator, such as $\frac{4}{4}$, is equivalent to 1.
- ▷ Multiplying the numerator and denominator of a fraction by the same number is the same as multiplying the fraction by 1. So, the product is equivalent to the original fraction.

✦ Generating Equivalent Fractions
(*Math Journal 2,* p. 356)

PARTNER ACTIVITY 

Have students turn to the Equivalent Names for Fractions table on journal page 356. Ask them to write in the table about 10 fractions that are equivalent to $\frac{1}{3}$.

Have students look for patterns in fractions that are equivalent to $\frac{1}{3}$. If possible, point out how these patterns relate to the Equivalent Fractions Rule.

Working in pairs, students use the Equivalent Fractions Rule to find three equivalent fractions for each fraction listed in the table except $\frac{1}{2}$ and $\frac{1}{3}$.

ONGOING ASSESSMENT

Students have had concrete experience generating equivalent fractions in *Third Grade Everyday Mathematics.* However, this is the first time they have been given a formal rule for generating such fractions. To check students' understanding of equivalent fractions, provide opportunities for students to verbally explain their answers using the Equivalent Fractions Rule.

Hiking

Luis is staying in a large state park that has 8 hiking trails. In the table at the right, each trail is labeled easy, moderate, or rugged, depending on how difficult that trail is for hiking.

Luis figures that it would take him about 20 minutes to walk 1 mile on an easy trail, about 30 minutes on a moderate trail, and about 40 minutes on a rugged trail.

State Park Trails

Trail	Miles	Type
Ice Age	$1\frac{1}{4}$	easy
Kettle	2	moderate
Pine	$\frac{3}{4}$	moderate
Bluff	$1\frac{3}{4}$	rugged
Cliff	$\frac{3}{4}$	rugged
Oak	$1\frac{1}{2}$	easy
Sky	$1\frac{1}{2}$	moderate
Badger	$3\frac{1}{2}$	moderate

1. About how long will it take Luis to walk the following trails?
   a. Kettle Trail: About 60 minutes
   b. Cliff Trail: About 30 minutes
   c. Oak Trail: About 30 minutes
   d. Bluff Trail: About 70 minutes
2. If Luis wants to hike for about $\frac{3}{4}$ of an hour, which trail should he choose? Sky Trail
3. If he wants to hike for about 25 minutes, which trail should he choose? Ice Age Trail
4. About how long would it take him to complete Pine Trail? About 22 to 23 minutes
5. Do you think Luis could walk Badger Trail in less than 2 hours? yes

   Explain. Sample answer: Badger is a moderate trail. Luis can walk 1 mile on a moderate trail in 30 minutes. So, he can walk 4 miles in 2 hours. Badger Trail is only $3\frac{1}{2}$ miles long, so Luis could walk it in less than 2 hours.

STUDENT PAGE

✦ *Math Journal 2,* p. 208

2 Ongoing Learning & Practice

✦ Solving "Fraction-of" Problems
(*Math Journal 2,* p. 208)

PARTNER ACTIVITY 

The problems on journal page 208 require more than one step. Encourage students to work them carefully. When discussing solution strategies with the class, remind students that the trail data given are estimates. The lengths of the trails are given to the nearest $\frac{1}{4}$ mile. The times Luis thinks it will take him to walk a mile are also estimates.

✦ Math Boxes 7.7 (*Math Journal 2,* p. 209)

INDEPENDENT ACTIVITY 

Mixed Review Math Boxes in this lesson are paired with Math Boxes in Lesson 7.5. The skill in Problem 1 is a prerequisite for Unit 8.

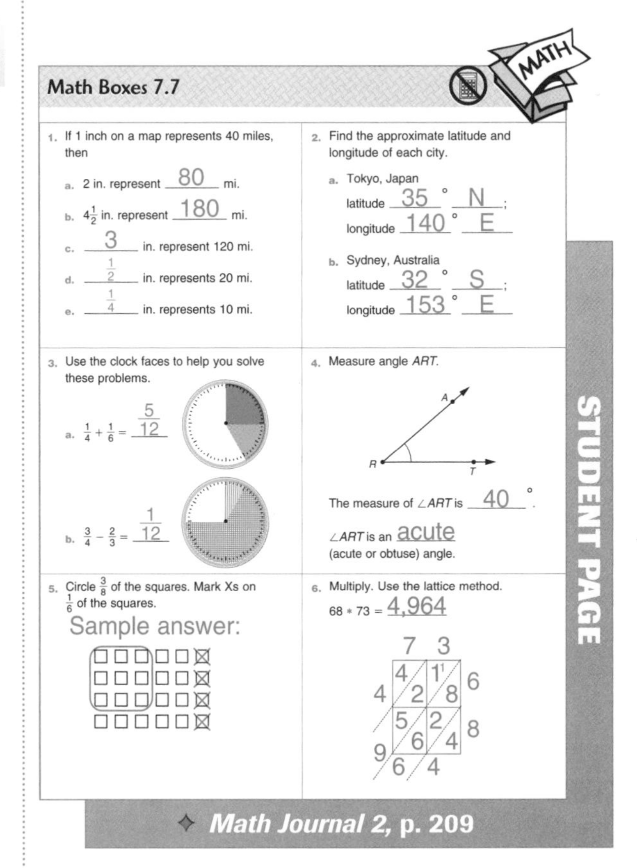

Math Boxes 7.7

1. If 1 inch on a map represents 40 miles, then
   a. 2 in. represent 80 mi.
   b. $4\frac{1}{2}$ in. represent 180 mi.
   c. 3 in. represent 120 mi.
   d. $\frac{1}{2}$ in. represents 20 mi.
   e. $\frac{1}{4}$ in. represents 10 mi.
2. Find the approximate latitude and longitude of each city.
   a. Tokyo, Japan: latitude 35° N; longitude 140° E
   b. Sydney, Australia: latitude 32° S; longitude 153° E
3. Use the clock faces to help you solve these problems.
   a. $\frac{1}{4} + \frac{1}{6} = \frac{5}{12}$
   b. $\frac{3}{4} - \frac{2}{3} = \frac{1}{12}$
4. Measure angle *ART*.

   The measure of ∠*ART* is 40°.

   ∠*ART* is an acute (acute or obtuse) angle.
5. Circle $\frac{3}{8}$ of the squares. Mark Xs on $\frac{1}{6}$ of the squares.

   Sample answer:
6. Multiply. Use the lattice method.

   68 * 73 = 4,964

STUDENT PAGE

✦ *Math Journal 2,* p. 209

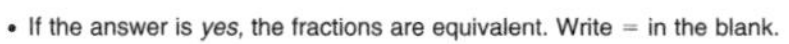

Equivalent Fractions

Study Link 7.7

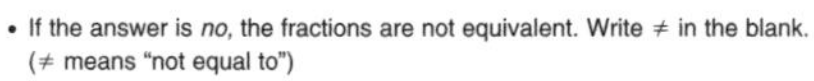

For each pair of fractions below, ask yourself: "If I multiply both the numerator and denominator of one fraction by the same number, will I get the other fraction?"

- If the answer is *yes*, the fractions are equivalent. Write = in the blank.
- If the answer is *no*, the fractions are not equivalent. Write ≠ in the blank. (≠ means "not equal to")

1. $\frac{1}{3}$ = $\frac{4}{12}$
2. $\frac{1}{4}$ ≠ $\frac{5}{12}$
3. $\frac{2}{3}$ = $\frac{4}{6}$
4. $\frac{6}{8}$ = $\frac{3}{4}$
5. $\frac{1}{2}$ = $\frac{6}{12}$
6. $\frac{3}{6}$ ≠ $\frac{2}{3}$
7. $\frac{2}{5}$ ≠ $\frac{6}{10}$
8. $\frac{2}{3}$ = $\frac{6}{9}$
9. $\frac{2}{6}$ ≠ $\frac{6}{12}$

In each box, write a number to make a fraction that is equivalent to the given fraction.

10. $\frac{4}{5} = \frac{\boxed{8}}{10}$
11. $\frac{30}{40} = \frac{\boxed{3}}{4}$
12. $\frac{15}{50} = \frac{3}{\boxed{10}}$
13. $\frac{2}{3} = \frac{12}{\boxed{18}}$
14. $\frac{8}{\boxed{12}} = \frac{2}{3}$
15. $\frac{\boxed{12}}{20} = \frac{3}{5}$

16. Margot says the value of a fraction doesn't change if you do the same thing to the numerator and denominator. Margot says that she added 2 to both the numerator and denominator in $\frac{1}{4}$ and got $\frac{3}{6}$.

$$\frac{1+2}{4+2} = \frac{3}{6}$$

Therefore, she says that $\frac{1}{4} = \frac{3}{6}$. How could you explain or show Margot that she is wrong?

Sample answer: You could tell her that the Equivalent Fractions Rule states that you will get an equivalent fraction if you multiply, not add, the same number to the numerator and denominator. Or, you could draw a picture to show that $\frac{1}{4}$ is not equal to $\frac{3}{6}$.

STUDY LINK MASTER

✦ Math Masters, p. 317

✦ Study Link 7.7 (*Math Masters*, p. 317)

Home Connection Students practice finding equivalent fractions. Point out that they are to write the symbols = or ≠ for Problems 1–9, and not the words "yes" or "no."

3 Options for Individualizing

✦ EXTRA PRACTICE Playing *Musical Name-Collection Boxes*

WHOLE-CLASS ACTIVITY  **15–30 min** 

Place several large sheets of butcher paper or other paper around the classroom. Make each sheet a name-collection box by writing a fraction such as the following in the upper left-hand corner: $\frac{2}{3}$, $\frac{3}{4}$, $\frac{5}{6}$, $\frac{1}{8}$, $\frac{5}{10}$, and $\frac{2}{5}$. Place a marker or pen next to each sheet.

Play music while students walk around. Stop the music. Students move quickly to the nearest name-collection box. Each student writes a fraction equivalent to the one shown in the upper left-hand corner, being careful not to repeat one already recorded on the paper. Repeat the procedure. To challenge students, you may want to limit the amount of time they have to write their answer. The activity becomes more difficult after each round of play.

7.8 Fractions and Decimals

OBJECTIVES **To rename fractions as decimals and decimals as fractions; and to explore the relationship between fractions and division.**

summaries	materials
1 Teaching the Lesson	
Students rename fractions as decimals and decimals as fractions. They also explore the relationship between fractions and division. [Numeration; Operations and Computation]	☐ *Math Journal 2,* pp. 210, 356, and 357 ☐ *Student Reference Book,* p. 44 ☐ Study Link 7.7 ☐ Transparency (*Math Masters,* p. 109; optional) ☐ base-10 blocks ☐ slate ☐ semipermanent chalk (optional) ***See* Advance Preparation**
2 Ongoing Learning & Practice	
Students use name-collection boxes for practice with equivalent fractions. [Numeration] Students practice and maintain skills through Math Boxes and Study Link activities.	☐ *Math Journal 2,* pp. 211 and 212 ☐ Study Link Master (*Math Masters,* p. 318)
3 Options for Individualizing	
Reteaching Students make a design with base-10 blocks and copy the design on a grid. [Numeration]	☐ Teaching Master (*Math Masters,* p. 110) ☐ base-10 blocks

Additional Information

Background Information For additional information on semipermanent chalk, see the *Teacher's Reference Manual.*

Advance Preparation If you are using an overhead transparency in Part 1, obtain a set of base-10 blocks for the overhead projector, if possible; otherwise, use regular base-10 blocks.

Getting Started

Mental Math and Reflexes

Write a fraction on the board. Students write an equivalent fraction on their slates. *Suggestions:*

Possible responses:

- $\frac{1}{5}$ $\frac{2}{10}, \frac{3}{15}$
- $\frac{50}{100}$ $\frac{5}{10}, \frac{25}{50}$
- $\frac{3}{4}$ $\frac{6}{8}, \frac{9}{12}$
- $\frac{6}{9}$ $\frac{2}{3}, \frac{12}{18}$

Math Message

Write the following fractions as decimals:

$\frac{1}{10}$ $\frac{7}{10}$ $\frac{32}{100}$ $\frac{9}{100}$

Study Link 7.7 Follow-Up

Review answers. For each pair of equivalent fractions, ask students to identify the number by which the numerator and denominator are multiplied. If students are having difficulty, have them compare fractions using their Fraction Cards.

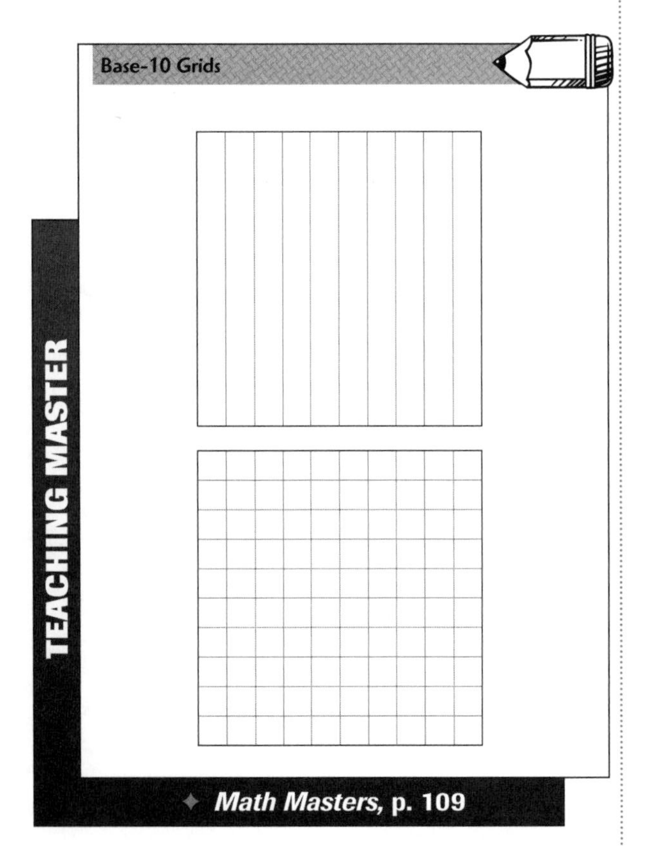

Math Masters, p. 109

1 Teaching the Lesson

Math Message Follow-Up
(*Math Masters,* p. 109)

WHOLE-CLASS DISCUSSION 

Display an overhead transparency of *Math Masters,* page 109 as you discuss the answers, or draw the grids on the board using semipermanent chalk. You can color the grid sections to show fractional parts or cover them with base-10 blocks.

Color or cover one column of the top grid.

- What fractional part of the square is this? $\frac{1}{10}$

$\frac{1}{10}$, or 0.1

- How would you write $\frac{1}{10}$ as a decimal? 0.1

Repeat with other fractions in tenths, including $\frac{3}{10}$ and $\frac{7}{10}$.

Next, color (or cover) one small square of the bottom grid on the transparency.

- What fractional part of the square is this? $\frac{1}{100}$

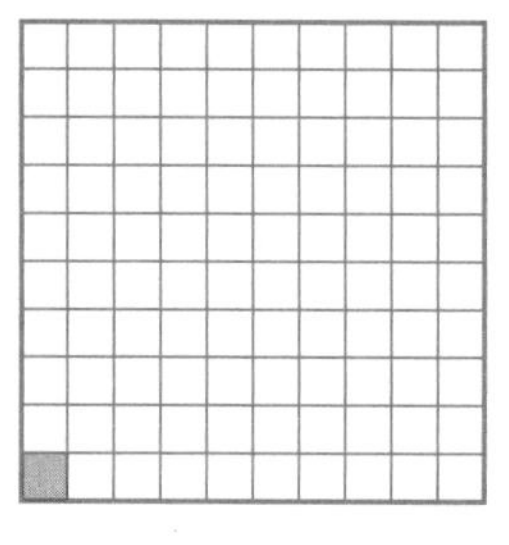

$\frac{1}{100}$, or 0.01

- How would you write $\frac{1}{100}$ as a decimal? 0.01

Repeat with other fractions in hundredths, including $\frac{32}{100}$ and $\frac{9}{100}$. Also, give students practice converting decimals into fractions; for example, 0.3, 0.25, and so on.

NOTE: Do not be concerned with reducing fractions to simplest form (lowest terms) when converting between decimals and fractions. At this stage, it is enough for students simply to make the conversions.

✦ Renaming Fractions as Decimals and Decimals as Fractions *(Math Journal 2,* pp. 210, 356, and 357)

PARTNER ACTIVITY

Students complete journal page 210. Circulate and provide assistance as needed. Then bring the class together to discuss answers, using the overhead transparency of *Math Masters,* page 109. For Problems 1–8, have students rename the fraction in tenths or hundredths and then rename it as a decimal. For each problem, ask by which number the numerator and denominator were multiplied to obtain the second fraction.

Ask students to record the decimals in the Equivalent Names for Fractions table on journal pages 356 and 357.

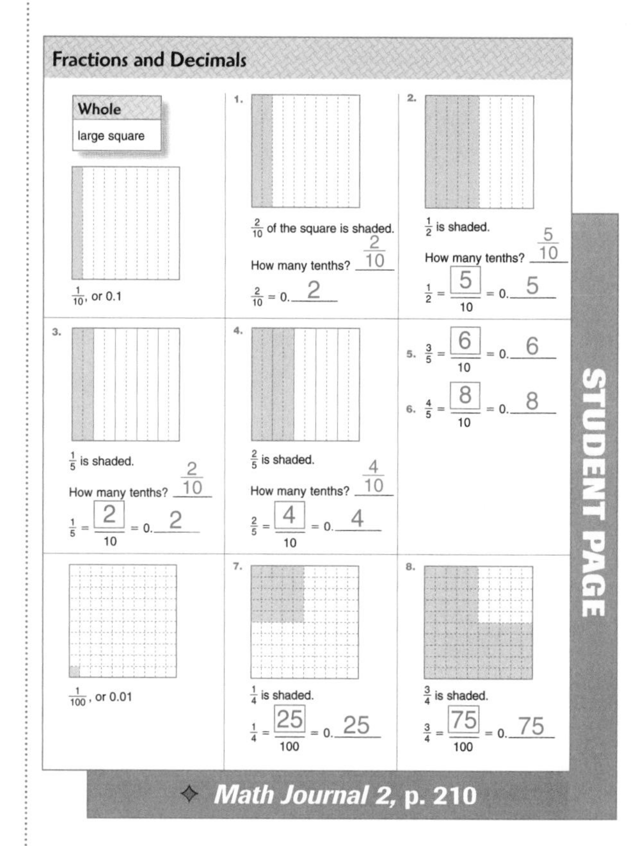

Fractions and Decimals

Whole: large square

$\frac{1}{10}$, or 0.1

1. $\frac{2}{10}$ of the square is shaded. How many tenths? $\frac{2}{10}$ $\frac{2}{10}$ = 0.2

2. $\frac{1}{2}$ is shaded. How many tenths? $\frac{5}{10}$ $\frac{1}{2} = \frac{5}{10}$ = 0.5

3. $\frac{1}{5}$ is shaded. How many tenths? $\frac{2}{10}$ $\frac{1}{5} = \frac{2}{10}$ = 0.2

4. $\frac{2}{5}$ is shaded. How many tenths? $\frac{4}{10}$ $\frac{2}{5} = \frac{4}{10}$ = 0.4

5. $\frac{3}{5} = \frac{6}{10}$ = 0.6

6. $\frac{4}{5} = \frac{8}{10}$ = 0.8

$\frac{1}{100}$, or 0.01

7. $\frac{1}{4}$ is shaded. $\frac{1}{4} = \frac{25}{100}$ = 0.25

8. $\frac{3}{4}$ is shaded. $\frac{3}{4} = \frac{75}{100}$ = 0.75

STUDENT PAGE

✦ *Math Journal 2,* p. 210

✦ Discussing Fractions and Division (*Student Reference Book,* p. 44)

WHOLE-CLASS DISCUSSION

Read and discuss "Fractions and Division" on page 44 of the *Student Reference Book.* Have students apply their understanding of division to equal-sharing division problems. *For example:*

- Nina and her mother baked 4 dozen cookies for the book club meeting. The club has 8 members. How many cookies are there for each member?

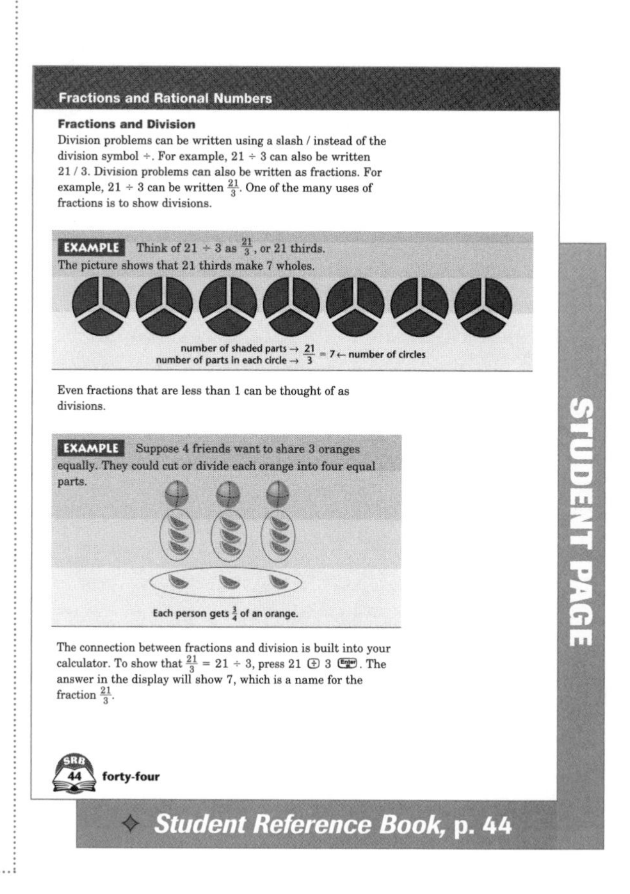

Fractions and Rational Numbers

Fractions and Division

Division problems can be written using a slash / instead of the division symbol ÷. For example, 21 ÷ 3 can also be written 21 / 3. Division problems can also be written as fractions. For example, 21 ÷ 3 can be written $\frac{21}{3}$. One of the many uses of fractions is to show divisions.

EXAMPLE Think of 21 ÷ 3 as $\frac{21}{3}$, or 21 thirds. The picture shows that 21 thirds make 7 wholes.

Even fractions that are less than 1 can be thought of as divisions.

EXAMPLE Suppose 4 friends want to share 3 oranges equally. They could cut or divide each orange into four equal parts.

Each person gets $\frac{3}{4}$ of an orange.

The connection between fractions and division is built into your calculator. To show that $\frac{21}{3}$ = 21 ÷ 3, press 21 ÷ 3 Enter. The answer in the display will show 7, which is a name for the fraction $\frac{21}{3}$.

SRB 44 forty-four

STUDENT PAGE

✦ *Student Reference Book,* p. 44

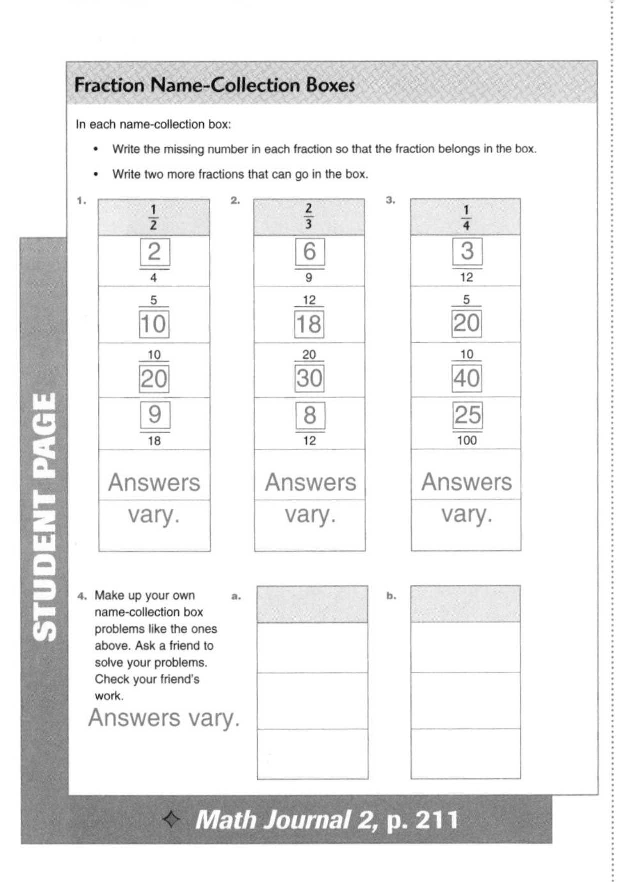
STUDENT PAGE

Fraction Name-Collection Boxes

In each name-collection box:

- Write the missing number in each fraction so that the fraction belongs in the box.
- Write two more fractions that can go in the box.

1. $\frac{1}{2}$	2. $\frac{2}{3}$	3. $\frac{1}{4}$
$\frac{2}{4}$	$\frac{6}{9}$	$\frac{3}{12}$
$\frac{5}{10}$	$\frac{12}{18}$	$\frac{5}{20}$
$\frac{10}{20}$	$\frac{20}{30}$	$\frac{10}{40}$
$\frac{9}{18}$	$\frac{8}{12}$	$\frac{25}{100}$
Answers vary.	Answers vary.	Answers vary.

4. Make up your own name-collection box problems like the ones above. Ask a friend to solve your problems. Check your friend's work.
Answers vary.

a. b.

✧ *Math Journal 2*, p. 211

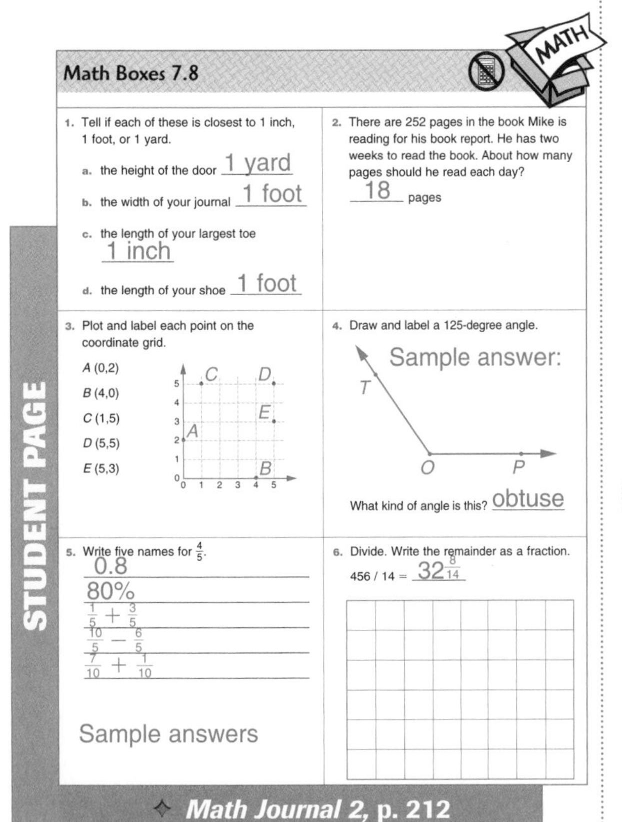
STUDENT PAGE

Math Boxes 7.8

1. Tell if each of these is closest to 1 inch, 1 foot, or 1 yard.
   a. the height of the door 1 yard
   b. the width of your journal 1 foot
   c. the length of your largest toe 1 inch
   d. the length of your shoe 1 foot

2. There are 252 pages in the book Mike is reading for his book report. He has two weeks to read the book. About how many pages should he read each day?
   18 pages

3. Plot and label each point on the coordinate grid.
   A (0,2)
   B (4,0)
   C (1,5)
   D (5,5)
   E (5,3)

4. Draw and label a 125-degree angle.
   Sample answer:
   What kind of angle is this? obtuse

5. Write five names for $\frac{4}{5}$.
   0.8
   80%
   $\frac{1}{5} + \frac{3}{5}$
   $\frac{10}{5} - \frac{6}{5}$
   $\frac{7}{10} + \frac{1}{10}$
   Sample answers

6. Divide. Write the remainder as a fraction.
   456 / 14 = $32\frac{8}{14}$

✧ *Math Journal 2*, p. 212

Four dozen equals 4 ∗ 12, or 48. The number models 48 / 8 = 6, 48 ÷ 8 = 6, and $\frac{48}{8} = 6$ fit this problem. The first and second number models suggest "dealing out" the 48 cookies to the 8 club members. When dealing is finished, each member has 6 cookies. The third number model, $\frac{48}{8} = 6$, suggests dividing each cookie into eighths and giving $\frac{1}{8}$ of each cookie to each person. When the 48 eighths each person has received are reassembled, they are equivalent to 6 cookies. Help students see that the net result—except for the crumbs—is the same as for "dealing out."

Also discuss problems in which the divisor is larger than the dividend. *For example:*

- Adam ordered 3 pizzas for his birthday party. There will be 5 people at the party. How much pizza is there for each person?

Point out that this problem and the cookie problem are both about sharing. The main difference is that in this problem, each share is less than one whole pizza. Draw 3 pizzas on the board or on the overhead transparency, and divide each one into fifths. If **A**dam's guests are named **B**ob, **C**harles, **D**arryl, and **E**d, the pizzas could be shared in the following way:

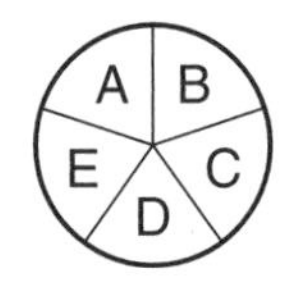

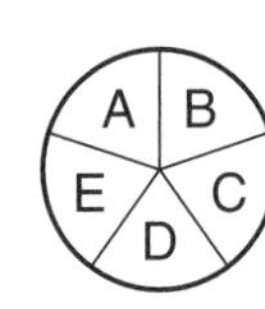

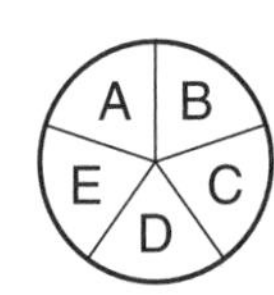

Help students see how the number model 3 / 5 = $\frac{3}{5}$ fits this problem. The left side, 3 / 5, suggests dividing 3 pizzas among 5 people. The right side, $\frac{3}{5}$, tells how much each person would get.

Explain that in high school and beyond, the symbol ÷ is almost never used for division. Division is usually shown with a slash (/) or a fraction bar (—).

2 Ongoing Learning & Practice

✦Using Fraction Name-Collection Boxes
(*Math Journal 2,* p. 211)

PARTNER ACTIVITY 

Students identify the missing numerator or denominator of equivalent fractions to complete name-collection boxes.

✦ Math Boxes 7.8 (*Math Journal 2,* p. 212)

INDEPENDENT ACTIVITY 

Mixed Review Math Boxes in this lesson are paired with Math Boxes in Lesson 7.6. The skill in Problem 1 is a prerequisite for Unit 8.

✦ Study Link 7.8 (*Math Masters,* p. 318)

Home Connection Students rename decimals as fractions and fractions as decimals. They color fractional parts of a 100-grid and write the value of the shaded part as a decimal and as a fraction.

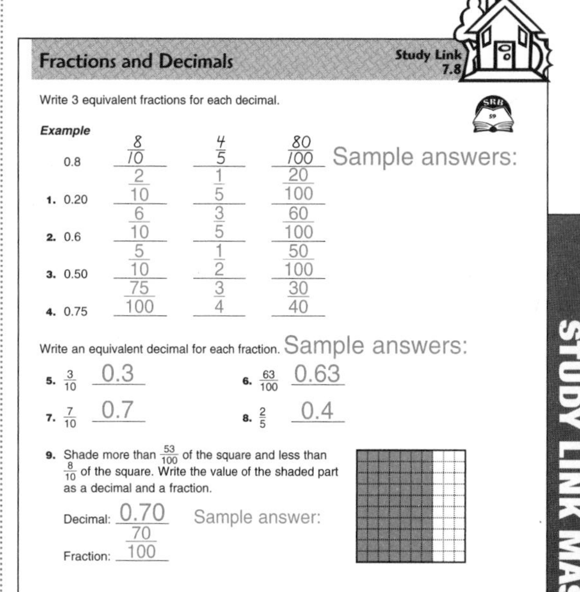

Fractions and Decimals — Study Link 7.8

Write 3 equivalent fractions for each decimal.

Example 0.8	$\frac{8}{10}$	$\frac{4}{5}$	$\frac{80}{100}$	Sample answers:
1. 0.20	$\frac{2}{10}$	$\frac{1}{5}$	$\frac{20}{100}$	
2. 0.6	$\frac{6}{10}$	$\frac{3}{5}$	$\frac{60}{100}$	
3. 0.50	$\frac{5}{10}$	$\frac{1}{2}$	$\frac{50}{100}$	
4. 0.75	$\frac{75}{100}$	$\frac{3}{4}$	$\frac{30}{40}$	

Write an equivalent decimal for each fraction. Sample answers:

5. $\frac{3}{10}$ 0.3 6. $\frac{63}{100}$ 0.63

7. $\frac{7}{10}$ 0.7 8. $\frac{2}{5}$ 0.4

9. Shade more than $\frac{53}{100}$ of the square and less than $\frac{8}{10}$ of the square. Write the value of the shaded part as a decimal and a fraction.

Decimal: 0.70 Sample answer:

Fraction: $\frac{70}{100}$

10. Shade more than $\frac{11}{100}$ of the square and less than $\frac{1}{4}$ of the square. Write the value of the shaded part as a decimal and a fraction.

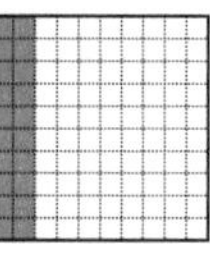

Decimal: 0.2 Sample answer:

Fraction: $\frac{2}{10}$

STUDY LINK MASTER

✦ *Math Masters,* p. 318

3 Options for Individualizing

✦ RETEACHING Creating Base-10 Block Designs (*Math Masters,* p. 110)

INDEPENDENT ACTIVITY  **30+ min** 

Students make a design on a base-10 block flat with cubes and then copy the design onto one of the grids shown on *Math Masters,* page 110. Students determine how much of the flat is covered by their cube design and express this number both as a decimal and as a fraction. Students may choose to exchange as many cubes as possible for longs, which would result in a certain number of longs (tenths) and cubes (hundredths).

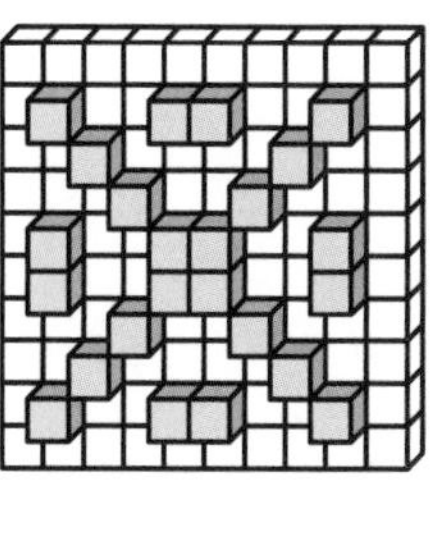

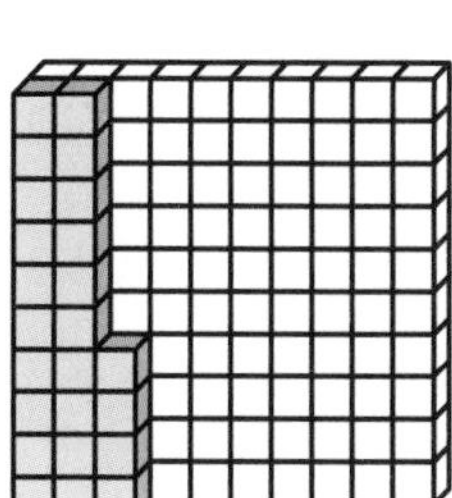

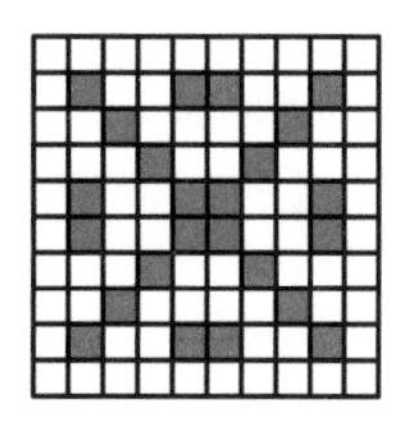

Decimal: 0.24

Fraction: $\frac{24}{100}$

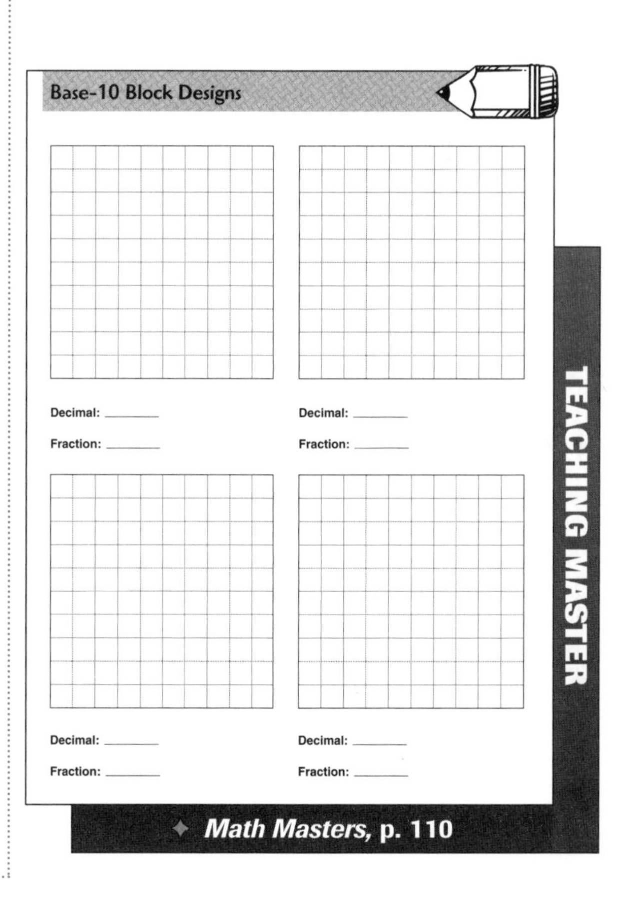

Base-10 Block Designs

Decimal: ______ Decimal: ______

Fraction: ______ Fraction: ______

Decimal: ______ Decimal: ______

Fraction: ______ Fraction: ______

TEACHING MASTER

✦ *Math Masters,* p. 110

7.9 Comparing Fractions

OBJECTIVE **To order sets of fractions.**

summaries	materials
1 Teaching the Lesson	
Students use Fraction Cards to determine whether a fraction is greater or less than another fraction, and they order sets of Fraction Cards from the smallest to the largest fraction. They also compare fractions with $\frac{1}{2}$ and write different sets of fractions in order. [Numeration]	☐ *Math Journal 2,* pp. 213 and 214 ☐ Study Link 7.8 ☐ Fraction Cards (see Lesson 7.4)
2 Ongoing Learning & Practice	
Students find fractional parts of money and lengths, and they shade fractional parts of regions. [Numeration] Students practice and maintain skills through Math Boxes and Study Link activities.	☐ *Math Journal 2,* pp. 215 and 216 ☐ Study Link Master (*Math Masters,* p. 319)
3 Options for Individualizing	
Enrichment Students use digits to create specified fractions. [Numeration]	

Additional Information

Vocabulary **(teacher)** • **unit fraction**

Getting Started

Mental Math and Reflexes

Write fraction addition and subtraction problems on the board. Students estimate whether the sum or difference is closest to 0, 1, or 2.

Suggestions

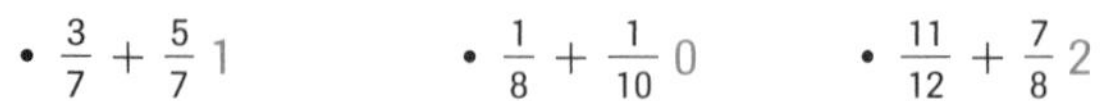

- $\frac{3}{7} + \frac{5}{7}$ 1
- $\frac{1}{8} + \frac{1}{10}$ 0
- $\frac{11}{12} + \frac{7}{8}$ 2
- $1\frac{1}{6} - \frac{7}{8}$ 0
- $1\frac{99}{100} - \frac{1}{5}$ 2
- $1\frac{9}{10} - \frac{15}{16}$ 1

Math Message

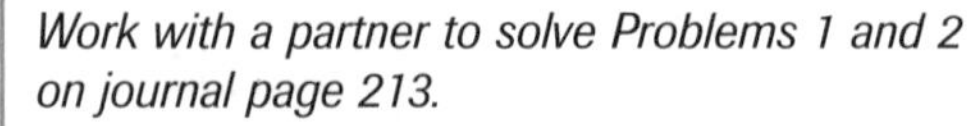

Work with a partner to solve Problems 1 and 2 on journal page 213.

Study Link 7.8 Follow-Up

Review answers. Ask students to explain how they solved Problems 9 and 10.

Teaching the Lesson

✦ Math Message Follow-Up (*Math Journal 2,* p. 213)

WHOLE-CLASS DISCUSSION

Students should have had no trouble concluding that Nancy ate more chocolate than Quinn (Problem 1), but they may have had more difficulty comparing the amounts eaten by Diego and Paula (Problem 2). Ask them to share their solution strategies. Students might have used any of these strategies:

- ▷ If you divide Diego's chocolate bar into 3 equal pieces and Paula's into 5 equal pieces, Diego's pieces will be larger than Paula's pieces. Therefore, there is more chocolate in two of Diego's pieces than in two of Paula's pieces. So Diego ate more chocolate than Paula did.
- ▷ Diego ate more than half a bar ($\frac{2}{3}$ is more than half). Paula ate less than half a bar ($\frac{2}{5}$ is less than half). So Diego ate more.
- ▷ Only $\frac{1}{3}$ of Diego's bar is left, but $\frac{3}{5}$ of Paula's bar is left. Since less of Diego's bar is left, he ate more.

Next, ask students who ate more, Diego or Kiana. Have them explain their answers. Students might have used any of the following strategies:

- ▷ If you divide Diego's chocolate bar into 6 equal pieces, he will eat 4 of the pieces, since $\frac{4}{6}$ is equivalent to $\frac{2}{3}$ of the bar. Since Diego ate $\frac{4}{6}$ of the bar and Kiana ate $\frac{5}{6}$ of a bar, Kiana ate more chocolate than Diego did.
- ▷ Kiana has only $\frac{1}{6}$ of her bar left, but Diego has $\frac{1}{3}$ left. Since $\frac{1}{3}$ is greater than $\frac{1}{6}$, Kiana has less left over. Therefore, Kiana must have eaten more.

Finally, have students determine who ate more, Diego or Nancy, and give their reasoning. Briefly discuss how they know Diego ate more.

✦ Ordering Fractions (Fraction Cards)

WHOLE-CLASS ACTIVITY

Have students compare fractions using their Fraction Cards. Have them look at fractions with the same numerator, then fractions with the same denominator, and finally mixed groups of fractions.

Comparing Fractions

Math Message: Eating Fractions

Quinn, Nancy, Diego, Paula, and Kiana were given 4 chocolate bars to share. All 4 bars were the same size.

1. Quinn and Nancy shared a chocolate bar. Quinn ate $\frac{1}{4}$ of the bar, and Nancy ate $\frac{2}{4}$.
   Who ate more? Nancy
   How much of the bar was left? $\frac{1}{4}$

2. Diego, Paula, and Kiana each ate part of the other chocolate bars. Diego ate $\frac{2}{3}$ of a bar, Paula ate $\frac{2}{5}$ of a bar, and Kiana ate $\frac{5}{6}$ of a bar.
   Who ate more, Diego or Paula? Diego
   How do you know? Sample answer: $\frac{2}{3}$ is more than $\frac{1}{2}$, and $\frac{2}{5}$ is less than $\frac{1}{2}$.

Comparing Fractions with $\frac{1}{2}$

Turn your Fraction Cards fraction-side up. Sort them into three piles:

- fractions less than $\frac{1}{2}$
- fractions equal to $\frac{1}{2}$
- fractions greater than $\frac{1}{2}$

You can turn the cards over to check your work. When you are finished, write the fractions in each pile in the correct box below.

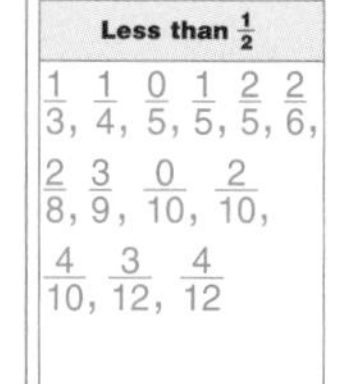

Less than ½
1/3, 1/4, 0/5, 1/5, 2/5, 2/6,
2/8, 3/9, 0/10, 2/10,
4/10, 3/12, 4/12

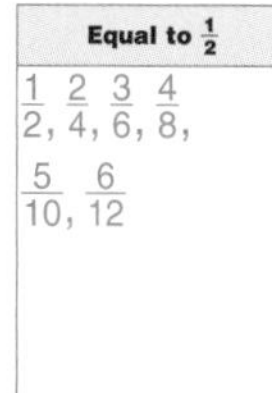

Equal to ½
1/2, 2/4, 3/6, 4/8,
5/10, 6/12

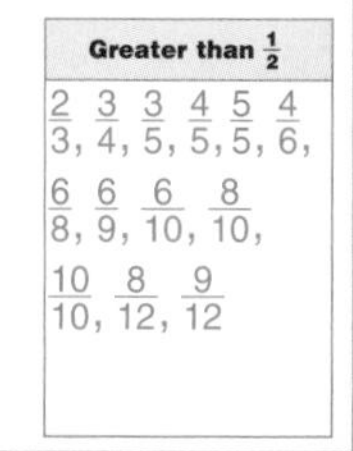

Greater than ½
2/3, 3/4, 3/5, 4/5, 5/5, 4/6,
6/8, 6/9, 6/10, 8/10,
10/10, 8/12, 9/12

STUDENT PAGE

✦ *Math Journal 2,* p. 213

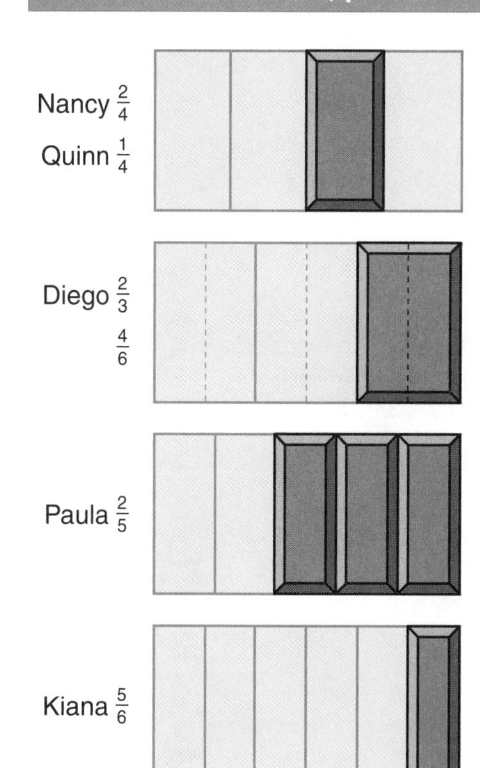

NOTE: Fractions with 1 in the numerator are called **unit fractions.**

Like Numerators

Tell students to take out all the Fraction Cards with 1 in the numerator ($\frac{1}{2}$, $\frac{1}{3}$, $\frac{1}{4}$, and $\frac{1}{5}$) and turn them fraction-side up. Ask them to line up the cards, from the smallest fraction (at the left) to the largest fraction (at the right). They can check by turning the cards over.

- What pattern do you notice? The larger the denominator, the smaller the fraction
- What is the reason for this pattern? As the denominator gets larger, the pieces get smaller because the whole is being divided into a greater number of pieces.

Like Denominators

Tell students to put the cards they just used back into the deck and then take out all the Fraction Cards with 10 in the denominator ($\frac{0}{10}$, $\frac{2}{10}$, $\frac{4}{10}$, $\frac{5}{10}$, $\frac{6}{10}$, $\frac{8}{10}$, and $\frac{10}{10}$). Ask them to turn the cards fraction-side up and arrange them in a row, from smallest fraction to largest fraction. They can check by turning the cards over.

- What pattern do you see? The larger the numerator, the larger the fraction
- What is the reason for this pattern? Since all the pieces are the same size, more pieces make a bigger fraction.

Different Numerators and Denominators

Tell students to put the cards they just used back into the deck, take out the cards for $\frac{1}{4}$, $\frac{2}{4}$, $\frac{2}{3}$, $\frac{2}{5}$, and $\frac{5}{6}$, and turn them fraction-side up. Have students line up these cards from smallest to largest fraction, using the following procedure:

▷ Tell students to place the $\frac{2}{4}$ card in front of them.

▷ Name one of the other cards ($\frac{1}{4}$, $\frac{2}{3}$, $\frac{2}{5}$, or $\frac{5}{6}$) and ask students whether the fraction is more or less than $\frac{2}{4}$. Also ask how they know.

▷ Direct students to place that card in the correct position—to the right or left of the $\frac{2}{4}$ card.

▷ Name the rest of the cards, one by one. Students place the cards in order, while you ask for justification for each card's placement. They can check by turning the cards over.

Have students work with partners to order the following Fraction Cards: $\frac{1}{2}$, $\frac{2}{10}$, $\frac{2}{6}$, $\frac{2}{3}$, and $\frac{3}{4}$. They should begin with the cards fraction-side up. They can check by turning the cards over. Circulate and assist as needed. When most students are finished, discuss their strategies.

STUDENT PAGE

Ordering Fractions

Write the fractions in order from smallest to largest.

1. $\frac{1}{4}$, $\frac{1}{2}$, $\frac{1}{9}$, $\frac{1}{5}$, $\frac{1}{100}$
   $\frac{1}{100}$ (smallest), $\frac{1}{9}$, $\frac{1}{5}$, $\frac{1}{4}$, $\frac{1}{2}$ (largest)

2. $\frac{2}{4}$, $\frac{2}{2}$, $\frac{2}{9}$, $\frac{2}{5}$, $\frac{2}{100}$
   $\frac{2}{100}$ (smallest), $\frac{2}{9}$, $\frac{2}{5}$, $\frac{2}{4}$, $\frac{2}{2}$ (largest)

3. $\frac{4}{10}$, $\frac{7}{10}$, $\frac{8}{10}$, $\frac{2}{10}$, $\frac{1}{10}$
   $\frac{1}{10}$ (smallest), $\frac{2}{10}$, $\frac{4}{10}$, $\frac{7}{10}$, $\frac{8}{10}$ (largest)

4. $\frac{4}{25}$, $\frac{1}{25}$, $\frac{7}{8}$, $\frac{6}{12}$, $\frac{7}{15}$
   $\frac{1}{25}$ (smallest), $\frac{4}{25}$, $\frac{7}{15}$, $\frac{6}{12}$, $\frac{7}{8}$ (largest)

5. a. Write 5 fractions that all have the same denominator. Answers vary.
   ___ ___ ___ ___ ___

   b. Ask a partner to put them in order from smallest to largest.
   ___ (smallest) ___ ___ ___ ___ (largest)

   c. Do you agree with your partner's answer? ________

✦ Math Journal 2, p. 214

Adjusting the Activity For those students who are having difficulty ordering fractions, consider giving them only two fractions at a time and having them decide which fraction is smaller.

✦ Comparing Fractions with $\frac{1}{2}$
(*Math Journal 2,* p. 213)

PARTNER ACTIVITY

Have students follow the directions at the bottom of journal page 213 to sort the Fraction Cards into three categories: less than $\frac{1}{2}$, equal to $\frac{1}{2}$, and greater than $\frac{1}{2}$.

✦ Ordering Fractions (*Math Journal 2,* p. 214)

PARTNER ACTIVITY

Students write fractions in order from smallest to largest.

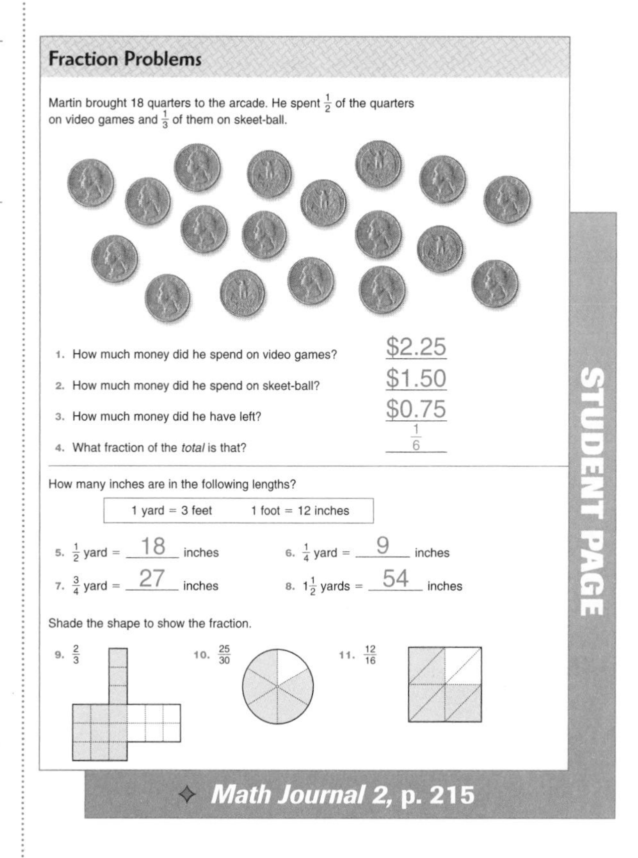

Fraction Problems

Martin brought 18 quarters to the arcade. He spent $\frac{1}{2}$ of the quarters on video games and $\frac{1}{3}$ of them on skee-ball.

1. How much money did he spend on video games? $2.25
2. How much money did he spend on skee-ball? $1.50
3. How much money did he have left? $0.75
4. What fraction of the *total* is that? $\frac{1}{6}$

How many inches are in the following lengths?

1 yard = 3 feet   1 foot = 12 inches

5. $\frac{1}{2}$ yard = 18 inches
6. $\frac{1}{4}$ yard = 9 inches
7. $\frac{3}{4}$ yard = 27 inches
8. $1\frac{1}{2}$ yards = 54 inches

Shade the shape to show the fraction.

9. $\frac{2}{3}$
10. $\frac{25}{30}$
11. $\frac{12}{16}$

STUDENT PAGE

✦ *Math Journal 2,* p. 215

Ongoing Learning & Practice

✦ Solving Fraction Problems
(*Math Journal 2,* p. 215)

INDEPENDENT ACTIVITY 

Students find fractional parts of money and lengths, and they shade fractional parts of regions.

✦ Math Boxes 7.9 (*Math Journal 2,* p. 216)

INDEPENDENT ACTIVITY 

Mixed Review Math Boxes in this lesson are paired with Math Boxes in Lesson 7.11. The skill in Problem 1 is a prerequisite for Unit 8.

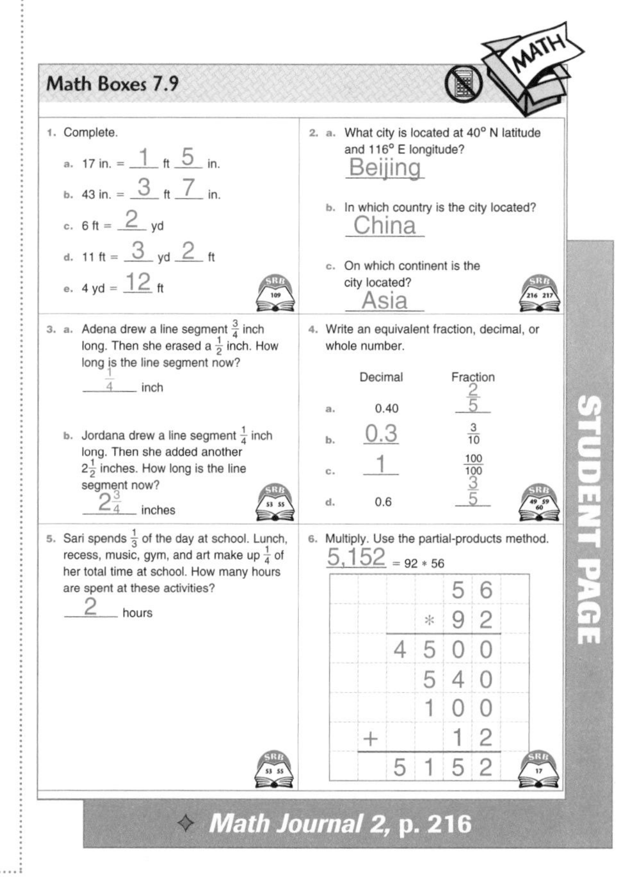

Math Boxes 7.9

1. Complete.
   a. 17 in. = 1 ft 5 in.
   b. 43 in. = 3 ft 7 in.
   c. 6 ft = 2 yd
   d. 11 ft = 3 yd 2 ft
   e. 4 yd = 12 ft

2. a. What city is located at 40° N latitude and 116° E longitude? Beijing
   b. In which country is the city located? China
   c. On which continent is the city located? Asia

3. a. Adena drew a line segment $\frac{3}{4}$ inch long. Then she erased a $\frac{1}{2}$ inch. How long is the line segment now? $\frac{1}{4}$ inch
   b. Jordana drew a line segment $\frac{1}{4}$ inch long. Then she added another $2\frac{1}{2}$ inches. How long is the line segment now? $2\frac{3}{4}$ inches

4. Write an equivalent fraction, decimal, or whole number.

	Decimal	Fraction
a.	0.40	$\frac{2}{5}$
b.	0.3	$\frac{3}{10}$
c.	1	$\frac{100}{100}$
d.	0.6	$\frac{3}{5}$

5. Sari spends $\frac{1}{3}$ of the day at school. Lunch, recess, music, gym, and art make up $\frac{1}{4}$ of her total time at school. How many hours are spent at these activities? 2 hours

6. Multiply. Use the partial-products method.
   5,152 = 92 * 56

		5	6
	*	9	2
4	5	0	0
	5	4	0
	1	0	0
+		1	2
5	1	5	2

STUDENT PAGE

✦ *Math Journal 2,* p. 216

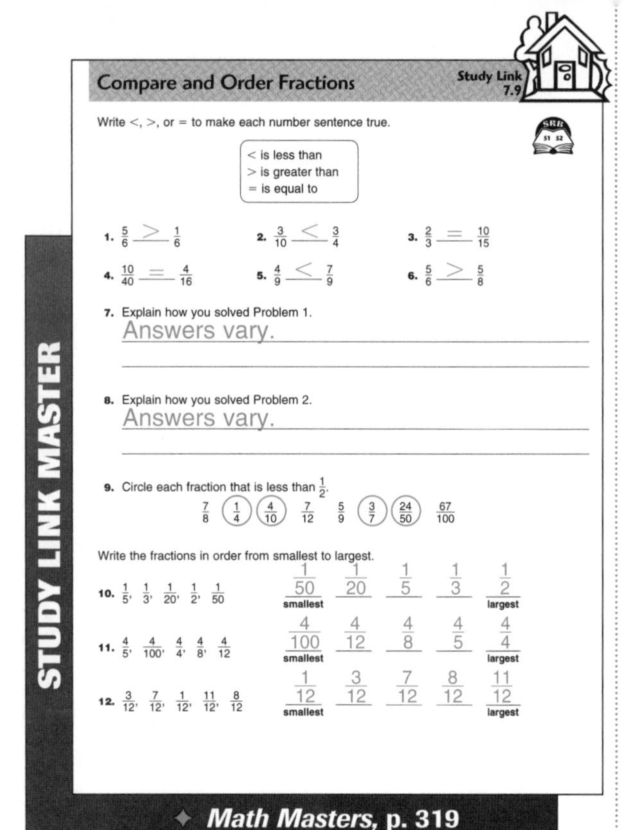

Compare and Order Fractions — Study Link 7.9

Write <, >, or = to make each number sentence true.

< is less than
> is greater than
= is equal to

1. $\frac{5}{6}$ > $\frac{1}{6}$
2. $\frac{3}{10}$ < $\frac{3}{4}$
3. $\frac{2}{3}$ = $\frac{10}{15}$
4. $\frac{10}{40}$ = $\frac{4}{16}$
5. $\frac{4}{9}$ < $\frac{7}{9}$
6. $\frac{5}{6}$ > $\frac{5}{8}$
7. Explain how you solved Problem 1.
   Answers vary.
8. Explain how you solved Problem 2.
   Answers vary.
9. Circle each fraction that is less than $\frac{1}{2}$.
   $\frac{7}{8}$ ($\frac{1}{4}$) ($\frac{4}{10}$) $\frac{7}{12}$ $\frac{5}{9}$ ($\frac{3}{7}$) ($\frac{24}{50}$) $\frac{67}{100}$

Write the fractions in order from smallest to largest.

10. $\frac{1}{5}$, $\frac{1}{3}$, $\frac{1}{20}$, $\frac{1}{2}$, $\frac{1}{50}$ — $\frac{1}{50}$ (smallest), $\frac{1}{20}$, $\frac{1}{5}$, $\frac{1}{3}$, $\frac{1}{2}$ (largest)
11. $\frac{4}{5}$, $\frac{4}{100}$, $\frac{4}{4}$, $\frac{4}{8}$, $\frac{4}{12}$ — $\frac{4}{100}$ (smallest), $\frac{4}{12}$, $\frac{4}{8}$, $\frac{4}{5}$, $\frac{4}{4}$ (largest)
12. $\frac{3}{12}$, $\frac{7}{12}$, $\frac{1}{12}$, $\frac{11}{12}$, $\frac{8}{12}$ — $\frac{1}{12}$ (smallest), $\frac{3}{12}$, $\frac{7}{12}$, $\frac{8}{12}$, $\frac{11}{12}$ (largest)

STUDY LINK MASTER

✦ *Math Masters,* p. 319

✦ Study Link 7.9 (*Math Masters,* p. 319)

Home Connection Students compare and order fractions.

3 Options for Individualizing

✦ ENRICHMENT Using Digits to Create Fractions

INDEPENDENT ACTIVITY  **5–15 min** 

Any fraction can be made from the digits 0, 1, 2, 3, 4, 5, 6, 7, 8, and 9. The fraction $\frac{3}{4}$ is made up of two digits, the fraction $\frac{23}{6}$ is made up of 3 digits, and so on. A fraction may not have a denominator of 0.

Challenge students to make the following fractions with two digits. For each problem, have them share their reasoning.

- ▷ The smallest possible fraction greater than 0 $\frac{1}{9}$
- ▷ The largest possible fraction $\frac{9}{1}$
- ▷ The largest fraction that is less than 1 $\frac{8}{9}$
- ▷ The smallest fraction that is greater than $\frac{1}{2}$ $\frac{5}{9}$

7.10 The ONE for Fractions

OBJECTIVE **To find the whole, or ONE, for given fractions.**

summaries	materials
1 Teaching the Lesson	
Students use pattern blocks and counters to find the ONE for given fractions, and they solve "What is the ONE?" problems. [Numeration]	□ *Math Journal 2,* pp. 217 and 218 □ Study Link 7.9 □ pattern blocks □ pattern blocks and counters for overhead (optional) □ beans, pennies, or other counters □ slate □ Geometry Template
2 Ongoing Learning & Practice	
Students play *Fraction Top-It* to provide practice in comparing fractions. [Numeration] Students practice and maintain skills through Math Boxes and Study Link activities.	□ *Math Journal 2,* p. 219 □ *Student Reference Book,* p. 197 □ Study Link Master (*Math Masters,* p. 320) □ Geometry Template (optional)
3 Options for Individualizing	
Enrichment Students make designs with pattern-block shapes, and they label each shape as a fraction of the design. [Numeration]	□ pattern blocks (hexagon, trapezoid, wide rhombus, and triangle) □ Geometry Template (optional)

Getting Started

Mental Math and Reflexes

Write fractions with denominators of 10 or 100 on the board and have students write the equivalent decimals on their slates. Then write decimals on the board and have students write the equivalent fractions on their slates. Do not insist that the fractions be in simplest form. *Suggestions:*

- $\frac{3}{10}$ 0.3
- $\frac{34}{100}$ 0.34
- $\frac{80}{100}$ 0.80, or 0.8
- 0.4 $\frac{4}{10}$
- 0.83 $\frac{83}{100}$
- 0.90 $\frac{90}{100}$

Math Message

Solve Problems 1 and 2 at the top of journal page 217.

Study Link 7.9 Follow-Up

Briefly go over the answers.

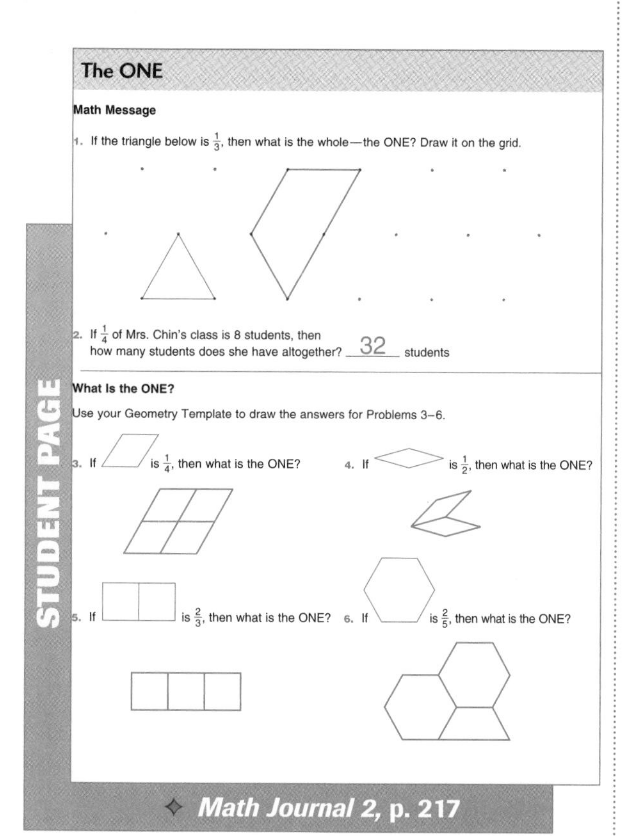
The ONE

Math Message

1. If the triangle below is $\frac{1}{3}$, then what is the whole—the ONE? Draw it on the grid.

2. If $\frac{1}{4}$ of Mrs. Chin's class is 8 students, then how many students does she have altogether? 32 students

What Is the ONE?

Use your Geometry Template to draw the answers for Problems 3–6.

3. If [shape] is $\frac{1}{4}$, then what is the ONE?

4. If [shape] is $\frac{1}{2}$, then what is the ONE?

5. If [shape] is $\frac{2}{3}$, then what is the ONE?

6. If [shape] is $\frac{2}{5}$, then what is the ONE?

✧ *Math Journal 2*, p. 217

Teaching the Lesson

✦ Math Message Follow-Up
(*Math Journal 2*, p. 217)

WHOLE-CLASS DISCUSSION 

Discuss students' answers. For Problem 2, have volunteers describe or show how they solved the problem.

✦ Using Pattern Blocks to Find the ONE

WHOLE-CLASS ACTIVITY

Pose problems like those below, in which a part is given and students are to find the whole, or ONE. Display one or two pattern blocks on the overhead projector and tell what fraction is represented by this block or pair of blocks. (Or you can draw the pattern blocks on the board or hold them up for the class to see.) Then direct students to use their pattern blocks to show what the ONE is. After each problem, discuss their solutions. *Suggestions:*

- If △ is $\frac{1}{2}$, then what is the ONE?
  1 wide rhombus or equivalent
- If ⏢ is $\frac{3}{4}$, then what is the ONE?
  2 wide rhombuses or equivalent
- If ⬡ is $\frac{2}{3}$, then what is the ONE?
  3 trapezoids or equivalent
- If ◻◻ is $\frac{1}{3}$, then what is the ONE?
  6 squares
- If ◇▱ is $\frac{1}{2}$, then what is the ONE?
  4 wide rhombuses

NOTE: The blocks that make up the ONE can often be arranged in several ways. Investigating various arrangements is worthwhile, but in this lesson, it doesn't matter how the blocks in the ONE are arranged.

✦ Using Counters to Find the ONE

WHOLE-CLASS ACTIVITY

Pose more problems, like those below, in which a part of a collection of objects is given and students are to find the ONE. Display beans, pennies, or other counters on the overhead projector and tell what fraction is represented. Ask students to use their slates to write the number of counters in the ONE.

- If ○○○ is $\frac{1}{2}$, then what is the ONE?
  6 counters
- If ○○○ is $\frac{1}{3}$, then what is the ONE?
  9 counters
- If ○○○○ is $\frac{2}{5}$, then what is the ONE?
  10 counters
- If ○○○○ is $\frac{2}{3}$, then what is the ONE?
  6 counters
- If ○○ is $\frac{1}{4}$, then what is the ONE?
  8 counters

✦ Solving "What Is the ONE?" Problems
(*Math Journal 2,* pp. 217 and 218)

PARTNER ACTIVITY

Students solve problems at the bottom of journal page 217 and on page 218, in which a fractional part is given and students identify the ONE.

Adjusting the Activity If students are having difficulty finding the ONE, encourage them to use their pattern blocks and counters when solving the problems.

What Is the ONE? (cont.)

Solve. If you wish, draw pictures at the bottom of the page to help you solve the problems.

7. If ○○○○○ is $\frac{1}{3}$, then what is the ONE? 15 counters
8. If ○○○○ is $\frac{1}{4}$, then what is the ONE? 16 counters
9. If 10 counters are $\frac{2}{5}$, then what is the ONE? 25 counters
10. If 12 counters are $\frac{3}{4}$, then what is the ONE? 16 counters
11. If $\frac{1}{5}$ of the cookies that Mrs. Jackson baked is 12, then how many cookies did she bake in all? 60 cookies
12. In Mr. Mendez's class, $\frac{3}{4}$ of the students take music lessons. That is, 15 students take music lessons. How many students are in Mr. Mendez's class? 20 students

STUDENT PAGE

✧ *Math Journal 2,* p. 218

Games

Fraction Top-It

Materials ☐ 1 deck of 32 Fraction Cards (*Math Journal 2*, Activity Sheets 5 and 6)

Players 2 to 4

Object of the game To collect the most cards.

Directions

Advance Preparation: Before beginning the game, write the fraction for the shaded part on the back of each card.

1. Deal the same number of cards, fraction-side up, to each player:
   - 16 cards each, if there are 2 players
   - 10 cards each, if there are 3 players
   - 8 cards each, if there are 4 players
2. Place the cards on the playing surface in front of each player, fraction-side up.
3. Starting with the dealer and going in a clockwise direction, each player plays one card.
4. Place cards on the table with the fraction-side showing.
5. The player with the largest fraction wins the round and takes the cards. Players may check who has the largest fraction by turning over the cards and comparing the amount shaded.
6. If there is a tie for the largest fraction, each player plays another card. The player with the largest fraction takes all the cards.
7. The player who takes the cards starts the next round. The game is over when all cards have been played.

The player who takes the most cards wins.

Fraction Cards 1

Fraction Cards 2

one hundred ninety-seven SRB 197

STUDENT PAGE

✧ *Student Reference Book*, p. 197

Ongoing Learning & Practice

✦ Playing *Fraction Top-It* (*Student Reference Book*, p. 197)

SMALL-GROUP ACTIVITY 

Go over the rules of *Fraction Top-It* with the class. Then divide the class into groups of 2, 3, or 4 to play the game.

✦ Math Boxes 7.10 (*Math Journal 2*, p. 219)

INDEPENDENT ACTIVITY

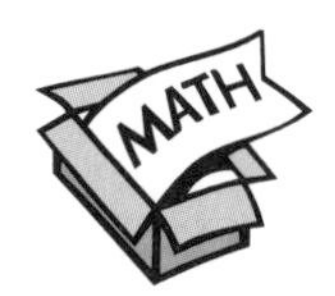

Mixed Review Math Boxes in this lesson are paired with Math Boxes in Lesson 7.12. The skill in Problem 1 is a prerequisite for Unit 8.

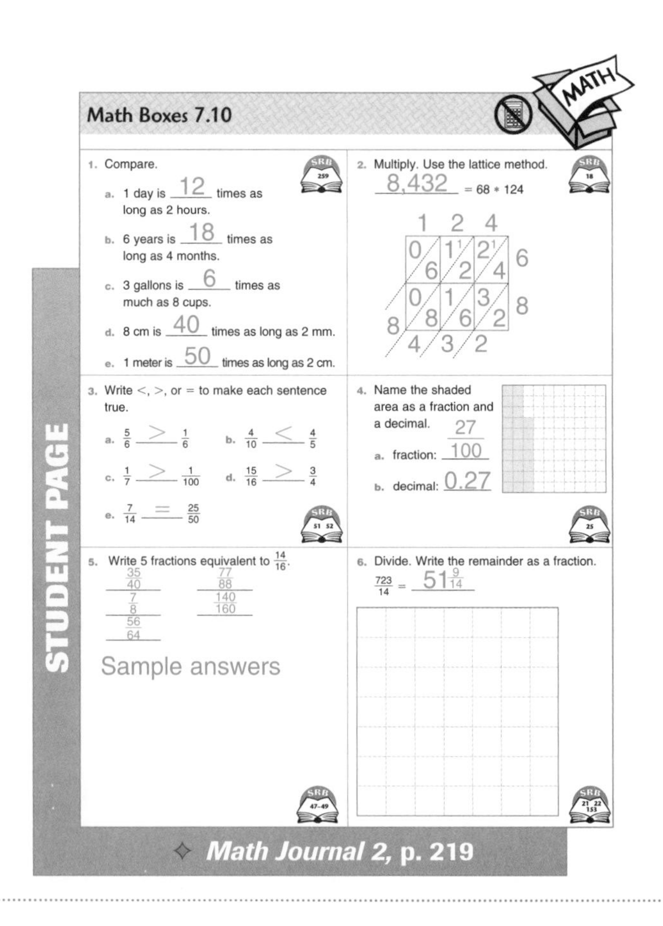

Math Boxes 7.10

1. Compare.
   a. 1 day is 12 times as long as 2 hours.
   b. 6 years is 18 times as long as 4 months.
   c. 3 gallons is 6 times as much as 8 cups.
   d. 8 cm is 40 times as long as 2 mm.
   e. 1 meter is 50 times as long as 2 cm.

SRB 259

2. Multiply. Use the lattice method.
   8,432 = 68 ∗ 124

SRB 18

3. Write <, >, or = to make each sentence true.
   a. $\frac{5}{6} > \frac{1}{6}$
   b. $\frac{4}{10} < \frac{4}{5}$
   c. $\frac{1}{7} > \frac{1}{100}$
   d. $\frac{15}{16} > \frac{3}{4}$
   e. $\frac{7}{14} = \frac{25}{50}$

SRB 51 52

4. Name the shaded area as a fraction and a decimal.
   a. fraction: $\frac{27}{100}$
   b. decimal: 0.27

SRB 25

5. Write 5 fractions equivalent to $\frac{14}{16}$.
   $\frac{35}{40}$, $\frac{7}{8}$, $\frac{56}{64}$, $\frac{77}{88}$, $\frac{140}{160}$
   Sample answers

SRB 47–49

6. Divide. Write the remainder as a fraction.
   $\frac{723}{14} = 51\frac{9}{14}$

SRB 21 22 155

STUDENT PAGE

✧ *Math Journal 2*, p. 219

✦ Study Link 7.10 (*Math Masters,* p. 320)

Home Connection Students solve "What is the ONE?" problems. For Problems 3–8, suggest that students use counters or pennies to help them find the answers.

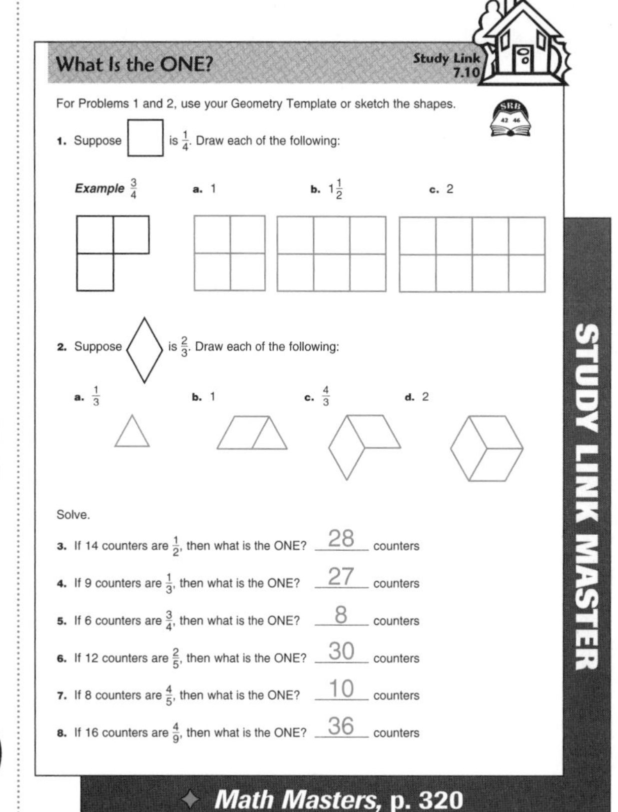

What Is the ONE? Study Link 7.10

For Problems 1 and 2, use your Geometry Template or sketch the shapes.

1. Suppose □ is $\frac{1}{4}$. Draw each of the following:

Example $\frac{3}{4}$ a. 1 b. $1\frac{1}{2}$ c. 2

2. Suppose ◇ is $\frac{2}{3}$. Draw each of the following:

a. $\frac{1}{3}$ b. 1 c. $\frac{4}{3}$ d. 2

Solve.

3. If 14 counters are $\frac{1}{2}$, then what is the ONE? 28 counters
4. If 9 counters are $\frac{1}{3}$, then what is the ONE? 27 counters
5. If 6 counters are $\frac{3}{4}$, then what is the ONE? 8 counters
6. If 12 counters are $\frac{2}{5}$, then what is the ONE? 30 counters
7. If 8 counters are $\frac{4}{5}$, then what is the ONE? 10 counters
8. If 16 counters are $\frac{4}{9}$, then what is the ONE? 36 counters

STUDY LINK MASTER

✦ *Math Masters,* p. 320

3 Options for Individualizing

✦ ENRICHMENT Naming Fractional Parts of a Region

INDEPENDENT ACTIVITY  **15–30 min** 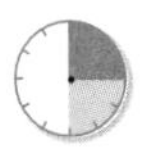

Art Link Have students use pattern blocks (hexagon, trapezoid, wide rhombus, and triangle) or the Geometry Template to draw and color a design. The design is the ONE. On each shape, students write what fraction of the design that shape represents. Students should compare their designs and note that the amount represented by a fraction depends on the whole or the ONE.

Portfolio Ideas

Example

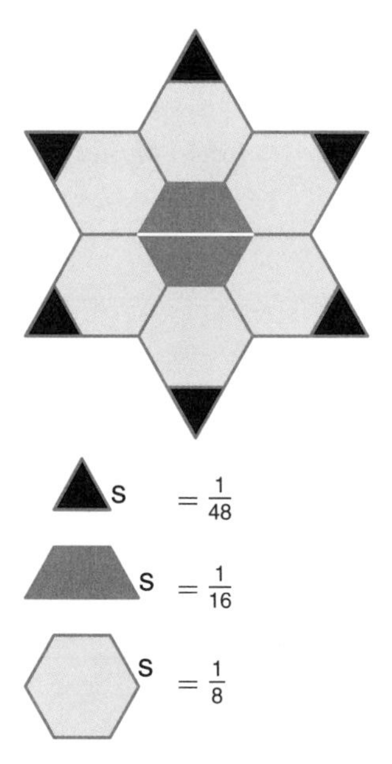

7.11 Probability, Fractions, and Spinners

OBJECTIVES **To review basic ideas of probability, including fairness and expected results; and to apply knowledge of fractions to spinners.**

summaries	materials
1 Teaching the Lesson	
Students review and apply basic concepts and vocabulary associated with chance events through hands-on activities with spinners. [Data and Chance]	□ *Math Journal 2,* p. 220 □ Study Link 7.10 □ Teaching Master (*Math Masters,* p. 111) □ coloring pencils, markers, or crayons (green, red, blue, and at least 3 other colors) □ straightedge □ 1 large (2") paper clip □ 2 pieces of removable tape □ data pad or chart paper (optional) □ slate
2 Ongoing Learning & Practice	
Students fill in missing fractions on number lines. [Numeration] Students practice and maintain skills through Math Boxes and Study Link activities.	□ *Math Journal 2,* pp. 221 and 222 □ Study Link Masters (*Math Masters,* pp. 321–323)
3 Options for Individualizing	
Reteaching Students use the words *impossible, maybe,* and *certain* to describe the likelihood of events. [Data and Chance] **Language Diversity** Students make a list of words that express the likelihood of an event. [Data and Chance] **Enrichment** Students read and discuss a book about probability. [Data and Chance]	□ *Do You Wanna Bet? Your Chance to Find Out about Probability* ***See* Advance Preparation**

Additional Information

Advance Preparation For the optional Enrichment activity in Part 3, obtain the book *Do You Wanna Bet? Your Chance to Find Out about Probability* by Jean Cushman (Clarion Books, 1991).

Vocabulary • **fair (die or spinner)** • **equal chance** • **expect** • **equally (more, less) likely**

Getting Started

Mental Math and Reflexes

Write pairs of fractions on the board and have students write the greater fraction in each pair on their slates. *Suggestions:*

- $\frac{3}{4}$ and $\frac{3}{8}$ $\frac{3}{4}$
- $\frac{6}{10}$ and $\frac{9}{10}$ $\frac{9}{10}$
- $\frac{5}{11}$ and $\frac{8}{14}$ $\frac{8}{14}$

Then write sets of fractions on the board and have students write the fractions from smallest to largest on their slates. *Suggestions:*

- $\frac{1}{2}, \frac{1}{3}, \frac{1}{8}, \frac{1}{20}, \frac{1}{5}$ $\frac{1}{20}, \frac{1}{8}, \frac{1}{5}, \frac{1}{3}, \frac{1}{2}$
- $\frac{4}{12}, \frac{9}{12}, \frac{7}{12}, \frac{1}{12}, \frac{11}{12}$ $\frac{1}{12}, \frac{4}{12}, \frac{7}{12}, \frac{9}{12}, \frac{11}{12}$

Math Message

Think of a game you like in which the players roll dice. Be prepared to explain how dice are used in the game.

Study Link 7.10 Follow-Up

Review answers.

1 Teaching the Lesson

Math Message Follow-Up

WHOLE-CLASS DISCUSSION 

Discuss the use of dice in games. *For example:*

- Dice are used to determine how far a player can move.
- Dice are used to determine numbers that are used in a game.
- You can't predict which number will come up on a die.
- It's important to have a **fair die**—that is, there must be an **equal chance** for it to land with any one of its faces on top.

Ask students what other devices they have used that serve the same purpose as dice. Spinners, egg cartons with numbered cups, coins, number cards, and so on

Spinning a Spinner (*Math Masters,* p. 111)

PARTNER ACTIVITY

Tell students that they are going to use spinners to experiment with situations in which they can't tell for sure what will happen.

Have students work with partners. Pass out *Math Masters,* page 111, and ask each partnership to tape it to a flat, level surface, such as the desktop. Show them how to make a paper-clip spinner and how to use the spinner. (*See margin on next page.*)

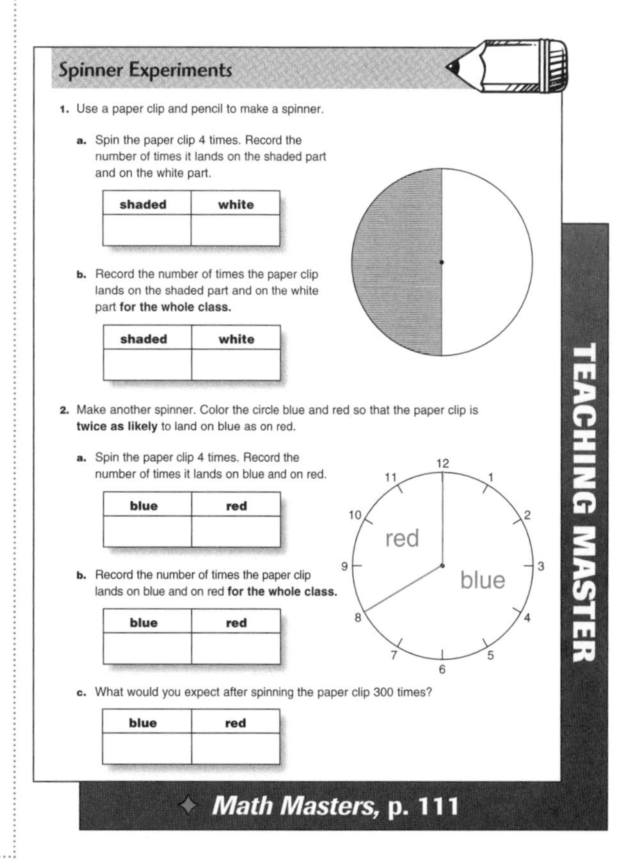

Spinner Experiments

1. Use a paper clip and pencil to make a spinner.

   a. Spin the paper clip 4 times. Record the number of times it lands on the shaded part and on the white part.

shaded	white

   b. Record the number of times the paper clip lands on the shaded part and on the white part **for the whole class.**

shaded	white

2. Make another spinner. Color the circle blue and red so that the paper clip is **twice as likely** to land on blue as on red.

   a. Spin the paper clip 4 times. Record the number of times it lands on blue and on red.

blue	red

   b. Record the number of times the paper clip lands on blue and on red **for the whole class.**

blue	red

   c. What would you expect after spinning the paper clip 300 times?

blue	red

Math Masters, p. 111

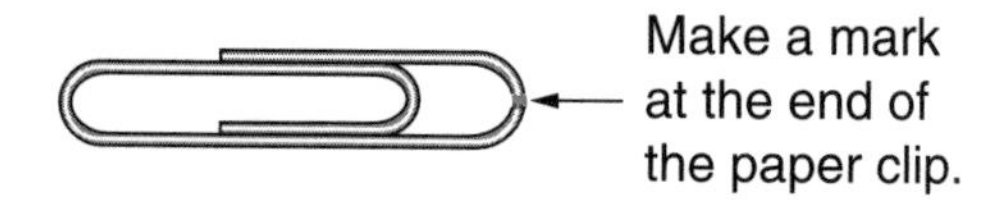
Make a mark
at the end of
the paper clip.

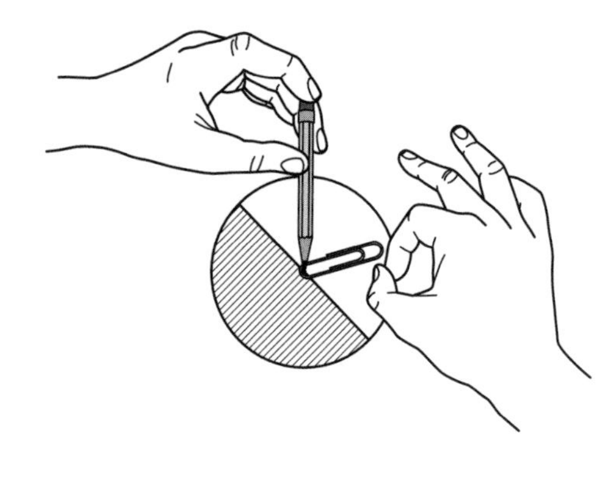

Discuss what constitutes a **fair spinner**—one in which the paper clip has an **equal chance** of landing on any part of the circle. A spinner may not spin fairly if it is placed on a surface that is not level.

Practice using the spinner. Here are two approaches:

▷ One partner holds the pencil. The other partner spins the paper clip with a flick of a finger.

▷ One partner holds the pencil and flicks the paper clip. The other partner records the results.

✦Doing Spinner Experiments
(*Math Masters,* p. 111)

WHOLE-CLASS ACTIVITY

Experiment 1

1. Partners use the first spinner on *Math Masters,* page 111. They spin the paper clip four times and record the results in Problem 1a.
2. Students report their results to you. You tally them on the class data pad or on the board.
3. You and the class find the class totals. Students record them in Problem 1b.

Ask students to summarize their results. Encourage language like the following:

▷ "The paper clip has the same chance of landing on the shaded part as on the white part."

▷ "If you spin the paper clip many times, it should land on white 1 out of 2 times."

▷ "Chances are, the paper clip will land on the white part half of the time and on the shaded part half of the time, because each part is half of the circle."

▷ "The chance of landing on the shaded part is 50% (or $\frac{1}{2}$)."

Experiment 2

Ask partners to color the second spinner on *Math Masters,* page 111, blue and red in such a way that the paper clip is twice as likely to land on blue as on red. Point out that the circle has been divided into 12 equal parts.

Bring the class together to share results and spinner designs. Students should have colored $\frac{2}{3}$ of the circle blue and $\frac{1}{3}$ red. Most students will have colored 8 consecutive equal parts blue, and the other 4 equal parts red.

NOTE: Encourage students to work in pencil until they are sure they have a correct solution. If they work in marker or crayon, errors will be harder to correct.

However, there are other possibilities—for example, 2 consecutive parts could be colored blue, followed by 1 red part, 2 blue parts, and so on.

When students' spinners are correct, repeat this procedure:

1. Partners use the blue-and-red spinner. They spin the paper clip four times and record the results in Problem 2a.
2. Students report their results to you. You tally them on the class data pad or on the board.
3. You and the class find the class totals. Students record them in Problem 2b.

Ask students to summarize their results. Encourage language like the following:

▷ "The paper clip is more likely to land on blue than on red."

▷ "If you spin many times, blue will come up twice as often."

▷ "It's hard to predict, but if you spin a lot of times, blue will come up about 2 out of 3 spins, or $\frac{2}{3}$ of the time."

▷ "There is a $\frac{2}{3}$ chance of landing on blue."

Finally, have students complete Problem 2c and discuss their answers. Make sure that they understand the meaning of the word **expect** in this context. One would *expect* the paper clip to land on red *about* 100 times, but this does not mean that it will do so *exactly* 100 times. In fact, it probably will *not* land on red exactly 100 times.

When students describe chance events, encourage them to use a variety of words and phrases, such as *likely, unlikely, 3 out of 4, three-fourths of the time, 75% chance, the chances are,* and *you can expect.*

✦ Designing Spinners (*Math Journal 2,* p. 220)

PARTNER ACTIVITY 

Students complete journal page 220. Circulate and assist students as needed. Then bring the class together to share results and spinner designs.

For Problem 1, students will probably divide the circle into 6 equal parts. Ask how they decided what size to make each part. $\frac{1}{6}$ of 12 = 2, so the circle can be divided into 6 equal parts by starting at 0 and counting by 2s.

Encourage students to use such phrases as "**equally likely,**" "equal chance," and "1 out of 6 chances of landing on red" when they discuss their spinner designs.

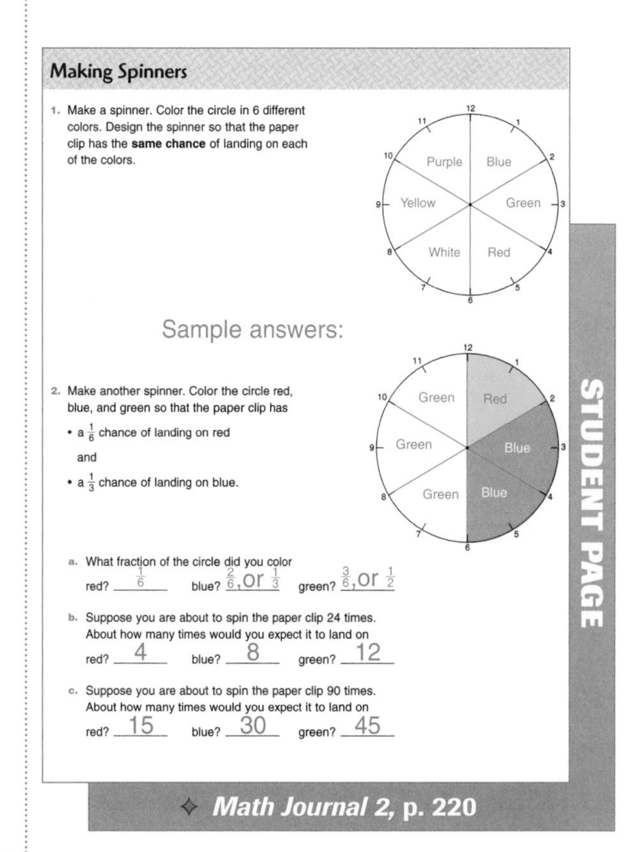

Making Spinners

1. Make a spinner. Color the circle in 6 different colors. Design the spinner so that the paper clip has the **same chance** of landing on each of the colors.

Sample answers:

2. Make another spinner. Color the circle red, blue, and green so that the paper clip has
   - a $\frac{1}{6}$ chance of landing on red

   and
   - a $\frac{1}{3}$ chance of landing on blue.

a. What fraction of the circle did you color red? $\frac{1}{6}$ blue? $\frac{2}{6}$, or $\frac{1}{3}$ green? $\frac{3}{6}$, or $\frac{1}{2}$

b. Suppose you are about to spin the paper clip 24 times. About how many times would you expect it to land on red? 4 blue? 8 green? 12

c. Suppose you are about to spin the paper clip 90 times. About how many times would you expect it to land on red? 15 blue? 30 green? 45

STUDENT PAGE

✧ *Math Journal 2,* p. 220

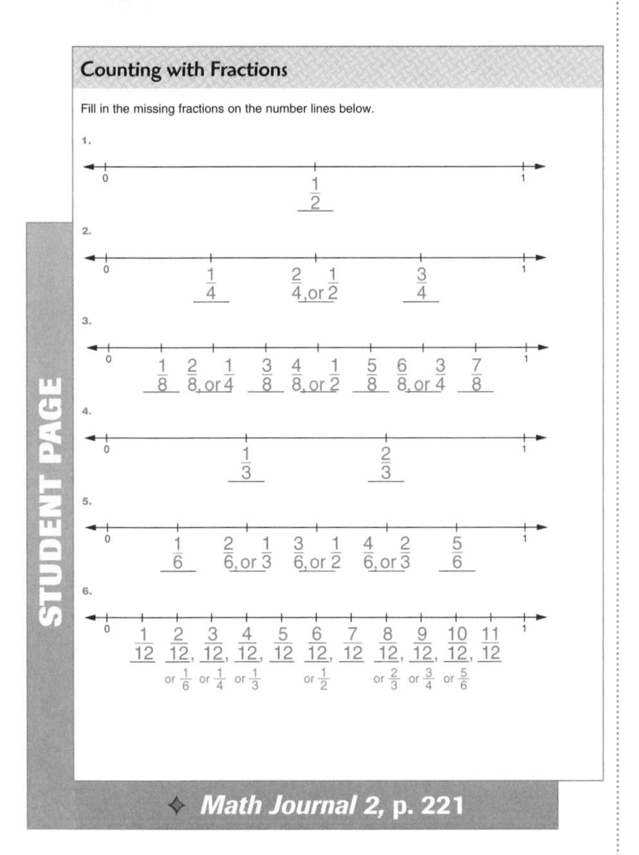
Counting with Fractions

Fill in the missing fractions on the number lines below.

1. 0, $\frac{1}{2}$, 1
2. 0, $\frac{1}{4}$, $\frac{2}{4}$, or $\frac{1}{2}$, $\frac{3}{4}$, 1
3. 0, $\frac{1}{8}$, $\frac{2}{8}$, or $\frac{1}{4}$, $\frac{3}{8}$, $\frac{4}{8}$, or $\frac{1}{2}$, $\frac{5}{8}$, $\frac{6}{8}$, or $\frac{3}{4}$, $\frac{7}{8}$, 1
4. 0, $\frac{1}{3}$, $\frac{2}{3}$, 1
5. 0, $\frac{1}{6}$, $\frac{2}{6}$, or $\frac{1}{3}$, $\frac{3}{6}$, or $\frac{1}{2}$, $\frac{4}{6}$, or $\frac{2}{3}$, $\frac{5}{6}$, 1
6. 0, $\frac{1}{12}$, $\frac{2}{12}$, $\frac{3}{12}$, $\frac{4}{12}$, $\frac{5}{12}$, $\frac{6}{12}$, $\frac{7}{12}$, $\frac{8}{12}$, $\frac{9}{12}$, $\frac{10}{12}$, $\frac{11}{12}$, 1
   or $\frac{1}{6}$ or $\frac{1}{4}$ or $\frac{1}{3}$ or $\frac{1}{2}$ or $\frac{2}{3}$ or $\frac{3}{4}$ or $\frac{5}{6}$

STUDENT PAGE

◆ *Math Journal 2,* p. 221

Math Boxes 7.11

1. Complete.
   a. 5 ft = 1 yd 2 ft
   b. $\frac{1}{3}$ yd = 12 in.
   c. 40 in. = 3 ft 4 in.
   d. 80 in. = 2 yd 8 in.
   e. 108 in. = 9 ft

2. a. What city is located at 60° N latitude and 110° W longitude? Fort Smith
   b. In which country is the city located? Canada
   c. On which continent is the city located? North America

3. a. Hannah drew a line segment $1\frac{5}{8}$ inches long. Then she erased a $\frac{1}{2}$ inch. How long is the line segment now? $1\frac{1}{8}$ inches
   b. Joshua drew a line segment $\frac{7}{8}$ inch long. Then he added another $\frac{3}{4}$ inch. How long is the line segment now? $1\frac{5}{8}$ inches

4. Write an equivalent fraction, decimal, or whole number.

	Decimal	Fraction
a.	0.70	$\frac{7}{10}$
b.	0.25	$\frac{25}{100}$
c.	1	$\frac{9}{9}$
d.	0.2	$\frac{2}{10}$

5. According to a survey of 800 students at Martin Elementary, about $\frac{3}{4}$ of them chose pizza as their favorite food. Of those who chose pizza, $\frac{1}{2}$ liked pepperoni topping the best. How many students liked pepperoni topping the best? 300 students

6. Multiply. Use the partial-products method.
   71 ∗ 38 = 2,698

	3	8
∗	7	1
2 1	0	0
5	6	0
	3	0
+		8
2 6	9	8

STUDENT PAGE

◆ *Math Journal 2,* p. 222

For Problem 2, students should color $\frac{1}{6}$ of the circle red, $\frac{1}{3}$ or $\frac{2}{6}$ of the circle blue, and the rest of the circle green. In discussing Problems 2b and 2c, give students plenty of opportunities to use the language of chance events and to compare the likelihood of the paper clip landing on the various colors. *For example:*

- ▷ "The paper clip is more likely to land on blue than on red, but less likely to land on blue than on green."
- ▷ "The paper clip is 3 times as likely to land on green as on red, and twice as likely to land on blue as on red."
- ▷ "The chance of landing on red is $\frac{1}{6}$, so $\frac{1}{6}$ of the circle should be red."
- ▷ "The chance of landing on red is 1 out of 6. That's 1 red for every 6 spins. So I would expect 4 reds if I spin 24 times."

NOTE: Remind students that the paper clip will not necessarily land on red exactly 4 times out of every 24 spins, or exactly 8 times on blue.

2 Ongoing Learning & Practice

◆ Identifying Fractions on Number Lines (*Math Journal 2,* p. 221)

INDEPENDENT ACTIVITY 

Students fill in the missing fractions on different number lines.

◆ Math Boxes 7.11 (*Math Journal 2,* p. 222)

INDEPENDENT ACTIVITY 

Mixed Review Math Boxes in this lesson are paired with Math Boxes in Lesson 7.9. The skill in Problem 1 is a prerequisite for Unit 8.

◆ Study Link 7.11 (*Math Masters,* pp. 321–323)

Home Connection Students design and describe spinners. Remind students that it would be better to use a pencil first when designing their spinners.

Also, in preparation for Lesson 8.1, students are asked to measure the distances between the appliances in their kitchens.

3 Options for Individualizing

✦ RETEACHING Judging the Likelihood of Events

SMALL-GROUP ACTIVITY  **5–15 min** 

Ask students to use the words *impossible, maybe,* and *certain* to describe the likelihood of events. *Suggestions:*

▷ It will get dark tonight.

▷ It may rain this afternoon.

▷ I will have an apple for lunch today.

▷ The sun will rise tomorrow.

▷ There will be math homework tonight.

▷ I will have four birthdays this year.

✦ LANGUAGE DIVERSITY Building Background for Mathematics Words

SMALL-GROUP ACTIVITY  **15–30 min** 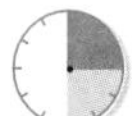

Language Arts Link Group a student learning English with a few proficient English speakers (or make this a whole-class activity). Have them think of as many words and phrases as they can that express the likelihood of an event occurring.

Examples

very unlikely	likely	extremely likely
extremely unlikely	50-50 chance	certain
impossible	maybe	sure

✦ ENRICHMENT Reading about Chance Events

SMALL-GROUP ACTIVITY  **15–30 min** 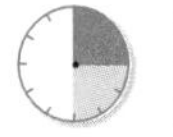

Literature Link Read and discuss the following book with students or have students read the book on their own:

Do You Wanna Bet? Your Chance to Find Out about Probability

Summary: Danny and Brian become involved in everyday probability situations, in and out of school.

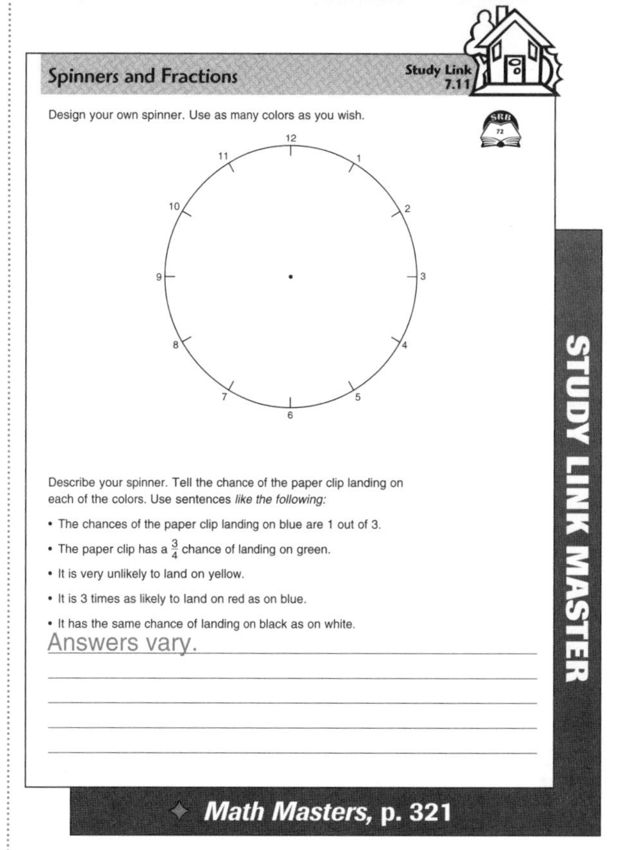

Spinners and Fractions Study Link 7.11

Design your own spinner. Use as many colors as you wish.

Describe your spinner. Tell the chance of the paper clip landing on each of the colors. Use sentences *like the following:*

- The chances of the paper clip landing on blue are 1 out of 3.
- The paper clip has a $\frac{3}{4}$ chance of landing on green.
- It is very unlikely to land on yellow.
- It is 3 times as likely to land on red as on blue.
- It has the same chance of landing on black as on white.

Answers vary.

STUDY LINK MASTER

✦ *Math Masters,* p. 321

Students must complete *Math Masters,* pages 322 and 323 and return them to class prior to Lesson 8.1.

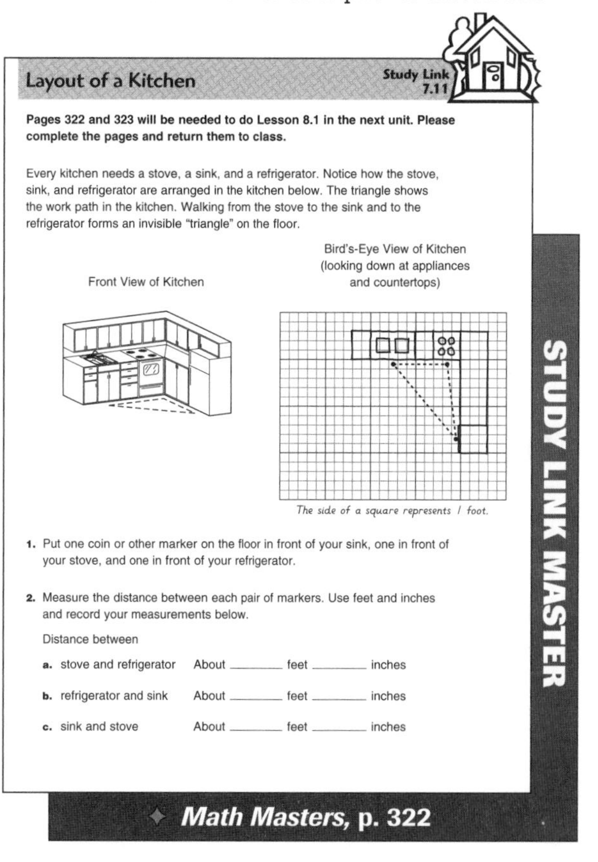

Layout of a Kitchen Study Link 7.11

Pages 322 and 323 will be needed to do Lesson 8.1 in the next unit. Please complete the pages and return them to class.

Every kitchen needs a stove, a sink, and a refrigerator. Notice how the stove, sink, and refrigerator are arranged in the kitchen below. The triangle shows the work path in the kitchen. Walking from the stove to the sink and to the refrigerator forms an invisible "triangle" on the floor.

The side of a square represents 1 foot.

1. Put one coin or other marker on the floor in front of your sink, one in front of your stove, and one in front of your refrigerator.

2. Measure the distance between each pair of markers. Use feet and inches and record your measurements below.

Distance between

a. stove and refrigerator About _____ feet _____ inches

b. refrigerator and sink About _____ feet _____ inches

c. sink and stove About _____ feet _____ inches

STUDY LINK MASTER

✦ *Math Masters,* p. 322

7.12 A Cube-Drop Experiment

OBJECTIVE **To compare predicted and actual results from an experiment with random outcomes.**

summaries	materials
1 Teaching the Lesson	
Students color a 10 by 10 grid. They determine the chance that a cm cube, dropped onto the grid, will land on a particular color. Then they perform this experiment and compare the results with their predictions. [Data and Chance]	□ *Math Journal 2,* pp. 223–225 □ Study Link 7.11 □ Teaching Master (*Math Masters,* p. 112) □ coloring pencils, markers, or crayons (yellow, red, green, blue) □ cm cube □ slate
2 Ongoing Learning & Practice	
Students identify fractional parts of number lines, collections of objects, and regions. [Numeration] Students practice and maintain skills through Math Boxes and Study Link activities.	□ *Math Journal 2,* pp. 226 and 227 □ Study Link Master (*Math Masters,* p. 324)
3 Options for Individualizing	
Enrichment Students combine results of 1,000 actual cube drops and compare them with expected results. [Data and Chance]	□ Teaching Masters (*Math Masters,* pp. 113 and 114) ***See* Advance Preparation**

Additional Information

Advance Preparation For the optional Enrichment activity in Part 3, make enough copies of *Math Masters,* page 113 so that there is a total of 20 "Results" slips.

Getting Started

Mental Math and Reflexes

Write fractions with denominators of 10 or 100 on the board and have students write the equivalent decimals on their slates. Then write decimals on the board and tell students to write the equivalent fractions on their slates. Do not insist that the fractions be written in simplest form.

Suggestions

- $\frac{2}{10}$ 0.2
- $\frac{73}{100}$ 0.73
- $\frac{50}{100}$ 0.50, or 0.5
- 0.9 $\frac{9}{10}$
- 0.24 $\frac{24}{100}$
- 0.60 $\frac{60}{100}$, or $\frac{6}{10}$

Math Message

Complete Problems 1 and 2 on journal page 223.

Study Link 7.11 Follow-Up

Briefly go over the answers.

Teaching the Lesson

✦ Math Message Follow-Up
(*Math Journal 2,* p. 223)

WHOLE-CLASS DISCUSSION

Discuss the answers (yellow 4, red 8, green 4, blue 8) and have students explain their reasoning. Ask whether students would be surprised if their predictions were not fulfilled exactly. They shouldn't be surprised. Discuss why the actual results for 24 spins might not match the prediction. The predictions are based on what is likely to happen; the actual outcomes will probably differ from the predictions.

Explain that this lesson involves an experiment in which they will compare their predictions with actual results.

✦ Predicting the Results of an Experiment
(*Math Journal 2,* p. 224; *Math Masters,* p. 112)

PARTNER ACTIVITY

Direct students to color the grid on *Math Masters,* page 112, according to the directions given beneath the grid.

Students can color the squares using any pattern they choose as long as they end up with the specified number of squares of each color. (Since half of the squares are to be white, students will actually *color* only 50 of the squares.)

Expected Spinner Results

1. If this spinner is spun 24 times, how many times do you expect it to land on each color? Fill in the table.

Answers vary.

Color	Expected Number in 24 Spins
red	
blue	
yellow	
green	
Total	24

2. Explain how you made your predictions.

STUDENT PAGE

✧ Math Journal 2, p. 223

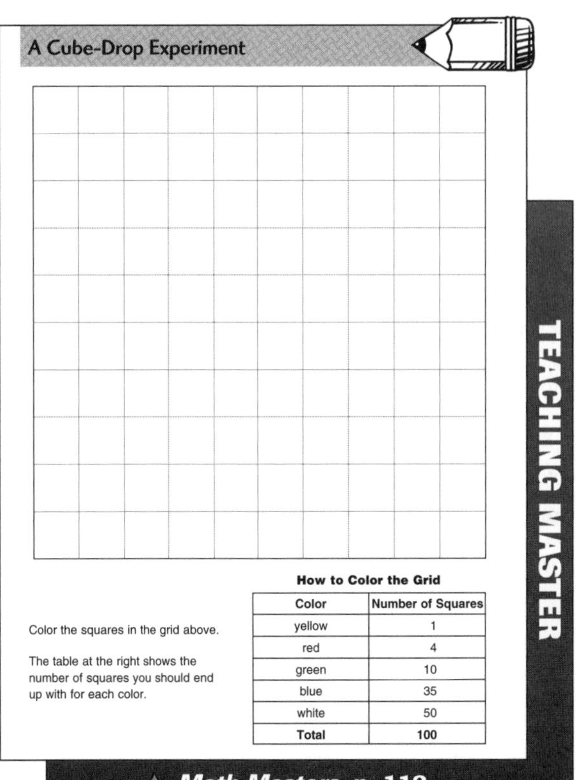

A Cube-Drop Experiment

Color the squares in the grid above.

The table at the right shows the number of squares you should end up with for each color.

How to Color the Grid

Color	Number of Squares
yellow	1
red	4
green	10
blue	35
white	50
Total	100

TEACHING MASTER

✧ Math Masters, p. 112

STUDENT PAGE

A Cube-Drop Experiment

Getting Ready

1. Follow the directions for coloring the grid on *Math Masters,* page 112. You may color the squares in any way. The colors can even form a pattern or a picture.
2. For this experiment, you are going to place your grid on the floor and hold a centimeter cube about 2 feet above the grid. Without aiming, you will let it drop onto the grid. You will then record the color of the square on which the cube finally lands.
   - If the cube does not land on the grid, the drop does not count.
   - If the cube lands on more than one color, record the color that is covered by most of the cube. If you can't tell, the toss does not count.

Making a Prediction Answers vary.

3. On which color is the cube *most likely* to land? ________
4. On which color is it *least likely* to land? ________
5. Suppose you were to drop the cube 100 times. How many times would you expect it to land on each color? Record your predictions below.

Predicted Results of 100 Cube Drops

Color	Number of Squares	Predicted Results Fraction	Predicted Results Percent
yellow	1	$\frac{1}{100}$	1 %
red	4		____%
green	10		____%
blue	35		____%
white	50		____%
Total	100	1	100%

✧ *Math Journal 2,* p. 224

Colors Landed On for 50 Cube Drops

w	w	w	b	w	r	g	b	b	b
y	w	b	w	w	b	r	w	b	w
w	g	w	w	b	w	b	b	b	w
w	b	w	w	w	b	w	b	b	w
w	w	b	g	w	w	w	w	w	w

Totals

y 1
r 2
g 3
b 16
w 28

Have students read about the cube-drop experiment on journal page 224. Then discuss it.

- If a cube is dropped onto the 100-grid, on which color is it most likely to land? White, since there are more white squares than any other colored squares
- On which color is it least likely to land? yellow

Have students complete the rest of the page on their own. Circulate and assist as needed.

Adjusting the Activity If students are having difficulty, remind them that dropping a cube onto a colored grid is very similar to spinning a spinner. For both the grid and the spinner, the chance of landing on a specific color *is the fraction of times you expect to land on that color.* For example, if 4 out of every 100 squares are colored red, then the chance of landing on red is $\frac{4}{100}$, or 4 out of 100, or 4%.

Bring the class together to share predictions. Encourage statements such as the following:

▷ "I colored only 1 square yellow out of 100 squares. So I should hit yellow about once out of every 100 drops. I say the chance of the cube landing on yellow is 1 out of 100."

▷ "White is easy. Half of the squares are white, so I should hit white half of the time. The chance for white is $\frac{1}{2}$."

▷ "For green, it's 10 out of 100. So I expect 10 greens if I toss 100 times. If I toss 500 times, I should get 5 times as many—that's 50 greens."

✦ Performing a Cube-Drop Experiment
(*Math Journal 2,* p. 225; *Math Masters,* p. 112)

PARTNER ACTIVITY

Go over the directions on journal page 225. Have partners take turns performing the experiment:

1. One partner drops a cube 50 times onto his or her 100-grid. The other partner records the results in the first partner's journal. (*See sample chart in margin.*)

2. Partners switch roles: The second partner drops a cube 50 times onto his or her 100-grid. The other partner records the results in the second partner's journal.
3. Students count the number of drops for each color and complete the "My Results for 50 Cube Drops" table on journal page 225. (See sample table below.)

My Results for 50 Cube Drops		
Color	**Number of Drops**	**Percent**
yellow	1	2%
red	2	4%
green	3	6%
blue	16	32%
white	28	56%
Total	**50**	**100%**

A Cube-Drop Experiment *(cont.)*

Doing the Experiment

You and your partner will each drop a centimeter cube onto your own colored grid.

6. One partner drops the cube. The other records the color in the grid below by writing a letter in one of the squares. Drop the cube a total of 50 times. (That will fill the grid.)

Write
y for yellow,
r for red,
g for green,
b for blue, and
w for white.

7. Then trade roles. Do another 50 drops, and record the results in the other partner's journal.

8. Count the number for each color.

Write it in the "Number of Drops" column.

Check that the total is 50.

My Results for 50 Cube Drops		
Color	**Number of Drops**	**Percent**
yellow		
red		
green		
blue		
white		
Total	**50**	**100%**

9. When you have finished, fill in the percent column in the table.

Example If your cube landed on blue 15 times out of 50 drops, this is the same as 30 times out of 100 drops, or 30% of the time.

STUDENT PAGE

✧ *Math Journal 2,* p. 225

ONGOING ASSESSMENT

This is a good opportunity to check students' recall of how to convert fractions to percents. Students should be familiar with converting fractions to percents because they calculated percent scores on the multiplication facts tests.

✦Comparing Actual and Expected Results
(*Math Journal 2,* pp. 224 and 225)

WHOLE-CLASS ACTIVITY

Bring the class together and have students compare their actual results with their predictions. Individual student results probably show a wide range. For example, some students may have hit a white square as many as 35 out of 50 tosses (70% of the time), while others may have done so only 15 times (30% of the time). Students should notice that while some individual results may be very close to the expected results, others may be far off.

Fractions of Sets and Wholes

1. Circle $\frac{1}{6}$ of the triangles. Mark Xs on $\frac{2}{3}$ of the triangles.

   Sample answer:

2. a. Shade $\frac{2}{5}$ of the pentagon.

   b. Shade $\frac{3}{5}$ of the pentagon.

3. There are 56 musicians in the school band: $\frac{1}{4}$ of the musicians play the flute, and $\frac{1}{8}$ play the trombone.

   a. How many musicians play the flute? 14

   b. How many musicians play the trombone? 7

4. Jennifer had 48 bean-bag animals in her collection. She sold 18 of them to another collector. What fraction of her collection did she sell? $\frac{3}{8}$

5. Complete.

   a. $\frac{3}{4}$ of 120 is 90.

   b. $\frac{2}{3}$ of 27 is 18.

   c. $\frac{5}{6}$ of 120 is 100.

   d. $\frac{3}{10}$ of 50 is 15.

   e. $\frac{4}{12}$ of 72 is 24.

6. Fill in the missing fractions on the number line.

   0, $\frac{1}{6}$, $\frac{2}{6}$, $\frac{3}{6}$, $\frac{4}{6}$, $\frac{5}{6}$, 1

STUDENT PAGE

Math Journal 2, p. 226

2 Ongoing Learning & Practice

Finding Fractions of Sets and Wholes (*Math Journal 2,* p. 226)

INDEPENDENT ACTIVITY 

Students identify fractional parts of number lines, collections of objects, and regions.

Math Boxes 7.12 (*Math Journal 2,* p. 227)

INDEPENDENT ACTIVITY 

Mixed Review Math Boxes in this lesson are paired with Math Boxes in Lesson 7.10. The skill in Problem 1 is a prerequisite for Unit 8.

Study Link 7.12 (*Math Masters,* p. 324)

Home Connection Students predict the results of a coin-tossing experiment, check their predictions by performing the experiment, and express the results with fractions.

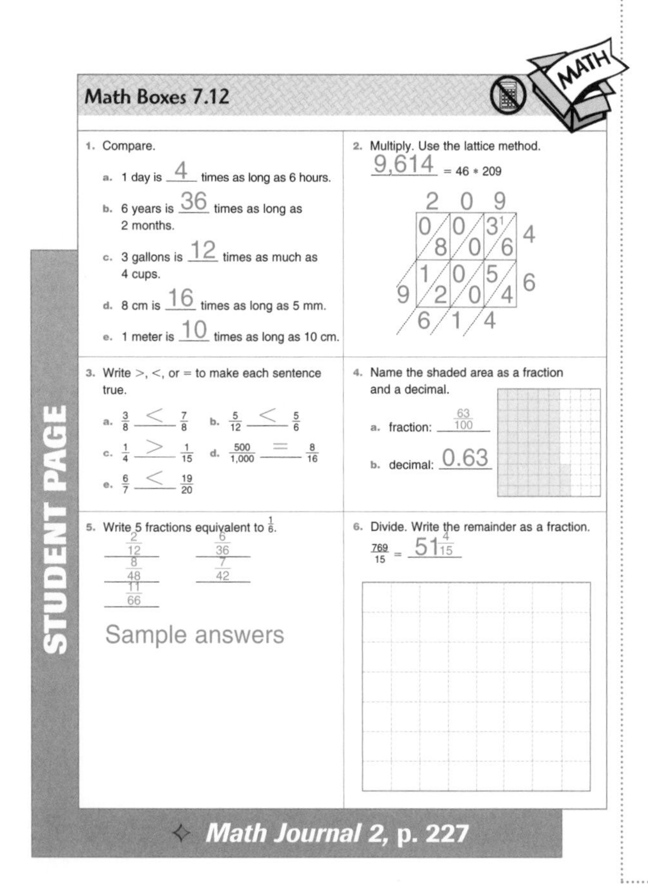

Math Boxes 7.12

1. Compare.

   a. 1 day is 4 times as long as 6 hours.

   b. 6 years is 36 times as long as 2 months.

   c. 3 gallons is 12 times as much as 4 cups.

   d. 8 cm is 16 times as long as 5 mm.

   e. 1 meter is 10 times as long as 10 cm.

2. Multiply. Use the lattice method.

   9,614 = 46 ∗ 209

3. Write >, <, or = to make each sentence true.

   a. $\frac{3}{8} < \frac{7}{8}$

   b. $\frac{5}{12} < \frac{5}{6}$

   c. $\frac{1}{4} > \frac{1}{15}$

   d. $\frac{500}{1,000} = \frac{8}{16}$

   e. $\frac{6}{7} < \frac{19}{20}$

4. Name the shaded area as a fraction and a decimal.

   a. fraction: $\frac{63}{100}$

   b. decimal: 0.63

5. Write 5 fractions equivalent to $\frac{1}{6}$.

   $\frac{2}{12}$, $\frac{6}{36}$, $\frac{8}{48}$, $\frac{7}{42}$, $\frac{11}{66}$

   Sample answers

6. Divide. Write the remainder as a fraction.

   $\frac{769}{15} = 51\frac{4}{15}$

STUDENT PAGE

Math Journal 2, p. 227

Chances Are ...

Study Link 7.12

1. You are going to toss 2 pennies 20 times. Make a prediction. How many times do you think the 2 pennies will come up as

   Sample answers:

   a. 2 heads? 5 times

   b. 2 tails? 5 times

   c. 1 head and 1 tail? 10 times

2. Now toss 2 pennies together 20 times. Record the results in the table. Answers vary.

A Penny Toss

Results	Number of Times
2 heads	
2 tails	
1 head and 1 tail	

3. What fraction of the tosses came up as

   a. 2 heads? ______

   b. 2 tails? ______ Answers vary.

   c. 1 head and 1 tail? ______

4. Suppose you were to flip the coins 1,000 times. What fraction do you think would come up as

   Sample answers:

   a. 2 heads? $\frac{1}{4}$

   b. 2 tails? $\frac{1}{4}$

   c. 1 head and 1 tail? $\frac{1}{2}$

5. Explain how you got your answers for Problem 4.

   Answers vary.

STUDY LINK MASTER

Math Masters, p. 324

3 Options for Individualizing

✦ ENRICHMENT Comparing Actual and Expected Results of 1,000 Cube Drops

(*Math Masters,* pp. 113 and 114)

WHOLE-CLASS ACTIVITY 15–30 min

Portfolio Ideas

Randomly select 20 students to report the results of their cube-dropping experiment on a "Results" slip, cut from *Math Masters,* page 113. Students combine the data into a "Class Results" table on *Math Masters,* page 114. The combined results will give students actual data on how many times a cube landed on each color for 1,000 cube drops.

NOTE: Select the results for 20 students, because data for 1,000 cube drops (20 * 50) can be easily converted into percents. If your class has fewer than 20 students, select an even number of students; that way, the total number of cube drops (even number * 50) will be a multiple of 100.

Have students compare the results for 1,000 cube drops with the predictions they made on journal page 224. The actual results should be very close to the expected results.

NOTE: When students calculate the percents on *Math Masters,* page 114, most of the answers will not be in whole percents. Students can either record them as percents in tenths or round them to the nearest whole percent. For example, 96 out of 1,000 is equivalent to 9.6 out of 100. This could be recorded either as 9.6% or 10%. If the answers are rounded, the total may not add up to 100%.

PLANNING AHEAD

Check to see that students will have completed Study Link 7.11, pages 322 and 323, in time for Lesson 8.1.

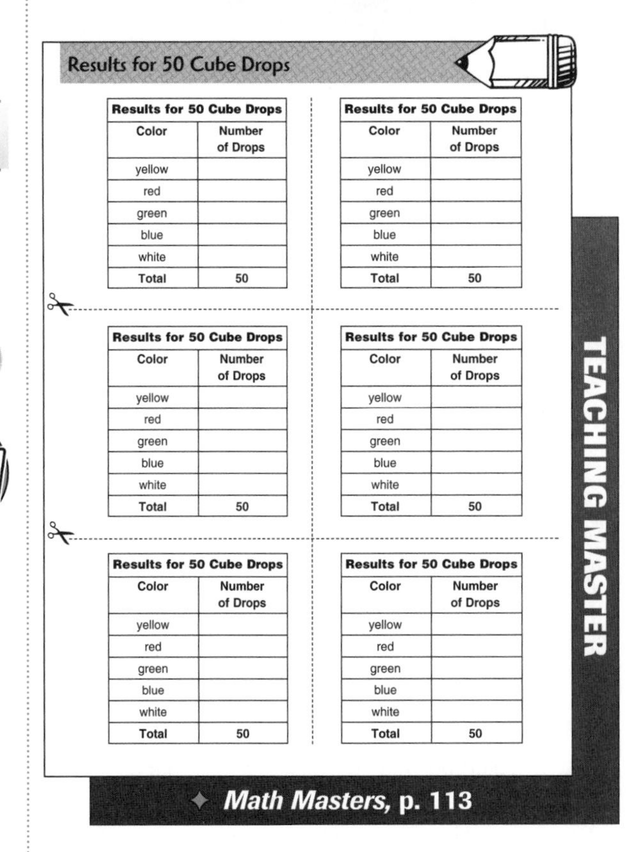

Results for 50 Cube Drops

Results for 50 Cube Drops	
Color	Number of Drops
yellow	
red	
green	
blue	
white	
Total	50

Results for 50 Cube Drops	
Color	Number of Drops
yellow	
red	
green	
blue	
white	
Total	50

Results for 50 Cube Drops	
Color	Number of Drops
yellow	
red	
green	
blue	
white	
Total	50

Results for 50 Cube Drops	
Color	Number of Drops
yellow	
red	
green	
blue	
white	
Total	50

Results for 50 Cube Drops	
Color	Number of Drops
yellow	
red	
green	
blue	
white	
Total	50

Results for 50 Cube Drops	
Color	Number of Drops
yellow	
red	
green	
blue	
white	
Total	50

TEACHING MASTER

✦ *Math Masters,* p. 113

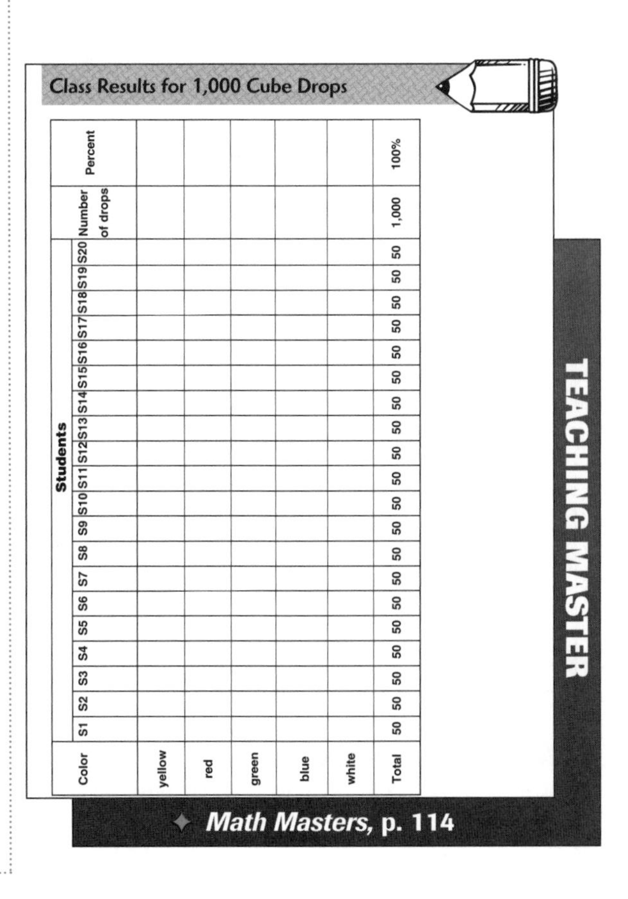

Class Results for 1,000 Cube Drops

	Color	yellow	red	green	blue	white	Total
Students	S1						50
	S2						50
	S3						50
	S4						50
	S5						50
	S6						50
	S7						50
	S8						50
	S9						50
	S10						50
	S11						50
	S12						50
	S13						50
	S14						50
	S15						50
	S16						50
	S17						50
	S18						50
	S19						50
	S20						50
Number of drops							1,000
Percent							100%

TEACHING MASTER

✦ *Math Masters,* p. 114

7.13 Unit 7 Review and Assessment

OBJECTIVE **To review and assess students' progress on the material covered in Unit 7.**

1 Assess Progress

learning goals	activities
7a **Beginning Goal** Add and subtract fractions. **(Lessons 7.4 and 7.5)**	❑ Slate Assessment, Problem 1 ❑ Written Assessment, Problem 16 ❑ Alternative Assessment Option
7b **Developing Goal** Rename fractions with denominators of 10 and 100 as decimals. **(Lesson 7.8)**	❑ Slate Assessment, Problem 2
7c **Developing Goal** Apply basic vocabulary and concepts associated with chance events. **(Lessons 7.11 and 7.12)**	❑ Written Assessment, Problems 14 and 15
7d **Developing Goal** Compare and order fractions. **(Lesson 7.9)**	❑ Oral Assessment, Problem 1 ❑ Written Assessment, Problems 5–10
7e **Developing Goal** Find equivalent fractions for given fractions. **(Lessons 7.6 and 7.7)**	❑ Oral Assessment, Problem 2 ❑ Written Assessment, Problems 1–4 and 7 ❑ Alternative Assessment Option
7f **Secure Goal** Identify the whole for fractions. **(Lessons 7.1, 7.3, and 7.10)**	❑ Written Assessment, Problems 11–13
7g **Secure Goal** Identify fractional parts of a collection of objects. **(Lesson 7.2)**	❑ Slate Assessment, Problem 3 ❑ Written Assessment, Problem 13
7h **Secure Goal** Identify fractional parts of regions. **(Lessons 7.1–7.3, 7.5, and 7.9)**	❑ Slate Assessment, Problem 4 ❑ Written Assessment, Problems 11, 12, 14, and 16

materials

- ☐ *Math Journal 2,* pp. 228, 356, and 357
- ☐ Study Link 7.12
- ☐ Teaching Masters (*Math Masters,* pp. 115 and 116)
- ☐ Assessment Masters (*Math Masters,* pp. 402 and 403)
- ☐ slate ☐ large paper clip ☐ straightedge

2 Build Background for Unit 6

summaries	materials
Students practice and maintain skills through Math Boxes and Study Link activities.	☐ *Math Journal 2,* p. 229 ☐ Study Link Masters (*Math Masters,* pp. 325–328)

Each **learning goal** listed above indicates a level of performance that might be expected at this point in the *Everyday Mathematics* K–6 curriculum. For a variety of reasons, the levels indicated may not accurately portray your class's performance.

Additional Information

Advance Preparation For additional information on assessment for Unit 7, see the *Assessment Handbook,* pages 57–59. For assessment checklists, see *Math Masters,* pages 438, 439, and 465–467.

Getting Started

Math Message

Complete the Time to Reflect *questions on journal page 228.*

Study Link 7.12 Follow-Up

Go over the answers with the class.

1 Assess Progress

Math Message Follow-Up
(*Math Journal 2,* p. 228)

WHOLE-CLASS DISCUSSION 

Have students share and discuss their answers. Students' responses to Problem 1 indicate their understanding of fraction notation. Problem 2 provides an opportunity to evaluate students' awareness of basic probability concepts outside the mathematics class. Problem 3 gives you insight into students' understanding of the importance of the whole, or ONE, for fractions.

Oral and Slate Assessments

WHOLE-CLASS ACTIVITY

If the suggested problems below are not appropriate for your class's level of performance, adjust the numbers or the problems themselves to better assess your students' abilities.

Oral Assessment Suggestions

1. Write pairs of fractions on the board. Have students identify the greater fraction and explain how they know it is greater. **Goal 7d**
   - $\frac{2}{5}$ and $\frac{2}{20}$ $\frac{2}{5}$ The fractions have like numerators. The smaller the denominator, the larger the fraction.
   - $\frac{4}{12}$ and $\frac{9}{12}$ $\frac{9}{12}$ The fractions have like denominators. The larger the numerator, the larger the fraction.
   - $\frac{5}{12}$ and $\frac{9}{16}$ $\frac{9}{16}$ $\frac{5}{12}$ is less than $\frac{1}{2}$, and $\frac{9}{16}$ is greater than $\frac{1}{2}$.

Time to Reflect

1. Suppose you had to explain to a first grader how to read the fraction $\frac{1}{6}$. What would you say?

2. How much does *chance* play a part in your life? Give at least two examples to support your answer.

3. When discussing fractions, why is it so important to know the value of the whole, or ONE? Give an example to support your answer.

STUDENT PAGE

Math Journal 2, p. 228

2. Write a fraction on the board. Students write an equivalent fraction and explain how they know that it is equivalent, using pictures or the Rule for Finding Equivalent Fractions. **Goal 7e**

Example

$\frac{2}{3} = \frac{4}{6}$: $\frac{2}{3}$ $\frac{2 * \mathbf{2}}{3 * \mathbf{2}} = \frac{4}{6}$

Slate Assessment Suggestions

1. Write a fraction addition or subtraction problem on the board. Students estimate whether the sum or difference is closest to 0, 1, or 2. **Goal 7a**
   - $\frac{4}{6} + \frac{3}{6}$ 1
   - $\frac{1}{20} + \frac{1}{6}$ 0
   - $\frac{9}{10} + \frac{15}{16}$ 2
   - $1\frac{1}{8} - \frac{11}{12}$ 0
   - $1\frac{49}{50} - \frac{1}{7}$ 2
   - $1\frac{8}{9} - \frac{13}{14}$ 1

2. Write fractions with denominators of 10 or 100 on the board and have students write the equivalent decimals. Then write decimals on the board and ask students to write a fraction equivalent for each. Do not insist that the fractions be in simplest form. **Goal 7b**
   - $\frac{8}{10}$ 0.8
   - $\frac{46}{100}$ 0.46
   - $\frac{30}{100}$ 0.30, or 0.3
   - 0.7 $\frac{7}{10}$
   - 0.98 $\frac{98}{100}$
   - 0.20 $\frac{20}{100}$

3. Pose "fraction-of" problems. **Goal 7g**
   - What is $\frac{1}{4}$ of 8? 2 $\frac{3}{4}$ of 8? 6
   - What is $\frac{1}{5}$ of 30? 6 $\frac{4}{5}$ of 30? 24
   - What is $\frac{2}{3}$ of 18? 12
   - What is $\frac{5}{6}$ of 12? 10

4. Students draw regions and shade fractional parts. **Goal 7h**
   - Draw a circle. Shade $\frac{1}{3}$ of it.
   - Draw a circle. Shade $\frac{1}{4}$ of it.
   - Draw a square. Shade $\frac{3}{4}$ of it.

✦ Written Assessment (*Math Masters,* pp. 402 and 403)

INDEPENDENT ACTIVITY 

Depending on the needs of students, you may want to work through an example together, reading a problem aloud, discussing it, and providing additional examples as necessary before students work the problem independently.

Each of the problems is listed below and paired with one or more of this unit's learning goals. Circulate and assist as students work.

- Write equivalent fractions. (Problems 1–4) **Goal 7e**
- Write $>$, $<$, or $=$ between each pair of fractions. (Problems 5–8) **Goal 7d**
- Write each set of fractions in order from smallest to largest. (Problems 9 and 10) **Goal 7d**
- Given the whole, determine the fraction of the whole. (Problem 11) **Goals 7f and 7h**
- Given the fraction of the whole, determine the whole. (Problem 12) **Goals 7f and 7h**
- Find a fractional part of a collection of things. (Problem 13) **Goals 7f and 7g**
- Determine the chance of a spinner landing on a color and express it as a fraction. (Problem 14) **Goals 7c and 7h**
- Perform a chance experiment. Record and analyze the results. (Problem 15) **Goal 7c**
- Solve a number story that involves addition of unlike fractions. (Problem 16) **Goals 7a and 7h**

NOTE: Partner and group work is a basic tenet of *Everyday Mathematics.* Problems 11–16 lend themselves to group assessment. You may wish to divide the class into groups of 3 or 4 students of mixed ability to solve these problems. Look for the following in students' group work:

▷ Use of manipulatives or pictures to model problems.

▷ Participation in group work: Do all students take part equally? Do some students dominate, while others take a "free ride?" Ask students if all of them participated fairly.

▷ Persistence in seeking an answer. Problem 16 is fairly difficult. Observe whether students continue to try or whether they give up easily when they don't get an answer quickly.

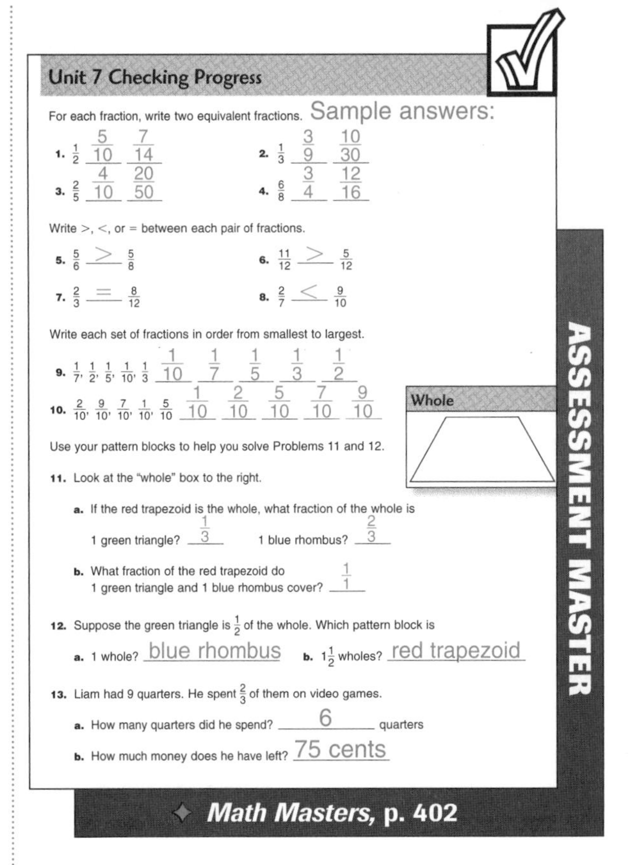

Unit 7 Checking Progress

For each fraction, write two equivalent fractions. Sample answers:

1. $\frac{1}{2}$ $\frac{5}{10}$ $\frac{7}{14}$
2. $\frac{1}{3}$ $\frac{3}{9}$ $\frac{10}{30}$
3. $\frac{2}{5}$ $\frac{4}{10}$ $\frac{20}{50}$
4. $\frac{6}{8}$ $\frac{3}{4}$ $\frac{12}{16}$

Write $>$, $<$, or $=$ between each pair of fractions.

5. $\frac{5}{6} > \frac{5}{8}$
6. $\frac{11}{12} > \frac{5}{12}$
7. $\frac{2}{3} = \frac{8}{12}$
8. $\frac{2}{7} < \frac{9}{10}$

Write each set of fractions in order from smallest to largest.

9. $\frac{1}{7}, \frac{1}{2}, \frac{1}{5}, \frac{1}{10}, \frac{1}{3}$ — $\frac{1}{10}$ $\frac{1}{7}$ $\frac{1}{5}$ $\frac{1}{3}$ $\frac{1}{2}$
10. $\frac{2}{10}, \frac{9}{10}, \frac{7}{10}, \frac{1}{10}, \frac{5}{10}$ — $\frac{1}{10}$ $\frac{2}{10}$ $\frac{5}{10}$ $\frac{7}{10}$ $\frac{9}{10}$

Use your pattern blocks to help you solve Problems 11 and 12.

Whole

11. Look at the "whole" box to the right.
    a. If the red trapezoid is the whole, what fraction of the whole is 1 green triangle? $\frac{1}{3}$ 1 blue rhombus? $\frac{2}{3}$
    b. What fraction of the red trapezoid do 1 green triangle and 1 blue rhombus cover? $\frac{1}{1}$
12. Suppose the green triangle is $\frac{1}{2}$ of the whole. Which pattern block is
    a. 1 whole? blue rhombus b. $1\frac{1}{2}$ wholes? red trapezoid
13. Liam had 9 quarters. He spent $\frac{2}{3}$ of them on video games.
    a. How many quarters did he spend? 6 quarters
    b. How much money does he have left? 75 cents

ASSESSMENT MASTER

✦ *Math Masters,* p. 402

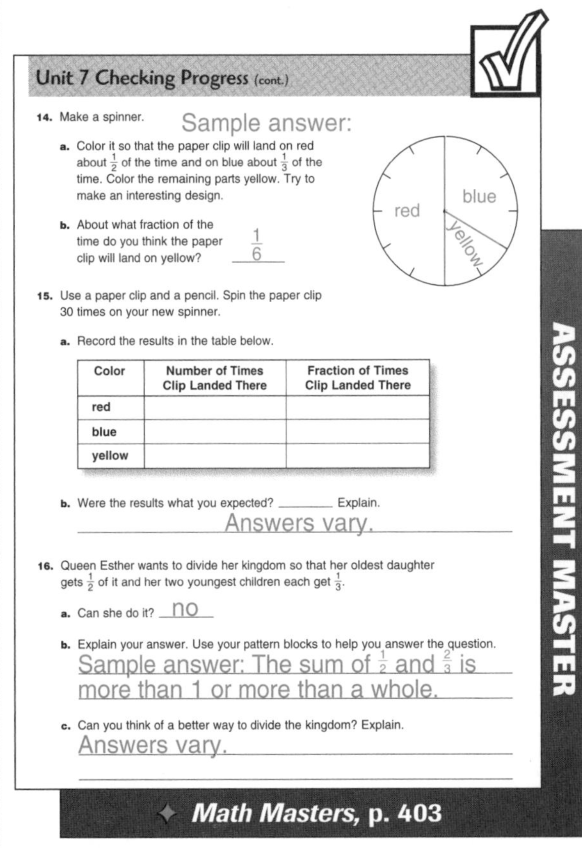

Unit 7 Checking Progress (cont.)

14. Make a spinner. Sample answer:
    a. Color it so that the paper clip will land on red about $\frac{1}{2}$ of the time and on blue about $\frac{1}{3}$ of the time. Color the remaining parts yellow. Try to make an interesting design.
    b. About what fraction of the time do you think the paper clip will land on yellow? $\frac{1}{6}$

15. Use a paper clip and a pencil. Spin the paper clip 30 times on your new spinner.
    a. Record the results in the table below.

Color	Number of Times Clip Landed There	Fraction of Times Clip Landed There
red		
blue		
yellow		

    b. Were the results what you expected? ______ Explain. Answers vary.

16. Queen Esther wants to divide her kingdom so that her oldest daughter gets $\frac{1}{2}$ of it and her two youngest children each get $\frac{1}{3}$.
    a. Can she do it? no
    b. Explain your answer. Use your pattern blocks to help you answer the question. Sample answer: The sum of $\frac{1}{2}$ and $\frac{2}{3}$ is more than 1 or more than a whole.
    c. Can you think of a better way to divide the kingdom? Explain. Answers vary.

ASSESSMENT MASTER

✦ *Math Masters,* p. 403

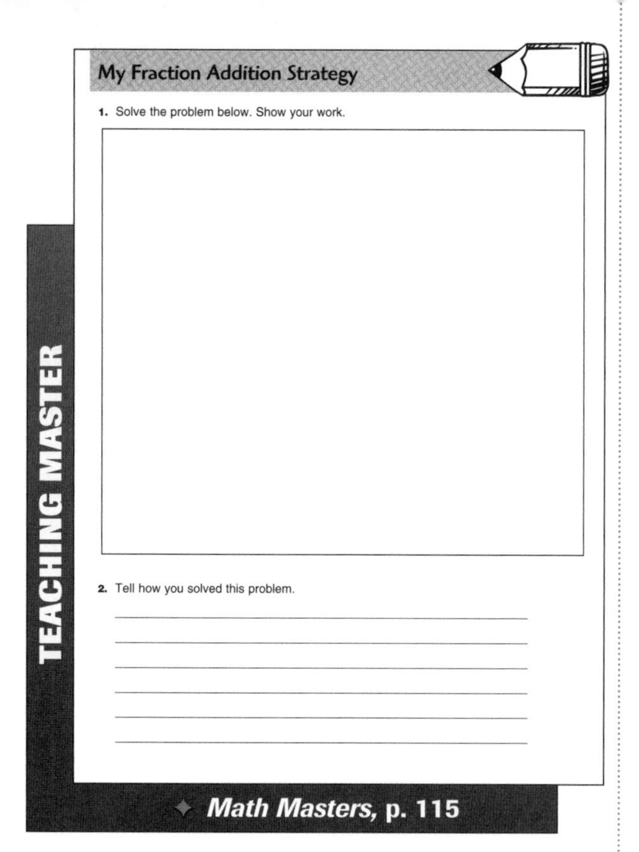
TEACHING MASTER

My Fraction Addition Strategy

1. Solve the problem below. Show your work.

2. Tell how you solved this problem.

✦ *Math Masters,* p. 115

✦ ALTERNATIVE ASSESSMENT OPTION

Describe a Fraction Addition or Subtraction Strategy (*Math Masters,* pp. 115 and 116)

INDEPENDENT ACTIVITY 

Portfolio Ideas

Write fraction addition and subtraction problems on the masters. Match them to the ability levels of individual students. For example, consider problems with like or unlike denominators. Ask students to solve a problem and then to describe the strategy that they used. Encourage the use of pattern blocks and clock faces.

✦ ALTERNATIVE ASSESSMENT OPTION

Collect Fraction Names (*Math Journal 2,* pp. 356 and 357)

INDEPENDENT ACTIVITY 

Students continue the work that they started in Lesson 7.6 on the Equivalent Names for Fractions table.

TEACHING MASTER

My Fraction Subtraction Strategy

1. Solve the problem below. Show your work.

2. Tell how you solved this problem.

✦ *Math Masters,* p. 116

2 Build Background for Unit 8

Math Boxes 7.13 (*Math Journal 2,* p. 229)

INDEPENDENT ACTIVITY 

Mixed Review The skills in Problems 1–6 are prerequisites for Unit 8.

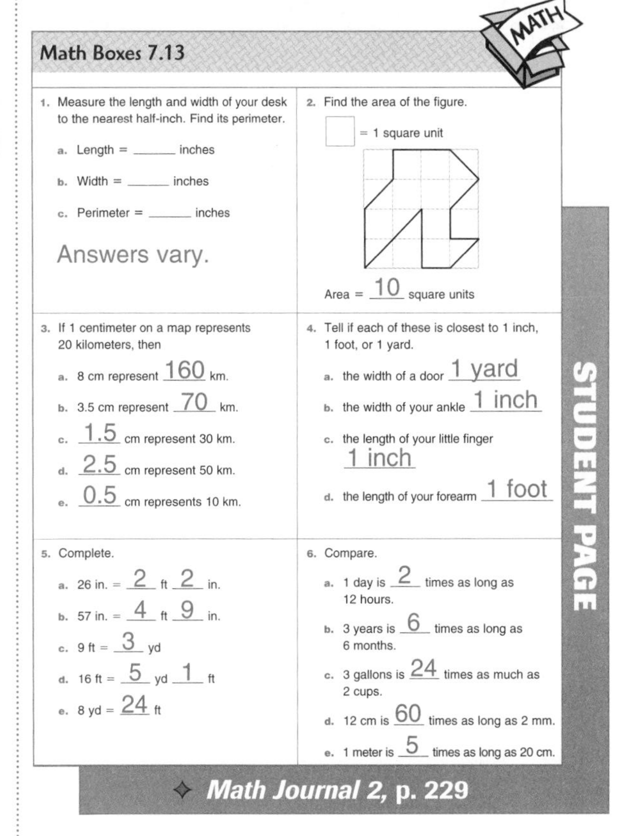

Math Boxes 7.13

1. Measure the length and width of your desk to the nearest half-inch. Find its perimeter.
   a. Length = ______ inches
   b. Width = ______ inches
   c. Perimeter = ______ inches

   Answers vary.

2. Find the area of the figure.
   □ = 1 square unit
   Area = 10 square units

3. If 1 centimeter on a map represents 20 kilometers, then
   a. 8 cm represent 160 km.
   b. 3.5 cm represent 70 km.
   c. 1.5 cm represent 30 km.
   d. 2.5 cm represent 50 km.
   e. 0.5 cm represents 10 km.

4. Tell if each of these is closest to 1 inch, 1 foot, or 1 yard.
   a. the width of a door 1 yard
   b. the width of your ankle 1 inch
   c. the length of your little finger 1 inch
   d. the length of your forearm 1 foot

5. Complete.
   a. 26 in. = 2 ft 2 in.
   b. 57 in. = 4 ft 9 in.
   c. 9 ft = 3 yd
   d. 16 ft = 5 yd 1 ft
   e. 8 yd = 24 ft

6. Compare.
   a. 1 day is 2 times as long as 12 hours.
   b. 3 years is 6 times as long as 6 months.
   c. 3 gallons is 24 times as much as 2 cups.
   d. 12 cm is 60 times as long as 2 mm.
   e. 1 meter is 5 times as long as 20 cm.

STUDENT PAGE

✧ Math Journal 2, p. 229

Study Link 7.13: Unit 8 Family Letter (*Math Masters,* pp. 325–328)

Home Connection This Study Link is a four-page newsletter that introduces parents and guardians to Unit 8's topics and terms. The letter also offers ideas for mathematics activities that are supportive of classroom work and can be done at home.

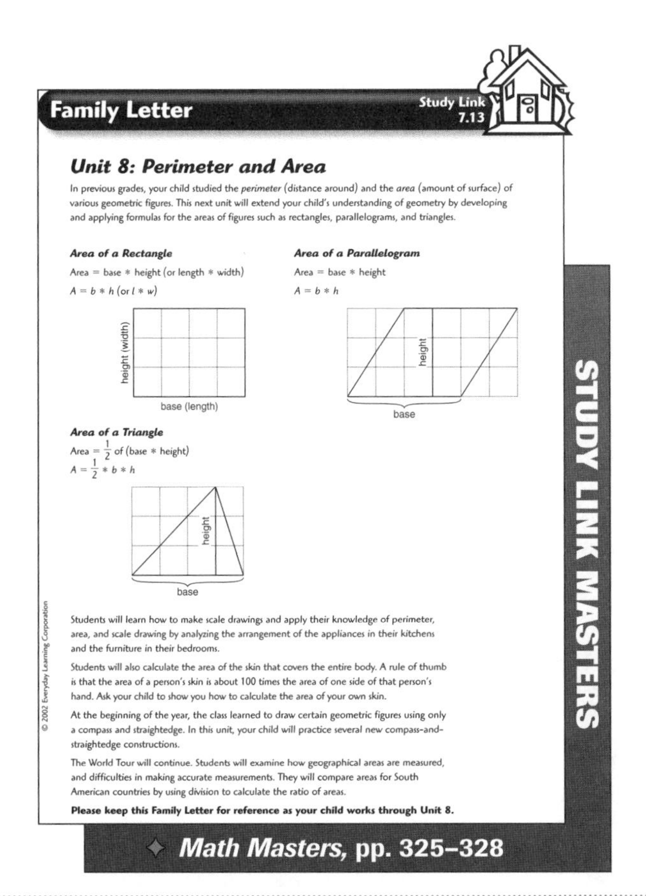

Family Letter — Study Link 7.13

Unit 8: Perimeter and Area

In previous grades, your child studied the *perimeter* (distance around) and the *area* (amount of surface) of various geometric figures. This next unit will extend your child's understanding of geometry by developing and applying formulas for the areas of figures such as rectangles, parallelograms, and triangles.

Area of a Rectangle
Area = base * height (or length * width)
$A = b * h$ (or $l * w$)

height (width)
base (length)

Area of a Parallelogram
Area = base * height
$A = b * h$

height
base

Area of a Triangle
Area = $\frac{1}{2}$ of (base * height)
$A = \frac{1}{2} * b * h$

height
base

Students will learn how to make scale drawings and apply their knowledge of perimeter, area, and scale drawing by analyzing the arrangement of the appliances in their kitchens and the furniture in their bedrooms.

Students will also calculate the area of the skin that covers the entire body. A rule of thumb is that the area of a person's skin is about 100 times the area of one side of that person's hand. Ask your child to show you how to calculate the area of your own skin.

At the beginning of the year, the class learned to draw certain geometric figures using only a compass and straightedge. In this unit, your child will practice several new compass-and-straightedge constructions.

The World Tour will continue. Students will examine how geographical areas are measured, and difficulties in making accurate measurements. They will compare areas for South American countries by using division to calculate the ratio of areas.

Please keep this Family Letter for reference as your child works through Unit 8.

STUDY LINK MASTERS

✧ Math Masters, pp. 325–328

Unit 8
Perimeter and Area

overview

The main objectives of this unit are to review perimeter and area concepts introduced earlier in *Everyday Mathematics;* to develop formulas as mathematical models for the areas of rectangles, parallelograms, and triangles; and to explore applications of area with the help of scale drawings.

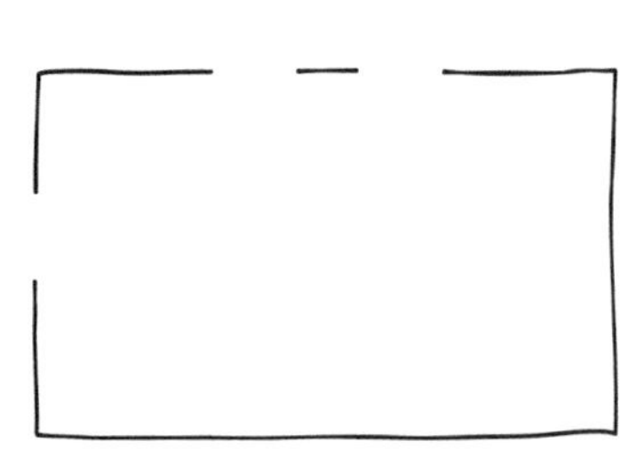

Figure 1: Students draw the classroom walls and leave openings for the doors and windows.

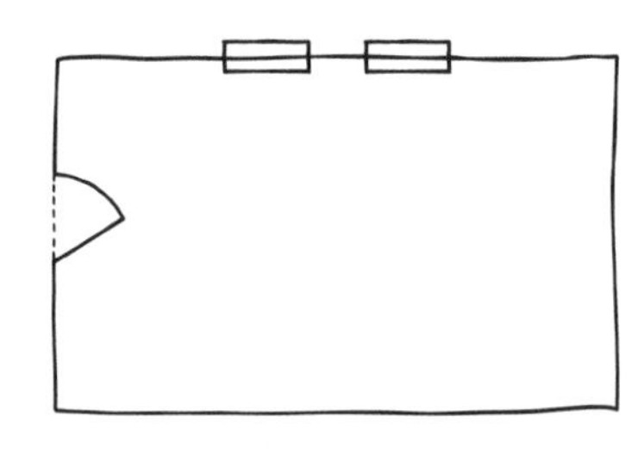

Figure 2: Students add symbols for doors and windows to their sketches.

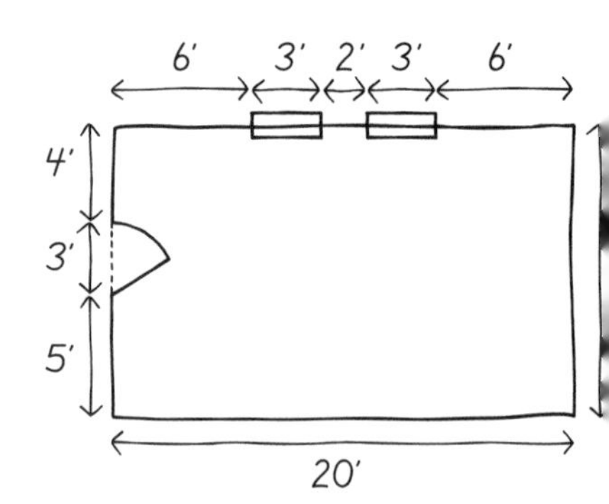

Figure 3: Students record accurate measurements on their sketches.

In Lesson 8.2, students make a rough floor plan of the classroom. They use this plan to create a scale drawing of the classroom on grid paper.

contents

Lesson	Objective	Page
8.1	**Kitchen Layouts and Perimeter** *To measure and add distances in feet and inches; to find the medians and other landmarks of sets of measurements; and to find the perimeters of triangles.*	596
8.2	**Scale Drawings** *To measure distances to the nearest foot; and to use measurements and a given scale to create a scale drawing on a grid.*	601
8.3	**Area** *To review basic area concepts; to estimate the area of a polygon by counting unit squares; and to use a scale drawing to find area.*	607
8.4	**What Is the Area of My Skin?** *To estimate the area of a surface having a curved boundary; and to convert measurements from one unit to another.*	611
8.5	**Formula for the Area of a Rectangle** *To develop and use a formula for the area of a rectangle.*	616
8.6	**Formula for the Area of a Parallelogram** *To review the properties of parallelograms; and to develop and use a formula for the area of a parallelogram.*	621
8.7	**Formula for the Area of a Triangle** *To develop and use a formula for the area of a triangle.*	627
8.8	**Geographical Area Measurements** *To examine how geographical areas are measured; and to use division to compare two quantities with like units.*	632
8.9	**Unit 8 Review and Assessment** *To review and assess students' progress on the material covered in Unit 8.*	637

UNIT 8

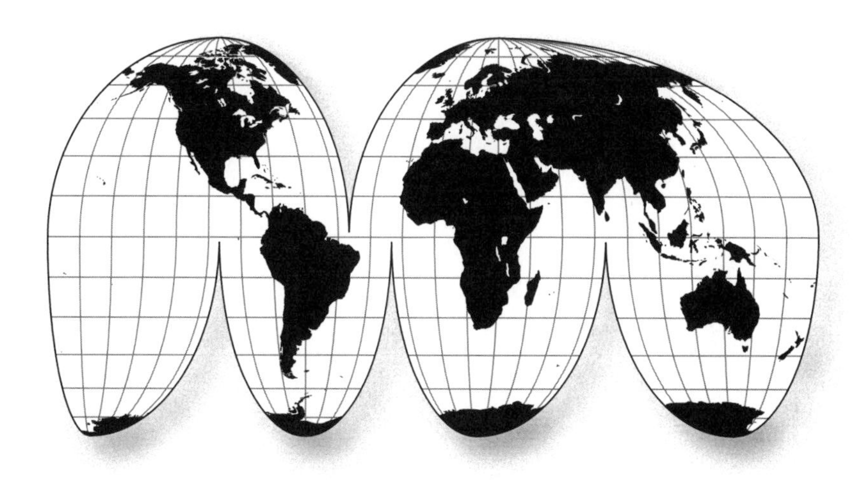

learning goals in perspective

learning goals	links to the past	links to the future
8a **Beginning Goal** Make and interpret scale drawings. **(Lessons 8.2, 8.3, and 8.5)**	Grade 3: Use a map scale to estimate the direct distance between two places. Grade 4: Use a map scale to estimate distances (Units 2 and 3). Estimate the lengths of non-linear paths drawn on square grids that include scale bars (Unit 6).	Grade 5: Use a map scale to estimate actual distances. Grade 6: Use a scale to calculate actual size from a scale drawing.
8b **Developing Goal** Use formulas to find areas of rectangles, parallelograms, and triangles. **(Lessons 8.5–8.8)**	Grade 2: Explore area and area units. Grade 3: Tile rectangles with pattern blocks; review the meaning of area and square units using models of square foot and square yard; discuss how to find the area of a room to be carpeted; use a geoboard to act out calculating areas of rectangles.	Grade 4: Use formulas to find volumes (Unit 11). Grade 5: Develop and apply formulas for areas of triangles and parallelograms. Identify personal references for metric and customary units of area. Grade 6: Use formulas to find perimeter, circumference, and area.
8c **Developing Goal** Find the perimeter of a polygon. **(Lessons 8.1, 8.2, and 8.7)**	Grade 2: Find perimeters of body parts, objects, and the classroom by measuring; find perimeters of polygons by measuring and adding lengths. Grade 3: Measure sides and find perimeters of straw polygons. Draw squares and rectangles with given perimeters.	Grade 5: Applications and maintenance. Grade 6: Use formulas to find perimeter, circumference, and area. Use graphing to investigate the relationship between the perimeter and area of a rectangle.
8d **Developing/Secure Goal** Find the area of a figure by counting unit squares and fractions of unit squares inside the figure. **(Lessons 8.3–8.7)**	Grade 2: Tile surfaces with pattern blocks, cards, and quarter-sheets of paper. Estimate areas using centimeter and inch grids; find areas of geoboard rectangles. Grade 3: Estimate areas of classroom surfaces, then measure with 1-foot or 1-yard squares. Find areas of rectangles by counting squares. Trace small objects on a centimeter grid to measure area.	Grade 5: Find areas of rectangles on grids. Use the rectangle method for finding areas of triangles and parallelograms.

assessment

ongoing • product • periodic

Informal Assessment

Math Boxes These *Math Journal* pages provide opportunities for cumulative review or assessment of concepts and skills.

Ongoing Assessment: Kid Watching Use the Ongoing Assessment suggestions in the following lessons to make quick, on-the-spot observations about students' understanding of:
- Measurement and Reference Frames **(Lesson 8.3, Part 1; Lesson 8.5, Part 3; Lesson 8.6, Part 1; and Lesson 8.7, Part 2)**
- Geometry **(Lesson 8.6, Part 1)**

Portfolio Ideas Samples of students' work may be obtained from the following assignments:
- Making a Scale Drawing of Your Bedroom **(Lesson 8.2)**
- Constructing Figures with a Compass and Straightedge **(Lesson 8.6)**
- Comparing Areas **(Lesson 8.7)**
- Using Division to Compare Numbers of Mammal Species **(Lesson 8.8)**
- Find the Area and Perimeter of an Irregular Figure **(Lesson 8.9)**
- Make Enlargements **(Lesson 8.9)**
- Solve Perimeter and Area Problems **(Lesson 8.9)**

Unit 8 Review and Assessment

Math Message Use the Time to Reflect questions in Lesson 8.9 to assess students' progress toward the following learning goals: **Goals 8a, 8b, and 8d**

Oral and Slate Assessments Use oral or slate assessments during Lesson 8.9 to assess students' progress toward the following learning goals: **Goals 8a–8d**

Written Assessment Use a written review during Lesson 8.9 to assess students' progress toward the following learning goals: **Goals 8a–8d**

Alternative Assessment Options Use independent alternative assessments in Lesson 8.9 to assess students' progress toward the following learning goals: **Goals 8b and 8c**

assessmenthandbook

For more information on how to use different types of assessment in Unit 8, see the Assessment Overview on pages 60–62 in the *Assessment Handbook*. The following Assessment Masters can be found in the *Math Masters* book:
- Unit 8 Checking Progress, pp. 404 and 405
- Unit 8 Class Checklist, p. 440
- Unit 8 Individual Profile of Progress, p. 441
- Class Progress Indicator, p. 467
- Interest Inventories, pp. 468 and 469
- Math Logs, pp. 470–472
- Self-Assessment Forms, pp. 473 and 474

problem solving

A process of modeling everyday situations using tools from mathematics

Encourage students to use a variety of strategies when attacking a given problem—and to explain those strategies. *Strategies students might use in this unit:*

- Drawing and using a picture
- Using estimation
- Making a model
- Using computation
- Using a formula
- Making a graph

Four Problem-Solving REPRESENTATIONS

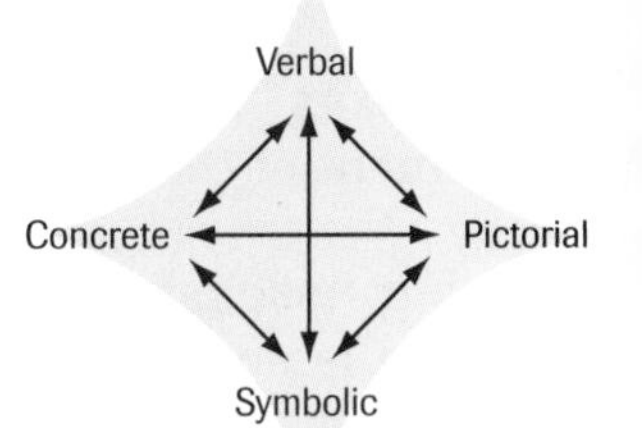

Lessons that teach *through* problem solving, not just *about* problem solving

Lesson	Activity	Lesson	Activity
8.1	Analyzing and rating the efficiency of kitchen arrangements	**8.4**	Finding the total area of skin on the body
8.2, 8.5	Making scale drawings: of the classroom, rectangles	**8.5–8.7**	Finding the areas of rectangles, parallelograms, and triangles
8.2	Finding the perimeter of given figures and drawing figures of given perimeters	**8.6**	Finding the largest area for a garden given the amount of fence for the perimeter
8.3	Finding the area of the classroom floor	**8.8**	Comparing the areas of countries and completing a picture graph
8.3	Solving probability problems involving spinners, dice, and coins		

For more information about problem solving in *Everyday Mathematics,* see the *Teacher's Reference Manual.*

cross-curricular links

social studies

- Students continue the World Tour by making an optional trip to a second country in South America. **(Lesson 8.4)**
- Students compare the area of Brazil with the area of other South American countries. **(Lesson 8.8)**

industrial arts

- Students examine a "work triangle," which shows distances between pairs of major kitchen appliances. **(Lesson 8.1)**

science

- Students use division to compare numbers of mammal species. **(Lesson 8.8)**

meeting INDIVIDUAL needs

UNIVERSAL ACCESS

✦ RETEACHING

The following features provide additional instructional support:

Adjusting the Activity

- **Lesson 8.1, Part 1**
- **Lesson 8.4, Part 1**

Options for Individualizing

- **Lesson 8.1** Investigating Perimeters on a Geoboard
- **Lesson 8.3** Investigating Geoboard Areas
- **Lesson 8.4** Converting Square Inches to Square Feet

✦ ENRICHMENT

The following features suggest some enrichment and extension activities found in this unit:

Adjusting the Activity

- **Lesson 8.3, Part 1**
- **Lesson 8.4, Part 2**
- **Lesson 8.6, Part 2**
- **Lesson 8.7, Part 1**
- **Lesson 8.8, Part 1**

Options for Individualizing

- **Lesson 8.2** Making a Scale Drawing of Your Bedroom
- **Lesson 8.6** Constructing Figures with a Compass and Straightedge
- **Lesson 8.7** Comparing Areas
- **Lesson 8.8** Using Division to Compare Numbers of Mammal Species

✦ LANGUAGE DIVERSITY

The following features suggest some ways to support students who are acquiring proficiency in English:

Adjusting the Activity

- **Lesson 8.6, Part 1**

Options for Individualizing

- **Lesson 8.2** Building Background for Mathematics Words

✦ MULTIAGE CLASSROOM

The following chart lists related lessons from Grades 3 and 5 that can help you meet your instructional needs:

Grade 3	3.4		3.5 3.6		3.5– 3.7			3.6
Grade 4	8.1	8.2	8.3	8.4	8.5	8.6	8.7	8.8
Grade 5	5.1– 5.3		9.4– 9.6	9.5	9.4	9.6	9.6	9.7

materials

lesson	math masters pages	manipulative kit items	other items
8.1	Study Link Masters, pp. 322, 323, and 329 Teaching Master, p. 117 ***See* Advance Preparation, p. 596**		scissors and transparent tape straightedge Geometry Template geoboard and rubber bands
8.2	Study Link Master, p. 330 Teaching Masters, p. 118 (optional); and pp. 119 and 120 transparency of Teaching Master, p. 118 (optional) ***See* Advance Preparation, p. 601**	1 tape measure per partnership	straightedge ruler tape measure scissors and transparent tape (or paste)
8.3	Study Link Master, p. 331 ***See* Advance Preparation, p. 607**		scissors and transparent tape Geometry Template masking tape geoboard and rubber bands
8.4	Study Link Master, p. 332 Teaching Masters, pp. 36–38 (optional); and p. 121 ***See* Advance Preparation, p. 611**		calculator scissors and transparent tape objects with flat, irregular shapes transparent or masking tape
8.5	Study Link Master, p. 333 ***See* Advance Preparation, p. 616**	1 six-sided die per partnership 36 cm cubes, 36 square pattern blocks, or a 7 by 7 geoboard and rubber bands per partnership	calculator ruler
8.6	Study Link Masters, pp. 334 and 335 Teaching Master, p. 122	straws and twist-ties compass ***See* Advance Preparation, p. 621**	centimeter ruler scissors and transparent tape index card or other square-corner device straightedge
8.7	Study Link Master, p. 336 Teaching Masters, pp. 123 and 124 transparency of Teaching Master, p. 20 (optional) Assessment Master, p. 475 (optional)		centimeter ruler scissors and transparent tape index card or other square-corner device straightedge ***See* Advance Preparation, p. 627**
8.8	Study Link Master, p. 337 Teaching Master, p. 125		world map or globe calculator
8.9	Study Link Masters, pp. 338–341 Teaching Masters, pp. 126–131 Assessment Masters, pp. 404 and 405		slate centimeter ruler scissors and transparent tape

planningtips

Pacing

Pacing depends on a number of factors, such as students' individual needs and how long your school has been using *Everyday Mathematics.* At the beginning of Unit 8, review your Content by Strand Poster to help you set a monthly pace.

← MOST CLASSROOMS →

FEBRUARY	MARCH	APRIL

Home Communication

Share Study Links 8.1–8.8 with families to help them understand the content and procedures in this unit. At the end of the unit, use Study Link 8.9 to introduce Unit 9. Supplemental information can be found in the *Home Connection Handbook*.

NCTM Standards

Standard	1	2	3	4	5	6	7	8	9	10
Unit 8 Lessons	8	5	2, 3, 5–7	1–8	1, 3	1–9	1–9	1–9	1–9	1–9

Content Standards
1 Number and Operations
2 Algebra
3 Geometry
4 Measurement
5 Data Analysis and Probability

Process Standards
6 Problem Solving
7 Reasoning and Proof
8 Communication
9 Connections
10 Representation

unit 8 content highlights

The discussion below highlights the major content ideas presented in Unit 8 and may help you establish instructional priorities.

Perimeter and Area (Lessons 8.1 and following)

Unit 8 begins with a review of perimeter (Lesson 8.1). Students use the measurements they made in Lesson 7.11 (*Math Masters,* pages 322 and 323) to evaluate the arrangement of appliances in their home kitchens. Then, in Lesson 8.2, they make scale drawings of their classroom. This activity serves several purposes:

▷ It provides practice in measuring lengths and in using a scale to make a scale drawing. Students use this skill again to make scale drawings of their bedrooms and their bedroom furniture in an optional activity in Lesson 8.2. They use their scale drawings to evaluate various arrangements of their bedroom furniture.

▷ Students use their scale drawings of the classroom floor to find the area of the floor in Lesson 8.3.

Length and *perimeter* (or *circumference*) are measures of distance along a linear path. *Area* is a measure of a finite amount of surface. This surface may be "flat" (for example, the interior of a rectangle), or it may be "curved" (for example, the surface of a cylinder or cone).

It is important to note that, like other measures, area always includes both a number and a unit. Units of area are typically *square units* based on linear units, such as a square yard, a square meter, and a square mile. Note that there are several units of area in which the word *square* does not appear; for example, an *acre* of land (now $\frac{1}{640}$ of a square mile) is said to have been based, a long time ago, on the amount of land a farmer could plow in one day. In the metric system, the *hectare* is used to measure land areas.

In most schoolbooks, the definition of area is based on the idea of "tiling," or covering a surface with identical unit squares, without gaps or overlaps, and then counting those units.

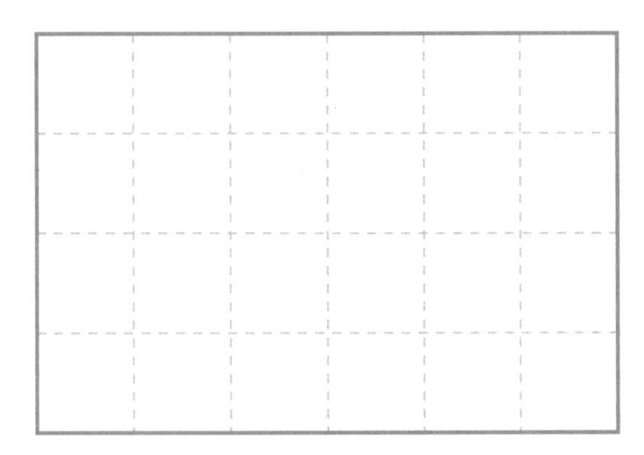

Use tiling to demonstrate area (discrete model).

If the surface is bounded by a rectangle, it is natural to arrange the tiles in an array, and to multiply the number of tiles per row by the number of rows. The usual formulas, $A = l * w$ or $A = b * h$, are then easily linked to array multiplication: area is equal to the number of square unit tiles in one row (equal to the length of the base in some linear unit) times the number of rows (equal to the width, or height, in that same linear unit). For other surfaces, defined by regular or irregular boundaries, tiling with square units can be thought of as (or actually done by) laying a grid of appropriate square units on the region and counting, estimating, or calculating how many squares it takes to cover that region.

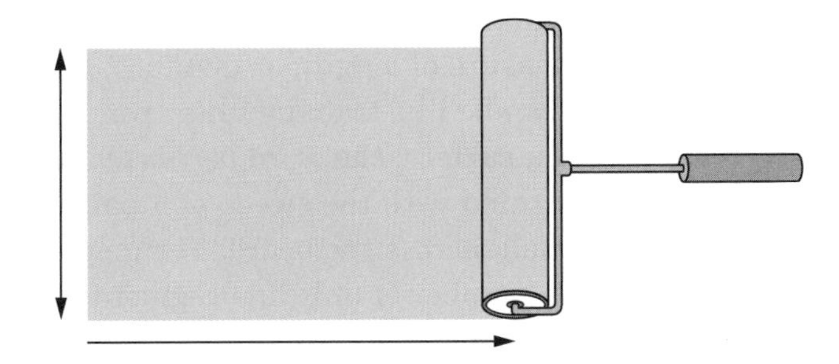

Use painting to demonstrate area (continuous model).

Another, more dynamic conception of area has proven to be useful in some applications and in more advanced mathematics courses. Imagine running a one-foot-wide paint roller on the floor of a rectangular room along one wall. For every foot the roller travels, 1 square foot of the floor is painted. Now suppose the room is 20 feet wide and the roller is the width of the room (a 20-foot-wide roller). Then, for every foot the roller travels along the length of the floor, 20 square feet of floor are painted. When the roller reaches the other side of the floor, the entire floor will have been painted. If you think of the floor as the interior of a rectangle, then the area of the rectangle is obtained not by counting squares (a *discrete* conception), but by sweeping the width of the rectangle across the interior of the rectangle, parallel to its base (a *continuous* conception). The area is simply the product of the length of the base and the width of the rectangle. In the classroom, this can be shown by rubbing the long part of a piece of chalk on the board to mark a rectangular surface—the further you sweep it along, the bigger the rectangle and the greater the area.

For most purposes, you will probably choose the traditional conception of area—counting or computing the number of square units required to cover a surface. However, the authors recommend that you also introduce the continuous conception, for it is easily extended to conceptions of *volume*. For example, students can think of the volume of a prism in terms of a prism that is gradually filled with water: The surface of the water is shaped like the base of the prism; the higher the level of the water, the more space it occupies and the greater the volume. This leads to the formula for the volume of a prism and a cylinder as the area of the base multiplied by the height. This formula for volume works no matter what the shape of the base.

Students often confuse perimeter with area, perhaps because they are not clear about the meaning of formulas they have been taught by rote. Perimeter is a measure of length, or distance; area is a measure of surface. Perimeter can be illustrated with a trundle wheel that rolls along the boundary of a surface; the word *perimeter* contains the word *rim*. Area can be illustrated with the sweep of a paint roller across a surface or a piece of chalk across the board. Perimeter is measured in units of length—the number of unit line segments from one point to another. Area is measured in square units—the number of unit squares needed to cover a surface. Occasionally remind your students of these basic differences.

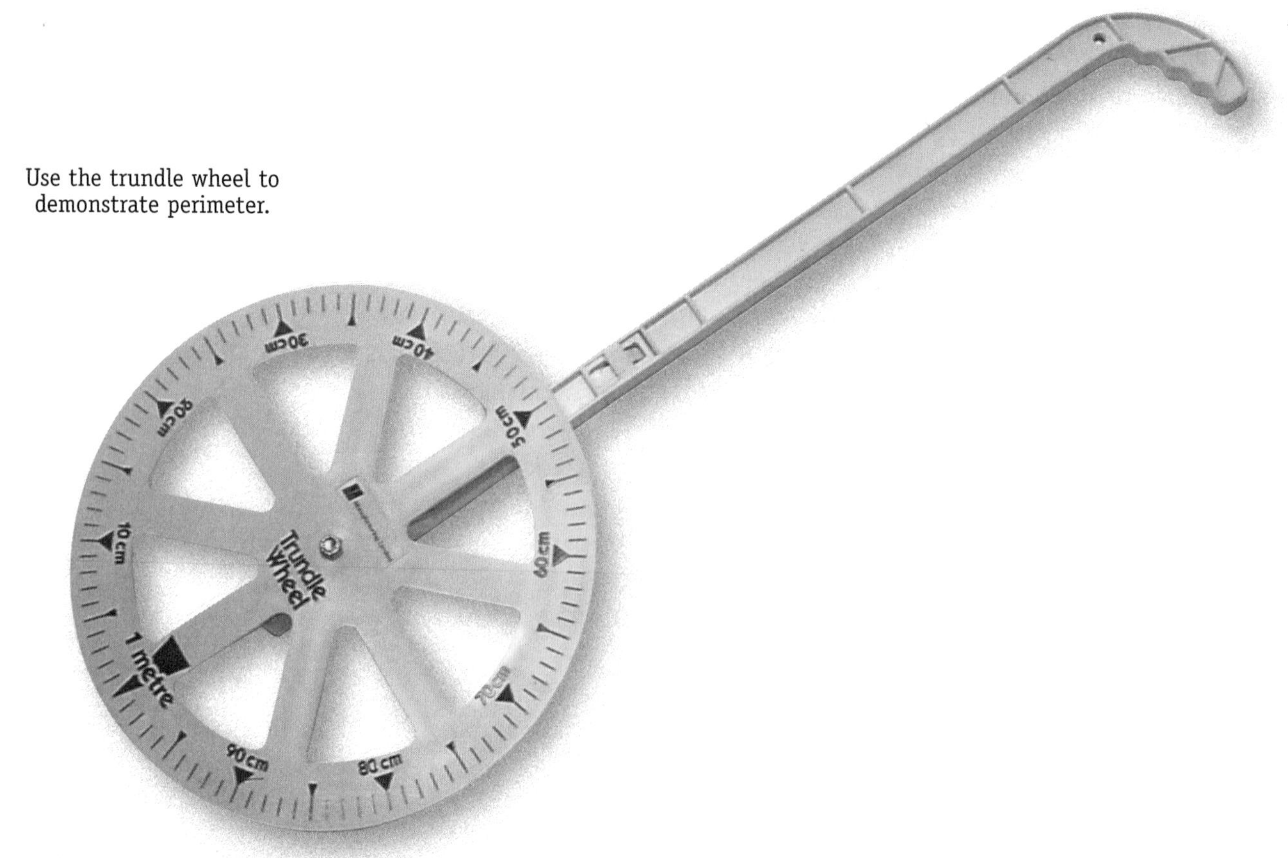

Use the trundle wheel to demonstrate perimeter.

Developing and Using Formulas (Lessons 8.4–8.8)

In Lessons 8.5, 8.6, and 8.7, students develop and use formulas for finding the area of rectangles, parallelograms, and triangles.

Lessons 8.4 and 8.8 deal with areas that are *not* calculated from formulas. In Lesson 8.4, students estimate the area of one side of their hand by tracing it onto a grid and counting squares and fractions of squares. Students then use this estimate to compute the area of the skin on their entire body by applying a rule of thumb (area of skin is about 100 times the area of one side of your hand). In Lesson 8.8, students learn about area measurements of some of the geographical features they have encountered on the World Tour. They use division and a calculator to compare areas of South American countries.

In this unit, the formula for the area of a rectangle (area = length of base times width, or height) is assumed as a basic "axiom." The formula for the area of a parallelogram is developed by cutting apart a parallelogram and rearranging the parts into a rectangular shape. Similarly, the formula for the area of a triangle is developed by cutting triangles and reassembling them to form parallelograms. Similar cut-and-paste methods will be used later in *Everyday Mathematics* to develop formulas for the areas of other 2-dimensional shapes—always with the idea of transforming a given shape into another shape of the same area, for which a formula is already known.

Once students learn a formula, they tend to use it without much thought as to its origin. It is important to remind students occasionally of why formulas make sense. Such derivations have the advantage of demonstrating an important mathematical process—one fact is taken as an "axiom" on which there is agreement, and other rules or relationships are developed from the axiom.

Most schoolbooks (and many standardized tests) express the formula for the area of a rectangle as the product of the *length* times the *width* ($A = l * w$). The formulas for the area of a parallelogram ($A = b * h$) and a triangle ($A = \frac{1}{2} * b * h$) are expressed in terms of the length of the *base* and the *height*. Students who have been taught only the formula $A = l * w$ will often mistakenly multiply the lengths of two adjacent sides when calculating the area of a parallelogram. Similar errors are made in finding the areas of triangles. While students should be familiar with the formula $A = l * w$, point out that since a rectangle is a special kind of parallelogram, it makes sense to use the formula $A = b * h$ for the area of a rectangle.

An added advantage to using the base-times-height formula is that it is consistent with the formulas used to find the volumes of many 3-dimensional figures. For example, no matter what the shape of the base, the volume of a prism is always equal to the area of a base multiplied by its height.

height

base

In most math textbooks, nearly every illustration in connection with the area of a polygon shows the base as a horizontal segment on which the figure "sits." But the base can be *any side,* and the height can be measured on a perpendicular to *whichever* side is designated as the base.

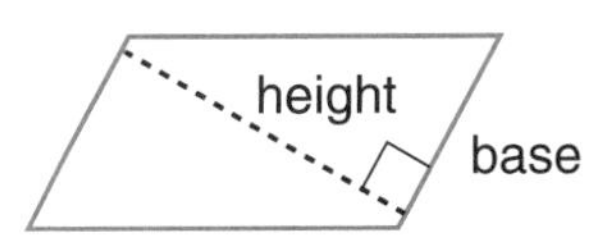

Two ways of designating the base and height of a parallelogram

Review and Assessment (Lesson 8.9)

The Unit 8 assessment in Lesson 8.9 includes oral, slate, and written assessments of the following concepts and skills:

- making and interpreting scale drawings
- using formulas to find the areas of rectangles, parallelograms, and triangles
- finding the perimeters of polygons
- finding the areas of irregular figures

For additional information on the following topics, see the *Teacher's Reference Manual:*

- area
- base and height
- floor plan
- formula
- length and width
- measurement
- perimeter
- scale drawing
- square units
- time-and-motion study
- variable
- work triangle

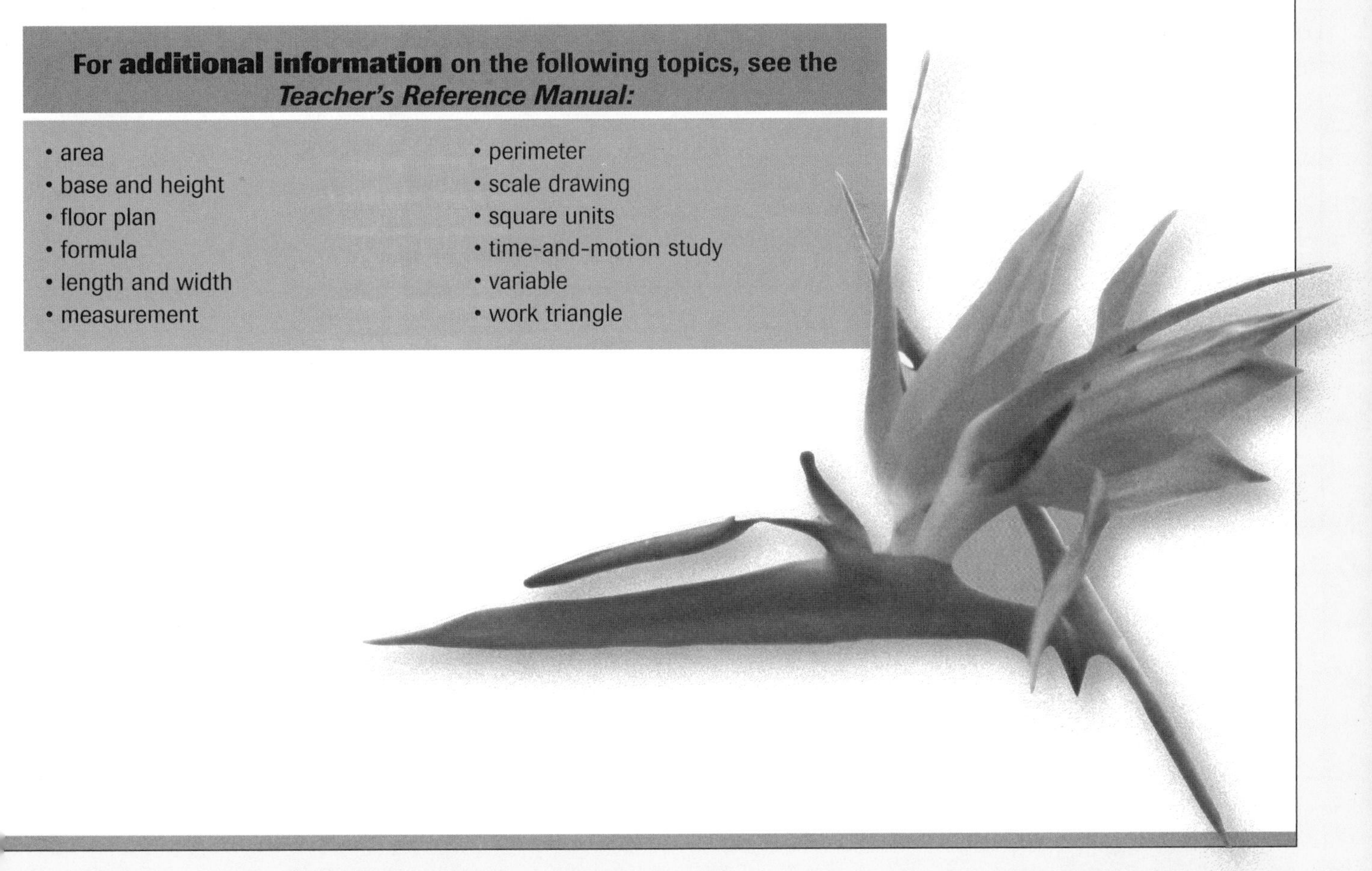

8.1 Kitchen Layouts and Perimeter

OBJECTIVES **To measure and add distances in feet and inches; to find the medians and other landmarks of sets of measurements; and to find the perimeters of triangles.**

summaries	materials
1 Teaching the Lesson	
Students describe their own kitchens and sketch the arrangements of three appliances in their kitchens. They calculate perimeters of the work triangles determined by these appliances and compare individual and class results to recommended distances between appliances. Then they find the minimum, maximum, mode, and median of the class perimeters. Students sketch work triangles that meet certain conditions. [Measurement and Reference Frames; Data and Chance]	☐ *Math Journal 2,* pp. 231–234 ☐ Study Link 7.11 (*Math Masters,* pp. 322 and 323) ☐ scissors and transparent tape ☐ straightedge ***See* Advance Preparation**
2 Ongoing Learning & Practice	
Students practice and maintain skills through Math Boxes and Study Link activities.	☐ *Math Journal 2,* p. 230 ☐ Study Link Master (*Math Masters,* p. 329) ☐ Geometry Template
3 Options for Individualizing	
Reteaching Students construct rectangles and squares of a given perimeter on a geoboard. [Measurement and Reference Frames]	☐ Teaching Master (*Math Masters,* p. 117) ☐ geoboard and rubber bands ***See* Advance Preparation**

Additional Information

Advance Preparation For Part 1, if students handed in *Math Masters,* pages 322 and 323, return these pages to them.

For the optional Reteaching activity in Part 3, make one copy of *Math Masters,* page 117 per 2 students.

Vocabulary • **time-and-motion study** • **work triangle** • **perimeter**

Getting Started

Mental Math and Reflexes

Remind students that 12 inches equal 1 foot. Remind them about symbols for feet (') and inches ("): 3' 10" is shorthand for 3 feet 10 inches. A measurement reported in feet and inches may be rewritten in a simpler form if there are more than 12 inches. For example, 2' 18" may be rewritten as 3' 6", because 18" = 1' 6".

Write mixed feet-and-inches measurements on the board. Students rewrite them in simpler form. *Suggestions:*

- 1' 15" 2' 3"
- 2' 22" 3' 10"
- 7' 18" 8' 6"
- 5' 27" 7' 3"

Math Message

Complete Parts 1 and 2 on journal page 232.

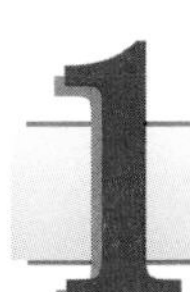

Teaching the Lesson

Math Message Follow-Up
(*Math Journal 2,* pp. 231 and 232; *Math Masters,* pp. 322 and 323)

WHOLE-CLASS DISCUSSION

Ask some students to describe the layout of the stove, sink, and refrigerator in their kitchens. Follow your usual group reading procedure to read journal page 231. Discuss the four types of layouts shown. Have students record the kind of layout they have in their homes.

Ask for a show of hands and tabulate on the board the number of students who have a one-wall kitchen, a U-shaped kitchen, a Pullman or galley kitchen, or an L-shaped kitchen. Ask:

- Do any students have "islands" in their kitchens? Some kitchens have island work areas that include a sink or stove. Share any sketches that show kitchen islands with the class.
- Why might a one-wall kitchen be less efficient than the other types? A person may have to walk longer distances from one appliance to another.

Each student should cut his or her kitchen sketch from *Math Masters,* page 323 and tape it onto journal page 232.

Rating the Efficiency of a Kitchen

WHOLE-CLASS DISCUSSION

Industrial Arts Link As a result of **time-and-motion studies,** kitchen efficiency experts have recommended minimum and maximum distances between each pair of major appliances (*see margin*).

Write these recommendations on the board. Then sketch a stove, sink, and refrigerator and connect them with line segments. The resulting triangle, called a **work triangle,** can be used to show distances between pairs of appliances (*see margin*).

Range of Distances between:
Stove and refrigerator: 4 feet to 9 feet
Refrigerator and sink: 4 feet to 7 feet
Sink and stove: 4 feet to 6 feet

Work triangle

6'

4' 3"

6' 10"

Kitchen Layouts and Kitchen Efficiency

Here are four common ways to arrange the appliances in a kitchen:

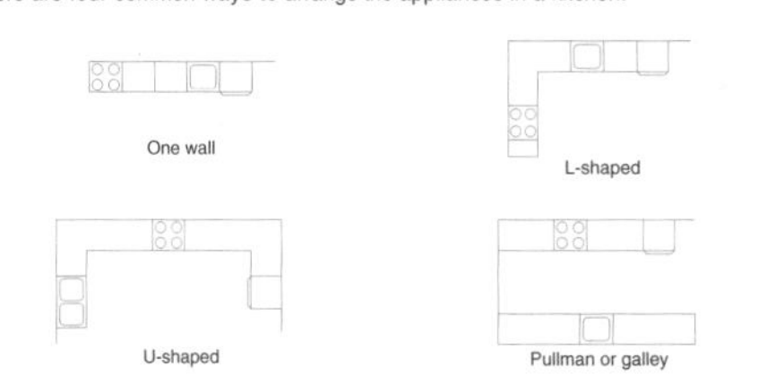

Pullman kitchens are usually found on passenger trains. **Galleys** are the kitchens on boats and airplanes. The kitchen areas on trains, boats, and airplanes are small. The cooking area is usually lined up against a single wall (a one-wall kitchen) or against two walls with a corridor between them (a Pullman or galley kitchen).

- What kind of kitchen layout do you have in your home? Circle one. Answers vary.

One wall L-shaped U-shaped Pullman or galley

Kitchen efficiency experts are people who study the ways we use our kitchens. They carry out **time-and-motion** studies to find how long it takes to do some kitchen tasks and how much a person has to move about in order to do them. They want to find the best ways to arrange the stove, the sink, and the refrigerator. In an efficient kitchen, a person should have to do very little walking to move from one appliance to another. However, the appliances should not be too close to each other, because the person would feel cramped.

A bird's-eye sketch is often drawn to see how well the appliances in a kitchen are arranged. The stove, the sink, and the refrigerator are connected with line segments as shown below. These segments form a triangle called a **work triangle.** The work triangle shows the distance between pairs of appliances.

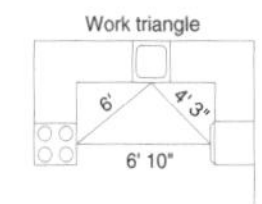

STUDENT PAGE

Math Journal 2, p. 231

Layout of My Kitchen

1. Copy the distances between your appliances from *Math Masters,* page 322.

Answers vary.

Between stove and refrigerator About ______ feet ______ inches

Between refrigerator and sink About ______ feet ______ inches

Between sink and stove About ______ feet ______ inches

2. Cut out the sketch of your kitchen from *Math Masters,* page 323 and tape it in the space below.

STUDENT PAGE

Math Journal 2, p. 232

Perimeter	Number of Triangles
less than 11 ft	/
11 ft	/
12 ft	///
13 ft	//
.	.
.	.

Tallying perimeters of work triangles

Remind students that the distance around a polygon is called its **perimeter.** Ask questions about the perimeter of a work triangle.

- What is the smallest perimeter of a work triangle that meets the experts' recommendations? $4 + 4 + 4 = 12$ feet
- What is the largest perimeter? $9 + 7 + 6 = 22$ feet
- What is a middle value for the range of recommended perimeters? The number halfway between 12 and 22 feet is 17 feet.

Analyzing Kitchen Arrangements
(*Math Journal 2,* pp. 232 and 233)

WHOLE-CLASS ACTIVITY

1. Ask students to use straightedges to connect the three appliances in their sketches on journal page 232 and write the distances between appliances on the sides of their triangles. Then have them find the perimeters of their work triangles (journal page 233, Problems 1–3).

Adjusting the Activity If students are having difficulty adding with mixed units, suggest that they think in terms of the partial-sums algorithm—add feet, and then add inches. For example, 6' + 4' 3" + 6' 10" = 16' 13" = 17' 1".

2. Have students report the perimeters of their own work triangles. You or a student tallies these perimeters on the board. To simplify the record-keeping, ignore the inches in the perimeter or round each perimeter to the nearest foot (*see margin*).
3. Have students find the minimum, maximum, mode, and median of the class perimeters and record them in Problem 4 on journal page 233. Ask:
   - Is the class median close to 17 feet—the median of the recommended perimeters?
   - Does anyone have a work triangle with a perimeter outside the recommended range (less than 12 feet or greater than 22 feet)? If so, share their sketches.
   - Does anyone have a work triangle in which the distance between two appliances is *outside* the recommended range, but whose *perimeter* is within the recommended range? (For example: the distance between stove and sink is 3 feet, but the perimeter is 14 feet.)

✦ Sketching Work Triangles of Given Perimeters (*Math Journal 2,* p. 234)

WHOLE-CLASS ACTIVITY

Students sketch work triangles that meet the following conditions:

▷ The perimeter is 21 feet.

▷ The length of each side is a whole number of feet.

▷ The length of each side is within the recommended range.

Ask students to share their solution strategies. One possible approach might be to establish the distance from sink to stove as 4, 5, or 6 feet.

▷ If the distance between sink and stove is 4 feet, then the sum of the other two distances must be 17 feet ($4 + 17 = 21$). But since this sum may not exceed 16 feet ($9 + 7$), the distance between sink and stove can't be 4 feet.

▷ If the distance between sink and stove is 5 feet, then the sum of the other two distances must be 16 feet ($5 + 16 = 21$). So the distance between stove and refrigerator would be 9 feet, and the distance between refrigerator and sink 7 feet.

▷ If the distance between sink and stove is 6 feet, then the sum of the other two distances must be 15 feet ($6 + 15 = 21$). Therefore, the other two distances would be either 8 feet and 7 feet or 9 feet and 6 feet.

2 Ongoing Learning & Practice

✦ Math Boxes 8.1 (*Math Journal 2,* p. 230)

INDEPENDENT ACTIVITY 

Mixed Review Math Boxes in this lesson are paired with Math Boxes in Lesson 8.3. The skill in Problem 1 is a prerequisite for Unit 9.

How Efficient Is My Kitchen?

Answer the questions below to see how well the appliances in your kitchen are arranged. Answers vary.

1. With a straightedge, draw a triangle connecting the appliances in your sketch on the facing page. Write the distances between the appliances on the sides of your triangle. This triangle is called a **work triangle.**

2. Find the **perimeter** of your work triangle. Show your work.

_____ feet _____ inches
_____ feet _____ inches
+ _____ feet _____ inches

The perimeter is about _____ feet _____ inches.

That's close to _____ feet.

3. Kitchen efficiency experts recommend the following distances between appliances:

Between stove and refrigerator:	4 feet to 9 feet
Between refrigerator and sink:	4 feet to 7 feet
Between sink and stove:	4 feet to 6 feet

Does your kitchen meet these recommendations? _____

4. How many students reported their work triangle perimeters? _____ students

The minimum perimeter is about _____ feet.

The maximum perimeter is about _____ feet.

The mode of the perimeters is about _____ feet.

The median perimeter is about _____ feet.

STUDENT PAGE

✦ *Math Journal 2,* p. 233

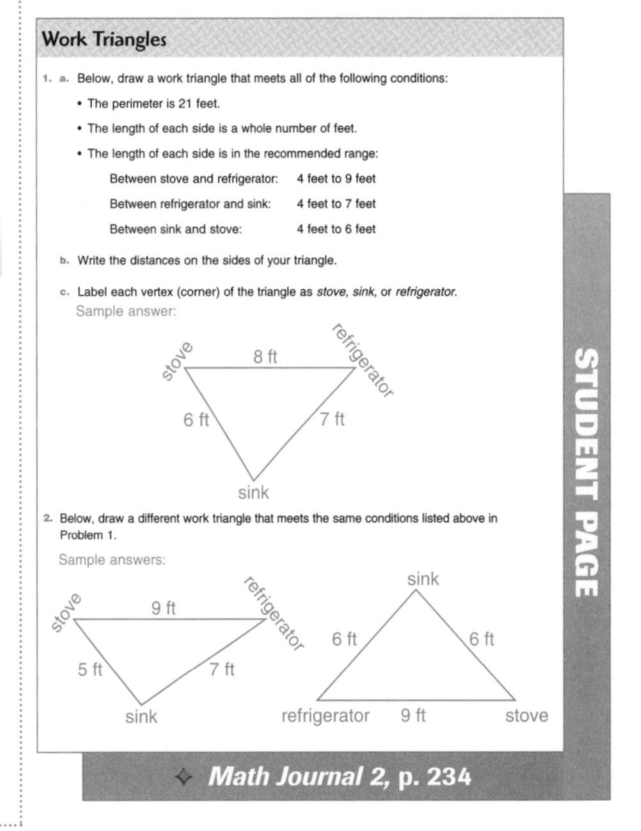
Work Triangles

1. a. Below, draw a work triangle that meets all of the following conditions:
   - The perimeter is 21 feet.
   - The length of each side is a whole number of feet.
   - The length of each side is in the recommended range:

Between stove and refrigerator:	4 feet to 9 feet
Between refrigerator and sink:	4 feet to 7 feet
Between sink and stove:	4 feet to 6 feet

   b. Write the distances on the sides of your triangle.

   c. Label each vertex (corner) of the triangle as *stove, sink,* or *refrigerator.*

Sample answer:

2. Below, draw a different work triangle that meets the same conditions listed above in Problem 1.

Sample answers:

STUDENT PAGE

✦ *Math Journal 2,* p. 234

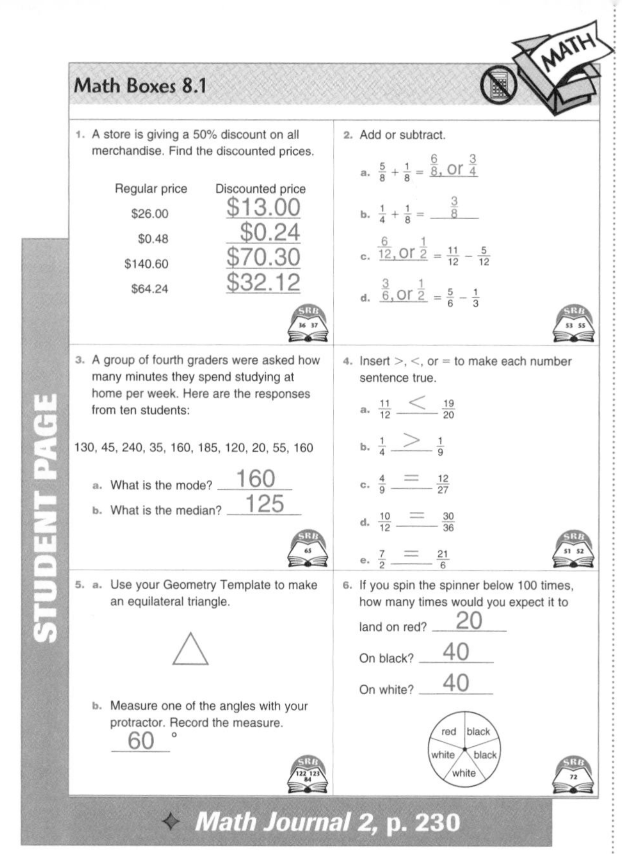
Math Boxes 8.1

1. A store is giving a 50% discount on all merchandise. Find the discounted prices.

Regular price	Discounted price
$26.00	$13.00
$0.48	$0.24
$140.60	$70.30
$64.24	$32.12

SRB 36 37

2. Add or subtract.

a. $\frac{5}{8} + \frac{1}{8} =$ $\frac{6}{8}$, or $\frac{3}{4}$

b. $\frac{1}{4} + \frac{1}{8} =$ $\frac{3}{8}$

c. $\frac{6}{12}$, or $\frac{1}{2}$ $= \frac{11}{12} - \frac{5}{12}$

d. $\frac{3}{6}$, or $\frac{1}{2}$ $= \frac{5}{6} - \frac{1}{3}$

SRB 53 55

3. A group of fourth graders were asked how many minutes they spend studying at home per week. Here are the responses from ten students:

130, 45, 240, 35, 160, 185, 120, 20, 55, 160

a. What is the mode? 160

b. What is the median? 125

SRB 65

4. Insert >, <, or = to make each number sentence true.

a. $\frac{11}{12}$ < $\frac{19}{20}$

b. $\frac{1}{4}$ > $\frac{1}{9}$

c. $\frac{4}{9}$ = $\frac{12}{27}$

d. $\frac{10}{12}$ = $\frac{30}{36}$

e. $\frac{7}{2}$ = $\frac{21}{6}$

SRB 51 52

5. a. Use your Geometry Template to make an equilateral triangle.

b. Measure one of the angles with your protractor. Record the measure. 60 °

SRB 122 123 84

6. If you spin the spinner below 100 times, how many times would you expect it to land on red? 20

On black? 40

On white? 40

red, black, white, black, white

SRB 72

Math Journal 2, p. 230

STUDENT PAGE

✦ Study Link 8.1 (*Math Masters,* p. 329)

Home Connection Students find the perimeters of work triangles. They should convert measures of 12 inches or more to feet and inches.

3 Options for Individualizing

✦ RETEACHING Investigating Perimeters on a Geoboard (*Math Masters,* p. 117)

PARTNER ACTIVITY **15–30 min** 

Students construct rectangles and squares of a given perimeter on a geoboard and record the lengths of the sides on *Math Masters,* page 117.

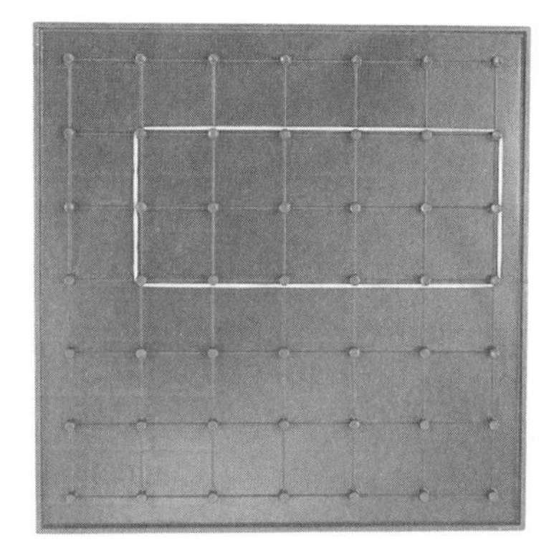

The perimeter of the rectangle is 14 units. The longer sides are each 5 units long, and the shorter sides are each 2 units long.

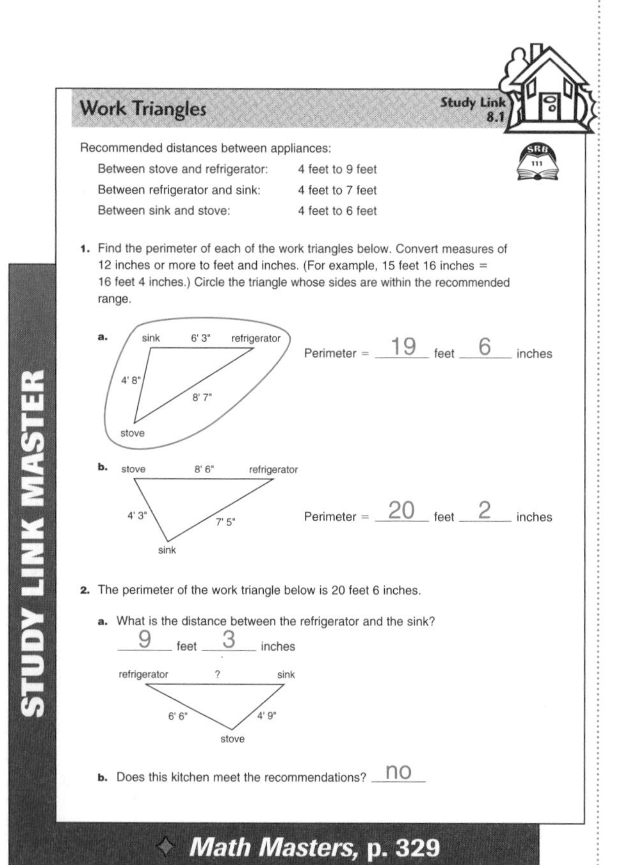
Work Triangles

Study Link 8.1

SRB 111

Recommended distances between appliances:

Between stove and refrigerator:	4 feet to 9 feet
Between refrigerator and sink:	4 feet to 7 feet
Between sink and stove:	4 feet to 6 feet

1. Find the perimeter of each of the work triangles below. Convert measures of 12 inches or more to feet and inches. (For example, 15 feet 16 inches = 16 feet 4 inches.) Circle the triangle whose sides are within the recommended range.

a. sink, 6' 3", refrigerator, 4' 8", 8' 7", stove

Perimeter = 19 feet 6 inches

b. stove, 8' 6", refrigerator, 4' 3", 7' 5", sink

Perimeter = 20 feet 2 inches

2. The perimeter of the work triangle below is 20 feet 6 inches.

a. What is the distance between the refrigerator and the sink? 9 feet 3 inches

refrigerator, ?, sink, 6' 6", 4' 9", stove

b. Does this kitchen meet the recommendations? no

Math Masters, p. 329

STUDY LINK MASTER

PLANNING AHEAD

Starting in Lesson 8.3, students will study area. Make and display unit squares with sides of length 1 inch, 1 foot, 1 yard, 1 centimeter, 1 decimeter, and 1 meter. Use any kind of paper. Label each square in two ways, such as *1 square inch* and *1 in.²*.

8.2 Scale Drawings

OBJECTIVES **To measure distances to the nearest foot; and to use measurements and a given scale to create a scale drawing on a grid.**

summaries	materials
1 Teaching the Lesson	
Students make a rough floor plan of the classroom. They use the rough floor plan to create a scale drawing of the classroom on grid paper. [Measurement and Reference Frames]	□ *Math Journal 2,* pp. 236 and 237 □ Study Link 8.1 □ Teaching Master (*Math Masters,* p. 118; optional) □ Transparency (*Math Masters,* p. 118; optional) □ straightedge □ 1 tape measure per partnership ***See*** **Advance Preparation**
2 Ongoing Learning & Practice	
Students measure figures and calculate their perimeters. They draw rectangles of a given perimeter. [Measurement and Reference Frames] Students practice and maintain skills through Math Boxes and Study Link activities.	□ *Math Journal 2,* pp. 235 and 238 □ Study Link Master (*Math Masters,* p. 330) □ ruler
3 Options for Individualizing	
Language Diversity Students think of as many ways of using the word *scale* as they can. [Measurement and Reference Frames] **Enrichment** Students make scale drawings of their bedrooms and bedroom furniture. [Measurement and Reference Frames]	□ Teaching Masters (*Math Masters,* pp. 119 and 120) □ tape measure □ straightedge □ scissors and transparent tape (or paste)

Additional Information

Background Information For additional information on scale drawings, see the *Teacher's Reference Manual.*

Advance Preparation For Part 1, measure the classroom before the lesson. The grid on journal page 237 will accommodate a classroom up to 25 feet by 30 feet. If your classroom is larger than that, make a copy of *Math Masters,* page 118, for each student. Students should cut out the grid and tape it to the journal page to create a double-size grid. A second option is to use only the grid on journal page 237 and to let $\frac{1}{4}$ inch represent 2 feet. This avoids copying, cutting, and taping the additional grid, but the scale will be harder to use than $\frac{1}{4}$ inch to 1 foot. Draw the following table on the board:

Dimensions of Classroom

Longer Side (feet)	Shorter Side (feet)

Vocabulary • **rough floor plan** • **scale drawing** • **scale**

Getting Started

Mental Math and Reflexes

Pose problems about scales. *Suggestions:*

- If 1 inch on a map represents 50 miles, then
  3 inches represent 150 miles. 8 inches represent 400 miles.
  $\frac{1}{2}$ inch represents 25 miles. $6\frac{1}{2}$ inches represent 325 miles.
- If $\frac{1}{4}$ inch on a drawing represents 1 foot, then
  1 inch represents 4 feet. $1\frac{3}{4}$ inches represent 7 feet.
  5 inches represent 20 feet. $10\frac{1}{2}$ inches represent 42 feet.

Math Message

Estimate:

The long side of our classroom is about ______ feet long.

The short side is about ______ feet long.

Write your estimates in the table on the board.

Study Link 8.1 Follow-Up

Briefly go over the answers. If students are having difficulty finding simpler names for measurements, do a few problems together.
For example, 18 feet 18 inches = 19 feet 6 inches.

1 Teaching the Lesson

✦Math Message Follow-Up

WHOLE-CLASS DISCUSSION 

Ask students to find the median of the estimates for the longer and shorter sides. Record them on the board. After students measure the classroom, you can compare the median estimates with their actual measurements.

✦Making a Rough Floor Plan of the Classroom

(*Math Journal 2,* p. 236)

PARTNER ACTIVITY 

Tell students that they are going to make a **rough floor plan** of the classroom. They will then use the rough plan to make a very accurate drawing of the classroom called a **scale drawing.**

STUDENT PAGE

A Floor Plan of My Classroom

When architects design a room or house, they usually make two drawings. The first drawing is called a **rough floor plan.** It is not carefully drawn. But the rough floor plan includes all of the information that is needed to make an accurate drawing. The second drawing is called a **scale drawing.** It is drawn on a grid and is very accurate.

Rough floor plan for a bedroom

Scale drawing for a bedroom
(1 grid length represents 1 foot.)

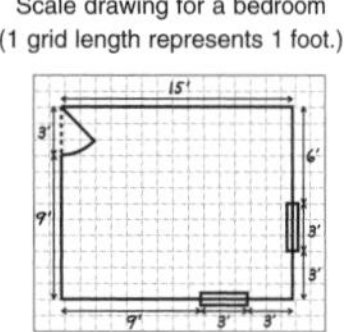

1. What information do you need to draw a rough floor plan?
   Sample answers: The shape of the room; locations of doors and windows; widths of doors, windows, and wall sections

Architects use these symbols to show windows and doors: window, door opening to left, door opening to right

2. Make a rough sketch of the outline of your classroom.

✧ *Math Journal 2,* p. 236

Ask students to look at the two drawings on journal page 236.

- ▷ The first drawing is a rough floor plan of a room. It is not carefully drawn, but it does include all of the information needed to make an accurate drawing.
- ▷ The second drawing is a scale drawing for the same room. It is drawn on a grid and is very accurate.

Have students discuss with their partners the information needed to make a rough floor plan of the classroom. They list this information in Part 1 on journal page 236 and then make a rough sketch of the outline of the classroom in Part 2. Circulate and assist as needed.

Bring the class together to discuss students' answers to Part 1. The list should include the following: the shape of the classroom; locations of doors and windows; widths of doors, windows, walls, and wall sections between doors and windows.

With students' help, draw a simple, rough floor plan of the classroom on the board. Students should add refinements to their own sketches in Part 2 on journal page 236, as you add them to your sketch.

1. Draw the walls and show the doors and windows (*see Figure 1*).
2. Show the symbols commonly used to represent doors and windows and add them to the sketch (*see Figure 2*).

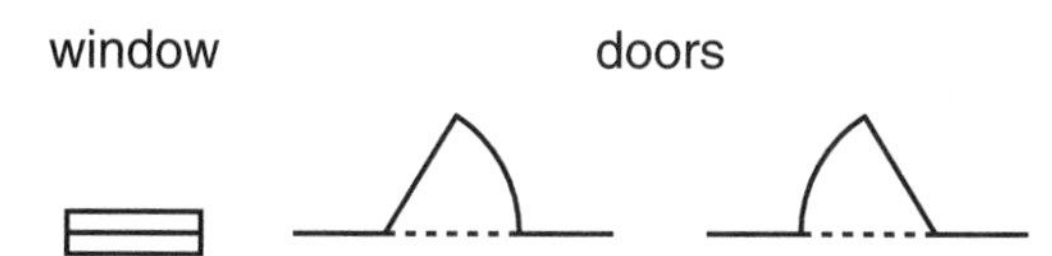

3. Give a measurement assignment to each partnership: For example, one pair of students measures the total length of a wall; another, the width of a window or door opening; another, the distance from a corner to a door or window; and so on. Ask students to make their measurements accurate to the nearest foot and to record them on the board sketch, using two-headed arrows (*see Figure 3*).
4. With the class, check the reported measurements:
   - ▷ The sum of the lengths of wall sections, windows, and door openings along each wall should be close to the total length of that wall.
   - ▷ Opposite walls should have nearly equal lengths (assuming the floor is rectangular).

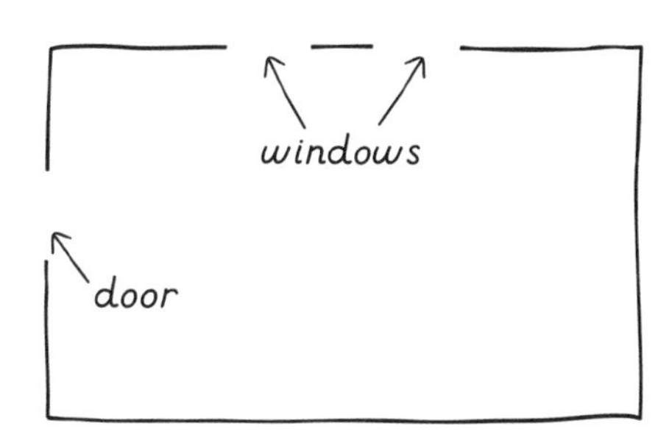

Figure 1

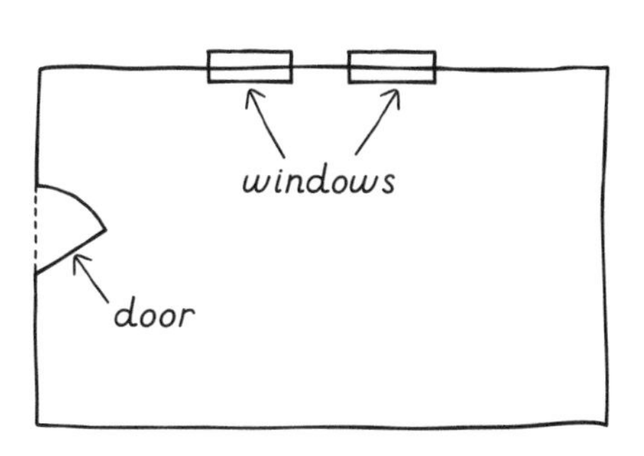

Figure 2

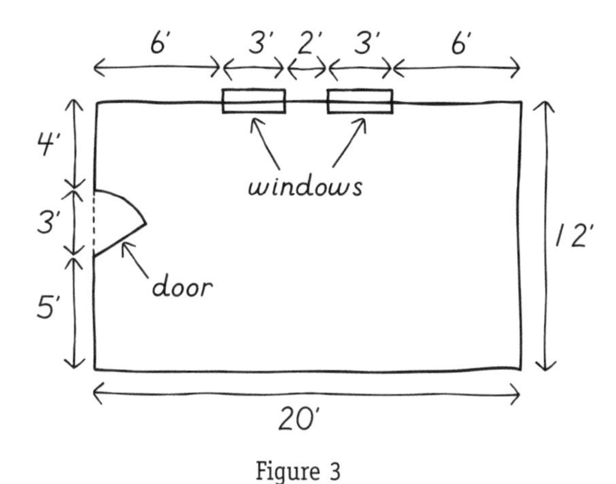

Figure 3

NOTE: Students measure to the nearest foot, so do not expect exact matches. If the floor is rectangular and opposite walls do not have the same length, revise one of the measurements so that they have equal lengths.

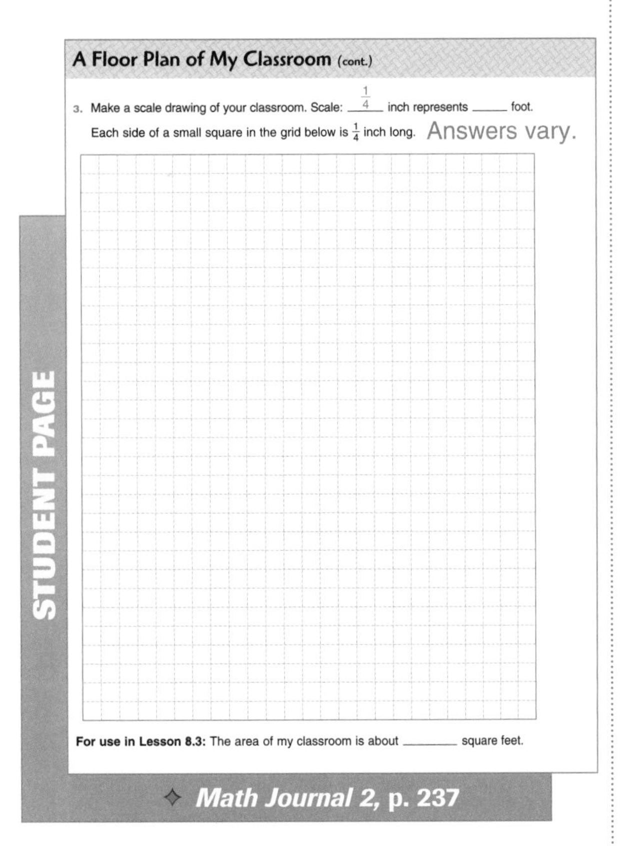
A Floor Plan of My Classroom (cont.)

3. Make a scale drawing of your classroom. Scale: $\frac{1}{4}$ inch represents ____ foot.
Each side of a small square in the grid below is $\frac{1}{4}$ inch long. Answers vary.

For use in Lesson 8.3: The area of my classroom is about _____ square feet.

STUDENT PAGE

✧ *Math Journal 2,* p. 237

✦ Making the Scale Drawing (*Math Journal 2,* pp. 236 and 237; *Math Masters,* p. 118)

WHOLE-CLASS ACTIVITY

NOTE: See Advance Preparation for suggestions of what to do if your classroom is larger than 25 feet by 30 feet.

Have students examine the grid on journal page 237. Explain that accurate floor plans are often drawn on this kind of grid. Ask:

- What is the length of the side of a small square? $\frac{1}{4}$ inch How many squares are in 1 inch? 4

Write "Scale: $\frac{1}{4}$ inch represents 1 foot" on the board and ask students to copy this onto the journal page. Tell them that this is the **scale** they will use in their scale drawings. (Write "Scale: $\frac{1}{4}$ inch represents 2 feet" instead, if you chose that option. Adjust the following steps accordingly.) Ask:

- How many small square sides are needed to represent a 6-foot wall? 6 A $2\frac{1}{2}$-foot door opening? $2\frac{1}{2}$
- On the scale drawing, what would be the length of a 14-foot wall? 14 small square sides, or $3\frac{1}{2}$ inches

The class now has all the information it needs to make the scale drawing. If you wish, use a transparency of a $\frac{1}{4}$-inch grid (*Math Masters,* page 118) to make the scale drawing of the classroom, as students follow your lead on journal page 237. Throughout this activity, remind students that the length of 1 grid square ($\frac{1}{4}$ inch) represents 1 foot of actual length.

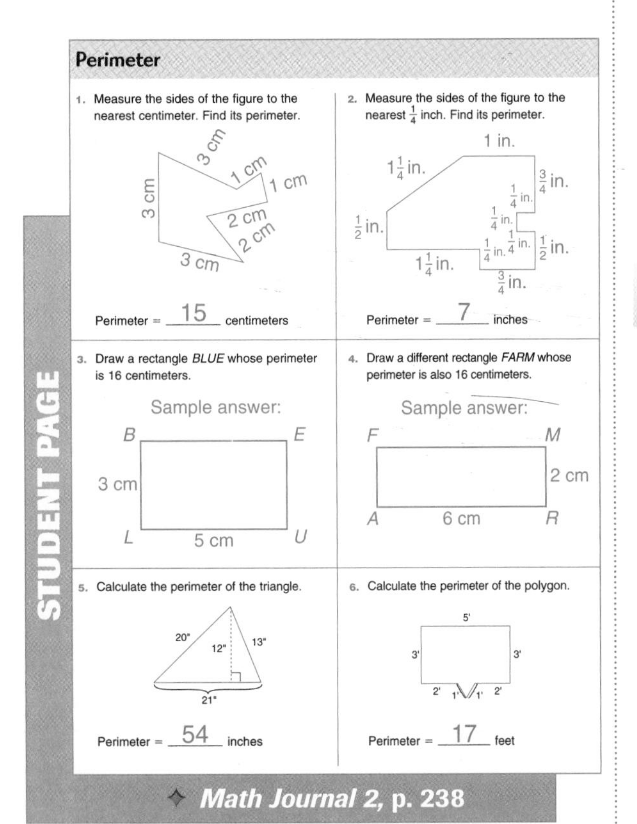
Perimeter

1. Measure the sides of the figure to the nearest centimeter. Find its perimeter.

Perimeter = 15 centimeters

2. Measure the sides of the figure to the nearest $\frac{1}{4}$ inch. Find its perimeter.

Perimeter = 7 inches

3. Draw a rectangle *BLUE* whose perimeter is 16 centimeters.

Sample answer:

4. Draw a different rectangle *FARM* whose perimeter is also 16 centimeters.

Sample answer:

5. Calculate the perimeter of the triangle.

Perimeter = 54 inches

6. Calculate the perimeter of the polygon.

Perimeter = 17 feet

STUDENT PAGE

✧ *Math Journal 2,* p. 238

2 Ongoing Learning & Practice

✦ Finding the Perimeter of Figures (*Math Journal 2,* p. 238)

INDEPENDENT ACTIVITY 

Students measure figures to the nearest centimeter and nearest $\frac{1}{4}$ inch and calculate the perimeter of each. They draw rectangles of a given perimeter.

✦Math Boxes 8.2 (*Math Journal 2,* p. 235)

INDEPENDENT ACTIVITY 

Mixed Review Math Boxes in this lesson are paired with Math Boxes in Lesson 8.4. The skill in Problem 1 is a prerequisite for Unit 9.

✦Study Link 8.2 (*Math Masters,* p. 330)

Home Connection Students solve problems involving scale. They will need a ruler to complete the page.

3 Options for Individualizing

✦LANGUAGE DIVERSITY Building Background for Mathematics Words

SMALL-GROUP ACTIVITY  **5–15 min** 

Group a student learning English with a few proficient English speakers and have them think of as many ways of using the word *scale* as they can.

Examples

▷ The map *scale* shows that 1 inch represents 50 miles.

▷ Julie's doll house is a *scale* model of her actual house.

▷ Every morning, my dad weighs himself on the bathroom *scale*. Today he weighs 182 pounds.

▷ The adventurers decided to *scale* the mountain. They think it will take about 4 days to get to the top.

▷ The body of a fish is covered with *scales*. The body of a human is covered with skin.

▷ Chris *scaled* the fish and then placed it on the grill to cook it.

▷ The trumpet players warmed up for the concert by playing *scales*.

▷ The class did very poorly on the test, so the teacher decided to *scale* it.

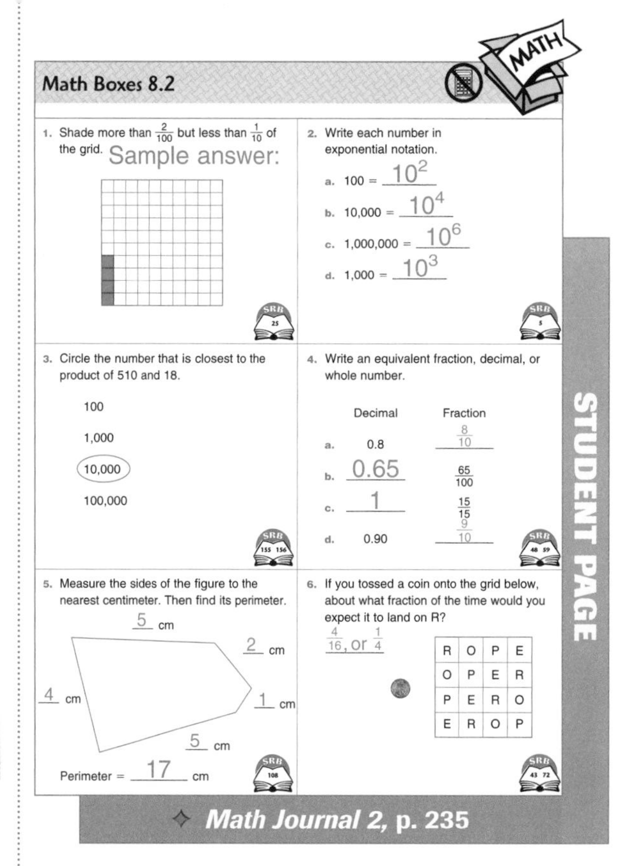

MATH
Math Boxes 8.2
1. Shade more than $\frac{2}{100}$ but less than $\frac{1}{10}$ of the grid. Sample answer:
2. Write each number in exponential notation.
a. 100 = 10^2
b. 10,000 = 10^4
c. 1,000,000 = 10^6
d. 1,000 = 10^3
3. Circle the number that is closest to the product of 510 and 18.
100
1,000
10,000
100,000
4. Write an equivalent fraction, decimal, or whole number.
Decimal
Fraction
a. 0.8 $\frac{8}{10}$
b. 0.65 $\frac{65}{100}$
c. 1 $\frac{15}{15}$
d. 0.90 $\frac{9}{10}$
5. Measure the sides of the figure to the nearest centimeter. Then find its perimeter.
5 cm
2 cm
4 cm
1 cm
5 cm
Perimeter = 17 cm
6. If you tossed a coin onto the grid below, about what fraction of the time would you expect it to land on R?
$\frac{4}{16}$, or $\frac{1}{4}$
R O P E
O P E R
P E R O
E R O P
STUDENT PAGE
Math Journal 2, p. 235

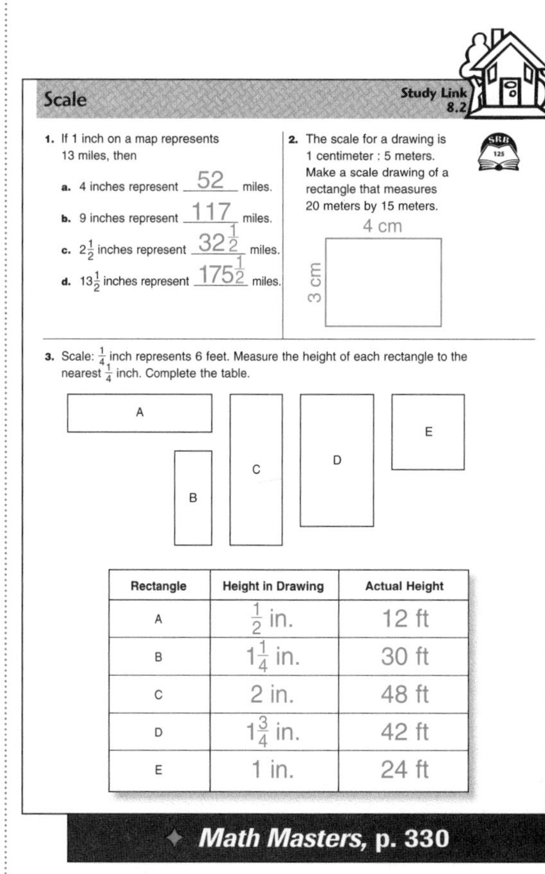

Rectangle	Height in Drawing	Actual Height
A	$\frac{1}{2}$ in.	12 ft
B	$1\frac{1}{4}$ in.	30 ft
C	2 in.	48 ft
D	$1\frac{3}{4}$ in.	42 ft
E	1 in.	24 ft

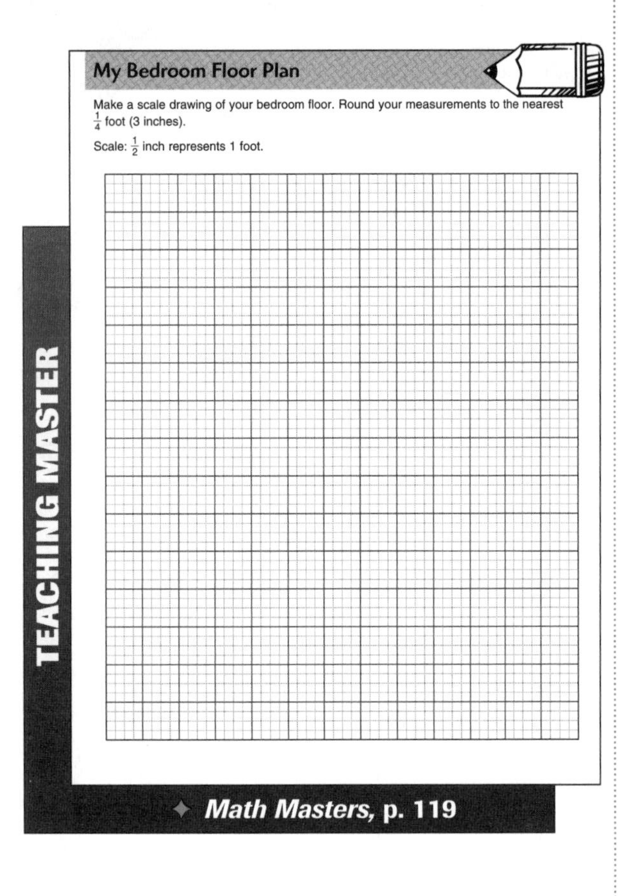
My Bedroom Floor Plan

Make a scale drawing of your bedroom floor. Round your measurements to the nearest $\frac{1}{4}$ foot (3 inches).

Scale: $\frac{1}{2}$ inch represents 1 foot.

TEACHING MASTER

Math Masters, p. 119

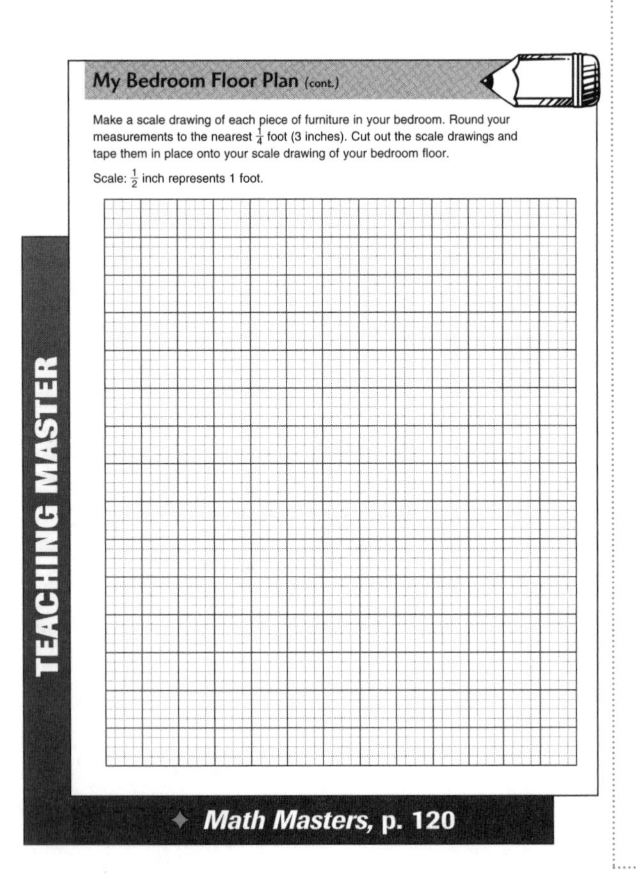
My Bedroom Floor Plan (cont.)

Make a scale drawing of each piece of furniture in your bedroom. Round your measurements to the nearest $\frac{1}{4}$ foot (3 inches). Cut out the scale drawings and tape them in place onto your scale drawing of your bedroom floor.

Scale: $\frac{1}{2}$ inch represents 1 foot.

TEACHING MASTER

Math Masters, p. 120

 ENRICHMENT Making a Scale Drawing of Your Bedroom (*Math Masters,* pp. 119 and 120)

INDEPENDENT ACTIVITY **30+ min**

Students make a scale drawing of their bedrooms on *Math Masters,* page 119. Then they make a scale drawing of the bird's-eye view of each piece of bedroom furniture on *Math Masters,* page 120. Students then cut out the drawings of the furniture and tape or paste them in place onto the scale drawings of their bedrooms.

Call students' attention to the scale to be used in the scale drawings: $\frac{1}{2}$ inch represents 1 foot. Since the sides of each larger square are divided into 4 equal parts, each part represents $\frac{1}{4}$ of a foot, or 3 inches.

Encourage students to think about ways to improve the layouts of their bedrooms.

▷ Would taking out or adding a piece of furniture make the room more comfortable?

▷ Would rearranging the furniture help?

▷ Can students think of ways to make better use of outside light? Of indoor light?

Students can experiment with various furniture arrangements on their scale drawings.

8.3 Area

OBJECTIVES **To review basic area concepts; to estimate the area of a polygon by counting unit squares; and to use a scale drawing to find area.**

summaries	materials
1 Teaching the Lesson	
Students review the meaning of area as a measure of a surface in square units and estimate polygon areas in square centimeters by counting unit squares. They use the scale drawing made in Lesson 8.2 to find the area of the classroom floor. [Measurement and Reference Frames]	☐ *Math Journal 2,* pp. 237 and 239 ☐ *Student Reference Book,* p. 113 ☐ Study Link 8.2 ***See* Advance Preparation**
2 Ongoing Learning & Practice	
Students solve probability problems. [Data and Chance] Students practice and maintain skills through Math Boxes and Study Link activities.	☐ *Math Journal 2,* pp. 240 and 241 ☐ Study Link Master (*Math Masters,* p. 331) ☐ scissors and transparent tape ☐ Geometry Template
3 Options for Individualizing	
Extra Practice Students compare areas of 1-yard and 1-meter squares. [Measurement and Reference Frames] **Reteaching** Students form polygons on their geoboards. They count squares and partial squares to find the areas of the polygons. [Geometry; Measurement and Reference Frames]	☐ masking tape ☐ geoboard and rubber bands ***See* Advance Preparation**

Additional Information

Advance Preparation For Part 1, display unit squares on a wall or bulletin board (see Planning Ahead on page 600 in Lesson 8.1). Put them in order of increasing size, with the metric unit squares in one row and the U.S. customary unit squares in another row.

For the optional Extra Practice activity in Part 3, outline two squares with masking tape on the floor: a 1-yard square and a 1-meter square.

Vocabulary • **area** • **square units**

Getting Started

Mental Math and Reflexes

Pose problems about perimeters of regular polygons. *Suggestions:*

- If a side of a regular octagon is 7 units long, what is the perimeter of the octagon? 56 units
- If the perimeter of a regular hexagon is 54 units, what is the length of one side? 9 units

Math Message

Read page 113 of your Student Reference Book. *Be ready to describe a situation in which you would need to know the area of a surface.*

Study Link 8.2 Follow-Up

Review answers.

1 Teaching the Lesson

✦ Math Message Follow-Up (*Student Reference Book,* p. 113)

WHOLE-CLASS DISCUSSION 

Use page 113 of the *Student Reference Book* to review basic area concepts. As part of the discussion, remind the class that **area** is a measure of the surface inside a shape. Area is commonly measured in **square units.**

▷ The area of a surface is the number of unit squares and fractions of unit squares needed to cover the surface, without overlaps and without gaps.

Call students' attention to the classroom display of unit squares and to alternative ways of writing the units: *square inch* or *in.*^{2}, *square meter* or *m*^{2}, and so on.

✦ Estimating Areas of Polygons by Counting Squares (*Math Journal 2,* p. 239)

PARTNER ACTIVITY 

Partners work on the problems while you circulate and assist where needed. For Problems 2–4, students should count whole squares and half squares to find the total area of each polygon. In Problems 5–7, a good strategy is to count whole squares first and then combine partial squares to form whole squares.

Point out that it is possible to estimate the areas of figures that do not have square corners. The unit squares need not fit neatly inside the figure. (In Lesson 8.4, students will estimate the areas of figures whose boundaries are not made of line segments.)

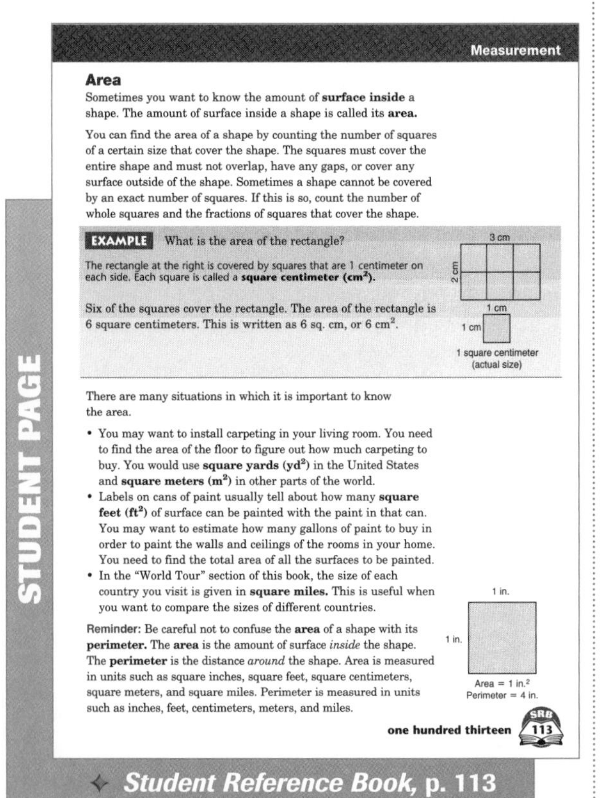

STUDENT PAGE

Measurement

Area

Sometimes you want to know the amount of **surface inside** a shape. The amount of surface inside a shape is called its **area.**

You can find the area of a shape by counting the number of squares of a certain size that cover the shape. The squares must cover the entire shape and must not overlap, have any gaps, or cover any surface outside of the shape. Sometimes a shape cannot be covered by an exact number of squares. If this is so, count the number of whole squares and the fractions of squares that cover the shape.

EXAMPLE What is the area of the rectangle?

The rectangle at the right is covered by squares that are 1 centimeter on each side. Each square is called a **square centimeter (cm^2).**

Six of the squares cover the rectangle. The area of the rectangle is 6 square centimeters. This is written as 6 sq. cm, or 6 cm^2.

1 square centimeter (actual size)

There are many situations in which it is important to know the area.

- You may want to install carpeting in your living room. You need to find the area of the floor to figure out how much carpeting to buy. You would use **square yards (yd^2)** in the United States and **square meters (m^2)** in other parts of the world.
- Labels on cans of paint usually tell about how many **square feet (ft^2)** of surface can be painted with the paint in that can. You may want to estimate how many gallons of paint to buy in order to paint the walls and ceilings of the rooms in your home. You need to find the total area of all the surfaces to be painted.
- In the "World Tour" section of this book, the size of each country you visit is given in **square miles.** This is useful when you want to compare the sizes of different countries.

Reminder: Be careful not to confuse the **area** of a shape with its **perimeter.** The **area** is the amount of surface *inside* the shape. The **perimeter** is the distance *around* the shape. Area is measured in units such as square inches, square feet, square centimeters, square meters, and square miles. Perimeter is measured in units such as inches, feet, centimeters, meters, and miles.

one hundred thirteen SRB 113

✦ *Student Reference Book,* p. 113

✦ Estimating the Area of the Classroom Floor (*Math Journal 2,* p. 237)

PARTNER ACTIVITY 

Have students turn to their scale drawings of the classroom on journal page 237. Make sure they understand that each grid square in their scale drawing represents 1 square foot of classroom floor.

Students work in pairs to find the area of the classroom from their scale drawings. Have students record the area at the bottom of the page. Circulate and assist as needed.

ONGOING ASSESSMENT

After a few minutes, bring the class together to share results and solution strategies. From the discussion, you can assess what students remember about finding the area of a rectangle. Did they simply count the squares in their scale drawing? Or did they use a more efficient method, such as counting the number of squares in one row, counting the number of rows, and then multiplying the number of rows by the number of squares in each row?

Adjusting the Activity Draw a grid on the board like the one shown in the margin. Challenge students to think of a way to estimate the area of the classroom floor in square yards. Possible strategies: (1) Since there are 3 feet in 1 yard, divide the scale drawing into larger 3 by 3 squares. Each 3 by 3 square represents 1 square yard. Count these larger squares and parts of squares. (2) Since 1 square yard = 9 square feet, find how many 9-square-foot units there are in the total area; that is, convert square feet to square yards by dividing the number of square feet by 9.

2 Ongoing Learning & Practice

✦ Solving Probability Problems (*Math Journal 2,* p. 240)

INDEPENDENT ACTIVITY 

Students solve problems involving spinners, dice, and coins.

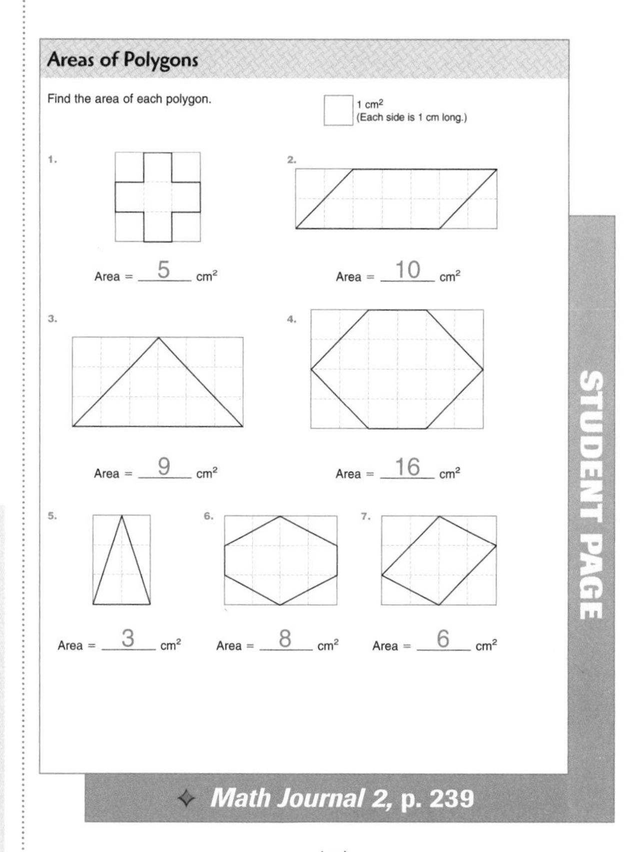

Areas of Polygons

Find the area of each polygon.

1 cm² (Each side is 1 cm long.)

1. Area = 5 cm²
2. Area = 10 cm²
3. Area = 9 cm²
4. Area = 16 cm²
5. Area = 3 cm²
6. Area = 8 cm²
7. Area = 6 cm²

STUDENT PAGE

✦ *Math Journal 2,* p. 239

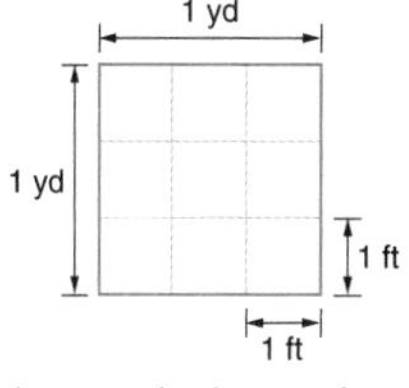

1 square yard = 9 square feet
$1\ yd^2 = 9\ ft^2$

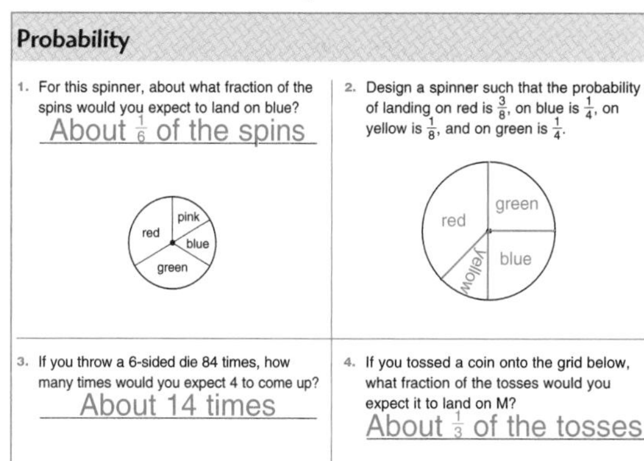

Probability

1. For this spinner, about what fraction of the spins would you expect to land on blue? About $\frac{1}{6}$ of the spins

2. Design a spinner such that the probability of landing on red is $\frac{3}{8}$, on blue is $\frac{1}{4}$, on yellow is $\frac{1}{8}$, and on green is $\frac{1}{4}$.

3. If you throw a 6-sided die 84 times, how many times would you expect 4 to come up? About 14 times

4. If you tossed a coin onto the grid below, what fraction of the tosses would you expect it to land on M? About $\frac{1}{3}$ of the tosses

M	A	P
P	M	A
A	P	M

5. If you throw a 6-sided die 96 times, how many times would you expect it to land on an odd number less than 5? About 32 times

6. You flip a coin 9 times, and each time the coin lands on heads. If you flip the same coin one more time, is it more likely to come up heads than tails or just as likely to come up heads as tails? Explain. Sample answer: For each toss, a coin has the same chance of coming up heads as coming up tails.

STUDENT PAGE

✦ *Math Journal 2,* p. 240

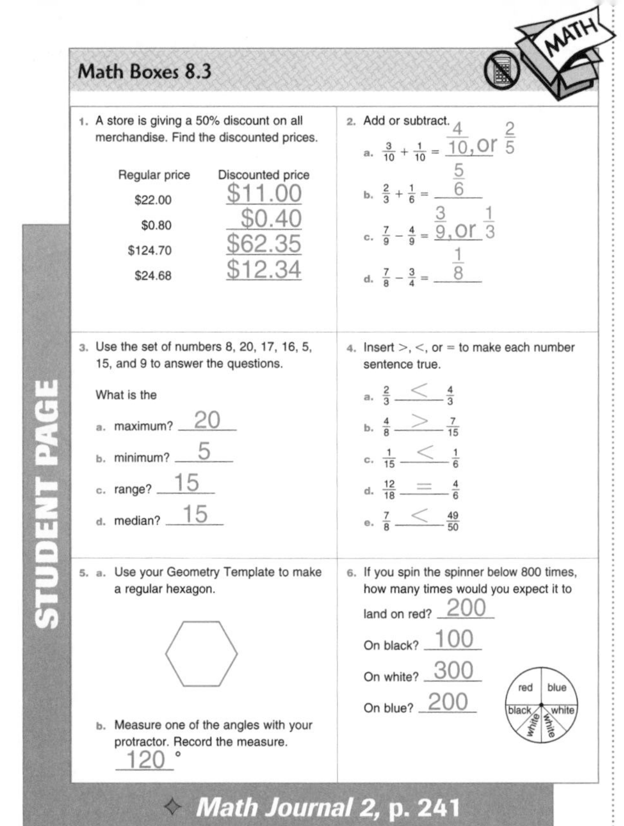
Math Boxes 8.3

1. A store is giving a 50% discount on all merchandise. Find the discounted prices.

Regular price	Discounted price
$22.00	$11.00
$0.80	$0.40
$124.70	$62.35
$24.68	$12.34

2. Add or subtract.
a. $\frac{3}{10} + \frac{1}{10} =$ $\frac{4}{10}$, or $\frac{2}{5}$
b. $\frac{2}{3} + \frac{1}{6} =$ $\frac{5}{6}$
c. $\frac{7}{9} - \frac{4}{9} =$ $\frac{3}{9}$, or $\frac{1}{3}$
d. $\frac{7}{8} - \frac{3}{4} =$ $\frac{1}{8}$

3. Use the set of numbers 8, 20, 17, 16, 5, 15, and 9 to answer the questions.
What is the
a. maximum? 20
b. minimum? 5
c. range? 15
d. median? 15

4. Insert >, <, or = to make each number sentence true.
a. $\frac{2}{3}$ < $\frac{4}{3}$
b. $\frac{4}{8}$ > $\frac{7}{15}$
c. $\frac{1}{15}$ < $\frac{1}{6}$
d. $\frac{12}{18}$ = $\frac{4}{6}$
e. $\frac{7}{8}$ < $\frac{49}{50}$

5. a. Use your Geometry Template to make a regular hexagon.
b. Measure one of the angles with your protractor. Record the measure. 120 °

6. If you spin the spinner below 800 times, how many times would you expect it to land on red? 200
On black? 100
On white? 300
On blue? 200

STUDENT PAGE

Math Journal 2, p. 241

Math Boxes 8.3 (*Math Journal 2,* p. 241)

INDEPENDENT ACTIVITY 

Mixed Review Math Boxes in this lesson are paired with Math Boxes in Lesson 8.1. The skill in Problem 1 is a prerequisite for Unit 9.

Study Link 8.3 (*Math Masters,* p. 331)

Home Connection Students cut a rectangle into pieces and then rearrange the pieces to make a new shape. They compare the area of the rectangle with the area of the new shape.

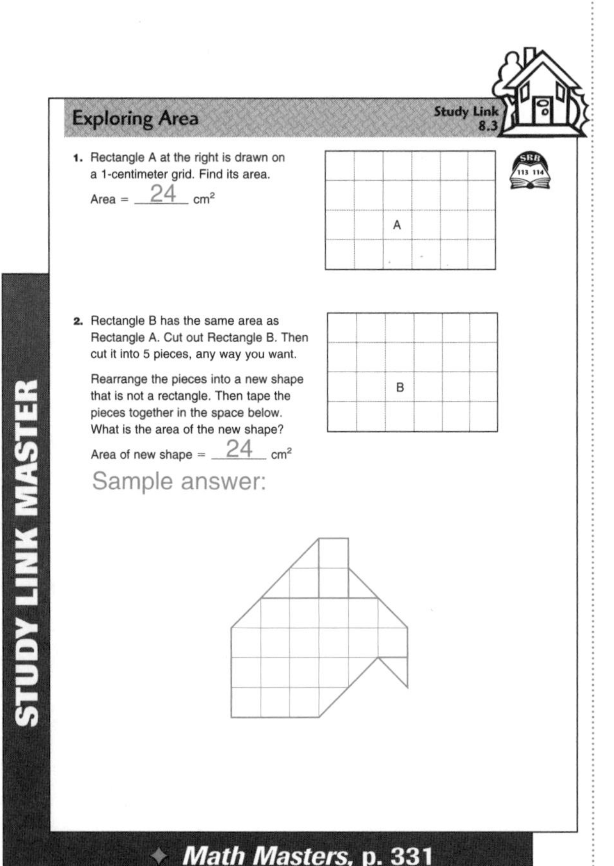
Exploring Area — Study Link 8.3

1. Rectangle A at the right is drawn on a 1-centimeter grid. Find its area.
Area = 24 cm²

2. Rectangle B has the same area as Rectangle A. Cut out Rectangle B. Then cut it into 5 pieces, any way you want.
Rearrange the pieces into a new shape that is not a rectangle. Then tape the pieces together in the space below. What is the area of the new shape?
Area of new shape = 24 cm²
Sample answer:

STUDY LINK MASTER

Math Masters, p. 331

3 Options for Individualizing

EXTRA PRACTICE Comparing Unit Squares

WHOLE-CLASS ACTIVITY  5–15 min 

Help students to visualize a square yard and a square meter. Use the 1-yard and 1-meter unit squares on the floor (see Advance Preparation). Have as many students as possible stand inside the 1-yard square, packed tightly together. Be sure that no one is uncomfortable. Count the number of students standing in the square.

Repeat the activity using the 1-meter square. (Expect to pack 2 or 3 more students within the square-meter area. A square meter is nearly 20% larger than a square yard.)

RETEACHING Investigating Geoboard Areas

PARTNER ACTIVITY  15–30 min

Tell students that the smallest square that can be formed on a geoboard has an area of one square unit.

Students use rubber bands to form polygons on their geoboards. They count squares and partial squares to find the areas of the polygons. Then they each form a polygon, find its area, and switch geoboards with their partner. They find the area of their partner's polygon and compare answers.

8.4 What Is the Area of My Skin?

OBJECTIVES **To estimate the area of a surface having a curved boundary; and to convert measurements from one unit to another.**

summaries	materials
1 Teaching the Lesson	
Students estimate the area of the front of their hand by tracing it on a 1-inch grid and counting squares. Then they use a rule of thumb to estimate their total skin area. Students convert measurements from square inches to square feet, and from square feet to square yards. [Measurement and Reference Frames]	□ *Math Journal 2,* pp. 242 and 243 □ Study Link 8.3 □ Teaching Master (*Math Masters,* p. 121) □ calculator □ scissors and transparent tape ***See*** **Advance Preparation**
2 Ongoing Learning & Practice	
Students resume the World Tour in South America. [multiple strands] Students practice and maintain skills through Math Boxes and Study Link activities.	□ *Math Journal 2,* p. 244; pp. 345–347 (optional) □ *Student Reference Book* □ Teaching Masters (*Math Masters,* pp. 36–38; optional) □ Study Link Master (*Math Masters,* p. 332)
3 Options for Individualizing	
Reteaching Students model the conversion of square inches to square feet. [Measurement and Reference Frames] **Extra Practice** Students place objects on a grid, trace their outline boundaries, and count grid squares to estimate their areas. [Measurement and Reference Frames]	□ *Math Journal 2,* p. 242 □ Teaching Master (*Math Masters,* p. 121) □ objects with flat, irregular surfaces □ calculator □ transparent or masking tape ***See*** **Advance Preparation**

Additional Information

Advance Preparation For Part 1, make 3 copies of *Math Masters,* page 121 (1-inch grid), for each student. Place copies near the Math Message.

For the optional Extra Practice activity in Part 3, students will need an additional copy of *Math Masters,* page 121 and objects with flat, irregular surfaces, such as eyeglasses, leaves, staplers, and tape dispensers.

Getting Started

Mental Math and Reflexes

Write mixed numbers on the board. Students enter these numbers into their calculators and read the display. Emphasize recognition that $\frac{1}{2} = 0.5$, $\frac{1}{4} = 0.25$, and $\frac{3}{4} = 0.75$. This skill is necessary for Lesson 8.5. *Suggestions:*

- $5\frac{3}{10}$ 5.3
- $1\frac{29}{100}$ 1.29
- $2\frac{1}{2}$ 2.5
- $3\frac{3}{4}$ 3.75
- $8\frac{1}{4}$ 8.25
- $10\frac{1}{2}$ 10.5

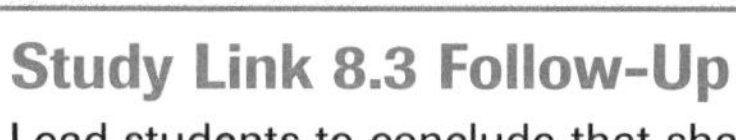

Math Message

Take 3 sheets of grid paper. Cut and tape the grids to make a square that measures 1 foot (12 inches) on each side. How many square inches are there in 1 square foot?

Study Link 8.3 Follow-Up

Lead students to conclude that shapes that look different can have the same area.

1 Teaching the Lesson

✦ Math Message Follow-Up
(*Math Journal 2,* p. 242)

WHOLE-CLASS DISCUSSION 

Each student should have made a square consisting of 12 rows with 12 one-inch squares in each row.

▷ Since $12 * 12 = 144$, there are 144 square inches in 1 square foot.

Students record this equivalency in Problem 1 on journal page 242. Have students keep their square feet to use in the following activity.

✦ Estimating the Area of Your Skin
(*Math Journal 2,* pp. 242 and 243)

PARTNER ACTIVITY

Divide the class into partnerships. Ask students to guess the total area of their skin in square feet and record it in Problem 2 on journal page 242. Have them refer to the 1-foot square they made to help them with their guess.

Tell them to use the following rule of thumb to check their guess:

Rule of Thumb: The area of your skin is about 100 times the area of the outline of your hand.

Then have partners follow these steps:

1. Trace the outline of your partner's hand on the grid on journal page 243.
2. Estimate the area of your own hand by counting grid squares (square inches) inside the tracing of your hand.
3. Use the rule of thumb to estimate the area of your skin (area of skin = 100 * area of hand).

Students record the results in Problems 3 and 4.

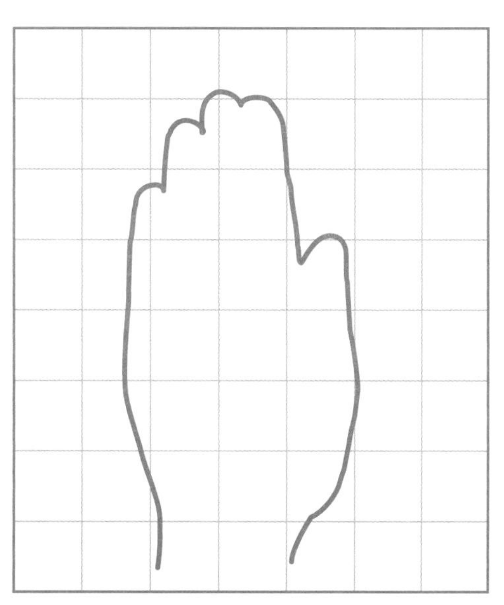

A student's fingers should be *closed* when his or her partner traces the hand outline on journal page 243.

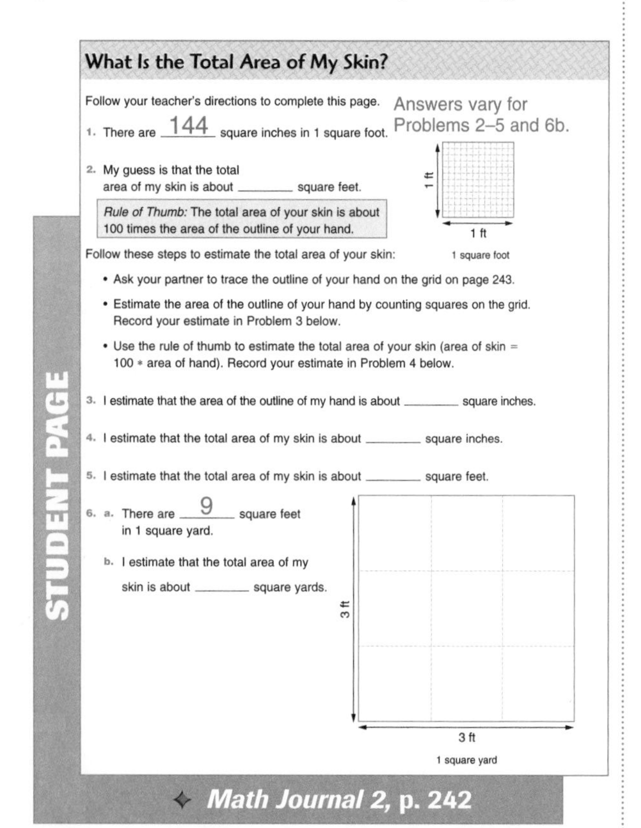

STUDENT PAGE

What Is the Total Area of My Skin?

Follow your teacher's directions to complete this page. Answers vary for Problems 2–5 and 6b.

1. There are 144 square inches in 1 square foot.
2. My guess is that the total area of my skin is about ______ square feet.

Rule of Thumb: The total area of your skin is about 100 times the area of the outline of your hand.

Follow these steps to estimate the total area of your skin:

- Ask your partner to trace the outline of your hand on the grid on page 243.
- Estimate the area of the outline of your hand by counting squares on the grid. Record your estimate in Problem 3 below.
- Use the rule of thumb to estimate the total area of your skin (area of skin = 100 * area of hand). Record your estimate in Problem 4 below.

3. I estimate that the area of the outline of my hand is about ______ square inches.
4. I estimate that the total area of my skin is about ______ square inches.
5. I estimate that the total area of my skin is about ______ square feet.
6. a. There are 9 square feet in 1 square yard.
   b. I estimate that the total area of my skin is about ______ square yards.

✦ Math Journal 2, p. 242

Sharing the Results of the Experiment
(*Math Journal 2,* pp. 242 and 243)

WHOLE-CLASS DISCUSSION

Bring the class together and ask students to describe how they estimated the area of a hand tracing. A good strategy is to count whole squares first and then combine partial squares to approximate whole squares.

Review the information students have obtained so far.

- In Problem 2, they *guessed* the total area of their skin *in square feet.*
- In Problem 4, they *estimated* the total area of their skin *in square inches.*

Ask students to check how close the guesses they made in Problem 2 are to their estimates in Problem 4.

- The guess and the estimate cannot be immediately compared, because the guess is in square feet, and the estimate is in square inches.
- Help students to convert their estimates in square inches to square feet. Have them record their square-foot estimates in Problem 5.

For example: Guess is 15 square feet. Estimate is 1,512 square inches. Convert 1,512 square inches to square feet. Use the fact that 144 square inches equal 1 square foot. You want to know how many 144s there are in 1,512. Use a calculator to divide 1,512 by 144. Since $1{,}512 \div 144 = 10.5$, 1,512 square inches equals 10.5 square feet.

Now ask students to convert their estimates to an approximate number of square yards (probably between 1 and 2) and record it in Problem 6. To convert to square yards, students divide the number of square feet by 9.

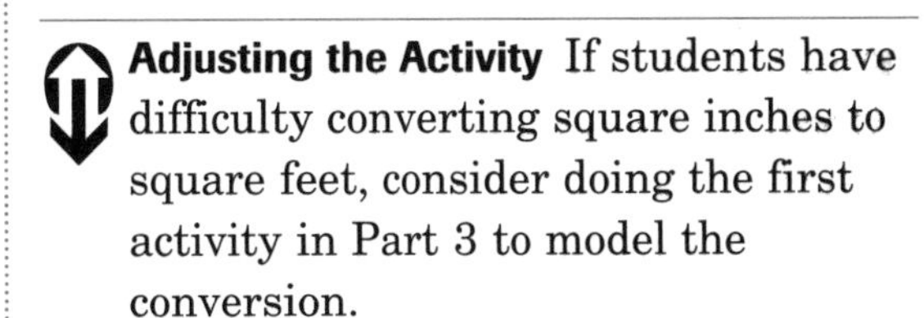

NOTE: You may want to discuss the difference between a guess and an estimate—an estimate is more systematic and usually more accurate than a guess.

Adjusting the Activity If students have difficulty converting square inches to square feet, consider doing the first activity in Part 3 to model the conversion.

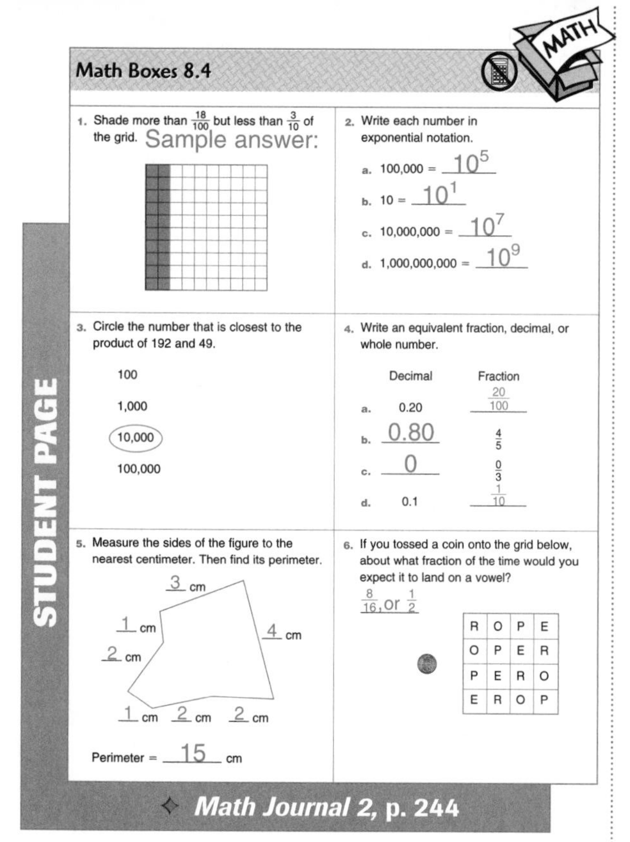

Math Boxes 8.4

1. Shade more than $\frac{18}{100}$ but less than $\frac{3}{10}$ of the grid. Sample answer:

2. Write each number in exponential notation.
   a. 100,000 = 10^5
   b. 10 = 10^1
   c. 10,000,000 = 10^7
   d. 1,000,000,000 = 10^9

3. Circle the number that is closest to the product of 192 and 49.
   100
   1,000
   (10,000)
   100,000

4. Write an equivalent fraction, decimal, or whole number.

	Decimal	Fraction
a.	0.20	$\frac{20}{100}$
b.	0.80	$\frac{4}{5}$
c.	0	$\frac{0}{3}$
d.	0.1	$\frac{1}{10}$

5. Measure the sides of the figure to the nearest centimeter. Then find its perimeter.
   3 cm, 4 cm, 1 cm, 2 cm, 1 cm, 2 cm, 2 cm
   Perimeter = 15 cm

6. If you tossed a coin onto the grid below, about what fraction of the time would you expect it to land on a vowel?
   $\frac{8}{16}$, or $\frac{1}{2}$

R	O	P	E
O	P	E	R
P	E	R	O
E	R	O	P

STUDENT PAGE

Math Journal 2, p. 244

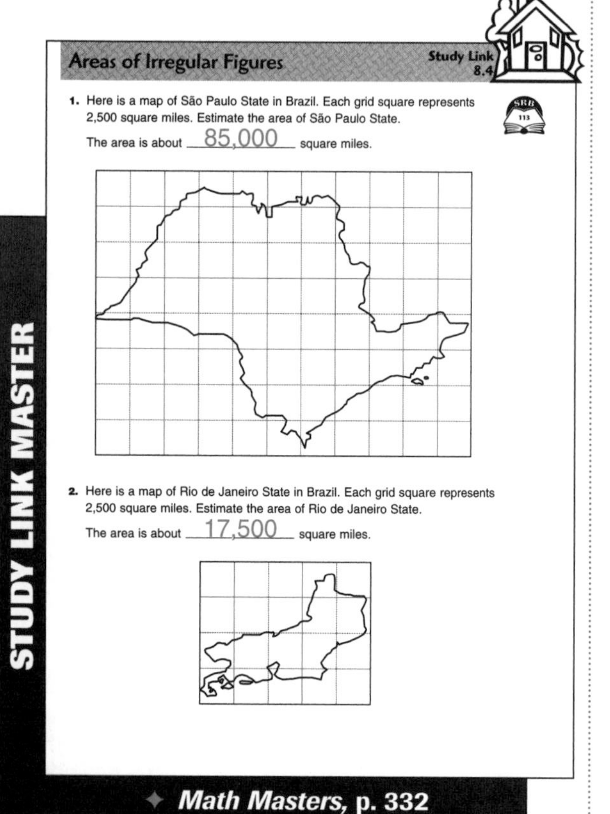

Areas of Irregular Figures Study Link 8.4

1. Here is a map of São Paulo State in Brazil. Each grid square represents 2,500 square miles. Estimate the area of São Paulo State.
   The area is about 85,000 square miles.

2. Here is a map of Rio de Janeiro State in Brazil. Each grid square represents 2,500 square miles. Estimate the area of Rio de Janeiro State.
   The area is about 17,500 square miles.

STUDY LINK MASTER

Math Masters, p. 332

2 Ongoing Learning & Practice

✦ World Tour Option: Visiting South America (*Math Journal 2*, pp. 345–347; *Student Reference Book; Math Masters*, pp. 36–38)

SMALL-GROUP ACTIVITY

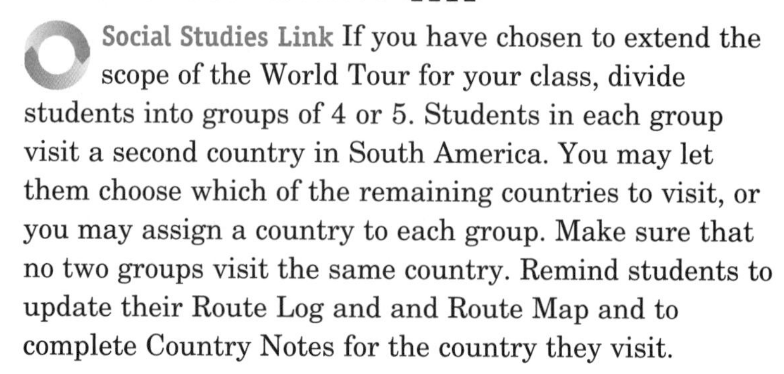

Social Studies Link If you have chosen to extend the scope of the World Tour for your class, divide students into groups of 4 or 5. Students in each group visit a second country in South America. You may let them choose which of the remaining countries to visit, or you may assign a country to each group. Make sure that no two groups visit the same country. Remind students to update their Route Log and and Route Map and to complete Country Notes for the country they visit.

Adjusting the Activity Have students determine the latitude and longitude of the capital city of the country they choose to visit. Encourage them to estimate to the nearest degree. Allow a 5° variance, but expect that most answers will not be off by more than a degree or two.

✦ Math Boxes 8.4 (*Math Journal 2*, p. 244)

INDEPENDENT ACTIVITY 

Mixed Review Math Boxes in this lesson are paired with Math Boxes in Lesson 8.2. The skill in Problem 1 is a prerequisite for Unit 9.

✦ Study Link 8.4 (*Math Masters*, p. 332)

Home Connection Students estimate the area of São Paulo State and Rio de Janeiro State in Brazil.

Options for Individualizing

✦ RETEACHING Converting Square Inches to Square Feet (*Math Journal 2,* p. 242)

WHOLE-CLASS ACTIVITY  **15–30 min** 

If students had difficulty converting square inches to square feet, try the following demonstration to model the conversion:

1. Find out which student in the group has the smallest estimated skin area (in square inches) and write it on the board. Assign a student with a calculator to be the "tabulator." The tabulator clears the calculator, so that the display shows 0.
2. Ask other students to come to the board, one at a time, with the 1-foot squares they made and tape them onto the board. For each square taped on the board, the tabulator adds 144 to the number in the calculator display and announces the total. Have students tape the first nine 1-foot squares into three rows with three squares in each row. Stop after the first nine squares to call students' attention to the fact that 9 square feet are equivalent to 1 square yard (*see margin*).
3. Students continue taping 1-foot squares next to the squares on the board until the tabulator's total is equal to or greater than the estimated area written on the board. Discuss how to use the taped squares on the board to find the approximate area in square feet. For example, 1,500 square inches is between 10 square feet ($10 * 144 = 1{,}440$) and 11 square feet ($11 * 144 = 1{,}584$).
4. Continue this process so that the other students can make estimates of their skin area in square feet. Have them record their estimates in Problem 5 on journal page 242.

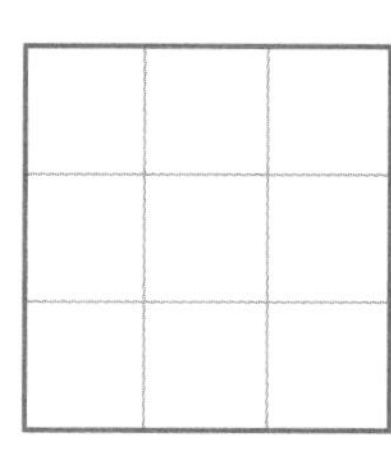

$9\ ft^2 = 1\ yd^2$

✦ EXTRA PRACTICE Estimating Areas of Irregular Regions (*Math Masters,* p. 121)

INDEPENDENT ACTIVITY  **5–15 min** 

Students place various objects that have flat, irregular surfaces on a grid and trace their outline boundaries. Then they count grid squares to estimate the areas.

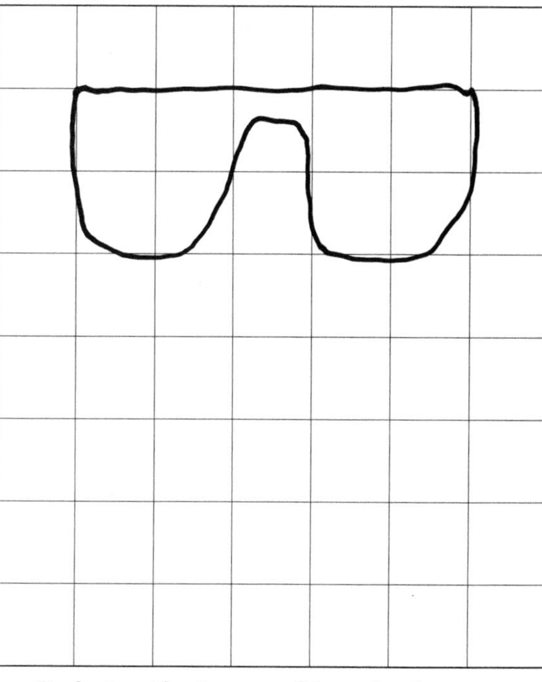

Students estimate areas of irregular shapes on *Math Masters,* page 121.

8.5 Formula for the Area of a Rectangle

OBJECTIVE **To develop and use a formula for the area of a rectangle.**

summaries	materials
1 Teaching the Lesson	
Students count squares to find the areas of rectangles and then develop a formula for the area of a rectangle. They use the formula to find the area of rectangles in which the length and/or width is not a whole number of units. [Geometry; Measurement and Reference Frames]	□ *Math Journal 2,* pp. 246 and 247 □ Study Link 8.4 □ calculator ***See* Advance Preparation**
2 Ongoing Learning & Practice	
Students draw rectangles according to a given scale. [Measurement and Reference Frames] Students practice and maintain skills through Math Boxes and Study Link activities.	□ *Math Journal 2,* pp. 245 and 248 □ Study Link Master (*Math Masters,* p. 333) □ ruler
3 Options for Individualizing	
Extra Practice Students roll a die to determine the dimensions of a rectangle. They build the rectangle with cubes, with pattern blocks, or on a geoboard, and then give the area of the rectangle. [Measurement and Reference Frames]	□ Per partnership: 1 six-sided die 36 cm cubes, 36 square pattern blocks, or a 7 by 7 geoboard and rubber bands

Additional Information

Advance Preparation For Part 1, draw the following table on the board:

Rectangle	Length of base	Width (height)	Area
A			
B			
C			

Vocabulary • **base** • **width** • **length** • **height** • **area** • **formula** • **variable**

Getting Started

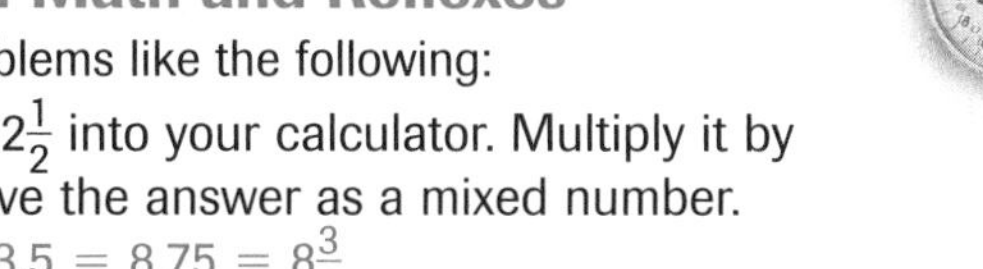

Mental Math and Reflexes

Pose problems like the following:

- Enter $2\frac{1}{2}$ into your calculator. Multiply it by $3\frac{1}{2}$. Give the answer as a mixed number.
  $2.5 * 3.5 = 8.75 = 8\frac{3}{4}$
- Enter $4\frac{1}{2}$ into your calculator. Multiply it by $4\frac{1}{2}$. Give the answer as a mixed number.
  $4.5 * 4.5 = 20.25 = 20\frac{1}{4}$

Math Message

Complete Problem 1 on journal page 246.

Study Link 8.4 Follow-Up

Students share estimation strategies. One approach is to combine areas of partial squares.

1 Teaching the Lesson

✦ Math Message Follow-Up
(*Math Journal 2,* p. 246)

WHOLE-CLASS DISCUSSION

Most students will simply count the number of squares in Rectangles A and B. For Rectangle C, some students may count the number of squares in one row 5, count the number of rows 6, and multiply. $6 * 5 = 30$, so the area equals 30 cm^2. Praise this approach, and use it to lead into the following activity.

✦ Developing a Formula for the Area of a Rectangle (*Math Journal 2,* p. 246)

WHOLE-CLASS ACTIVITY

Remind students how to write a number model for the area of Rectangle A: There are 2 rows with 4 squares in each row, for a total of 8 squares. Two rows of 4 squares each is equivalent to $2 * 4 = 8$ squares. Have students record this information in the table in Problem 2 on journal page 246. They can complete the table for Rectangles B and C on their own.

Rectangle	Number of squares per row	Number of rows	Total number of squares	Number model
A	4	2	8	$2 * 4 = 8$
B				
C				

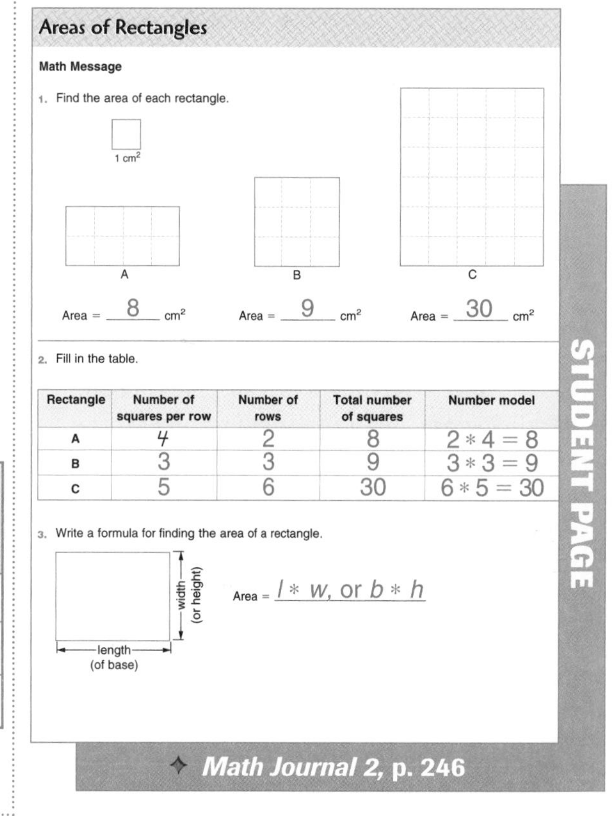

Areas of Rectangles

Math Message

1. Find the area of each rectangle.

1 cm^2

A: Area = 8 cm^2 B: Area = 9 cm^2 C: Area = 30 cm^2

2. Fill in the table.

Rectangle	Number of squares per row	Number of rows	Total number of squares	Number model
A	4	2	8	$2 * 4 = 8$
B	3	3	9	$3 * 3 = 9$
C	5	6	30	$6 * 5 = 30$

3. Write a formula for finding the area of a rectangle.

Area = $l * w$, or $b * h$

STUDENT PAGE

✦ *Math Journal 2,* p. 246

Draw a rectangle on the board. Choose one of the sides (for example, the side on which the rectangle "sits") and call it the **base.** (Any side could be designated as the base.) Explain that the shortest distance between the base and the side opposite the base is called the **width** of the rectangle. In a rectangle, the width is the length of a side adjacent to the base.

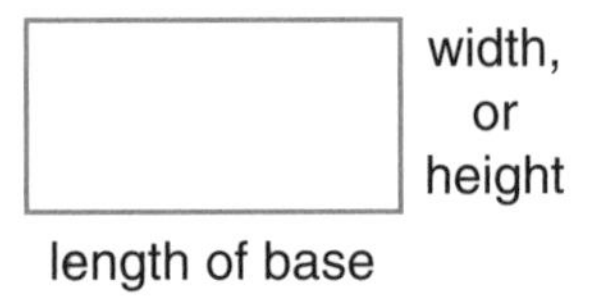

The *length of the base* of a rectangle is often simply called the **length,** and the width is also called the **height.**

If you have not already copied the following table onto the board, do that now. Ask students to help you fill it out.

Rectangle	Length of base	Width (height)	Area
A	4 cm	2 cm	8 cm^2
B	3 cm	3 cm	9 cm^2
C	5 cm	6 cm	30 cm^2

Summary: If the length of the base and the width of a rectangle are known, the area can be found by multiplying:

Area of a rectangle = length of the base * width of the rectangle

Such a rule is called a **formula.** It can be abbreviated as

$$A = l * w$$

In the formula, the letter A stands for *area of a rectangle,* the letter l for *length of the base,* and the letter w for *width of the rectangle.*

An alternative formula for the area of a rectangle is

$$A = b * h$$

Here the letter b stands for *length of the base* and the letter h for the *height of the rectangle.*

Have students record a formula for the area of a rectangle in Problem 3 on journal page 246. Remind the class that the letters in a formula are called **variables.** They can take on any value; that is, their values may *vary.*

NOTE: Since a rectangle is a special kind of parallelogram, and the usual formula for the area of a parallelogram is $A = b * h$, the authors will usually use this form of the formula for the area of a rectangle. However, in certain contexts, the formula $A = l * w$ is preferable.

Although the word *base* refers to a side of a parallelogram, it is also often used to mean the length of that side.

✦ Using a Formula to Find the Area of Rectangles (*Math Journal 2*, p. 247)

PARTNER ACTIVITY 

In this set of problems, students find the area of rectangles in which the length of the base and/or the height is not a whole number.

Ask partners to count squares to find the area of the rectangles in Problem 4 on journal page 247 and to record the results in the first column in the table.

Bring the class together to share results. Students should note that all rectangles except D contain half-squares, and that Rectangles G and I contain quarter-squares. Make sure that students understand how to count the partial squares. *For example:*

- ▷ Rectangle E—4 half-squares are the same as 2 squares.
- ▷ Rectangle F—6 half-squares are the same as 3 squares.
- ▷ Rectangle G—2 half-squares are the same as 1 square, and 4 quarter-squares are the same as 1 square.
- ▷ Rectangle H—5 half-squares are the same as $2\frac{1}{2}$ squares.
- ▷ Rectangle I—8 half-squares are the same as 4 squares; Rectangle I also has a quarter-square.

Next, have students record the length of the base and the height of each rectangle. Then have them find the area by using a calculator to multiply the base times the height. Remind students that when using a calculator, they need to rename $\frac{1}{2}$ as 0.5. For example, the height of Rectangle E is $2\frac{1}{2}$ centimeters, which is entered in the calculator as 2.5. The calculator display for the area of Rectangle I is 20.25. This is equivalent to $20\frac{1}{4}$ square centimeters.

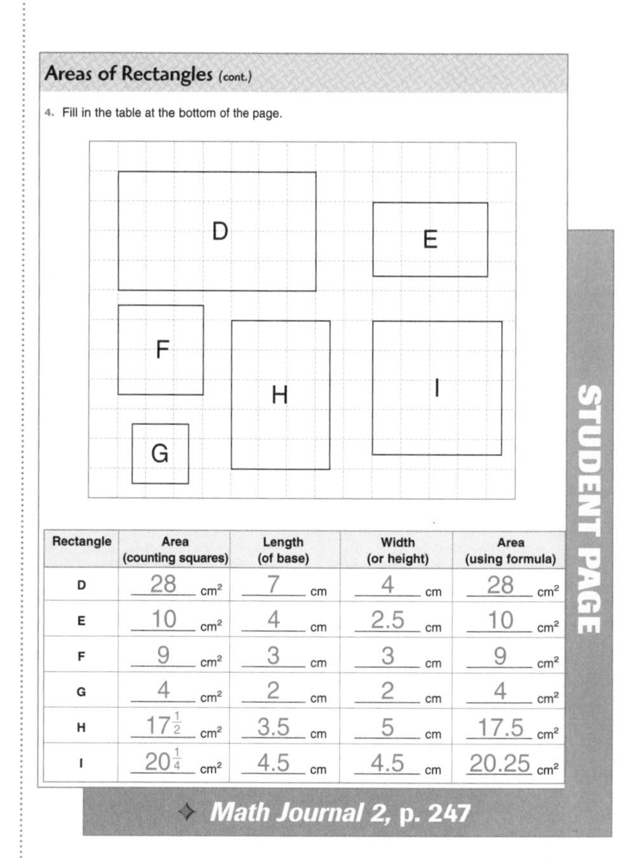

Areas of Rectangles (cont.)

4. Fill in the table at the bottom of the page.

Rectangle	Area (counting squares)	Length (of base)	Width (or height)	Area (using formula)
D	28 cm²	7 cm	4 cm	28 cm²
E	10 cm²	4 cm	2.5 cm	10 cm²
F	9 cm²	3 cm	3 cm	9 cm²
G	4 cm²	2 cm	2 cm	4 cm²
H	$17\frac{1}{2}$ cm²	3.5 cm	5 cm	17.5 cm²
I	$20\frac{1}{4}$ cm²	4.5 cm	4.5 cm	20.25 cm²

STUDENT PAGE

✦ *Math Journal 2*, p. 247

2 Ongoing Learning & Practice

✦ Drawing to Scale (*Math Journal 2*, p. 248)

INDEPENDENT ACTIVITY 

Students draw rectangles according to given scales.

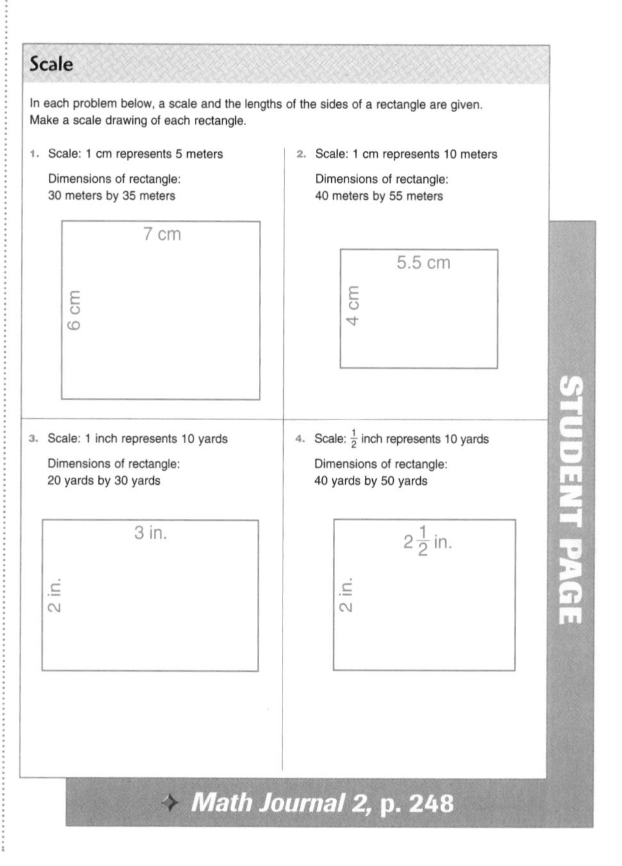

Scale

In each problem below, a scale and the lengths of the sides of a rectangle are given. Make a scale drawing of each rectangle.

1. Scale: 1 cm represents 5 meters
   Dimensions of rectangle:
   30 meters by 35 meters

2. Scale: 1 cm represents 10 meters
   Dimensions of rectangle:
   40 meters by 55 meters

3. Scale: 1 inch represents 10 yards
   Dimensions of rectangle:
   20 yards by 30 yards

4. Scale: $\frac{1}{2}$ inch represents 10 yards
   Dimensions of rectangle:
   40 yards by 50 yards

STUDENT PAGE

✦ *Math Journal 2*, p. 248

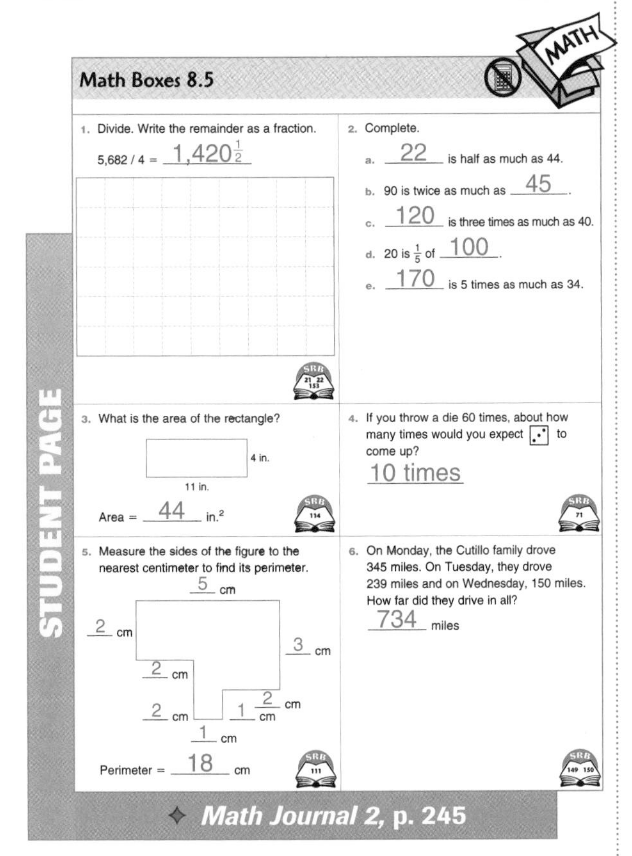

STUDENT PAGE

Math Boxes 8.5

1. Divide. Write the remainder as a fraction.
   5,682 / 4 = $1,420\frac{1}{2}$

2. Complete.
   a. 22 is half as much as 44.
   b. 90 is twice as much as 45.
   c. 120 is three times as much as 40.
   d. 20 is $\frac{1}{5}$ of 100.
   e. 170 is 5 times as much as 34.

3. What is the area of the rectangle?
   4 in.; 11 in.
   Area = 44 in.^{2}

4. If you throw a die 60 times, about how many times would you expect ⚂ to come up?
   10 times

5. Measure the sides of the figure to the nearest centimeter to find its perimeter.
   5 cm; 2 cm; 3 cm; 2 cm; 2 cm; 2 cm; 1 cm; 1 cm
   Perimeter = 18 cm

6. On Monday, the Cutillo family drove 345 miles. On Tuesday, they drove 239 miles and on Wednesday, 150 miles. How far did they drive in all?
   734 miles

✦ *Math Journal 2*, p. 245

✦ Math Boxes 8.5 (*Math Journal 2,* p. 245)

INDEPENDENT ACTIVITY

Mixed Review Math Boxes in this lesson are paired with Math Boxes in Lesson 8.7. The skill in Problem 1 is a prerequisite for Unit 9.

✦ Study Link 8.5 (*Math Masters,* p. 333)

Home Connection Students practice finding the areas of rectangles, using the dimensions of a tennis court. Then they answer a question about area and explain their reasoning.

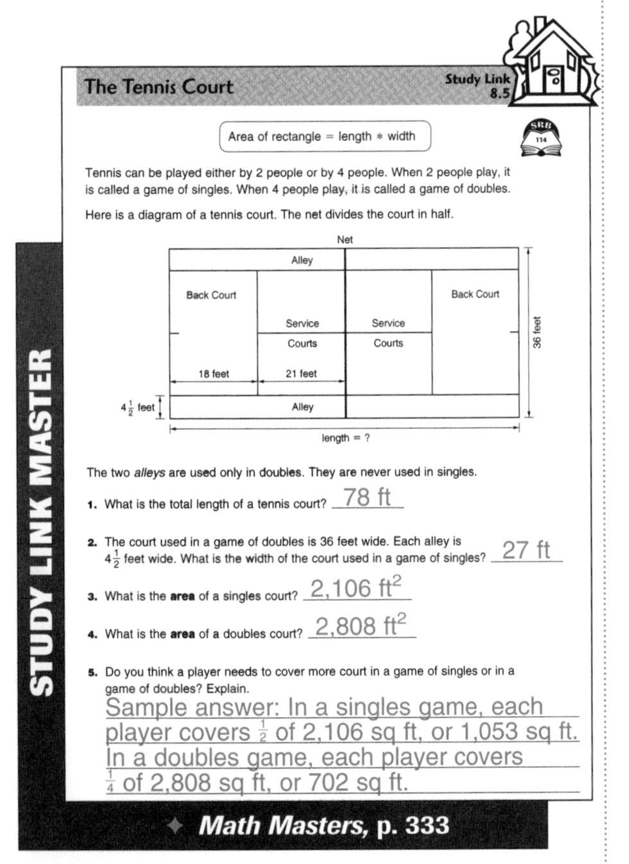

STUDY LINK MASTER

The Tennis Court Study Link 8.5

Area of rectangle = length ∗ width

Tennis can be played either by 2 people or by 4 people. When 2 people play, it is called a game of singles. When 4 people play, it is called a game of doubles.

Here is a diagram of a tennis court. The net divides the court in half.

The two *alleys* are used only in doubles. They are never used in singles.

1. What is the total length of a tennis court? 78 ft
2. The court used in a game of doubles is 36 feet wide. Each alley is $4\frac{1}{2}$ feet wide. What is the width of the court used in a game of singles? 27 ft
3. What is the **area** of a singles court? 2,106 ft^2
4. What is the **area** of a doubles court? 2,808 ft^2
5. Do you think a player needs to cover more court in a game of singles or in a game of doubles? Explain.
   Sample answer: In a singles game, each player covers $\frac{1}{2}$ of 2,106 sq ft, or 1,053 sq ft. In a doubles game, each player covers $\frac{1}{4}$ of 2,808 sq ft, or 702 sq ft.

✦ *Math Masters*, p. 333

3 Options for Individualizing

✦ EXTRA PRACTICE Finding the Area of Rectangles

PARTNER ACTIVITY  **15–30 min** 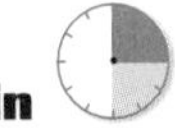

Partners take turns rolling a die. The first roll represents the length of the base of a rectangle. The second roll represents the height of the rectangle.

Partners build the rectangle with cm cubes, with square pattern blocks, or on a geoboard. Then they give the area of the rectangle in square units.

For example: First roll 4, second roll 3

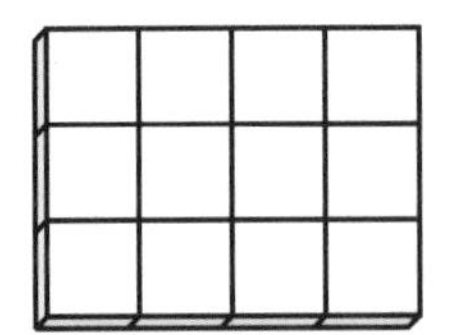

Area: 12 square units

ONGOING ASSESSMENT

Observe the strategies students use to build the rectangle and find its area. Expect that some students will still count squares. Others will not need to build the rectangle in order to calculate the area; they will simply find the product of the two rolls of the die.

8.6 Formula for the Area of a Parallelogram

OBJECTIVES To review the properties of parallelograms; and to develop and use a formula for the area of a parallelogram.

summaries	materials
1 Teaching the Lesson	
Students construct models of parallelograms and use them to review properties of parallelograms. Students cut apart and rearrange parallelogram shapes; they develop and use a formula for the area of a parallelogram. [Geometry; Measurement and Reference Frames]	□ *Math Journal 2,* pp. 250–252 □ Study Link 8.5 □ Teaching Master (*Math Masters,* p. 122) □ centimeter ruler □ straws and twist-ties □ scissors and transparent tape □ index card or other square-corner device ***See* Advance Preparation**
2 Ongoing Learning & Practice	
Students find the largest possible area of a rectangular garden whose perimeter is given. [Measurement and Reference Frames] Students practice and maintain skills through Math Boxes and Study Link activities.	□ *Math Journal 2,* pp. 249 and 253 □ Study Link Masters (*Math Masters,* pp. 334 and 335)
3 Options for Individualizing	
Enrichment Students construct figures with a compass and straightedge. [Geometry]	□ *Student Reference Book,* pp. 100, 103, and 104 □ compass □ straightedge

Additional Information

Advance Preparation Parts 1 and 2 may take a total of two days. For Part 1, each student will need 2 short straws, 2 long straws, and 4 twist-ties. Pairs of straws should be the same length. Place them near the Math Message.

Vocabulary • **base** • **height** • **perpendicular**

Getting Started

Mental Math and Reflexes

Pose scale problems like the following:

- If 1 inch on a map represents 40 miles, then
  2 inches represent 80 miles.
  $\frac{1}{4}$ inch represents 10 miles.
  $5\frac{1}{2}$ inches represent 220 miles.
- If $\frac{1}{2}$ inch on a map represents 25 miles, then
  1 inch represents 50 miles.
  2 inches represent 100 miles.
  $1\frac{1}{2}$ inches represent 75 miles.

Math Message

Take 2 short straws, 2 long straws, and 4 twist-ties. Use them to construct a parallelogram.

Study Link 8.5 Follow-Up

Review answers. Discuss the answer to Problem 5. While the area of the doubles court is greater than the area of the singles court, a singles player has to cover all of one-half of the singles court; a doubles player has to cover all of only one-quarter of the doubles court.

1 Teaching the Lesson

✦ Math Message Follow-Up

WHOLE-CLASS DISCUSSION

Invite volunteers to show their constructions and describe how they made them. After a brief discussion, move directly to the next activity.

✦ Reviewing the Properties of Parallelograms

WHOLE-CLASS ACTIVITY

Ask students to tell what they know about parallelograms, using their straw constructions as models, while you list the properties they name on the board. The list should include the following:

▷ A parallelogram is a four-sided polygon, called a quadrangle or quadrilateral.

▷ Opposite sides of a parallelogram are parallel.

▷ Opposite sides of a parallelogram are the same length.

▷ Rectangles and squares are special kinds of parallelograms.

Have students form a rectangle with their straw constructions, and then ask them to pull gently on the opposite corners. They should get a parallelogram that is not a rectangle. Ask the following questions:

- Does the perimeter remain the same? yes
- Does the area remain the same? yes

ONGOING ASSESSMENT

Take this opportunity to check students' understanding of terms such as *quadrangle, quadrilateral, opposite sides, parallel sides, perimeter,* and *area.*

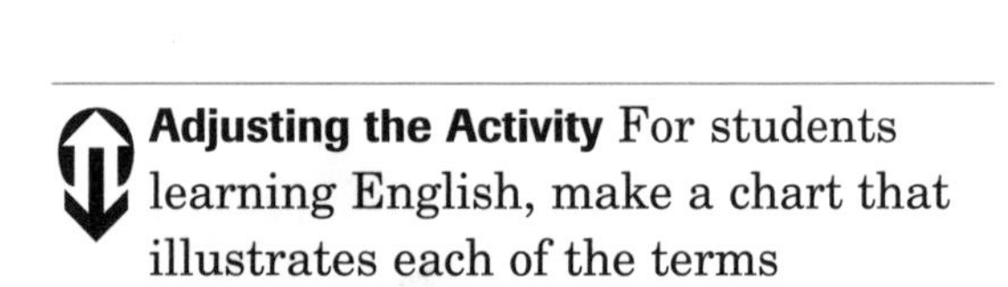

Adjusting the Activity For students learning English, make a chart that illustrates each of the terms mentioned in Ongoing Assessment.

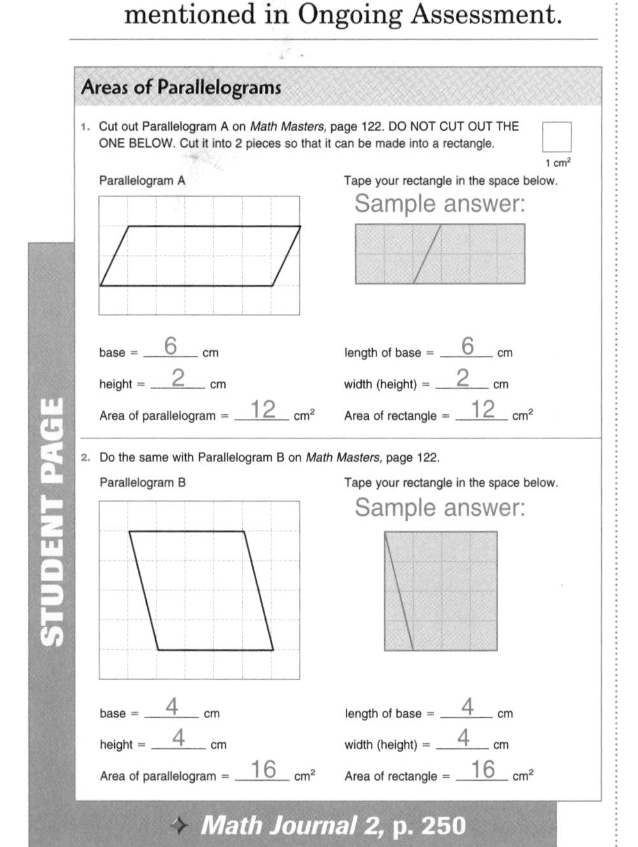

STUDENT PAGE

Areas of Parallelograms

1. Cut out Parallelogram A on *Math Masters,* page 122. DO NOT CUT OUT THE ONE BELOW. Cut it into 2 pieces so that it can be made into a rectangle.

1 cm²

Parallelogram A

Tape your rectangle in the space below.

Sample answer:

base = 6 cm

height = 2 cm

Area of parallelogram = 12 cm²

length of base = 6 cm

width (height) = 2 cm

Area of rectangle = 12 cm²

2. Do the same with Parallelogram B on *Math Masters,* page 122.

Parallelogram B

Tape your rectangle in the space below.

Sample answer:

base = 4 cm

height = 4 cm

Area of parallelogram = 16 cm²

length of base = 4 cm

width (height) = 4 cm

Area of rectangle = 16 cm²

✦ *Math Journal 2,* p. 250

Draw a parallelogram on the board. Choose one of the sides, for example, the side on which the parallelogram "sits," and call it the **base.** Label the base in your drawing. Explain that *base* is also used to mean *length of the base.*

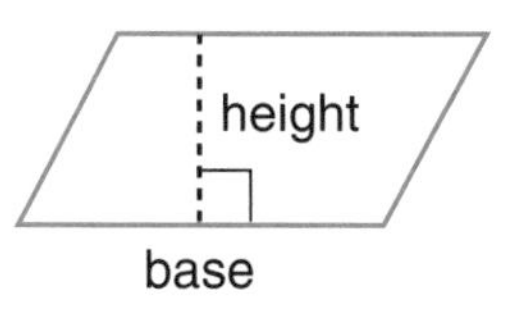

Height is the distance perpendicular to the base of a figure.

The shortest distance between the base and the side opposite the base is called the **height** of the parallelogram. Draw and label a dashed line to show the height. Include a right-angle symbol. Point out that the dashed line can be drawn anywhere between the two sides as long as it is **perpendicular** to (forms a right angle with) the base.

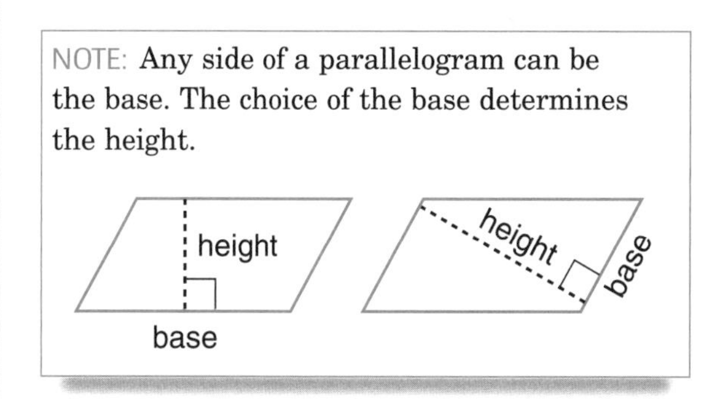
NOTE: Any side of a parallelogram can be the base. The choice of the base determines the height.

Remind students that rectangles are parallelograms whose corners are right angles. If you think of one side of a rectangle as its *base,* then the length of an adjacent side is its *height.*

✦ Developing a Formula for Finding the Area of a Parallelogram (*Math Journal 2,* pp. 250 and 251; *Math Masters,* p. 122)

WHOLE-CLASS ACTIVITY

Ask the class to turn to journal page 250 while you distribute copies of *Math Masters,* page 122. Point out that Parallelogram A is the same on both the journal page and the master.

NOTE: There are two drawings of each parallelogram on *Math Masters,* page 122 so that students can try again if they don't succeed the first time in making a rectangle out of the parallelogram.

Guide students through the following activity:

1. Cut out Parallelogram A from the master.
2. Cut the parallelogram into two pieces along one of the vertical grid lines.
3. Tape the pieces together to form a rectangle.

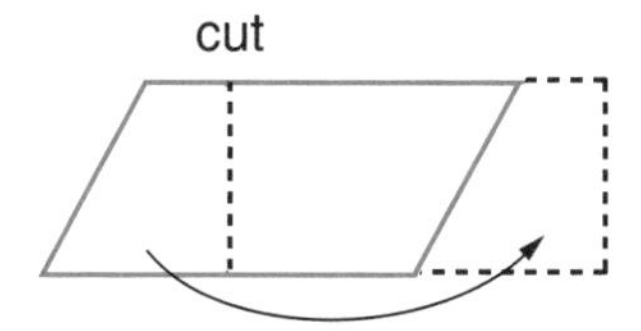

4. Tape this rectangle in the space next to the parallelogram in the journal.

   Discuss the relationship between the parallelogram and the rectangle.

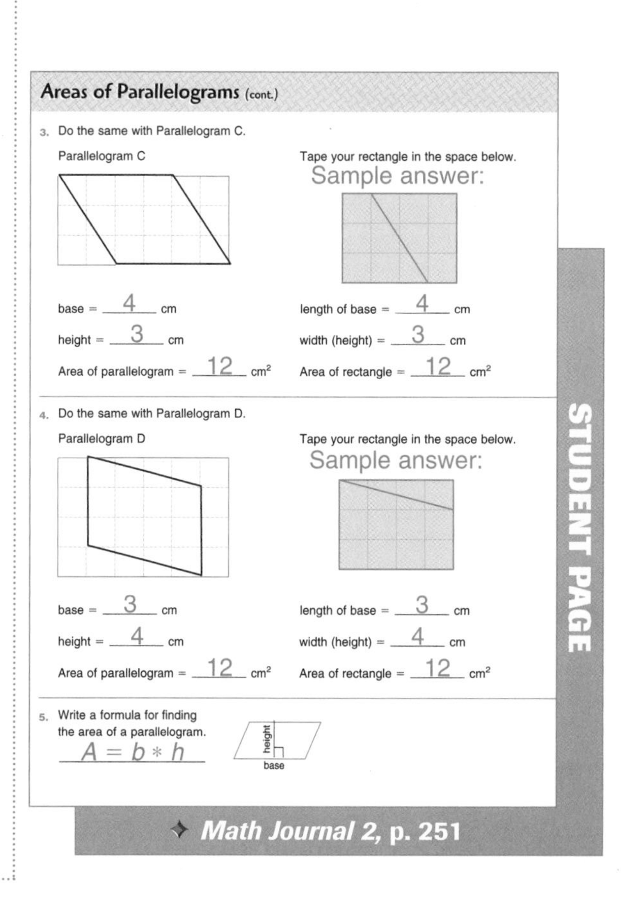
Areas of Parallelograms (cont.)

3. Do the same with Parallelogram C.

Parallelogram C

Tape your rectangle in the space below.

Sample answer:

base = 4 cm

height = 3 cm

Area of parallelogram = 12 cm²

length of base = 4 cm

width (height) = 3 cm

Area of rectangle = 12 cm²

4. Do the same with Parallelogram D.

Parallelogram D

Tape your rectangle in the space below.

Sample answer:

base = 3 cm

height = 4 cm

Area of parallelogram = 12 cm²

length of base = 3 cm

width (height) = 4 cm

Area of rectangle = 12 cm²

5. Write a formula for finding the area of a parallelogram.

$A = b * h$

height
base

STUDENT PAGE

✦ *Math Journal 2,* p. 251

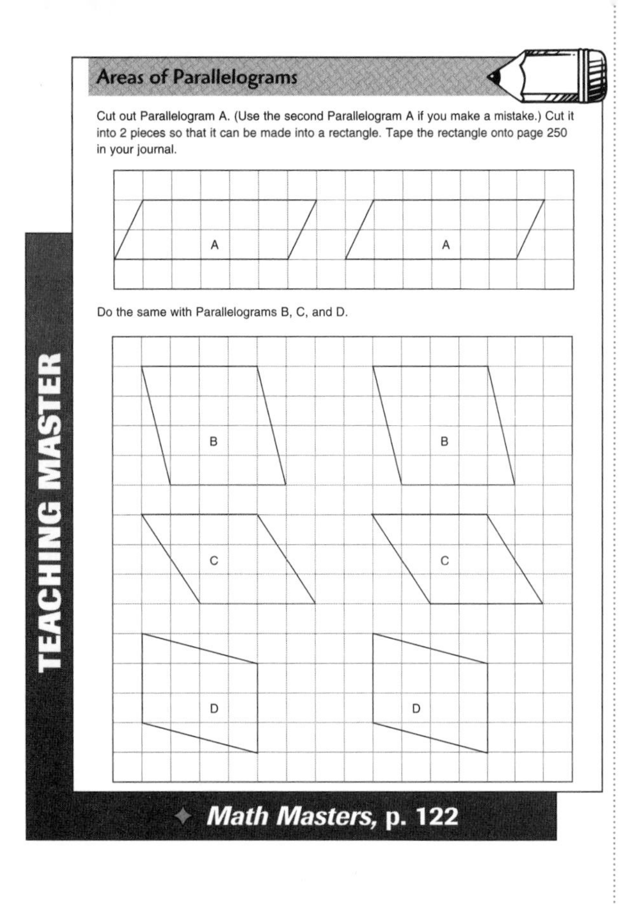
TEACHING MASTER

Areas of Parallelograms

Cut out Parallelogram A. (Use the second Parallelogram A if you make a mistake.) Cut it into 2 pieces so that it can be made into a rectangle. Tape the rectangle onto page 250 in your journal.

A A

Do the same with Parallelograms B, C, and D.

B B

C C

D D

✦ *Math Masters*, p. 122

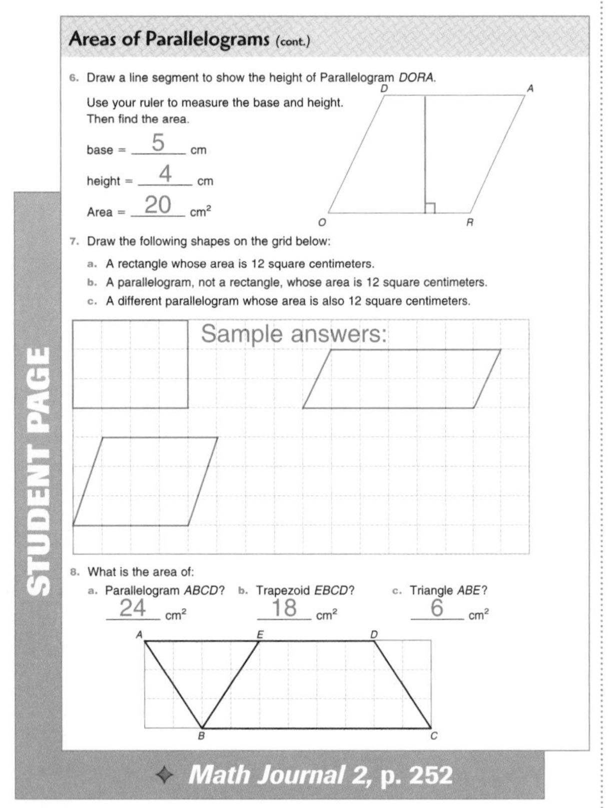
STUDENT PAGE

Areas of Parallelograms (cont.)

6. Draw a line segment to show the height of Parallelogram *DORA*.

Use your ruler to measure the base and height. Then find the area.

base = 5 cm

height = 4 cm

Area = 20 cm²

7. Draw the following shapes on the grid below:

a. A rectangle whose area is 12 square centimeters.

b. A parallelogram, not a rectangle, whose area is 12 square centimeters.

c. A different parallelogram whose area is also 12 square centimeters.

Sample answers:

8. What is the area of:

a. Parallelogram *ABCD*? 24 cm²

b. Trapezoid *EBCD*? 18 cm²

c. Triangle *ABE*? 6 cm²

✦ *Math Journal 2*, p. 252

- Why must the parallelogram and the rectangle both have the same area? The rectangle was constructed from the parallelogram. Nothing was lost.

5. Record the dimensions and area of the parallelogram and the rectangle. Length of base of parallelogram and length of base of rectangle = 6 cm; height of parallelogram and width (height) of rectangle = 2 cm; area of each figure = 12 cm²

Have students repeat these steps with Parallelograms B, C, and D, working on their own or with a partner.

Bring students together to develop a formula for the area of a parallelogram. Their line of reasoning might go something like this:

▷ The area of each parallelogram is the same as the area of the rectangle that was made from it.

▷ The area of the rectangle is equal to the length of its base times its width (height).

▷ The length of the base of the parallelogram is equal to the length of the base of the rectangle. The height of that parallelogram is equal to the width (height) of that rectangle. Therefore, the area of the parallelogram is equal to the length of its base times its height.

Using variables:

$$A = b * h$$

where b is the length of the base and h the height.

Have students record the formula at the bottom of journal page 251.

✦ Solving Area Problems
(*Math Journal 2,* p. 252)

PARTNER ACTIVITY 

Work with the whole class on Problem 6 on journal page 252. Students can place an index card (or other square-corner device) on top of the shape, align the bottom edge of the card with the base, and then use the edge of the card to draw a line for the height. They will need a centimeter ruler to measure the length of the base and the height.

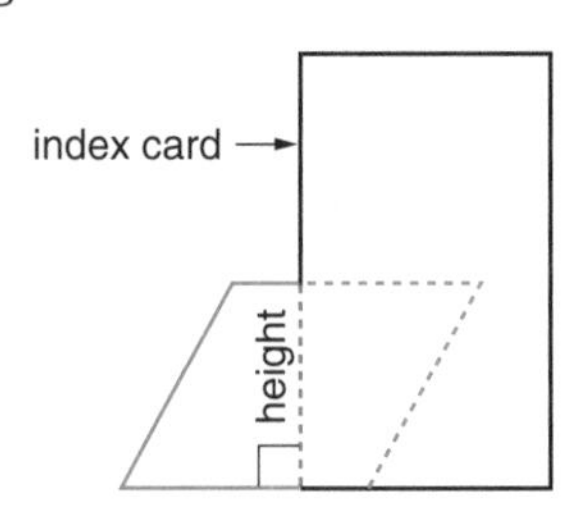

Drawing the height of a parallelogram

Have students work with their partners or in small groups to complete Problems 7 and 8. Circulate and assist as needed. Then bring students together to discuss their solutions.

▷ Problem 7 illustrates the fact that shapes that don't look the same can have the same area.

▷ Problem 8b lends itself to a variety of solution strategies. Some students may have partitioned the trapezoid into a rectangle flanked by two triangles (*see margin*). The rectangle covers 12 grid squares. If one triangle were cut apart and placed next to the other triangle to form a rectangle, the pair would cover 6 squares. The rectangle and two triangles cover $12 + 6 = 18 \text{ cm}^2$.

▷ Problem 8c can be solved without using a formula for the area of a triangle. The parallelogram area minus the trapezoid area is the triangle area. $24 - 18 = 6 \text{ cm}^2$

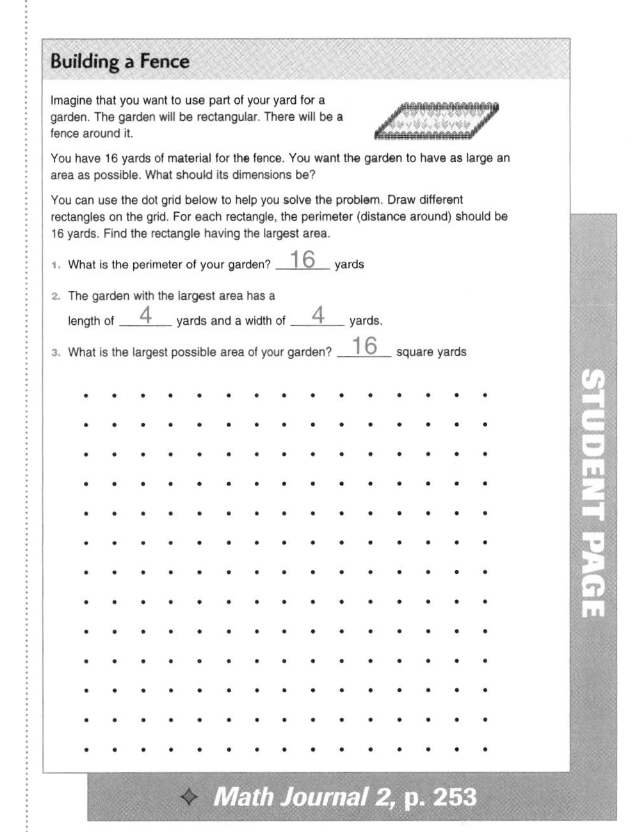

Building a Fence
Imagine that you want to use part of your yard for a garden. The garden will be rectangular. There will be a fence around it.
You have 16 yards of material for the fence. You want the garden to have as large an area as possible. What should its dimensions be?
You can use the dot grid below to help you solve the problem. Draw different rectangles on the grid. For each rectangle, the perimeter (distance around) should be 16 yards. Find the rectangle having the largest area.
1. What is the perimeter of your garden? 16 yards
2. The garden with the largest area has a length of 4 yards and a width of 4 yards.
3. What is the largest possible area of your garden? 16 square yards
STUDENT PAGE
Math Journal 2, p. 253

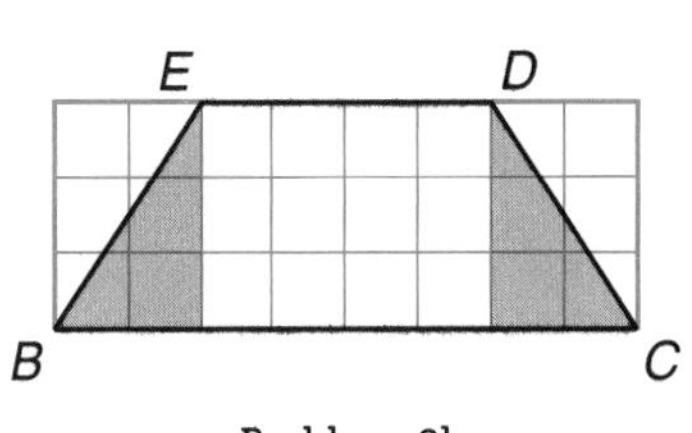

Problem 8b

2 Ongoing Learning & Practice

✦Building a Fence (*Math Journal 2*, p. 253)

PARTNER ACTIVITY

Students find the largest possible area for a rectangular garden whose perimeter is 16 yards. When students share results, be sure to list all possible whole-number dimensions of the rectangle.

Dimensions (yd)	Area (yd^2)
1 by 7	7
2 by 6	12
3 by 5	15
4 by 4	16

Adjusting the Activity Challenge students to find the area of rectangles whose length and width are not whole numbers of yards. For example, if the dimensions of a rectangle are $3\frac{1}{2}$ yd by $4\frac{1}{2}$ yd, the perimeter is 16 yd and the area is $15\frac{3}{4}$ yd^2.

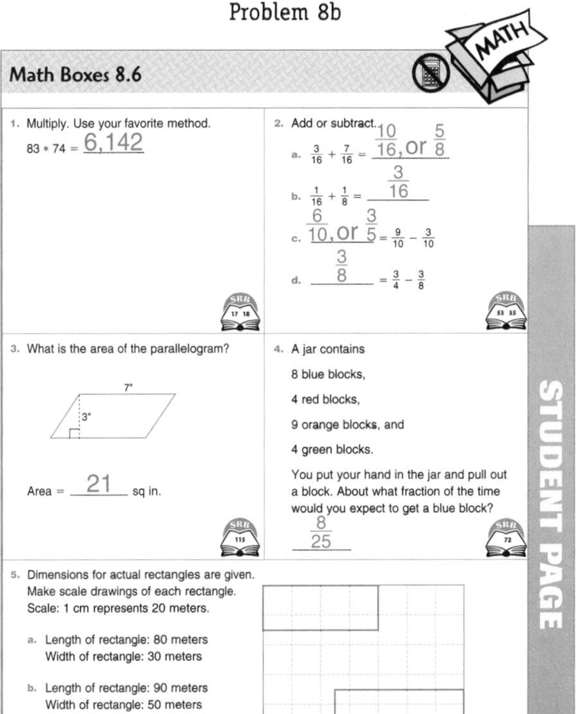

Math Boxes 8.6
MATH
1. Multiply. Use your favorite method.
83 * 74 = 6,142
2. Add or subtract.
a. 3/16 + 7/16 = 10/16, or 5/8
b. 1/16 + 1/8 = 3/16
c. 6/10, or 3/5 = 9/10 − 3/10
d. 3/8 = 3/4 − 3/8
3. What is the area of the parallelogram?
7"
3"
Area = 21 sq in.
4. A jar contains
8 blue blocks,
4 red blocks,
9 orange blocks, and
4 green blocks.
You put your hand in the jar and pull out a block. About what fraction of the time would you expect to get a blue block?
8/25
5. Dimensions for actual rectangles are given. Make scale drawings of each rectangle. Scale: 1 cm represents 20 meters.
a. Length of rectangle: 80 meters
Width of rectangle: 30 meters
b. Length of rectangle: 90 meters
Width of rectangle: 50 meters
STUDENT PAGE
Math Journal 2, p. 249

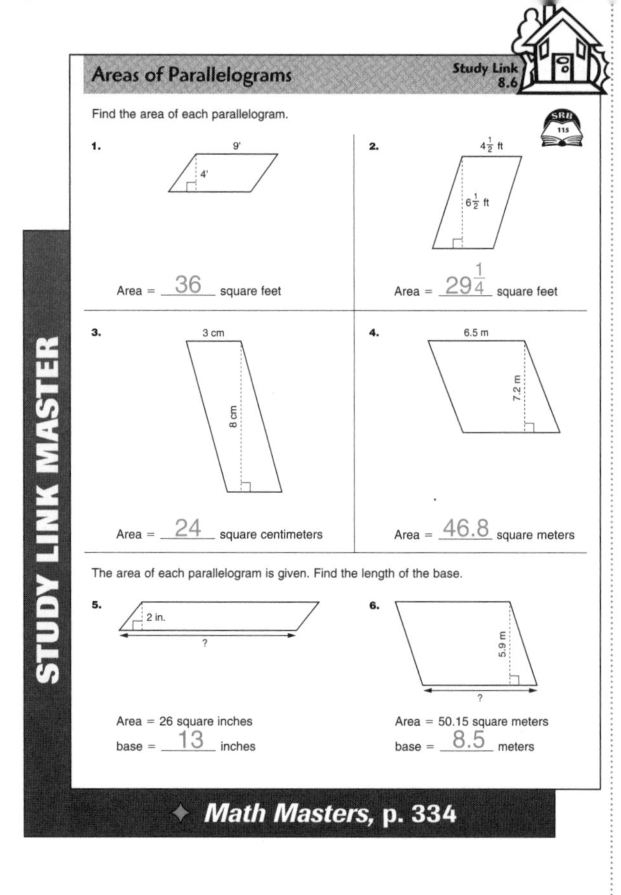
Areas of Parallelograms — Study Link 8.6

Find the area of each parallelogram.

1. (base 9', height 4')
Area = 36 square feet

2. (base $4\frac{1}{2}$ ft, height $6\frac{1}{2}$ ft)
Area = $29\frac{1}{4}$ square feet

3. (base 3 cm, height 8 cm)
Area = 24 square centimeters

4. (base 6.5 m, height 7.2 m)
Area = 46.8 square meters

The area of each parallelogram is given. Find the length of the base.

5. (height 2 in., base ?)
Area = 26 square inches
base = 13 inches

6. (height 5.9 m, base ?)
Area = 50.15 square meters
base = 8.5 meters

STUDY LINK MASTER

✦ *Math Masters,* p. 334

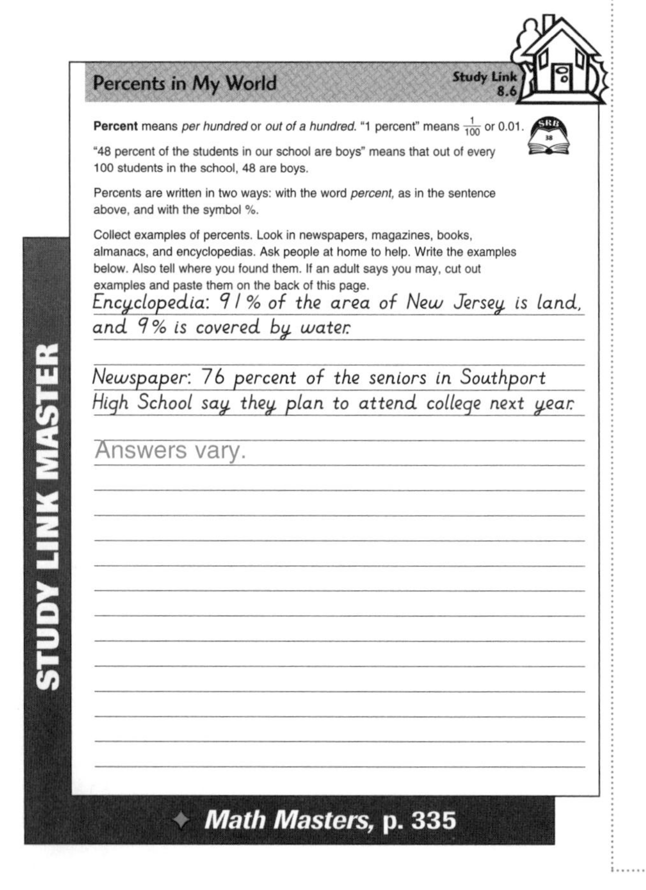
Percents in My World — Study Link 8.6

Percent means *per hundred* or *out of a hundred.* "1 percent" means $\frac{1}{100}$ or 0.01.

"48 percent of the students in our school are boys" means that out of every 100 students in the school, 48 are boys.

Percents are written in two ways: with the word *percent,* as in the sentence above, and with the symbol %.

Collect examples of percents. Look in newspapers, magazines, books, almanacs, and encyclopedias. Ask people at home to help. Write the examples below. Also tell where you found them. If an adult says you may, cut out examples and paste them on the back of this page.

Encyclopedia: 91% of the area of New Jersey is land, and 9% is covered by water.

Newspaper: 76 percent of the seniors in Southport High School say they plan to attend college next year.

Answers vary.

STUDY LINK MASTER

✦ *Math Masters,* p. 335

✦ Math Boxes 8.6 (*Math Journal 2,* p. 249)

INDEPENDENT ACTIVITY 

Mixed Review Math Boxes in this lesson are paired with Math Boxes in Lesson 8.8. The skill in Problem 1 is a prerequisite for Unit 9.

✦ Study Link 8.6 (*Math Masters,* pp. 334 and 335)

Home Connection Students calculate the area of parallelograms on *Math Masters,* page 334.

NOTE: *Math Masters,* page 335 should be completed before Lesson 9.1, in which students share and discuss examples of percents they have collected.

3 Options for Individualizing

✦ ENRICHMENT Constructing Figures with a Compass and Straightedge (*Student Reference Book,* pp. 100, 103, and 104)

INDEPENDENT ACTIVITY  **30+ min**

Students who enjoyed doing constructions in the past may want to try these new constructions in their spare time. The *Student Reference Book* pages show how to construct a parallelogram and how to draw perpendicular line segments.

Assign one or more of the *Student Reference Book* pages. Tell students to complete a Check Your Understanding problem by following the steps listed above the problem.

8.7 Formula for the Area of a Triangle

OBJECTIVE **To develop and use a formula for the area of a triangle.**

summaries	materials
1 Teaching the Lesson	
Students arrange triangles to form parallelograms. They develop and use a formula for finding the area of a triangle. [Geometry; Measurement and Reference Frames]	□ *Math Journal 2,* pp. 254–256 □ Teaching Master (*Math Masters,* p. 123) □ Transparency (*Math Masters,* p. 20; optional) □ centimeter ruler □ scissors and transparent tape □ index card or other square-corner device ***See* Advance Preparation**
2 Ongoing Learning & Practice	
Students solve perimeter and area problems on a grid. [Geometry; Measurement and Reference Frames] Students practice and maintain skills through Math Boxes and Study Link activities.	□ *Math Journal 2,* pp. 257 and 258 □ Study Link Master (*Math Masters,* p. 336) □ Assessment Master (*Math Masters,* p. 475; optional) □ straightedge
3 Options for Individualizing	
Enrichment Students cut apart a regular hexagon and use the pieces to make area comparisons. [Geometry; Measurement and Reference Frames]	□ Teaching Master (*Math Masters,* p. 124) □ scissors ***See* Advance Preparation**

Additional Information

Background Information For additional information on base and height, see the *Teacher's Reference Manual.*

Advance Preparation This lesson may take two days. For the optional Enrichment activity in Part 3, make a copy of *Math Masters,* page 124 for each group of 2 to 4 students.

Vocabulary • **equilateral triangle** • **isosceles triangle** • **base** • **height**

Getting Started

Mental Math and Reflexes

Draw the following parallelogram on the board:

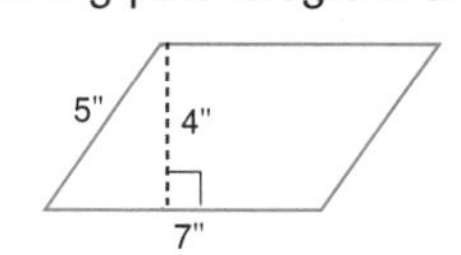

Ask students to find the area 28 square inches and the perimeter. 24 inches, or 2 feet Watch for students who find the area by multiplying the length of the base (7 inches) by the length of the slanted side (5 inches), instead of by the height (4 inches).

Math Message

Make a list of everything that you know about triangles.

Study Link 8.6 Follow-Up

Review answers.

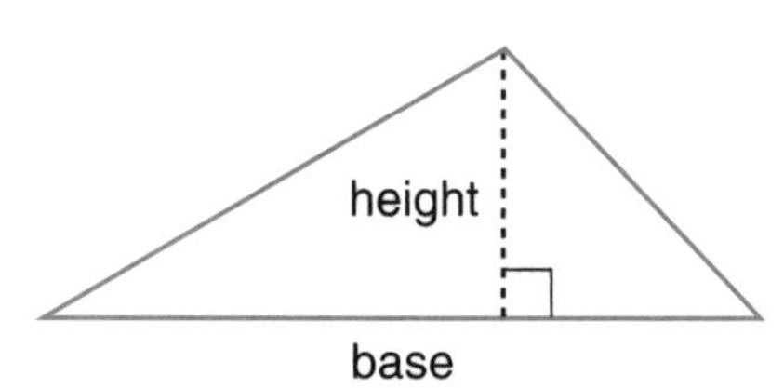

The height of a triangle is measured along a line segment perpendicular to the base.

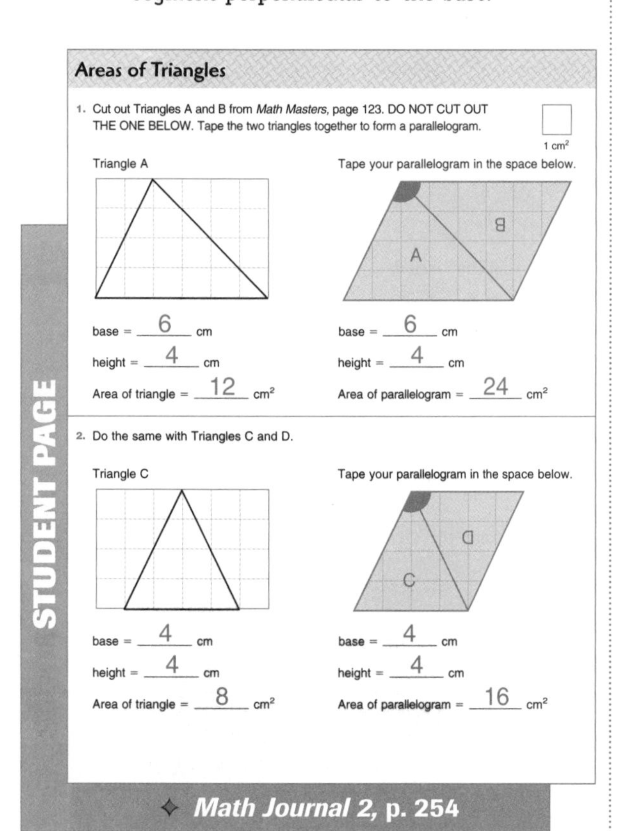

Areas of Triangles

1. Cut out Triangles A and B from *Math Masters,* page 123. DO NOT CUT OUT THE ONE BELOW. Tape the two triangles together to form a parallelogram.

1 cm²

Triangle A

Tape your parallelogram in the space below.

base = 6 cm
height = 4 cm
Area of triangle = 12 cm²

base = 6 cm
height = 4 cm
Area of parallelogram = 24 cm²

2. Do the same with Triangles C and D.

Triangle C

Tape your parallelogram in the space below.

base = 4 cm
height = 4 cm
Area of triangle = 8 cm²

base = 4 cm
height = 4 cm
Area of parallelogram = 16 cm²

STUDENT PAGE

✧ *Math Journal 2,* p. 254

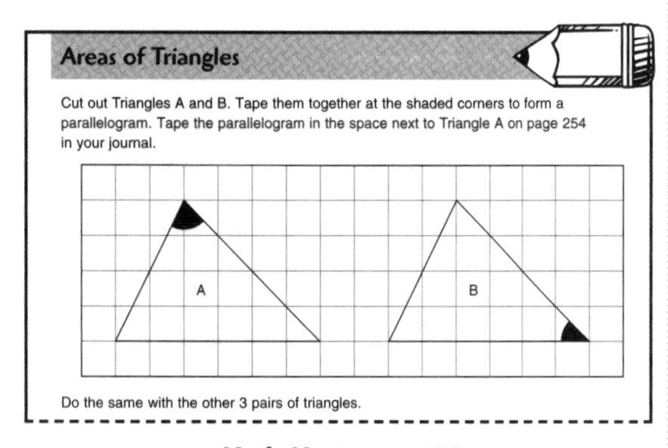

Areas of Triangles

Cut out Triangles A and B. Tape them together at the shaded corners to form a parallelogram. Tape the parallelogram in the space next to Triangle A on page 254 in your journal.

Do the same with the other 3 pairs of triangles.

Math Masters, p.123

1 Teaching the Lesson

✦ Math Message Follow-Up

WHOLE-CLASS DISCUSSION 

As students share their responses, write them on the board. The list might include the following properties:

▷ A triangle is a three-sided polygon.

▷ The sum of the measures of the angles of a triangle is 180°.

▷ A triangle has three vertices.

▷ A triangle is a convex polygon.

▷ An **equilateral triangle** is a triangle in which all three sides have the same measure, and all three angles have the same measure. An equilateral triangle is a regular polygon.

▷ An **isosceles triangle** is a triangle in which two sides have the same measure.

✦ Developing a Formula for Finding the Area of a Triangle (*Math Journal 2,* pp. 254 and 255; *Math Masters,* p. 123)

WHOLE-CLASS ACTIVITY

Draw a triangle on the board. Choose one of the sides—the side on which the triangle "sits," for example—and call it the **base.** Label the base in your drawing. Explain that *base* is also used to mean *length of the base.*

The shortest distance from the vertex above the base to the base is called the **height** of the triangle. Draw a dashed line to show the height and label it. Include a right-angle symbol (*see margin*).

NOTE: As with parallelograms, any side of a triangle can be the base. The choice of the base determines the height.

Ask the class to turn to journal page 254 while you distribute copies of *Math Masters,* page 123. Point out that Triangles A and B on the master are the same as

Triangle A on the journal page. Then guide students through the following activity:

1. Cut out Triangles A and B from the master.
2. Tape the triangles together at the shaded corners to form a parallelogram. (Partners can help each other: One partner holds the triangles in place while the other tapes them together.)
3. Tape the parallelogram in the space next to Triangle A in the journal.

   Discuss the relationship between the area of the triangle and the area of the parallelogram. Triangles A and B have the same area. Therefore, the area of either triangle is half the area of the parallelogram.
4. Record the dimensions and area of the triangle and of the parallelogram. Base of triangle and of parallelogram = 6 cm; height of triangle and of parallelogram = 4 cm; area of parallelogram = 24 cm^2; area of triangle = $\frac{1}{2}$ the area of parallelogram = 12 cm^2.

Have students repeat these steps with Triangles C and D, E and F, and G and H. Then bring the class together to state a rule and write a formula for the area of a triangle.

The rule can be stated as follows:

If the length of the base and the height of a triangle are the same as the length of the base and the height of a parallelogram, then:

Area of the triangle = $\frac{1}{2}$ the Area of the parallelogram,

or

Area of the triangle = $\frac{1}{2}$ of (base * height)

Using variables:

$$A = \frac{1}{2} \text{ of } (b * h) \quad \text{or} \quad A = \frac{1}{2} * (b * h)$$

where b is the length of the base and h is the height.

Have students record the formula at the bottom of journal page 255.

✦ Solving Area Problems

(*Math Journal 2,* p. 256; *Math Masters,* p. 20)

PARTNER ACTIVITY 

Work with the whole class on Problem 6. Students can place an index card (or other square-corner device) on top of the triangle, align the bottom edge of the card with the base (making sure that one edge of the card passes through point S), and then draw a line for the height. Students will need a centimeter ruler to measure the base and the height (*see margin*).

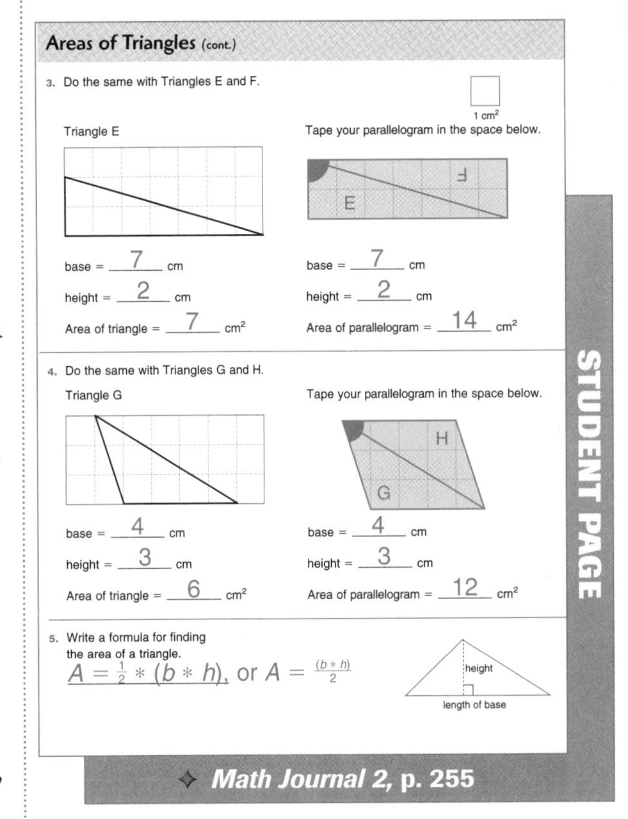

Areas of Triangles (cont.)
3. Do the same with Triangles E and F.
1 cm²
Triangle E
Tape your parallelogram in the space below.
E
F
base = 7 cm
height = 2 cm
Area of triangle = 7 cm²
base = 7 cm
height = 2 cm
Area of parallelogram = 14 cm²
4. Do the same with Triangles G and H.
Triangle G
Tape your parallelogram in the space below.
H
G
base = 4 cm
height = 3 cm
Area of triangle = 6 cm²
base = 4 cm
height = 3 cm
Area of parallelogram = 12 cm²
5. Write a formula for finding the area of a triangle.
A = ½ ∗ (b ∗ h), or A = (b ∗ h)/2
height
length of base
STUDENT PAGE

✦ *Math Journal 2,* p. 255

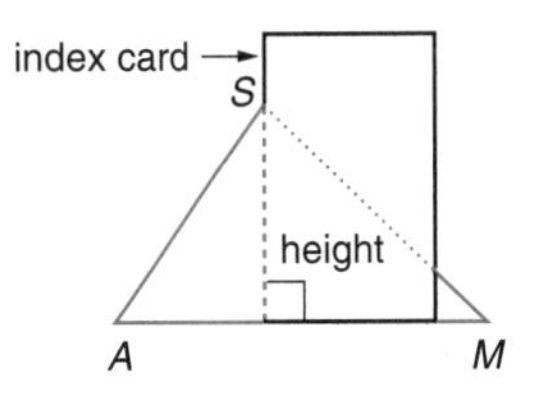

Drawing the height of a triangle

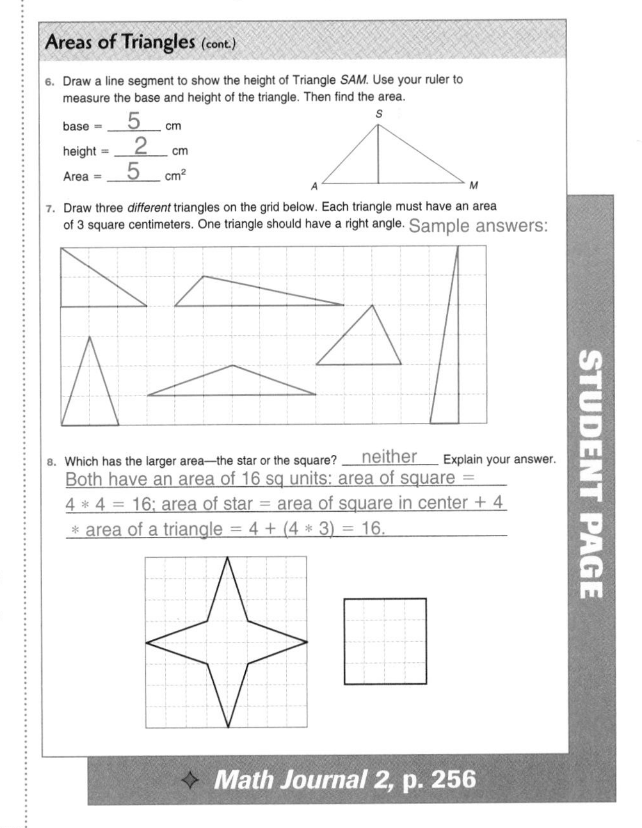

Areas of Triangles (cont.)
6. Draw a line segment to show the height of Triangle SAM. Use your ruler to measure the base and height of the triangle. Then find the area.
base = 5 cm
height = 2 cm
Area = 5 cm²
S
A
M
7. Draw three different triangles on the grid below. Each triangle must have an area of 3 square centimeters. One triangle should have a right angle. Sample answers:
8. Which has the larger area—the star or the square? neither Explain your answer.
Both have an area of 16 sq units: area of square = 4 ∗ 4 = 16; area of star = area of square in center + 4 ∗ area of a triangle = 4 + (4 ∗ 3) = 16.
STUDENT PAGE

✦ *Math Journal 2,* p. 256

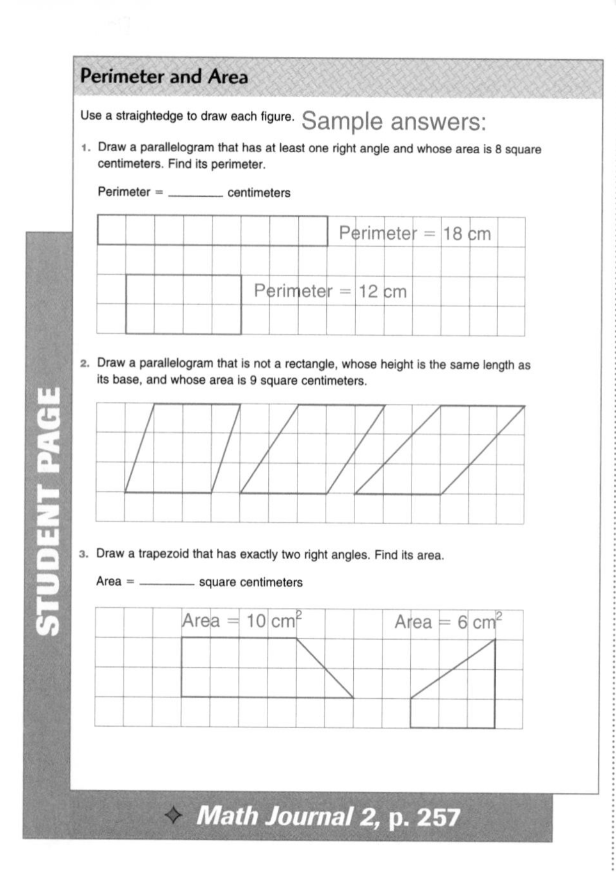

STUDENT PAGE

Perimeter and Area

Use a straightedge to draw each figure. Sample answers:

1. Draw a parallelogram that has at least one right angle and whose area is 8 square centimeters. Find its perimeter.

   Perimeter = ______ centimeters

   Perimeter = 18 cm

   Perimeter = 12 cm

2. Draw a parallelogram that is not a rectangle, whose height is the same length as its base, and whose area is 9 square centimeters.

3. Draw a trapezoid that has exactly two right angles. Find its area.

   Area = ______ square centimeters

   Area = 10 cm²

   Area = 6 cm²

✦ *Math Journal 2,* p. 257

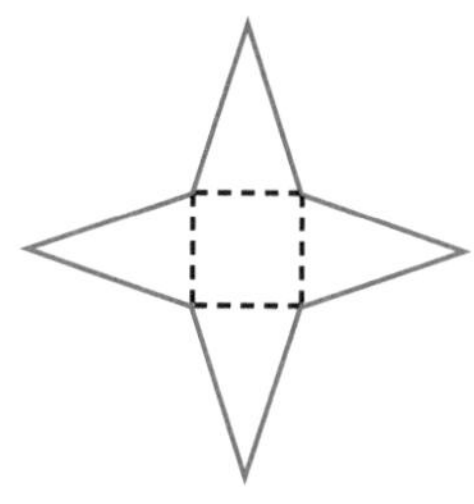

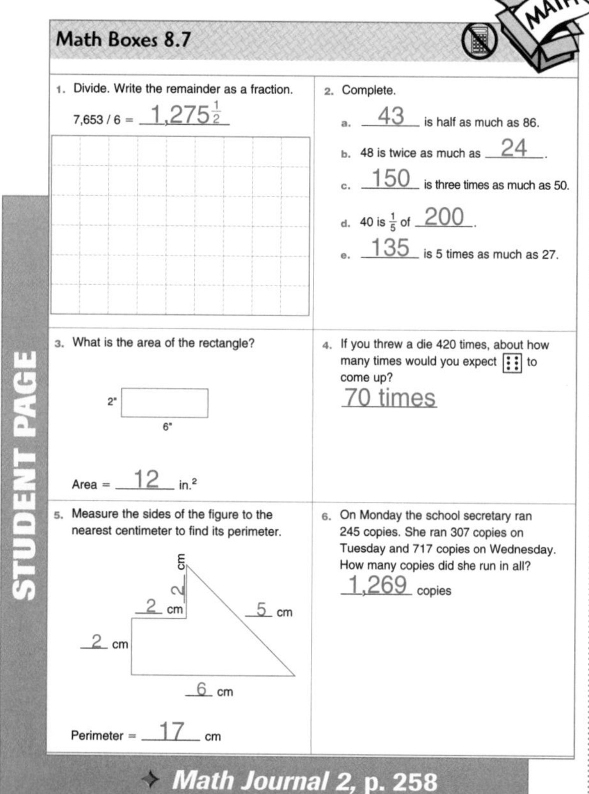

STUDENT PAGE

Math Boxes 8.7

1. Divide. Write the remainder as a fraction.

   7,653 / 6 = $1,275\frac{1}{2}$

2. Complete.

   a. 43 is half as much as 86.

   b. 48 is twice as much as 24.

   c. 150 is three times as much as 50.

   d. 40 is $\frac{1}{5}$ of 200.

   e. 135 is 5 times as much as 27.

3. What is the area of the rectangle?

   2" 6"

   Area = 12 in.²

4. If you threw a die 420 times, about how many times would you expect ⚃ to come up?

   70 times

5. Measure the sides of the figure to the nearest centimeter to find its perimeter.

   2 cm, 2 cm, 5 cm, 2 cm, 6 cm

   Perimeter = 17 cm

6. On Monday the school secretary ran 245 copies. She ran 307 copies on Tuesday and 717 copies on Wednesday. How many copies did she run in all?

   1,269 copies

✦ *Math Journal 2,* p. 258

Adjusting the Activity On the board, draw a triangle that has an obtuse angle as one of its base angles. Challenge students to draw the height of the triangle. Demonstrate by extending the base along the side of the obtuse angle, and drawing a perpendicular line from the opposite vertex to the extended base. *For example:*

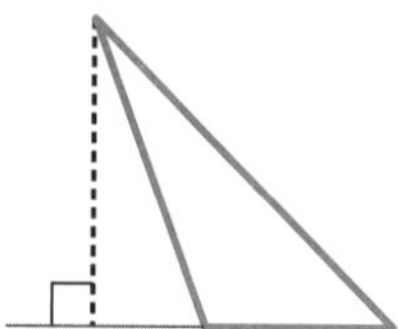

Students work with partners or in small groups to complete Problems 7 and 8. Circulate and assist as needed. Then bring the class together to discuss solutions.

▷ There are many possibilities for Problem 7. You can use a transparency of a 1-cm grid (*Math Masters,* page 20) on the overhead projector to display a number of them.

▷ It may surprise some students that the star and the square in Problem 8 have the same area. One way to find the area of the star is to think of it as a square with a triangle attached to each of its sides (*see margin*).

2 Ongoing Learning & Practice

✦ Solving Perimeter and Area Problems
(*Math Journal 2,* p. 257)

INDEPENDENT ACTIVITY 

Students solve problems that involve drawing polygons and finding areas and perimeters. Briefly go over the answers with the class.

▷ The parallelogram in Problem 2 is not a rhombus, because its sides are not all the same length.

▷ To find the area of the trapezoid in Problem 3, decompose the trapezoid into a rectangle and a triangle. Use the appropriate formula to find the area of each, and then add the two areas.

ONGOING ASSESSMENT

Consider asking students to respond to the following question on an Exit Slip (*Math Masters*, page 475):

- How could you help a friend remember the difference between the *perimeter* of a figure and its *area?*

If no one mentions it, point out that the word *rim* can be found in the term *perimeter.*

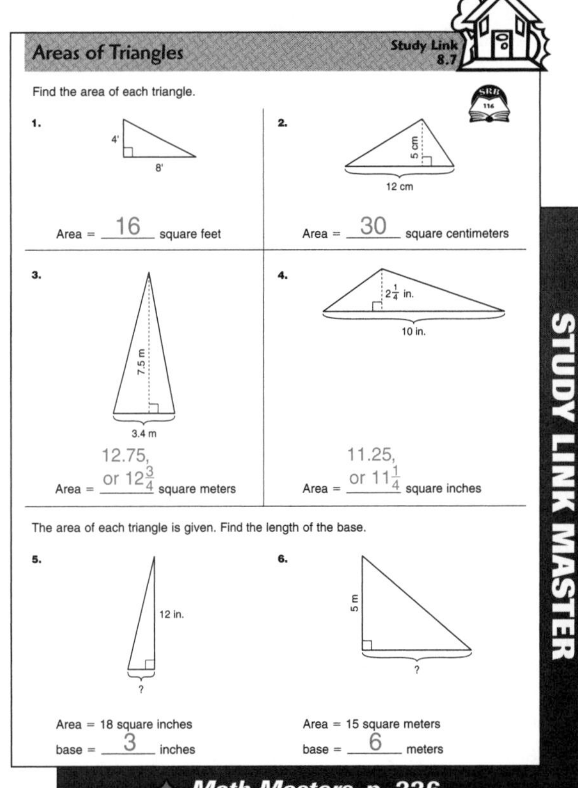
Areas of Triangles

Study Link 8.7

Find the area of each triangle.

1. 4', 8' — Area = 16 square feet
2. 5 cm, 12 cm — Area = 30 square centimeters
3. 7.5 m, 3.4 m — Area = 12.75, or $12\frac{3}{4}$ square meters
4. $2\frac{1}{4}$ in., 10 in. — Area = 11.25, or $11\frac{1}{4}$ square inches

The area of each triangle is given. Find the length of the base.

5. 12 in., ? — Area = 18 square inches, base = 3 inches
6. 5 m, ? — Area = 15 square meters, base = 6 meters

STUDY LINK MASTER

Math Masters, p. 336

Math Boxes 8.7 (*Math Journal 2*, p. 258)

INDEPENDENT ACTIVITY 

Mixed Review Math Boxes in this lesson are paired with Math Boxes in Lesson 8.5. The skill in Problem 1 is a prerequisite for Unit 9.

Study Link 8.7 (*Math Masters*, p. 336)

Home Connection Students calculate the area of triangles. They continue to work on *Math Masters*, page 335, which should be completed before Lesson 9.1.

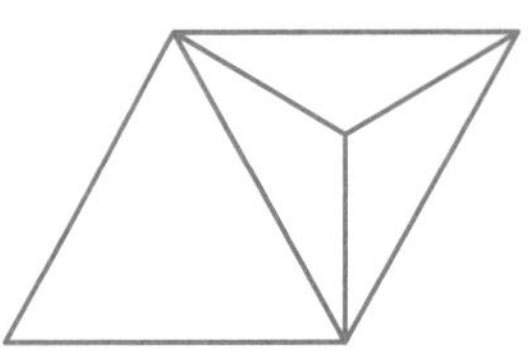

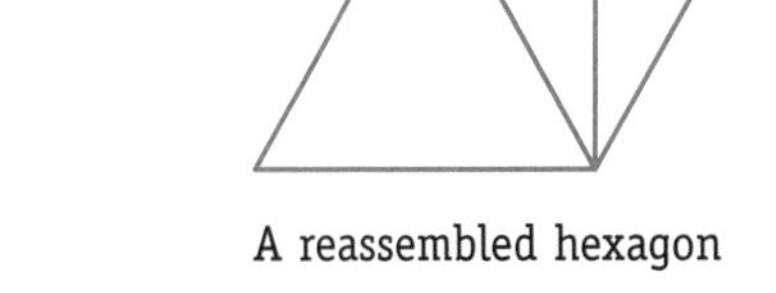

A reassembled hexagon

3 Options for Individualizing

ENRICHMENT Comparing Areas (*Math Masters*, p. 124)

SMALL-GROUP ACTIVITY  **15–30 min** 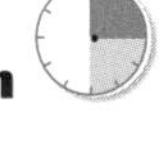

Distribute a copy of *Math Masters*, page 124 to each group. Tell groups to follow the directions and answer the questions.

Portfolio Ideas

▷ In Step 2, the figure should look like the one shown in the margin.

The area of the rhombus is the same as the area of the hexagon. It is possible for two different shapes to have the same area.

▷ In Step 3, the three smaller triangles exactly cover the equilateral triangle. The area of the hexagon is twice the area of the larger triangle.

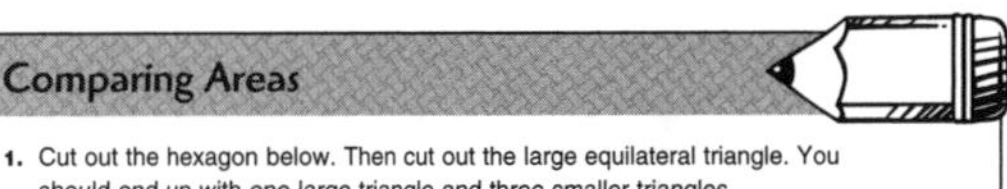
Comparing Areas

1. Cut out the hexagon below. Then cut out the large equilateral triangle. You should end up with one large triangle and three smaller triangles.
2. Use the large triangle and the three smaller triangles to form a rhombus.
   a. Is the area of the rhombus the same as the area of the hexagon you started with? yes
   b. Is it possible for two different shapes to have the same area? yes
3. Put the pieces back together to form a hexagon with an equilateral triangle inside.

   How can you show that the area of the hexagon is twice the area of the large triangle?
   Sample answer: The three smaller triangles cover the equilateral triangle. Six of the smaller triangles cover the entire hexagon.

There are 4 triangles in the hexagon.

- The large triangle is called an **equilateral triangle.** All 3 sides are the same length.
- The smaller triangles are called **isosceles triangles.** Each of these triangles has 2 sides that are the same length.

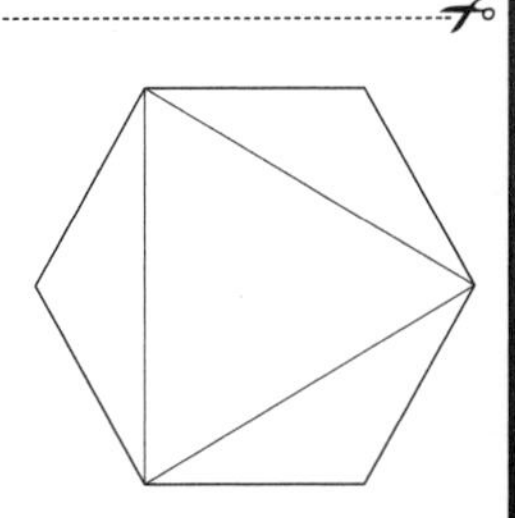

TEACHING MASTER

Math Masters, p. 124

8.8 Geographical Area Measurements

OBJECTIVES **To examine how geographical areas are measured; and to use division to compare two quantities with like units.**

summaries	materials
1 Teaching the Lesson	
Students examine how geographical areas are measured and the difficulties involved in making accurate measurements. They compare country areas by guessing and then using division to calculate the ratio of areas. [Measurement and Reference Frames; Operations and Computation]	□ *Math Journal 2,* pp. 260 and 261 □ *Student Reference Book,* pp. 230, 231, and 239 □ Study Link 8.7 □ world map or globe □ calculator
2 Ongoing Learning & Practice	
Students find areas of a rectangle, a parallelogram, and a triangle. They count squares to find the area of an irregular figure and draw a rectangle with a given area and perimeter. [Measurement and Reference Frames] Students practice and maintain skills through Math Boxes and Study Link activities.	□ *Math Journal 2,* pp. 259 and 262 □ Study Link Master (*Math Masters,* p. 337)
3 Options for Individualizing	
Enrichment Students use division to compare numbers of mammal species. [Operations and Computation]	□ Teaching Master (*Math Masters,* p. 125) □ calculator

Additional Information

Background Information For additional information on area, see the *Teacher's Reference Manual.*

Getting Started

Mental Math and Reflexes

Write numbers on the board. Students round them to specified places.

Suggestions

- 440,762

  Round to the nearest 100. 440,800 The nearest 1,000. 441,000
  The nearest 10,000. 440,000
- 1,073,518

  Round to the nearest 100. 1,073,500 The nearest 1,000. 1,074,000
  The nearest 10,000. 1,070,000

Math Message

Read page 239 of the Student Reference Book.

Study Link 8.7 Follow-Up

Review answers.

1 Teaching the Lesson

✦ Math Message Follow-Up
(Student Reference Book, p. 239)

WHOLE-CLASS DISCUSSION 

Students discuss page 239 of the *Student Reference Book.* Listed below are some of the ideas that should emerge from the discussion.

▷ It is often difficult to make accurate area measurements of land forms.

▷ People do not always agree on where the borders of a country are located, or even on the definition of a land form.

▷ Boundaries may change, due to cultivation of the land, political events, or changes in climate.

Students may be surprised to learn that places where the water is always frozen, called tundras, are actually considered deserts.

✦ Comparing Country Areas
(Math Journal 2, pp. 260 and 261; Student Reference Book, pp. 230 and 231)

WHOLE-CLASS ACTIVITY

Social Studies Link Ask students to turn to the map of South America on pages 230 and 231 of the *Student Reference Book.* The country in South America with the largest area is Brazil. Use the classroom world map or a globe to compare Brazil and the United States, and mention that they have nearly the same area. (The United States is about 10% larger.)

Tell students that they will be comparing the areas of other countries in South America to Brazil's area. Since Brazil and the United States have nearly the same area, these comparisons will be nearly the same as if they compared the areas of other South American countries to the area of the United States.

STUDENT PAGE

World Tour

Geographical Area Measurements

The heights of mountains and the depths of oceans are obtained *directly.* We find heights and depths by measuring the Earth itself.

The areas of countries and the areas of oceans are found *indirectly.* We measure very accurate maps or satellite pictures. The countries and oceans themselves are not measured.

Countries, oceans, and deserts have irregular boundaries. To measure their areas, scientists count grid squares. They place a transparent grid of squares on a map. Then they count the squares and parts of squares that cover the region being measured. The squares are drawn to the same scale as the map.

There are several reasons that it is hard to measure the following regions accurately:

Area of a country. Sometimes people disagree about the exact boundary of a country. So the area may depend on which boundary is being used to measure.

Area of a lake, sea, or ocean. Some bodies of water have shorelines that shift greatly depending on the level of the water. So it is very hard to accurately measure the area that is covered by water.

The world's oceans are not separated from one another by shorelines. Sometimes people disagree on the boundaries between the oceans. This makes it difficult to measure the areas of oceans.

Area of a desert. Measuring desert areas is very hard. Desert boundaries may change because the climate changes. When land is cultivated, a desert boundary shifts. Also, scientists do not agree on what a desert actually is. Some define a desert as land that cannot be used for raising crops. Others define it as land that cannot be used for either crops or grazing. There are deserts that are hot and dry only part of the year. Some deserts are dry all year because it is very hot. Other deserts are dry all year because it is very cold and the water is always frozen. Very cold deserts are known as *tundras.*

two hundred thirty-nine 

✧ *Student Reference Book,* p. 239

STUDENT PAGE

Comparing Country Areas

Brazil is the largest country in South America. Brazil's area is about 3,300,000 square miles. The area of the United States is about 3,500,000 square miles. So Brazil is nearly the same size as the United States.

Fill in the table below. This will help you to compare the areas of other countries in South America to Brazil's area. Round quotients in Part 4 to the nearest tenth.

Sample answers:

Country	(1) Guess the number of times it would fit in the area of Brazil	(2) Area	(3) Area (rounded to the nearest 10,000)	(4) Divide the rounded areas: Brazil area ÷ country area
Ecuador	30	109,500 mi²	110,000 mi²	3,300,000 ÷ 110,000 = 30
Argentina	3	1,068,300 mi²	1,070,000 mi²	3,300,000 ÷ 1,070,000 = 3.1
Paraguay	20	157,000 mi²	160,000 mi²	3,300,000 ÷ 160,000 = 20.6
Peru	6	496,200 mi²	500,000 mi²	3,300,000 ÷ 500,000 = 6.6
Uruguay	50	68,000 mi²	70,000 mi²	3,300,000 ÷ 70,000 = 47.1
Chile	10	292,300 mi²	290,000 mi²	3,300,000 ÷ 290,000 = 11.4

Math Journal 2, p. 260

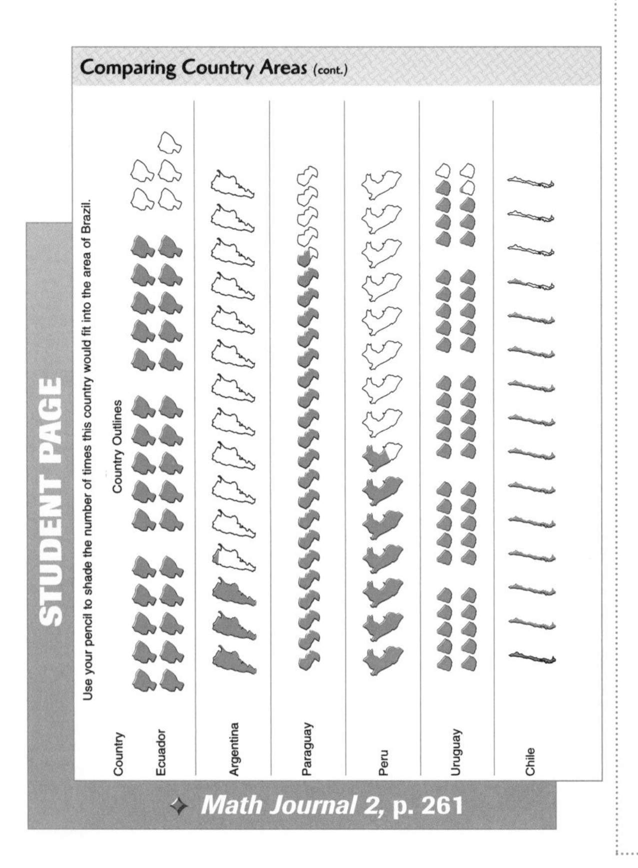
STUDENT PAGE
Comparing Country Areas (cont.)
Use your pencil to shade the number of times this country would fit into the area of Brazil.
Country
Country Outlines
Ecuador
Argentina
Paraguay
Peru
Uruguay
Chile

Math Journal 2, p. 261

Have students find Ecuador on the map. Use the following routine to compare the areas of Ecuador and Brazil. Students fill in the first line of the table on journal page 260 as you work through the steps.

▷ *Guess how many times larger Brazil is than Ecuador.* Ask students to imagine that they have many paper cutouts that are the size and shape of Ecuador. About how many cutouts would it take to cover Brazil? Said another way, how many Ecuadors would fill up Brazil? Expect answers that range from 20 to 50.

▷ *Round the areas of Brazil and Ecuador to the nearest 10,000 square miles.* The area of Ecuador is given in column (2) on the journal page as 109,500 square miles. The rounded area is 110,000 square miles.

Brazil's area is reported (at the top of the journal page) as 3,300,000 square miles. Rounding to the nearest 10,000 square miles will have no effect.

Ecuador's area is about 110,000 square miles. Brazil's area is about 3,300,000 square miles.

▷ *Estimate how many times larger Brazil is than Ecuador.* Point out that students need to figure out how many 110,000s there are in 3,300,000. Write 3,300,000 ÷ 110,000 on the board, and have students use their calculators to divide. 3,300,000 ÷ 110,000 = 30 Brazil is about 30 times the size of Ecuador. About 30 cutouts or copies of Ecuador would fit inside the boundary of Brazil.

▷ *Complete the picture graph.* The table on journal page 261 shows multiple copies of the outline of Ecuador. Ask students to shade in the first 30 of these outlines. The 30 shaded figures represent the estimate just made, that Brazil is 30 times the size of Ecuador.

NOTE: Students used division to solve equal-sharing and equal-grouping problems in Unit 6. The activity here introduces a third use of division: to compare two quantities that are measured with the same unit. The guessing procedure suggested above, whereby students are asked to imagine how many copies of the smaller quantity are needed to "fit into" or equal the larger quantity, will remind them that division can be used to solve comparison problems. We will return to division uses, including ratio comparisons, in Unit 9.

Students work with partners to complete journal pages 260 and 261. Make sure they understand that the different country areas are always compared to Brazil's area. If necessary, solve one or two additional comparison problems as a whole class, until students catch on.

In most cases, the division of Brazil's area by the area of another country will lead to a decimal answer. For example, Brazil's area divided by Peru's is 3,300,000 mi^2 ÷ 500,000 mi^2 = 6.6. Students should shade 6 full copies of Peru, and then shade $\frac{6}{10}$ of another copy.

Adjusting the Activity Offer practice using the calculator's memory keys. Have students do repeated divisions in which the dividend is 3,300,000. If they enter this dividend into the memory, they will not have to key it in each time.

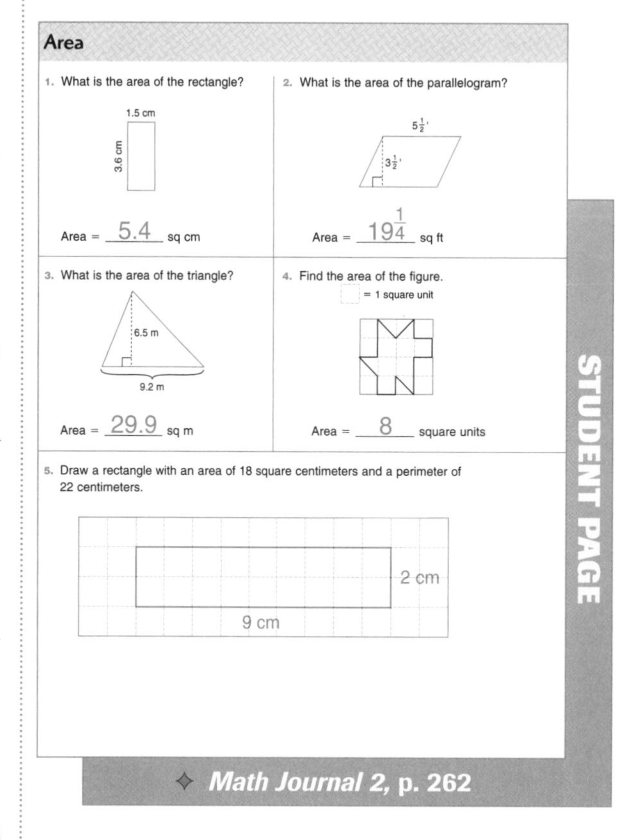

Area

1. What is the area of the rectangle? (1.5 cm; 3.6 cm) Area = 5.4 sq cm
2. What is the area of the parallelogram? ($5\frac{1}{2}$'; $3\frac{1}{2}$') Area = $19\frac{1}{4}$ sq ft
3. What is the area of the triangle? (6.5 m; 9.2 m) Area = 29.9 sq m
4. Find the area of the figure. (□ = 1 square unit) Area = 8 square units
5. Draw a rectangle with an area of 18 square centimeters and a perimeter of 22 centimeters. (2 cm; 9 cm)

STUDENT PAGE

✦ *Math Journal 2,* p. 262

Ongoing Learning & Practice

✦ Finding Areas (*Math Journal 2,* p. 262)

INDEPENDENT ACTIVITY 

Students use formulas to find the area of a rectangle, a parallelogram, and a triangle. They count squares to find the area of an irregular figure. Students draw a rectangle with a given area and perimeter.

✦ Math Boxes 8.8 (*Math Journal 2,* p. 259)

INDEPENDENT ACTIVITY 

Mixed Review Math Boxes in this lesson are paired with Math Boxes in Lesson 8.6. The skill in Problem 1 is a prerequisite for Unit 9.

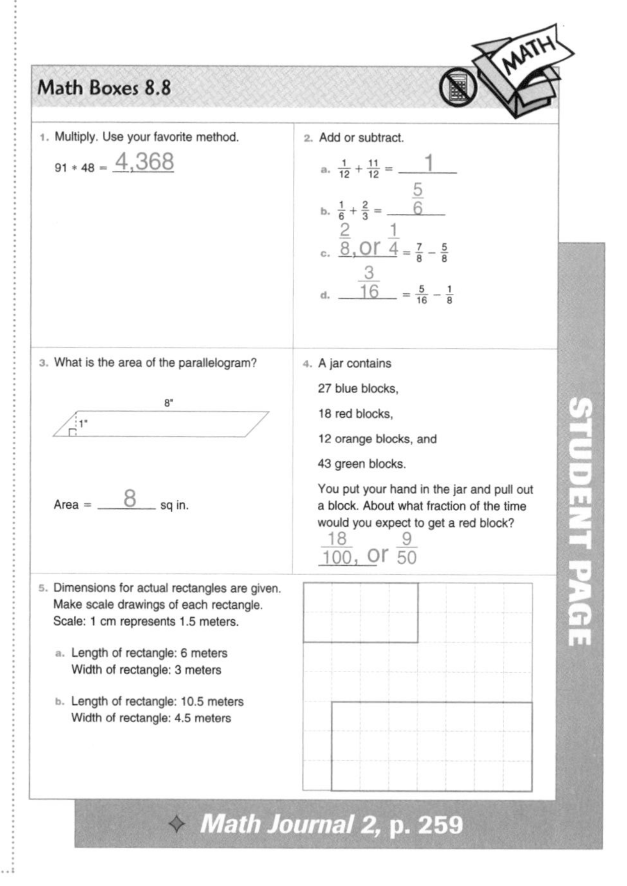

Math Boxes 8.8

1. Multiply. Use your favorite method. 91 ∗ 48 = 4,368
2. Add or subtract.
   a. $\frac{1}{12} + \frac{11}{12} = 1$
   b. $\frac{1}{6} + \frac{2}{3} = \frac{5}{6}$
   c. $\frac{2}{8}$, or $\frac{1}{4}$ $= \frac{7}{8} - \frac{5}{8}$
   d. $\frac{3}{16} = \frac{5}{16} - \frac{1}{8}$
3. What is the area of the parallelogram? (8"; 1") Area = 8 sq in.
4. A jar contains 27 blue blocks, 18 red blocks, 12 orange blocks, and 43 green blocks. You put your hand in the jar and pull out a block. About what fraction of the time would you expect to get a red block? $\frac{18}{100}$, or $\frac{9}{50}$
5. Dimensions for actual rectangles are given. Make scale drawings of each rectangle. Scale: 1 cm represents 1.5 meters.
   a. Length of rectangle: 6 meters; Width of rectangle: 3 meters
   b. Length of rectangle: 10.5 meters; Width of rectangle: 4.5 meters

STUDENT PAGE

✦ *Math Journal 2,* p. 259

STUDY LINK MASTER

Daily Newspapers

Study Link 8.8

Use the information in the table below to estimate the answers to the questions.

Country	Number of Daily Newspapers
India	1,802
United States	1,533
Germany	406
Turkey	400
Brazil	320
Mexico	310
Russia	292
Pakistan	223
Argentina	190
Greece	168

Source: The Top 10 of Everything 1999

1. India has about 6 times as many daily newspapers as which three countries? Russia, Mexico and Brazil
2. Which two countries have about $\frac{1}{2}$ as many daily newspapers as Germany? Pakistan and Argentina
3. The United States has about 5 times as many daily newspapers as Mexico.
4. India has about 10, or 11 times as many daily newspapers as Greece.
5. Greece has about $\frac{1}{2}$ as many daily newspapers as Brazil.
6. India has about 9, or 10 times as many daily newspapers as Argentina.

Math Masters, p. 337

TEACHING MASTER

Mammal Species

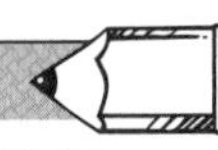

One of the major achievements of science is a system for classifying plants and animals. It was developed by Carolus Linnaeus (luh • knee´ • us) over 200 years ago. It is still in use today. In this system, a group of animals that are similar in form and that reproduce together is called a *species*. (The plural of *species* is *species*.)

Linnaeus's Classification System

	Bear	Rhinoceros
Kingdom	Animalia	Animalia
Phylum	Chordata	Chordata
Class	Mammalia	Mammalia
Order	Carnivora	Perissodactyla
Family	Ursidae	Rhinocerotidae
Genus and Species	*Ursus arctos* (Brown bear), *Ursus americanus* (American black bear), *Ursus maritimus* (Polar bear), *Selenarctos thibetanus* (Asiatic black bear), *Melursus ursinus* (Sloth bear), *Tremarctos ornatus* (Spectacled bear), *Helarctos malayanus* (Sun bear)	*Rhinoceros unicornis* (Indian rhino), *Rhinoceros sondaicus* (Javan rhino), *Dicerorhinus sumatrensis* (Sumatran rhino), *Diceros bicornis* (Black rhino), *Ceratotherium simum* (White or Square-lipped rhino)

Scientists have identified over 4,000 species of mammals. According to this system, jackrabbits of the northern plains form one species. Snowshoe hares of the western mountains form another.

Species that share a number of features are grouped into *genera* (plural of *genus*), and genera are grouped into *families*. There are 44 different rabbit and hare species. Each species has some unique feature that makes it different from all other species in the rabbit and hare family.

Number of Species in the Family

Family	Species	Family	Species
Koala	1	Dolphin	32
Elephant	2	Deer	34
White whale	3	Rabbit & hare	44
Great ape	4	Kangaroo & wallaby	50
Rhinoceros	5	Opossum	75
Porpoise	6	Monkey	127
Bear	7	Shrew	246
Pig	9	Squirrel	267
Hedgehog & moonrat	17	Bat	950
Armadillo	20	Mouse & rat	1,082

Source: Simon and Schuster's Guide to Mammals

Math Masters, p. 125

✦ Study Link 8.8 (*Math Masters*, p. 337)

Home Connection Students compare the number of daily newspapers in different countries. They use data in a table to estimate answers to given questions.

3 Options for Individualizing

✦ ENRICHMENT Using Division to Compare Numbers of Mammal Species (*Math Masters*, p. 125)

INDEPENDENT ACTIVITY  **15–30 min** 

Science Link Students read the essay about mammal species on *Math Masters*, page 125. They use data in a table to write and solve problems like the one below.

Sample Problem and Solution

There are how many times as many species of shrews (246) as species of pigs (9)?

There are about 27 times as many species of shrews as species of pigs.

8.9 Unit 8 Review and Assessment

OBJECTIVE **To review and assess students' progress on the material covered in Unit 8.**

1 Assess Progress

learning goals	activities
8a **Beginning Goal** Make and interpret scale drawings. **(Lessons 8.2, 8.3, and 8.5)**	❑ Slate Assessment, Problem 1 ❑ Written Assessment, Problems 8–11
8b **Developing Goal** Use formulas to find areas of rectangles, parallelograms, and triangles. **(Lessons 8.5–8.8)**	❑ Oral Assessment, Problem 1 ❑ Written Assessment, Problems 3–7 ❑ Alternative Assessment Option
8c **Developing Goal** Find the perimeter of a polygon. **(Lessons 8.1, 8.2, and 8.7)**	❑ Oral Assessment, Problem 1 ❑ Written Assessment, Problems 1, 3–5, and 9 ❑ Alternative Assessment Option
8d **Developing/Secure Goal** Find the area of a figure by counting unit squares and fractions of unit squares inside the figure. **(Lessons 8.3–8.7)**	❑ Oral Assessment, Problem 1 ❑ Written Assessment, Problems 2 and 11

materials

- ☐ *Math Journal 2,* p. 263
- ☐ Study Link 8.8
- ☐ Teaching Masters (*Math Masters,* pp. 126–131)
- ☐ Assessment Masters (*Math Masters,* pp. 404 and 405)
- ☐ slate ☐ centimeter ruler ☐ scissors and transparent tape

2 Build Background for Unit 9

summaries	materials
Students practice and maintain skills through Math Boxes and Study Link activities.	☐ *Math Journal 2,* p. 264 ☐ Study Link Masters (*Math Masters,* pp. 338–341)

Each **learning goal** listed above indicates a level of performance that might be expected at this point in the *Everyday Mathematics* K–6 curriculum. For a variety of reasons, the levels indicated may not accurately portray your class's performance.

Additional Information

Advance Preparation For additional information on assessment for Unit 8, see the *Assessment Handbook,* pages 60–62. For assessment checklists, see *Math Masters,* pages 440, 441, and 465–467.

Getting Started

Math Message

Complete the Time to Reflect *questions on journal page 263.*

Study Link 8.8 Follow-Up

Review answers.

Time to Reflect

1. Which do you think is more difficult—making a rough sketch of something or making a scale drawing of something? Explain your answer.
Accept all reasonable answers. Most students will likely say that making a scale drawing is more difficult because it requires more accuracy than a rough sketch.

2. Think about the decorating and upkeep that your family might do to your home. When might they need to know the *area* of something?
Sample answers: To buy a new carpet; to put in a new kitchen or bathroom floor; to paint a room; to plan a garden; to choose furniture for a room

3. Which area would it take you longer to paint—20 square yards or 20 square meters?
20 square meters

STUDENT PAGE

✧ *Math Journal 2,* p. 263

Assess Progress

✦ Math Message Follow-Up
(*Math Journal 2,* p. 263)

WHOLE-CLASS DISCUSSION

Students share their answers. For Problem 3, display unit squares so that students can visually compare a square yard and a square meter. Explain that the square meter has an area that is about 20% larger than the area of a square yard.

✦ Oral and Slate Assessments

WHOLE-CLASS ACTIVITY

If the suggested problems below are not appropriate for your class's level of performance, adjust the numbers or the problems themselves to better assess your students' abilities.

Oral Assessment Suggestion

1. Students explain the differences between *area* and *perimeter.* Look for responses such as the following: **Goals 8b, 8c, and 8d**

▷ The perimeter of a polygon is the distance around the polygon. The area of a polygon is a measure of the surface inside the polygon.

▷ To find the perimeter of a polygon, you can add the lengths of its sides. To find the area of an irregular polygon, you can count unit squares and fractions of unit squares inside the polygon. To find the area of a rectangle, parallelogram, or triangle, you can use a formula.

▷ Perimeter is measured in units such as inches, feet, and centimeters. Area is measured in units such as square inches, square feet, and square centimeters.

Slate Assessment Suggestions

1. Pose problems that require students to interpret a scale. **Goal 8a**

   If $\frac{1}{2}$ inch on a map represents 30 miles, then

   - 1 inch represents __60__ miles.
   - $\frac{1}{4}$ inch represents __15__ miles.
   - 2 inches represent __120__ miles.
   - $1\frac{3}{4}$ inches represent __105__ miles.

2. Write mixed feet-and-inches measurements on the board. Students rewrite them in simpler form.

   - 1' 18" 2' 6"
   - 3' 20" 4' 8"
   - 5' 25" 7' 1"

3. Pose "fraction-of" problems.

   - What is $\frac{1}{2}$ of 64? 32
   - What is $\frac{1}{3}$ of 24? 8
   - What is $\frac{3}{4}$ of 20? 15

4. Pose "times-as-many" problems.

   - What number is 2 times as many as 49? 98
   - What number is 3 times as many as 25? 75
   - What number is 4 times as many as 15? 60

5. Write numbers on the board. Students round the numbers to a given place.

   - Round 436 to the nearest 10. 440
   - Round 1,571 to the nearest 100. 1,600
   - Round 43,299 to the nearest 1,000. 43,000 To the nearest 10,000. 40,000

NOTE: Some of the slate assessment suggestions relate to learning goals that have been addressed in previous units. Now is a good time to evaluate students' progress toward those goals.

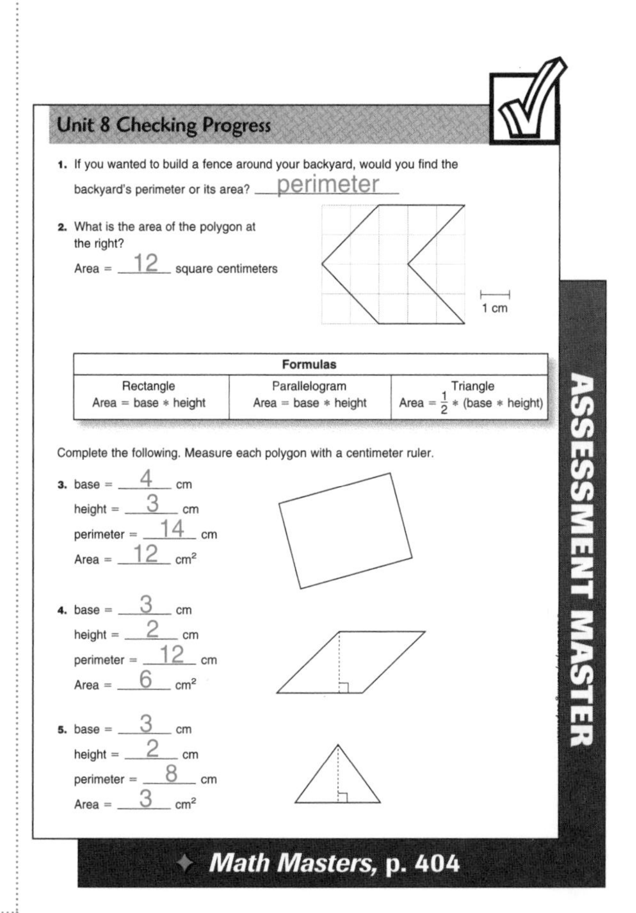
Unit 8 Checking Progress

1. If you wanted to build a fence around your backyard, would you find the backyard's perimeter or its area? __perimeter__

2. What is the area of the polygon at the right?

   Area = __12__ square centimeters

Formulas		
Rectangle Area = base * height	Parallelogram Area = base * height	Triangle Area = $\frac{1}{2}$ * (base * height)

Complete the following. Measure each polygon with a centimeter ruler.

3. base = __4__ cm
height = __3__ cm
perimeter = __14__ cm
Area = __12__ cm^2

4. base = __3__ cm
height = __2__ cm
perimeter = __12__ cm
Area = __6__ cm^2

5. base = __3__ cm
height = __2__ cm
perimeter = __8__ cm
Area = __3__ cm^2

Math Masters, p. 404

ASSESSMENT MASTER

Unit 8 Checking Progress *(cont.)*

6. Mrs. Lopez wants to tile her dining room floor. The room is 12 feet wide and 21 feet long. How many 1-square-foot tiles does she need to cover the floor?
   Answer: 252 tiles

7. Suppose Mrs. Lopez chooses tiles that are 6 inches on each side. How many 6-inch tiles would she need in order to cover her dining room floor?

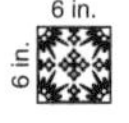

   Answer: 1,008 tiles
   Explain how you got your answer.
   It takes four 6-inch tiles to cover one 12-inch tile, so she would need $4 * 252$ tiles = 1,008 tiles.

Below is a scale drawing of a very large forest. A river runs along the northwest border of the forest. Use the scale to answer the following questions:

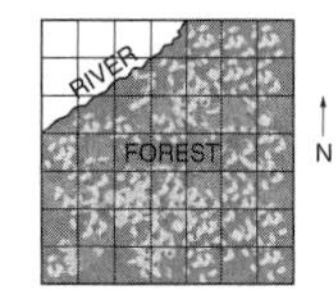

Scale: $\frac{1}{4}$ inch represents 10 miles

8. What is the length of the river along the northwest border?
   About 50 miles

9. What is the perimeter of the boundary of the forest?
   About 260 miles

10. How many square miles does each little square in the scale drawing represent?
    About 100 square miles

11. What is the area of the forest?
    About 4,300 square miles

✦ *Math Masters,* p. 405

TEACHING MASTER

Area and Perimeter

1. Find the area of the polygon below *without* counting squares.
   Hint: Divide the polygon into figures for which you can calculate the areas: rectangles, parallelograms, and triangles. Use a formula to find the area of each of the figures.
   Total area of polygon = 126 cm^2

2. Find the perimeter of the polygon. Use a centimeter ruler.
   Perimeter = 48 cm

Sample answer:

10 cm
24 sq cm
12 cm
5 cm
6 sq cm
48 sq cm
8 cm
24 sq cm
24 sq cm
10 cm
1 cm
3 cm

✦ *Math Masters* p. 126

✦ Written Assessment
(*Math Masters,* pp. 404 and 405)

INDEPENDENT ACTIVITY 

Depending on the needs of your students, you may want to work through an example together, reading a problem aloud, discussing it, and providing additional examples as necessary before students work the problem independently.

Each of the problems is listed below and paired with one or more of this unit's learning goals.

- Decide whether perimeter or area is the more appropriate measure. (Problem 1) **Goal 8c**
- Find the area of an irregular polygon. (Problem 2) **Goal 8d**
- Use formulas to find the area of a rectangle, parallelogram, and triangle. Also find the perimeter of each figure. (Problems 3–5) **Goals 8b and 8c**
- Solve number stories involving area. (Problems 6 and 7) **Goal 8b**
- Use a scale drawing to estimate a distance and to find the perimeter of a region. (Problems 8 and 9) **Goals 8a and 8c**
- Use a scale drawing to estimate the area of regions. (Problems 10 and 11) **Goals 8a and 8d**

NOTE: The problems on *Math Masters,* page 404 assess the basic concepts and skills presented in this unit. The problems on *Math Masters,* page 405 are more challenging; the emphasis is on applying the concepts and skills in problem-solving situations. While students may work independently on all the problems on both masters, you might consider having them work on *Math Masters,* page 405 with a partner or in small groups.

Students who do well on the problems on *Math Masters,* page 404 are progressing satisfactorily. Do not expect most students to solve all the problems on *Math Masters,* page 405. Those who do well on this part of the assessment exhibit a high level of understanding and problem-solving skill.

Problem notes

▷ Problem 2 can be solved by counting squares and half-squares. Some students may have noticed that the polygon consists of two parallelograms, each having the same area. Thus, they can find the area of one polygon using the formula, and then double the result. Another method is to move the triangular part from the left side of the polygon to the right side; the resulting figure is a 3-cm by 4-cm rectangle.

▷ For Problems 6 and 7, point out that while there are twice as many 6-inch tiles as 1-foot tiles along each side of the floor, 4 times as many 6-inch tiles are needed to cover the floor.

▷ One way to find the area of the forest in Problem 11 is to count squares and partial squares. Another way is to partition the forest into a 7 by 4 rectangle, a 3 by 3 square, and a right triangle. Using this method, the area of the forest is represented by 43 squares in the scale drawing. This is equivalent to an actual area of 4,300 square miles.

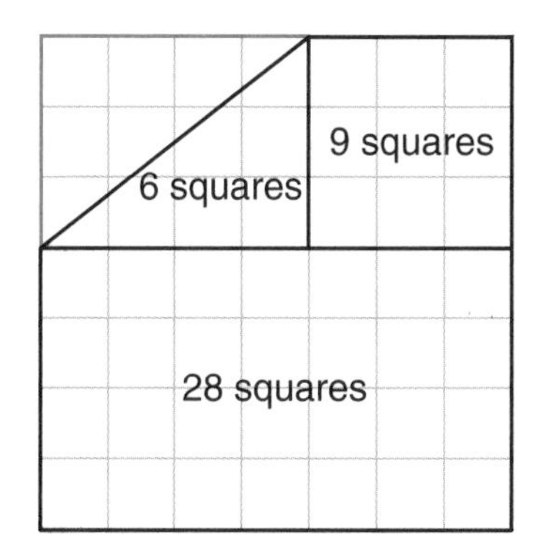

$6 + 9 + 28 = 43$ squares

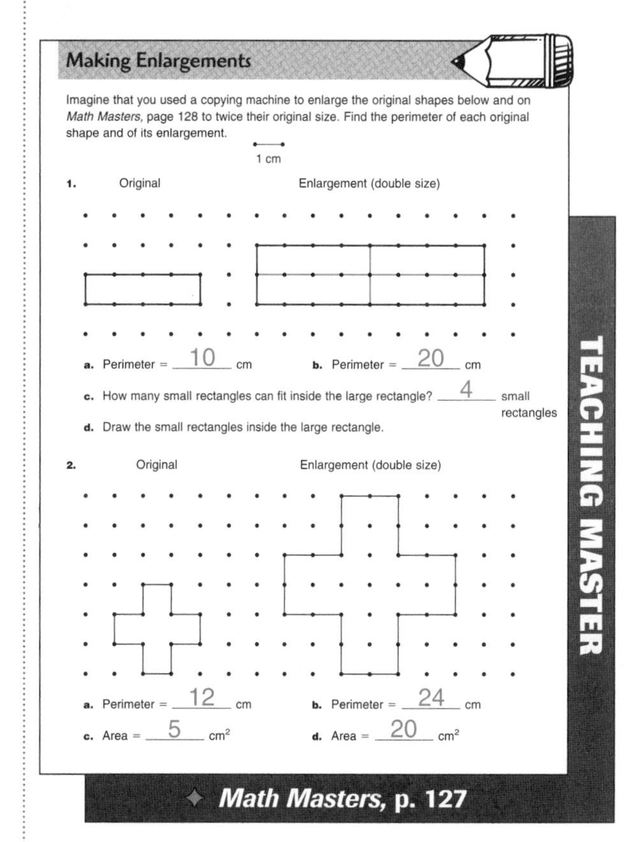

Making Enlargements

Imagine that you used a copying machine to enlarge the original shapes below and on *Math Masters,* page 128 to twice their original size. Find the perimeter of each original shape and of its enlargement.

1 cm

1. Original — Enlargement (double size)

a. Perimeter = 10 cm
b. Perimeter = 20 cm
c. How many small rectangles can fit inside the large rectangle? 4 small rectangles
d. Draw the small rectangles inside the large rectangle.

2. Original — Enlargement (double size)

a. Perimeter = 12 cm
b. Perimeter = 24 cm
c. Area = 5 cm²
d. Area = 20 cm²

TEACHING MASTER

✦ **Math Masters, p. 127**

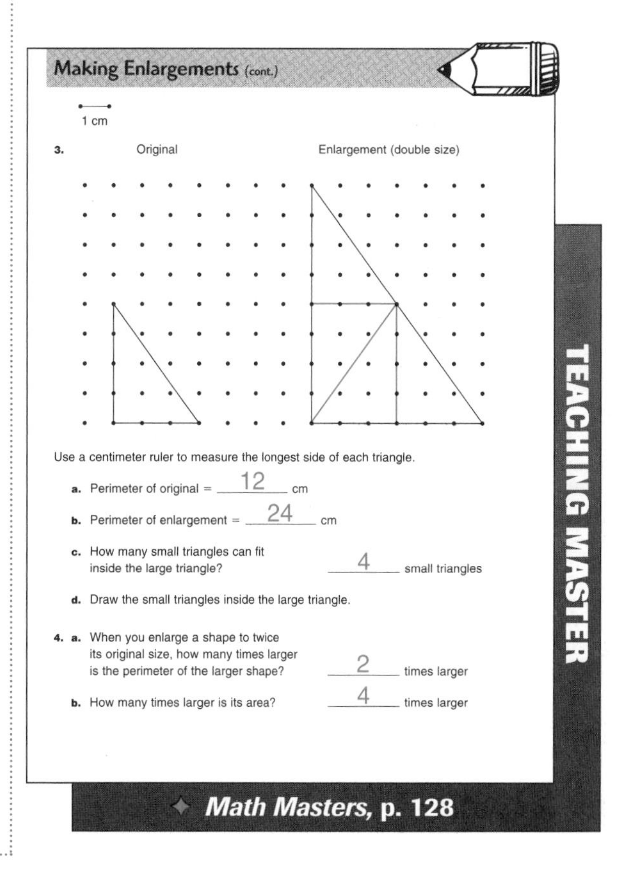

Making Enlargements (cont.)

1 cm

3. Original — Enlargement (double size)

Use a centimeter ruler to measure the longest side of each triangle.

a. Perimeter of original = 12 cm
b. Perimeter of enlargement = 24 cm
c. How many small triangles can fit inside the large triangle? 4 small triangles
d. Draw the small triangles inside the large triangle.

4. a. When you enlarge a shape to twice its original size, how many times larger is the perimeter of the larger shape? 2 times larger
b. How many times larger is its area? 4 times larger

TEACHING MASTER

✦ **Math Masters, p. 128**

✦ ALTERNATIVE ASSESSMENT OPTION

Find the Area and Perimeter of an Irregular Figure (*Math Masters,* p. 126)

INDEPENDENT ACTIVITY 

Students find the area and perimeter of an irregular polygon. Counting squares to find the area is not permitted; students are encouraged to divide the polygon into figures and then use a formula to calculate the area of each figure.

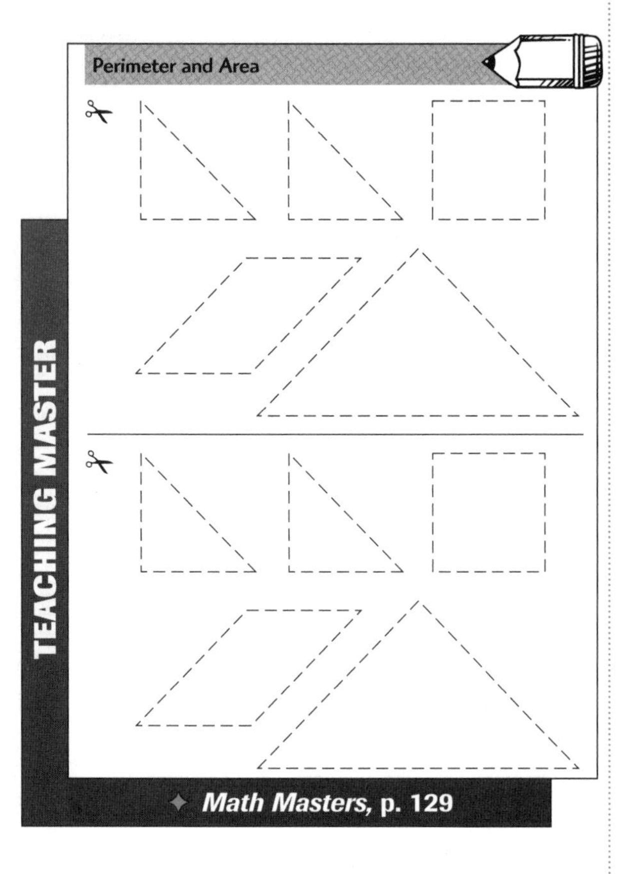
TEACHING MASTER

Perimeter and Area

✦ *Math Masters,* p. 129

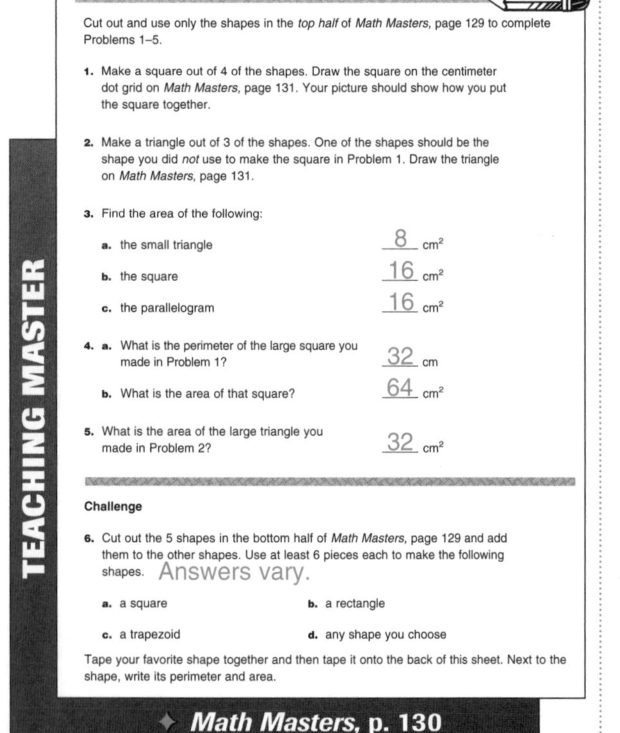
TEACHING MASTER

Perimeter and Area (cont.)

Cut out and use only the shapes in the *top half* of *Math Masters,* page 129 to complete Problems 1–5.

1. Make a square out of 4 of the shapes. Draw the square on the centimeter dot grid on *Math Masters,* page 131. Your picture should show how you put the square together.

2. Make a triangle out of 3 of the shapes. One of the shapes should be the shape you did *not* use to make the square in Problem 1. Draw the triangle on *Math Masters,* page 131.

3. Find the area of the following:

   a. the small triangle 8 cm^2

   b. the square 16 cm^2

   c. the parallelogram 16 cm^2

4. a. What is the perimeter of the large square you made in Problem 1? 32 cm

   b. What is the area of that square? 64 cm^2

5. What is the area of the large triangle you made in Problem 2? 32 cm^2

Challenge

6. Cut out the 5 shapes in the bottom half of *Math Masters,* page 129 and add them to the other shapes. Use at least 6 pieces each to make the following shapes. Answers vary.

   a. a square
   b. a rectangle
   c. a trapezoid
   d. any shape you choose

Tape your favorite shape together and then tape it onto the back of this sheet. Next to the shape, write its perimeter and area.

✦ *Math Masters,* p. 130

One solution strategy is to partition the polygon as shown below. Find the area of Triangle A (6 cm^2), Parallelogram B (96 cm^2), and Rectangle C (24 cm^2). Total area = 126 cm^2. Another solution strategy can be found on the reduction of *Math Masters,* page 126. See page 640.

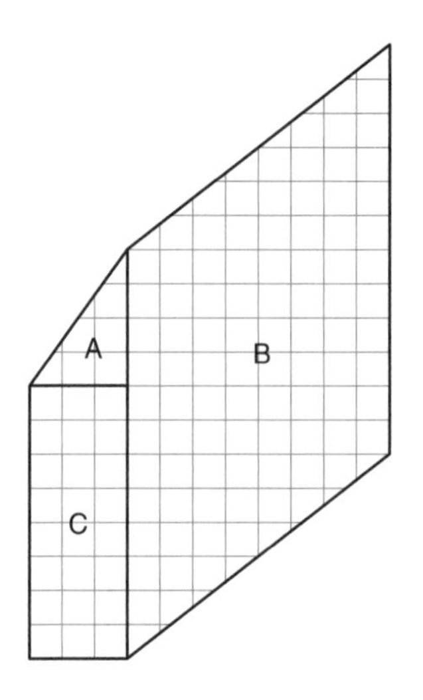

✦ ALTERNATIVE ASSESSMENT OPTION

Make Enlargements

(*Math Masters,* pp. 127 and 128)

INDEPENDENT ACTIVITY 

Students determine what effect doubling the sides of a polygon has on its perimeter and its area.

✦ ALTERNATIVE ASSESSMENT OPTION

Solve Perimeter and Area Problems

(*Math Masters,* pp. 129–131)

INDEPENDENT ACTIVITY 

Portfolio Ideas

Students explore ways of combining various 2-dimensional shapes to form new shapes. The new shapes are then used to check students' understanding of perimeter and area. The following are possible solutions to Problem 6.

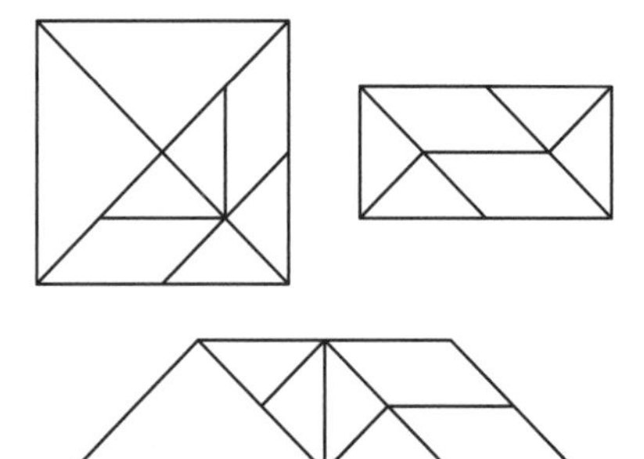

2 Build Background for Unit 9

✦ Math Boxes 8.9 (*Math Journal 2,* p. 264)

INDEPENDENT ACTIVITY 

Mixed Review The skills in Problems 1–4 are prerequisites for Unit 9.

✦ Study Link 8.9: Unit 9 Family Letter (*Math Masters,* pp. 338–341)

Home Connection This Study Link is a four-page newsletter that introduces parents and guardians to Unit 9's topics and terms. The letter also offers ideas for mathematics activities that are supportive of classroom work and can be done at home.

PLANNING AHEAD

Remind students to complete Study Link 8.6 (*Math Masters,* page 335) before the class begins Lesson 9.1.

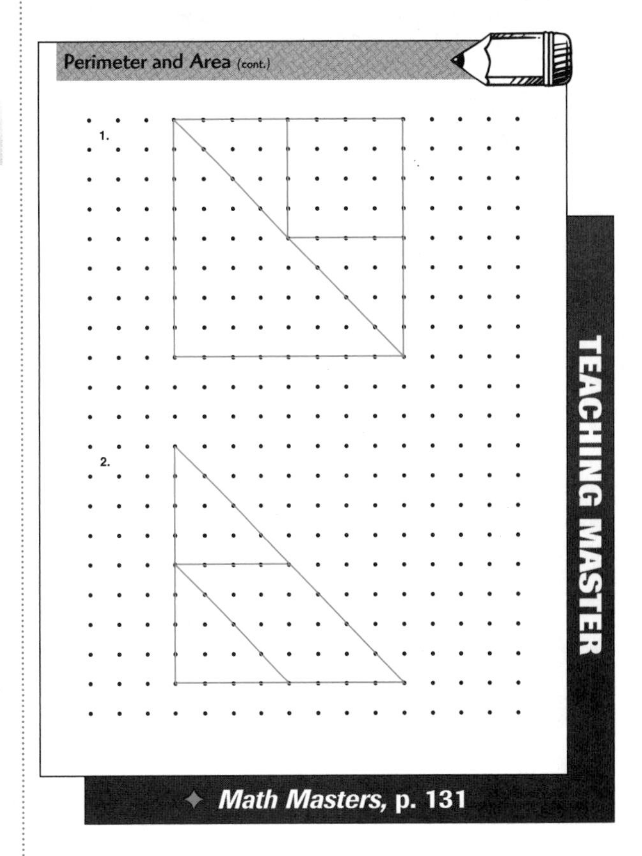

Family Letter Study Link 8.9

Unit 9: Percents

In Unit 9, we will be studying percents and their uses in everyday situations. Your child should begin finding examples of percents in newspapers and magazines, on food packages, on clothing labels, and so on, and bring them to class. Students' collections will be used to illustrate a variety of percent applications.

As we study percents, your child will learn equivalent values for percents, fractions, and decimals. For example, 50% is equivalent to the fraction $\frac{1}{2}$ and to the decimal 0.5. The class will develop the understanding that **percent** always refers to a **part out of 100.**

Converting "easy" fractions, such as $\frac{1}{2}$, $\frac{1}{3}$, $\frac{1}{10}$, and $\frac{3}{4}$, to decimal and percent equivalents should become automatic for your child. Such fractions are common in percent situations and are helpful with "more difficult" fractions, decimals, and percents. To aid in memorizing the "easy" fraction/percent equivalencies, your child will play *Fraction/Percent Concentration.*

"Easy" Fractions	Decimals	Percents
$\frac{1}{2}$	0.50	50%
$\frac{1}{4}$	0.25	25%
$\frac{3}{4}$	0.75	75%
$\frac{2}{5}$	0.40	40%
$\frac{7}{10}$	0.70	70%
$\frac{2}{2}$	1.00	100%

Throughout the unit, your child will use a calculator to convert fractions to percents and will learn how to use the percent key [%] to calculate discounts, sale prices, and percents of discount.

As part of the World Tour, your child will explore population data, such as literacy rates and percents of people who live in rural and urban areas.

Finally, the class will begin to apply the multiplication and division algorithms to problems that contain decimals. The approach used in *Everyday Mathematics* is quite simple: Students solve the problems as if the numbers were whole numbers. Then they estimate the answers to help them locate the decimal point in the exact answer. In this unit, we begin with fairly simple problems. Your child will solve progressively more difficult problems in *Fifth* and *Sixth Grade Everyday Mathematics.*

Please keep this Family Letter for reference as your child works through Unit 9.

STUDY LINK MASTERS

✦ *Math Masters,* pp. 338–341

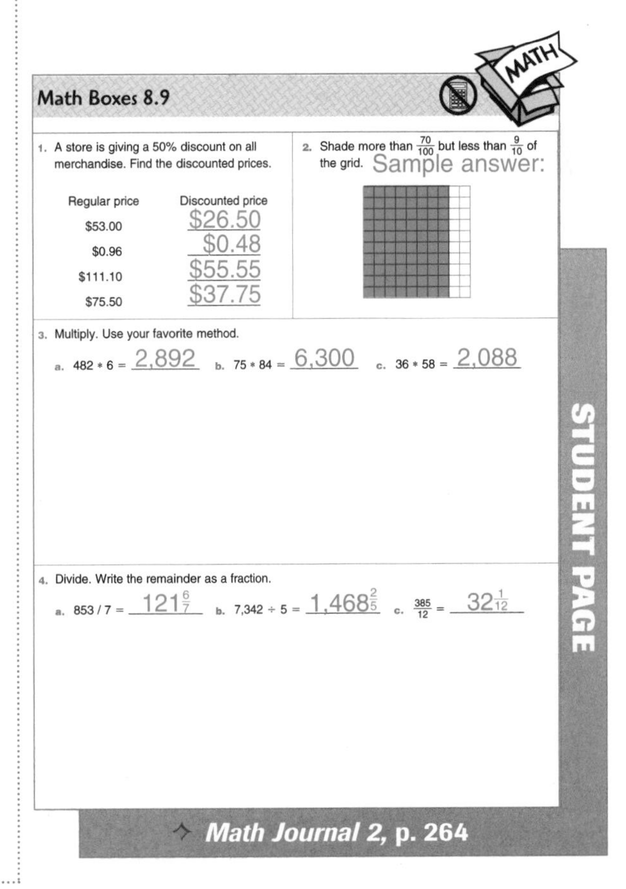

Math Boxes 8.9

1. A store is giving a 50% discount on all merchandise. Find the discounted prices.

Regular price	Discounted price
$53.00	$26.50
$0.96	$0.48
$111.10	$55.55
$75.50	$37.75

2. Shade more than $\frac{70}{100}$ but less than $\frac{9}{10}$ of the grid. Sample answer:

3. Multiply. Use your favorite method.

a. 482 ∗ 6 = 2,892 b. 75 ∗ 84 = 6,300 c. 36 ∗ 58 = 2,088

4. Divide. Write the remainder as a fraction.

a. 853 / 7 = $121\frac{6}{7}$ b. 7,342 ÷ 5 = $1,468\frac{2}{5}$ c. $\frac{385}{12}$ = $32\frac{1}{12}$

STUDENT PAGE

✦ *Math Journal 2,* p. 264

Unit 9
Percents

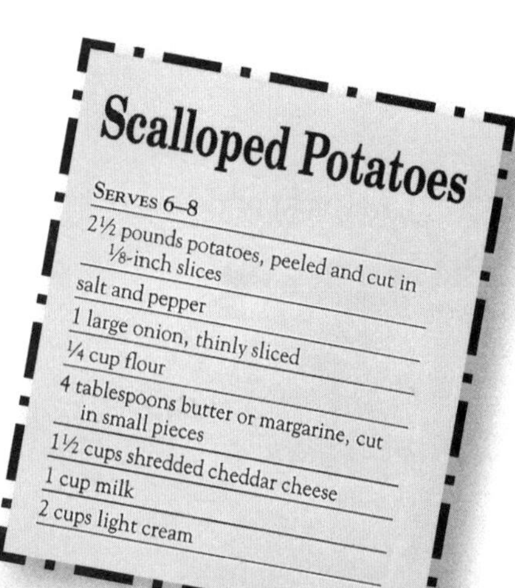

Scalloped Potatoes
Serves 6–8
2½ pounds potatoes, peeled and cut in ⅛-inch slices
salt and pepper
1 large onion, thinly sliced
¼ cup flour
4 tablespoons butter or margarine, cut in small pieces
1½ cups shredded cheddar cheese
1 cup milk
2 cups light cream

overview

Everyday Mathematics emphasizes the fact that many different names can be given to any number. Unit 9 focuses on the links among fraction, decimal, and percent names for numbers, with a special emphasis on percents.

Percent names are useful when comparing ratios because they represent fractions with the common denominator 100. For example, if 7 out of 12 boys and 4 out of 9 girls in a class prefer watching TV over listening to the radio, one can compare these ratios by converting them to percents: $\frac{7}{12}$ is equal to about 58% and $\frac{4}{9}$ is equal to about 44%. The percent names make it easier to compare these ratios.

In the first seven lessons of Unit 9, students will practice conversions among fractions, decimals, and percents. They will use grid pictures, the multiplication rule for renaming fractions, memorization of simple conversions, and a calculator for more complex conversions. In the last two lessons, they will begin to apply whole number multiplication and division algorithms to multiplication and division with decimals.

contents

Lesson	Objective	Page
9.1	**Fractions, Decimals, and Percents** *To use percents to describe real-life situations; and to practice naming equivalencies among fractions, decimals, and percents.*	656
9.2	**Converting "Easy" Fractions to Decimals and Percents** *To rename "easy" fractions (fourths, fifths, and tenths) as decimals and percents; and to solve percent problems by using equivalent fractions.*	662
9.3	**Using a Calculator to Convert Fractions to Decimals** *To rename any fraction as a decimal by using a calculator; and to memorize fraction/percent equivalencies for "easy" fractions (fourths, fifths, and tenths).*	668
9.4	**Using a Calculator to Convert Fractions to Percents** *To rename fractions as percents using a calculator; and to solve number stories involving discounts expressed as percents.*	674
9.5	**Conversions among Fractions, Decimals, and Percents** *To look up and record numerical data; to rename fractions as percents using a calculator; and to rename decimals as percents.*	680
9.6	**Comparing the Results of a Survey** *To organize and tabulate survey data; and to use percents to compare quantities expressed as fractions with unlike denominators.*	686
9.7	**Comparing Population Data** *To rank and compare data that are reported as percents; and to display ranked data by coloring maps.*	692
9.8	**Multiplication of Decimals** *To multiply decimals by whole numbers; and to practice the partial-products and lattice methods for multiplication.*	698
9.9	**Division of Decimals** *To divide decimals by whole numbers; and to practice the partial-quotients division algorithm introduced in Unit 6.*	704
9.10	**Unit 9 Review and Assessment** *To review and assess students' progress on the material covered in Unit 9.*	710

learning goals in perspective

learning goals	links to the past	links to the future
9a **Beginning Goal** Use an estimation strategy to divide decimals by whole numbers. **(Lesson 9.9)**	Grade 3: Model and solve division number stories using arrays, multiplication/division diagrams, and number models. Review division as equal sharing and equal grouping. Practice division facts. Extend decimal notation to tenths and hundredths using money and base-10 blocks.	Grade 5: Make magnitude estimates for quotients of whole numbers and decimals divided by whole numbers. Divide decimal numbers by whole numbers with no remainders. Grade 6: Extend the partial-quotients algorithm to decimal divisors. Use the method to find quotients to any given number of decimal places and to rename fractions as decimals.
9b **Beginning Goal** Use an estimation strategy to multiply decimals by whole numbers. **(Lesson 9.8)**	Grade 3: Model and solve multiplication number stories using arrays, multiplication/division diagrams, and number models. Practice multiplication facts. Extend decimal notation to tenths and hundredths using money and base-10 blocks. Grade 4: Estimate the magnitude of a product of multidigit numbers (Unit 5).	Grade 5: Make magnitude estimates to place decimal points in products. Extend the partial-products algorithm and lattice method to decimals. Grade 6: Multiply decimals.
9c **Developing Goal** Find a percent or a fraction of a number. **(Lessons 9.1–9.3 and 9.6)**	Grade 3: Name fractional parts of regions and sets of objects. Fold rectangles to find fractions of fractions.	Grades 5 and 6: Solve percent-of problems. Find the whole, given a percent of the whole.
9d **Developing Goal** Convert between "easy" fractions (fourths, fifths, and tenths), decimals, and percents. **(Lessons 9.1–9.3)**	Grade 3: Find equivalent fractions using Fraction Cards; identify fractions on a fraction number line. Find fraction/decimal equivalents.	Grade 5: Develop reflex recognition of "easy" fraction-decimal equivalents. Grade 6: Applications and maintenance.
9e **Secure Goal** Convert between hundredths-fractions, decimals, and percents. **(Lessons 9.1 and 9.2)**	Grade 3: Find fraction/decimal equivalents. Grade 4: Find equivalent names for decimals (Unit 4).	Grade 4: Start a table of equivalent fractions and fraction/decimal equivalents (Unit 10). Grades 5 and 6: Applications and extensions, including games to promote reflex recognition of fraction/decimal/percent equivalents, and practice with equivalent rates and ratios.
9f **Secure Goal** Use a calculator to rename any fraction as a decimal or percent. **(Lessons 9.3–9.5 and 9.7)**	Grade 3: Read and display numbers on a calculator. Perform operations on a calculator. Play *Beat the Calculator.*	Grade 5: Use a calculator to find decimal equivalents. Grade 6: Use a calculator to rename fractions as decimals and percents.

assessment

ongoing • product • periodic

Informal Assessment

Ongoing Assessment: Kid Watching Use the Ongoing Assessment suggestions in the following lessons to make quick, on-the-spot observations about students' understanding of:

- Numeration **(Lesson 9.1, Part 1 and Lesson 9.5, Part 1)**
- Operations and Computation **(Lesson 9.2, Part 2; Lesson 9.6, Part 2; Lesson 9.8, Part 1; and Lesson 9.9, Part 1)**

Portfolio Ideas Samples of students' work may be obtained from the following assignments:

- Making a Percent Booklet or Poster **(Lesson 9.1)**
- Writing and Solving "Percent-of" Number Stories **(Lesson 9.2)**
- Solving Challenging Discount Number Stories **(Lesson 9.4)**
- Graphing Survey Results **(Lesson 9.6)**
- Ranking Countries and Coloring a Map to Show Literacy Data **(Lesson 9.7)**
- Writing and Solving Division Number Stories with Decimals **(Lesson 9.9)**
- Find the "Fraction-of" and "Percent-of" a Design; Describe a Decimal Division Strategy; Describe a Decimal Multiplication Strategy **(Lesson 9.10)**

Unit 9 Review and Assessment

Math Message Use Time to Reflect Questions 1–3 in Lesson 9.10 to assess students' progress toward the following learning goals: **Goals 9c–9e**

Oral and Slate Assessments Use oral or slate assessments during Lesson 9.10 to assess students' progress toward the following learning goals: **Goals 9a–9e**

Written Assessment Use a written review during Lesson 9.10 to assess students' progress toward the following learning goals: **Goals 9a–9f**

Alternative Assessment Options Use independent alternative assessments in Lesson 9.10 to assess students' progress toward the following learning goals: **Goals 9a–9c and 9f**

assessmenthandbook

For more information on how to use different types of assessment in Unit 9, see the Assessment Overview on pages 63–65 in the *Assessment Handbook*. The following Assessment Masters can be found in the *Math Masters* book:

- Unit 9 Checking Progress, pp. 406–408
- Unit 9 Class Checklist, p. 442
- Unit 9 Individual Profile of Progress, p. 443
- Class Progress Indicator, p. 467
- Interest Inventories, pp. 468 and 469
- Math Logs, pp. 470–472
- Self-Assessment Forms, pp. 473 and 474

problem solving

A process of modeling everyday situations using tools from mathematics

Encourage students to use a variety of strategies when attacking a given problem—and to explain those strategies. *Strategies students might use in this unit:*

- Using number sense
- Using computation
- Finding a pattern
- Using data in a table
- Making a table
- Drawing a picture
- Using estimation
- Writing a problem

Four Problem-Solving
REPRESENTATIONS

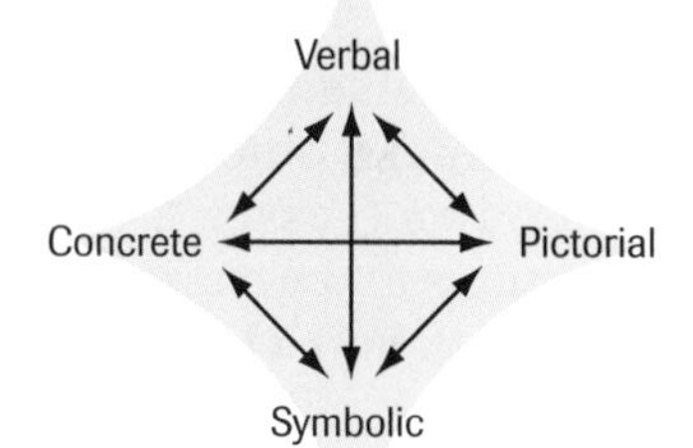

Lessons that teach *through* problem solving, not just *about* problem solving

Lesson	Activity	Lesson	Activity
9.1	Writing equivalent names for percents in various situations	**9.6**	Tabulating survey results; making predictions by comparing data expressed as percents
9.2	Solving "percent-of" number stories	**9.7**	Listing in order the populations of countries and coloring maps to display the data
9.3	Identifying a pattern when renaming a variety of fractions as decimals	**9.8**	Solving problems involving multiplication of decimals
9.4	Solving number stories involving discounts given as percents	**9.9**	Solving number stories involving division of decimals
9.5	Renaming "number-of" data as percents		

For more information about problem solving in *Everyday Mathematics,* see the *Teacher's Reference Manual.*

cross-curricular links

language arts

- Students think of words that begin with *cent-*. **(Lesson 9.1)**

science

- Students examine circle graphs and read books showing information about rain forests. **(Lesson 9.4)**

literature

- Students read books about fraction equivalencies: *Gator Pie* by Louise Mathews and *Eating Fractions* by Bruce McMillan. **(Lesson 9.3)**
- Students learn about ways that data can be compared by reading *Incredible Comparisons* by Russell Ash. **(Lesson 9.6)**

social studies

- Students continue the World Tour by flying from Brasília, Brazil, to Beijing, China. **(Lesson 9.5)**
- Students discuss population data. **(Lesson 9.7)**

consumer

- Students solve number stories involving discounts on items. **(Lesson 9.4)**

meeting INDIVIDUAL needs

UNIVERSAL ACCESS

✦ RETEACHING

The following features provide additional instructional support:

Adjusting the Activity

- **Lesson 9.3, Part 2**
- **Lesson 9.4, Part 1**
- **Lesson 9.9, Part 1**

Options for Individualizing

- **Lesson 9.1** Creating Base-10 Block Designs
- **Lesson 9.3** Finding Fraction Equivalencies in Literature
- **Lesson 9.8** Using the Lattice Method to Position Decimal Points
- **Lesson 9.8** Multiplying Whole Numbers
- **Lesson 9.9** Dividing Whole Numbers

✦ ENRICHMENT

The following features suggest some enrichment and extension activities found in this unit:

Adjusting the Activity

- **Lesson 9.1, Part 1**
- **Lesson 9.4, Part 1**
- **Lesson 9.5, Part 1**
- **Lesson 9.5, Part 2**
- **Lesson 9.6, Part 1**

Options for Individualizing

- **Lesson 9.1** Making a Percent Booklet or Poster
- **Lesson 9.3** Playing *Getting to One*
- **Lesson 9.4** Solving Challenging Discount Number Stories
- **Lesson 9.4** Estimating What Percent of a Circle Graph Is Shaded
- **Lesson 9.6** Graphing Survey Results
- **Lesson 9.6** Reading about Comparisons
- **Lesson 9.7** Ranking Countries and Coloring a Map to Show Literacy Data
- **Lesson 9.9** Writing and Solving Division Number Stories with Decimals

✦ LANGUAGE DIVERSITY

The following features suggest some ways to support students who are acquiring proficiency in English:

Adjusting the Activity

- **Lesson 9.5, Part 2**

Options for Individualizing

- **Lesson 9.2** Writing and Solving "Percent-of" Number Stories
- **Lesson 9.4** Building Background for Mathematics Words

✦ MULTIAGE CLASSROOM

The following chart lists related lessons from Grades 3 and 5 that can help you meet your instructional needs:

Grade 3	8.4 8.5	8.4 8.5	8.4 8.5			11.7			
Grade 4	9.1	9.2	9.3	9.4	9.5	9.6	9.7	9.8	9.9
Grade 5	6.8	6.8 8.8		5.8	5.8 6.8		3.2	2.8	4.4

materials

lesson	math masters pages	manipulative kit items	other items
9.1	Study Link Masters, pp. 335, 342, and 343 Teaching Masters, pp. 132 and 133 ***See* Advance Preparation, p. 656**	base-10 blocks	
9.2	Study Link Master, p. 344 Teaching Masters, p. 20 or 80 (optional); and pp. 134 and 135 ***See* Advance Preparation, p. 662**		scissors
9.3	Study Link Master, p. 345 Teaching Masters, pp. 136 and 137		envelope or small plastic bag calculator *Gator Pie* *Eating Fractions* ***See* Advance Preparation, p. 668**
9.4	Study Link Master, p. 346 Teaching Masters, pp. 138 and 139		calculator Fraction/Percent Tiles (see Lesson 9.3) *Life in the Rain Forest* *Inside the Amazing Amazon* *The Brazilian Rain Forest* *Rain Forest* ***See* Advance Preparation, p. 674**
9.5	Study Link Master, p. 347 Teaching Masters, pp. 36–38 (optional); and p. 140		calculator
9.6	Study Link Master, p. 348 Teaching Master, p. 20 or 80 (optional) transparency of Teaching Master, p. 141 (optional) ***See* Advance Preparation, p. 686**		calculator *Incredible Comparisons*
9.7	Study Link Master, p. 349 Teaching Masters, pp. 142 and 143 ***See* Advance Preparation, p. 692**		red, green, and blue pencils or markers per partnership slate
9.8	Study Link Master, p. 350 Teaching Masters, p. 20 or 80 (optional); and p. 144		Fraction/Percent Tiles (see Lesson 9.3)
9.9	Study Link Master, p. 351 Teaching Masters, p. 20 or 80 (optional); and p. 145		
9.10	Study Link Masters, pp. 352–355 Teaching Masters, pp. 146–148 Assessment Masters, pp. 406–408		markers or crayons calculator

planningtips

Pacing

Pacing depends on a number of factors, such as students' individual needs and how long your school has been using *Everyday Mathematics.* At the beginning of Unit 9, review your Content by Strand Poster to help you set a monthly pace.

FEBRUARY	MARCH	APRIL
	←MOST CLASSROOMS→	

Home Communication

Share Study Links 9.1–9.9 with families to help them understand the content and procedures in this unit. At the end of the unit, use Study Link 9.10 to introduce Unit 10. Supplemental information can be found in the *Home Connection Handbook.*

NCTM Standards

Standard	1	2	3	4	5	6	7	8	9	10
Unit 9 Lessons	1–9				1, 4–7	1–10	1–10	1–10	1–10	1–10

Content Standards
1 Number and Operations
2 Algebra
3 Geometry
4 Measurement
5 Data Analysis and Probability

Process Standards
6 Problem Solving
7 Reasoning and Proof
8 Communication
9 Connections
10 Representation

PRACTICE *through* Games

Everyday Mathematics uses games to help students develop good fact power and other math skills.

- *Getting to One* to practice estimation and using trial-and-error to find mystery numbers **(Lesson 9.3)**
- *Fraction/Percent Concentration* to help students memorize the "easy" fraction/percent equivalents **(Lessons 9.3, 9.4, and 9.8)**

unit 9 content highlights

The discussion below highlights the major content ideas presented in Unit 9 and may help you establish instructional priorities.

Conversions among Fractions, Decimals, and Percents (Lessons 9.1–9.5)

Students begin their work with fraction/decimal/percent names for numbers by exploring pictorial representations of such numbers on a 10 by 10 grid. They use these representations to restate percent situations as fractions and decimals. In particular, they find and memorize equivalencies for "easy" fractions (halves, fourths, fifths, and tenths).

One way to convert a fraction to a percent is to first rename it as a fraction with a denominator of 100. This can be done for "easy" fractions by using the multiplication rule for equivalent fractions.

Example

$$\frac{3}{5} = \frac{3 * 20}{5 * 20} = \frac{60}{100}$$
$$\frac{60}{100} = 0.60 = 60\%$$

NOTE: Terminating and repeating decimals will be covered formally in *Sixth Grade Everyday Mathematics.*

More complicated fractions, which do not lend themselves to conversions by the multiplication rule, can be renamed as decimals by dividing the numerator by the denominator with the help of a calculator.

Example

$$\frac{3}{7} = 3 \div 7 = 0.428571 \ldots$$

To convert the decimal to a percent, multiply it by 100 and attach the percent symbol to the result.

$0.428571 = (0.428571 * 100)\% = 42.8571\%$, or 43%, rounded to the nearest percent

This percent key is referenced throughout Unit 9.

The percent key on a calculator is really not needed, since the percent equivalent of any ratio or fraction can be calculated by using the division key and multiplying by 100. The authors include a discussion of the percent key mainly to take one more "mystery" off the keypad.

Solving Problems Involving Percents (Lessons 9.4–9.7)

As was mentioned in the Overview, solving percent problems often involves conversions among fractions, decimals, and percents. In Lessons 9.4–9.7, students use their conversion skills to solve a variety of problems.

- ▷ In Lesson 9.4, students solve problems that involve percents of discount. These problems are simple enough so that students can do the conversions without the use of a calculator.
- ▷ In Lesson 9.5, students use World Tour data to answer questions, such as the following:
  What percent of the world population lives in China?
  What percent of the world's land area belongs to Russia?
- ▷ For Study Link 9.1, students conduct a survey. They analyze the results of the survey in Lesson 9.6. In order to compare the results, they need to convert various ratios to percents.
- ▷ In Lesson 9.7, students create color-coded maps to organize and represent certain population data.

About 20% of the world's population lives in China.

Multiplication and Division with Decimals
(Lessons 9.8 and 9.9)

The approach to multiplication and division of decimals used in *Everyday Mathematics* is based on two assumptions:

▷ The same multiplication and division algorithms may be used for whole numbers and decimals.

▷ The placement of the decimal point in the answer can be determined by making a rough estimate of the answer.

Example $42 * 23.8 = ?$

Step 1: Estimate the product: $40 * 20 = 800$, or $50 * 20 = 1,000$; so $42 * 23.8$ will be about 800 or 1,000.

Step 2: Multiply the numbers, leaving out the decimal point.

$$\begin{array}{r} 238 \\ *\ 42 \\ \hline 9996 \end{array}$$

Step 3: Insert the decimal point in the answer. Since the estimated product is close to 1,000, the exact product must be 999.6.

Example $259.2 \div 8 = ?$

Step 1: Estimate the quotient: 259.2 is close to 260, and $260 \div 8$ is between 30 and 40.

Step 2: Divide the numbers, leaving out the decimal point.

$$2592 \div 8 = 324$$

Step 3: Insert the decimal point in the answer. Since the estimated quotient is between 30 and 40, the exact quotient must be 32.4.

Review and Assessment (Lesson 9.10)

Lesson 9.10 includes oral, slate, and written assessments of the following concepts and skills:

- using an estimation strategy to divide and multiply decimals by whole numbers
- finding a percent or a fraction of a number
- identifying equivalencies among fractions, decimals, and percents
- using a calculator to rename a fraction as a decimal or a percent

If you are planning a quarterly assessment for Units 7–9, you may want to refer to the *Assessment Handbook.* The quarterly learning goals Class Checklist and Individual Profile of Progress checklist (*Math Masters,* pages 458–460) are useful tools for keeping track of students' progress.

For additional information on the following topics, see the *Teacher's Reference Manual:*

- calculators
- decimals
- division algorithms
- fractions
- graphs
- key sequences
- multiplication algorithms
- percents

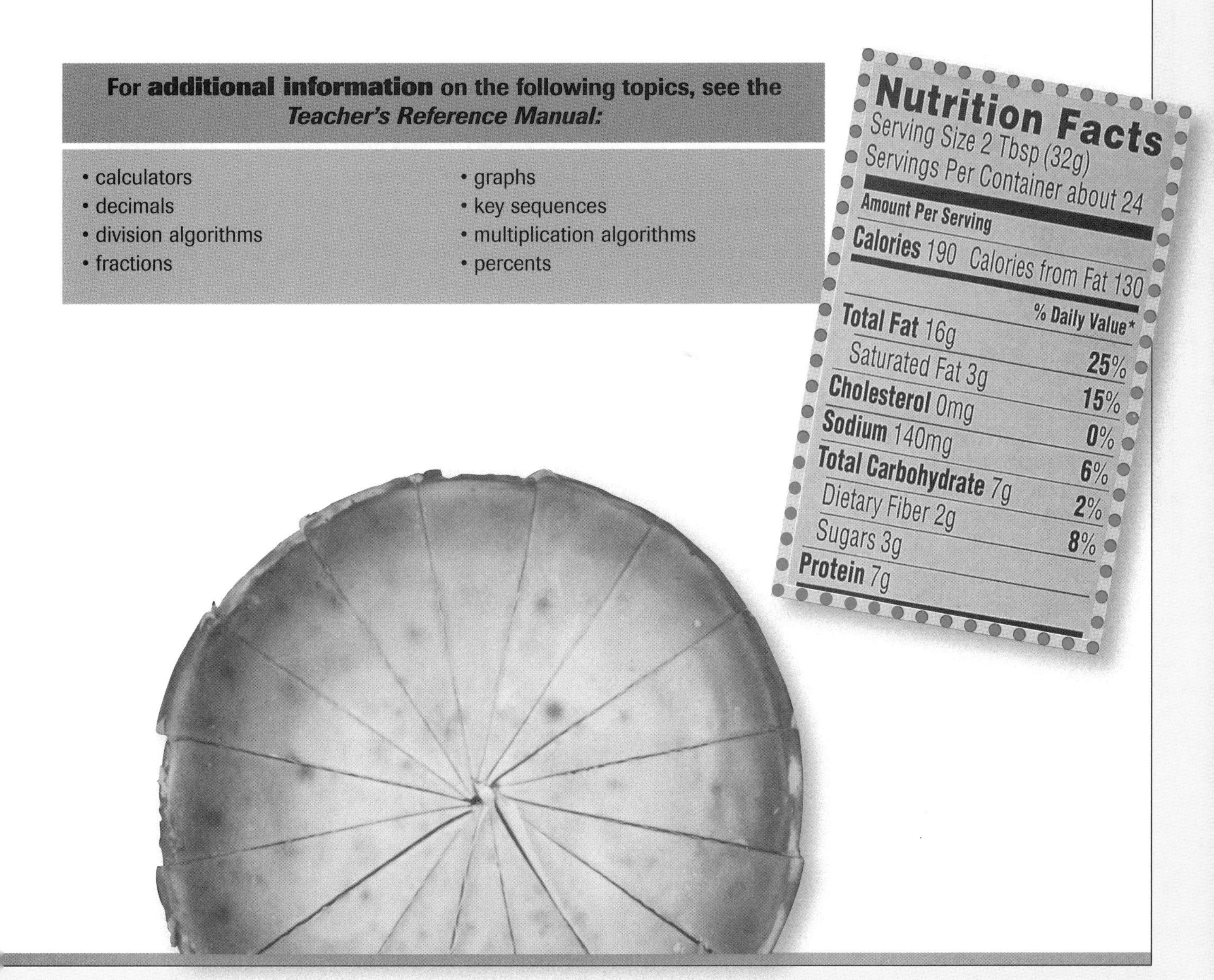

Nutrition Facts
Serving Size 2 Tbsp (32g)
Servings Per Container about 24
Amount Per Serving
Calories 190 Calories from Fat 130
% Daily Value*
Total Fat 16g
Saturated Fat 3g 25%
Cholesterol 0mg 15%
Sodium 140mg 0%
Total Carbohydrate 7g 6%
Dietary Fiber 2g 2%
Sugars 3g 8%
Protein 7g

9.1 Fractions, Decimals, and Percents

OBJECTIVES **To use percents to describe real-life situations; and to practice naming equivalencies among fractions, decimals, and percents.**

summaries	materials
1 Teaching the Lesson	
Students discuss uses of percents in everyday life. They represent various percent situations by shading 10 by 10 grid squares, and they restate each percent situation using a fraction name and a decimal name. [Numeration]	□ *Math Journal 2,* pp. 265–267 □ Study Link 8.6 (*Math Masters,* p. 335)
2 Ongoing Learning & Practice	
Students practice and maintain skills through Math Boxes and Study Link activities.	□ *Math Journal 2,* p. 268 □ Study Link Masters (*Math Masters,* pp. 342 and 343) ***See*** **Advance Preparation**
3 Options for Individualizing	
Enrichment Students collect examples of percents and display them in a booklet or poster display. [Numeration] **Reteaching** Students make designs on a 10 by 10 grid and express the amount covered by the design as a fraction, decimal, and percent. [Numeration]	□ Teaching Masters (*Math Masters,* pp. 132 and 133) □ base-10 blocks (1 flat, 5 longs, and up to 50 cubes)

Additional Information

Background Information For additional information on the following topics, see the *Teacher's Reference Manual:* decimals; fractions; and percents.

Advance Preparation For Part 2, Study Link Master, page 343 will ask students to conduct a survey among family members, neighbors, and friends. The results of the survey will be used later, for Lesson 9.6.

Vocabulary • **percent** • **100% box**

Getting Started

Mental Math and Reflexes

Draw figures like the following on the board and have students use formulas to find the area. *Suggestions:*

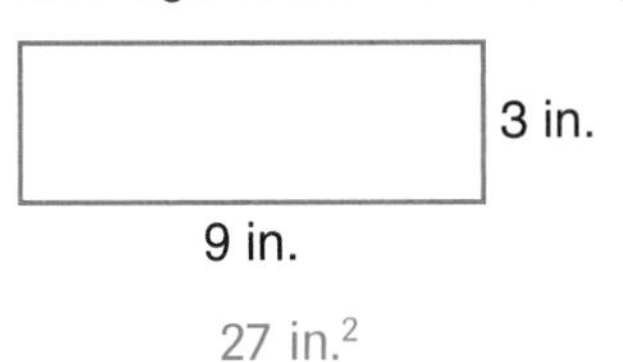

27 in.^{2}

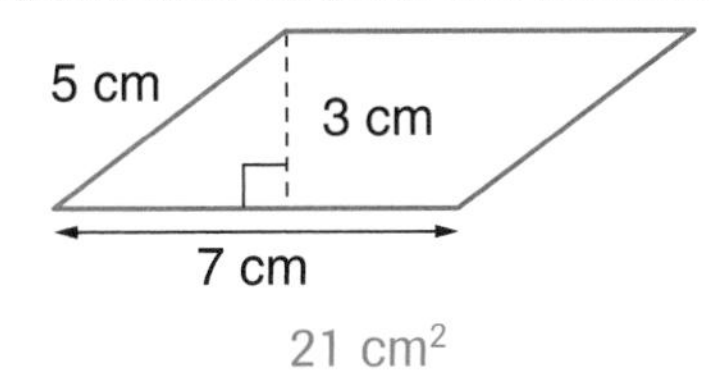

21 cm^2

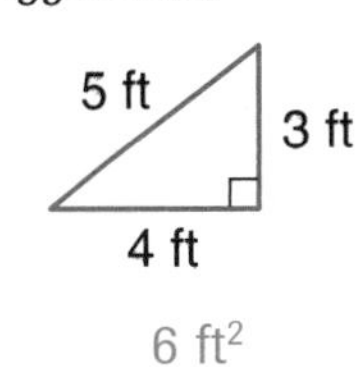

6 ft^2

Math Message

Be ready to discuss the examples of percents you collected on Study Link 8.6.

1 Teaching the Lesson

✦ Math Message Follow-Up
(*Math Masters,* p. 335)

WHOLE-CLASS DISCUSSION 

Students share the examples they collected of uses of **percents.** To help them better understand the meaning of percents, encourage them to restate each percent situation in a variety of ways.

Example: Candidate Reed got 50% of the votes.

This can be restated as follows:

"For every 100 votes cast, Reed got 50 votes."

"If 100 people had voted, Reed would have gotten 50 votes."

"Reed got 50 out of every 100 votes cast."

"Reed got $\frac{50}{100}$ of the votes cast."

Emphasize that "50 out of 100" *does not mean that exactly 100 votes were cast* but that Reed got 50 votes for every 100 votes that were cast. (Since $\frac{50}{100}$ equals $\frac{1}{2}$, Reed got half the votes cast.) If this had been a school council election, there might have been fewer than 100 votes cast—say, 60 votes. Then, Reed would have gotten 50% of 60 votes, or 30 votes. If it had been an election for mayor, there probably would have been many more than 100 votes, perhaps 30,000 votes. Then Reed would have gotten 50% of 30,000 votes, or 15,000 votes.

Percents in My World — Study Link 8.6

Percent means *per hundred* or *out of a hundred.* "1 percent" means $\frac{1}{100}$ or 0.01.

"48 percent of the students in our school are boys" means that out of every 100 students in the school, 48 are boys.

Percents are written in two ways: with the word *percent,* as in the sentence above, and with the symbol %.

Collect examples of percents. Look in newspapers, magazines, books, almanacs, and encyclopedias. Ask people at home to help. Write the examples below. Also tell where you found them. If an adult says you may, cut out examples and paste them on the back of this page.

Encyclopedia: 91% of the area of New Jersey is land, and 9% is covered by water.

Newspaper: 76 percent of the seniors in Southport High School say they plan to attend college next year.

Answers vary.

STUDY LINK MASTER

✦ *Math Masters,* p. 335

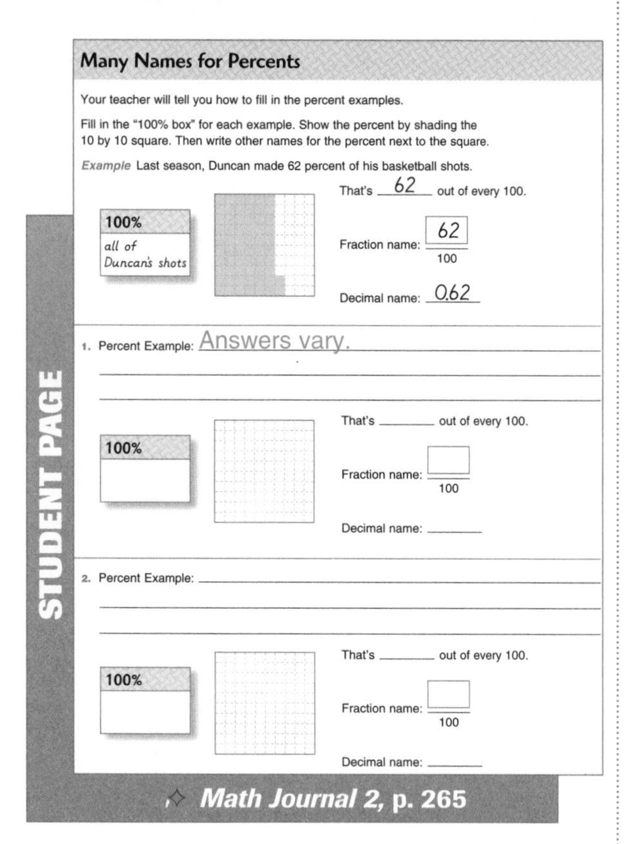
STUDENT PAGE

Many Names for Percents

Your teacher will tell you how to fill in the percent examples.

Fill in the "100% box" for each example. Show the percent by shading the 10 by 10 square. Then write other names for the percent next to the square.

Example Last season, Duncan made 62 percent of his basketball shots.

100%
all of Duncan's shots

That's 62 out of every 100.

Fraction name: $\frac{62}{100}$

Decimal name: 0.62

1. Percent Example: Answers vary.

100%

That's ____ out of every 100.

Fraction name: $\frac{\square}{100}$

Decimal name: ____

2. Percent Example: ____

100%

That's ____ out of every 100.

Fraction name: $\frac{\square}{100}$

Decimal name: ____

Math Journal 2, p. 265

Remind students that, just as with fractions, a percent always represents a *percent of something.* The "something" is the whole 100%, which is the entire object, or the entire collection of objects, or the entire quantity being considered (the ONE). In the example on page 657, the whole is the total number of votes cast. The total number of votes cast is 100 percent of the votes. The **"100% box"** serves the same purpose for percents as the "whole box" does for fractions: It helps focus students' attention on the whole, or 100%.

Language Arts Link The word *percent* comes from the Latin *per centum: Per* means *for,* and *centum* means *one hundred.* Ask students if they can think of other words that begin with *cent-:* cent ($\frac{1}{100}$ of a dollar); century (100 years); centennial (100th anniversary); centipede (looks like it has 100 legs); centimeter ($\frac{1}{100}$ of a meter).

✦Making Up Equivalent Names for Percents

(*Math Journal 2,* p. 265)

WHOLE-CLASS ACTIVITY

Discuss the example on journal page 265: "Last season, Duncan made 62 percent of his basketball shots."

▷ The 10 by 10 square represents the whole (100%)—in this case, all of the shots Duncan attempted.

▷ The 10 by 10 square is made up of 100 small squares. Each small square is $\frac{1}{100}$ or 1% of the whole. A decimal name for $\frac{1}{100}$ is 0.01.

▷ Sixty-two small squares are shaded. These shaded squares represent the number of shots Duncan made out of every 100 shots he took.

▷ Had Duncan taken 100 shots, he would have made 62 shots. This can also be stated as a fraction, $\frac{62}{100}$ of his shots; or as a decimal, 0.62 of his shots.

Make sure that students understand that the statement does *not* mean he took exactly 100 shots and made exactly 62 of them. For example, he might have taken just 50 shots and made 31 of them, or taken 200 shots and made 124 of them.

Now select two of the examples of percents that students collected and discussed during the Math Message Follow-Up. Work as a class to complete Problems 1 and 2 on journal page 265. Have students write a brief description for each percent example. Then fill in the 100% box, shade the grid to show the percent, and write the fraction and decimal names for the percent.

Adjusting the Activity Journal pages 265–267 prompt students to provide an equivalent "hundredths-fraction" for the percent example. Some students may wonder why they need to write a fraction such as $\frac{25}{100}$ when it can be written in simplest form as $\frac{1}{4}$. Encourage these students to write both forms whenever possible.

✦ Making Up Equivalent Names for Percents
(*Math Journal 2,* pp. 266 and 267)

PARTNER ACTIVITY 

Students complete journal pages 266 and 267. For Problems 5–7, students may have difficulty deciding what the "whole" is and how to fill in the 100% box.

- ▷ Problem 5: The example does not mention a specific time period. The whole (100%) could logically be "1 day" or any longer period (week, month, year). Any period shorter than 1 day could be problematic; for example, cats are much more likely to be active at night and to sleep a lot during the day.
- ▷ Problem 6: 40% will be deducted from the original price for any item sold. So the whole (100%) is the "original price of an item."
- ▷ Problem 7: Whatever the cost of carpet may be, the buyer must pay 20% of that cost at the time of purchase. So the whole (100%) is the "cost of the carpet."

ONGOING ASSESSMENT

Discuss several of the percent examples. For each example, be sure to ask the following questions:

- **What is the whole? (Percent of what?)**
- **What do the shaded squares represent?**
- **Can you change each statement by replacing the percent with the phrase "*x* out of *y*"? Can you change it by replacing the percent with a fraction? With a decimal? (Have students respond using complete sentences.)**

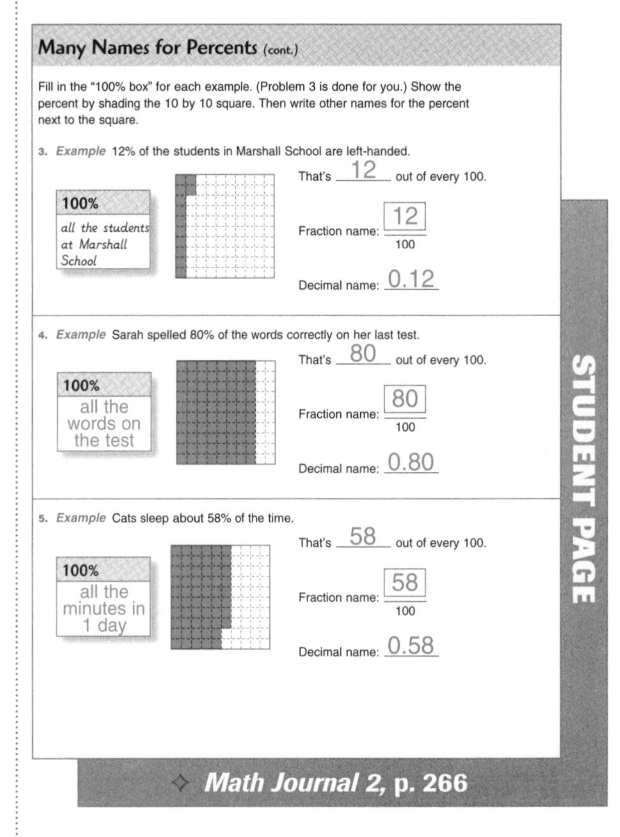

Many Names for Percents (cont.)

Fill in the "100% box" for each example. (Problem 3 is done for you.) Show the percent by shading the 10 by 10 square. Then write other names for the percent next to the square.

3. *Example* 12% of the students in Marshall School are left-handed.

100%: all the students at Marshall School

That's 12 out of every 100.

Fraction name: $\frac{12}{100}$

Decimal name: 0.12

4. *Example* Sarah spelled 80% of the words correctly on her last test.

100%: all the words on the test

That's 80 out of every 100.

Fraction name: $\frac{80}{100}$

Decimal name: 0.80

5. *Example* Cats sleep about 58% of the time.

100%: all the minutes in 1 day

That's 58 out of every 100.

Fraction name: $\frac{58}{100}$

Decimal name: 0.58

STUDENT PAGE

✧ *Math Journal 2,* p. 266

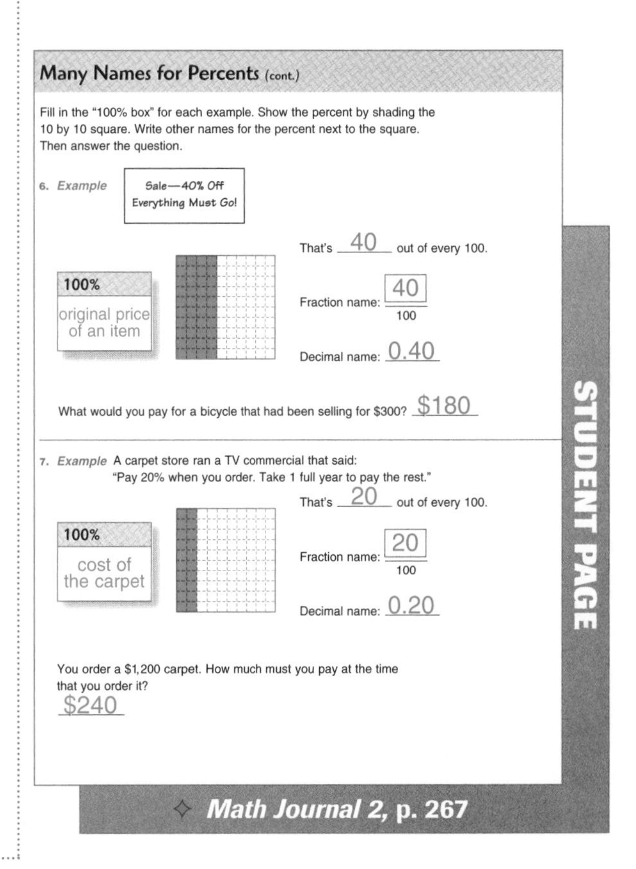

Many Names for Percents (cont.)

Fill in the "100% box" for each example. Show the percent by shading the 10 by 10 square. Write other names for the percent next to the square. Then answer the question.

6. *Example* Sale—40% Off Everything Must Go!

100%: original price of an item

That's 40 out of every 100.

Fraction name: $\frac{40}{100}$

Decimal name: 0.40

What would you pay for a bicycle that had been selling for $300? $180

7. *Example* A carpet store ran a TV commercial that said: "Pay 20% when you order. Take 1 full year to pay the rest."

100%: cost of the carpet

That's 20 out of every 100.

Fraction name: $\frac{20}{100}$

Decimal name: 0.20

You order a $1,200 carpet. How much must you pay at the time that you order it? $240

STUDENT PAGE

✧ *Math Journal 2,* p. 267

2 Ongoing Learning & Practice

✦ Math Boxes 9.1 (*Math Journal 2,* p. 268)

INDEPENDENT ACTIVITY 

Mixed Review Math Boxes in this lesson are paired with Math Boxes in Lesson 9.3. The skill in Problem 1 is a prerequisite for Unit 10.

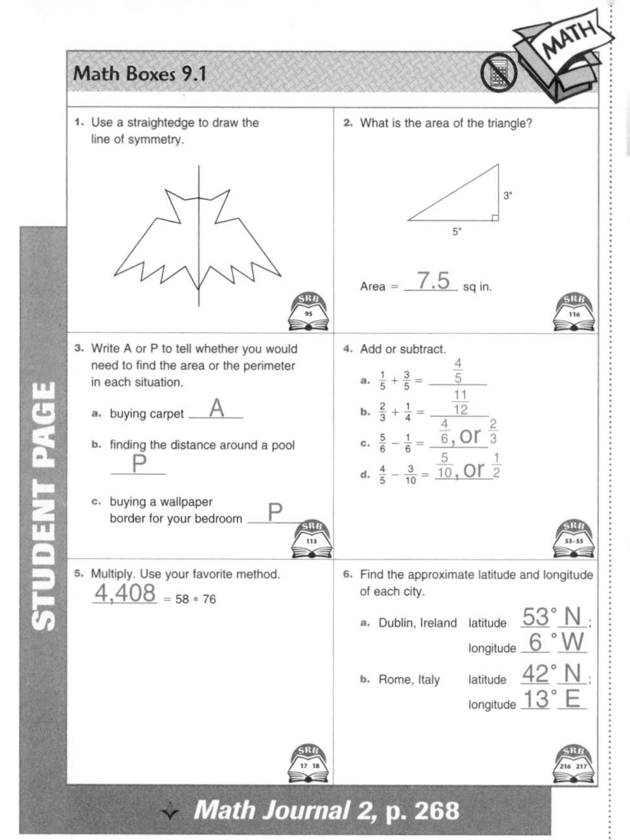

STUDENT PAGE

Math Boxes 9.1

1. Use a straightedge to draw the line of symmetry.

2. What is the area of the triangle? (3", 5")
Area = 7.5 sq in.

3. Write A or P to tell whether you would need to find the area or the perimeter in each situation.
   a. buying carpet A
   b. finding the distance around a pool P
   c. buying a wallpaper border for your bedroom P

4. Add or subtract.
   a. $\frac{1}{5} + \frac{3}{5} = \frac{4}{5}$
   b. $\frac{2}{3} + \frac{1}{4} = \frac{11}{12}$
   c. $\frac{5}{6} - \frac{1}{6} = \frac{4}{6}$, or $\frac{2}{3}$
   d. $\frac{4}{5} - \frac{3}{10} = \frac{5}{10}$, or $\frac{1}{2}$

5. Multiply. Use your favorite method.
   4,408 = 58 * 76

6. Find the approximate latitude and longitude of each city.
   a. Dublin, Ireland latitude 53° N; longitude 6° W
   b. Rome, Italy latitude 42° N; longitude 13° E

✧ Math Journal 2, p. 268

✦ Study Link 9.1
(*Math Masters,* pp. 342 and 343)

Home Connection Students name equivalencies among fractions, decimals, and percents. They shade grids to represent fractions, decimals, and percents.

In preparation for Lesson 9.6, students will need to conduct a survey using the second page of the Study Link. The results will be used as data for the activity in Lesson 9.6. Advise students to read the instructions for each question. They will not need to ask everyone each question on the survey.

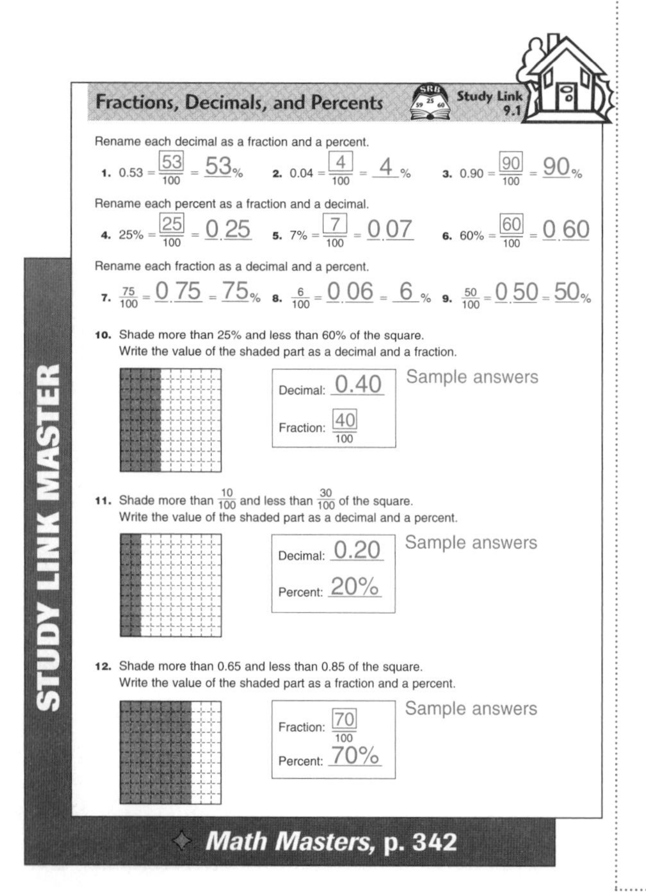

STUDY LINK MASTER

Fractions, Decimals, and Percents — Study Link 9.1

Rename each decimal as a fraction and a percent.

1. $0.53 = \frac{53}{100} = 53\%$
2. $0.04 = \frac{4}{100} = 4\%$
3. $0.90 = \frac{90}{100} = 90\%$

Rename each percent as a fraction and a decimal.

4. $25\% = \frac{25}{100} = 0.25$
5. $7\% = \frac{7}{100} = 0.07$
6. $60\% = \frac{60}{100} = 0.60$

Rename each fraction as a decimal and a percent.

7. $\frac{75}{100} = 0.75 = 75\%$
8. $\frac{6}{100} = 0.06 = 6\%$
9. $\frac{50}{100} = 0.50 = 50\%$

10. Shade more than 25% and less than 60% of the square.
Write the value of the shaded part as a decimal and a fraction.
Decimal: 0.40
Fraction: $\frac{40}{100}$
Sample answers

11. Shade more than $\frac{10}{100}$ and less than $\frac{30}{100}$ of the square.
Write the value of the shaded part as a decimal and a percent.
Decimal: 0.20
Percent: 20%
Sample answers

12. Shade more than 0.65 and less than 0.85 of the square.
Write the value of the shaded part as a fraction and a percent.
Fraction: $\frac{70}{100}$
Percent: 70%
Sample answers

✧ Math Masters, p. 342

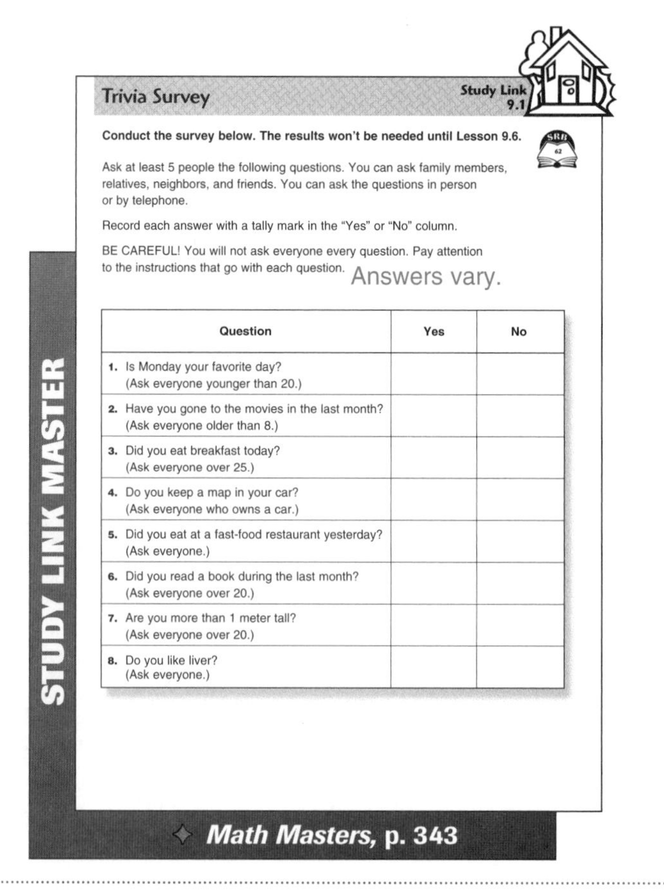

STUDY LINK MASTER

Trivia Survey — Study Link 9.1

Conduct the survey below. The results won't be needed until Lesson 9.6.

Ask at least 5 people the following questions. You can ask family members, relatives, neighbors, and friends. You can ask the questions in person or by telephone.

Record each answer with a tally mark in the "Yes" or "No" column.

BE CAREFUL! You will not ask everyone every question. Pay attention to the instructions that go with each question. Answers vary.

Question	Yes	No
1. Is Monday your favorite day? (Ask everyone younger than 20.)		
2. Have you gone to the movies in the last month? (Ask everyone older than 8.)		
3. Did you eat breakfast today? (Ask everyone over 25.)		
4. Do you keep a map in your car? (Ask everyone who owns a car.)		
5. Did you eat at a fast-food restaurant yesterday? (Ask everyone.)		
6. Did you read a book during the last month? (Ask everyone over 20.)		
7. Are you more than 1 meter tall? (Ask everyone over 20.)		
8. Do you like liver? (Ask everyone.)		

✧ Math Masters, p. 343

Options for Individualizing

✦ ENRICHMENT Making a Percent Booklet or Poster (*Math Masters,* p. 132)

INDEPENDENT ACTIVITY  **15–30 min** 

Students continue to look for examples of uses of percents and present them in a booklet or on a poster. For each example, have students cut out a slip from *Math Masters,* page 132, describe the example, and fill in the 100% box and the equivalency statements.

Hold brief sharing sessions of students' work during the next few days and occasionally throughout the rest of the school year, so that students may be exposed to a variety of percent situations.

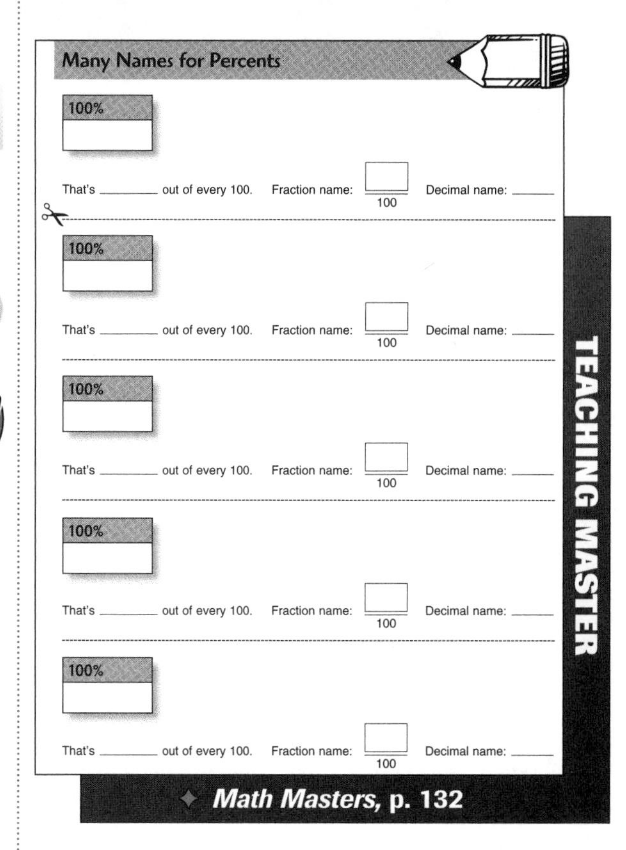
Many Names for Percents

100%

That's ______ out of every 100. Fraction name: $\frac{\square}{100}$ Decimal name: ______

100%

That's ______ out of every 100. Fraction name: $\frac{\square}{100}$ Decimal name: ______

100%

That's ______ out of every 100. Fraction name: $\frac{\square}{100}$ Decimal name: ______

100%

That's ______ out of every 100. Fraction name: $\frac{\square}{100}$ Decimal name: ______

100%

That's ______ out of every 100. Fraction name: $\frac{\square}{100}$ Decimal name: ______

TEACHING MASTER

✦ *Math Masters,* p. 132

✦ RETEACHING Creating Base-10 Block Designs (*Math Masters,* p. 133)

INDEPENDENT ACTIVITY  **30+ min** 

Students use cubes to make a design on a flat and then copy the design onto one of the grids on *Math Masters,* page 133. Students determine how much of the flat is covered by their cube design and express this amount as a fraction, decimal, and percent. As an aid to counting cubes, some students may choose to exchange as many cubes as possible for longs, resulting in a certain number of longs (tenths) and cubes (hundredths).

NOTE: This Reteaching activity was also suggested in Lesson 7.8. However, in that lesson, it was limited to fraction and decimal equivalencies.

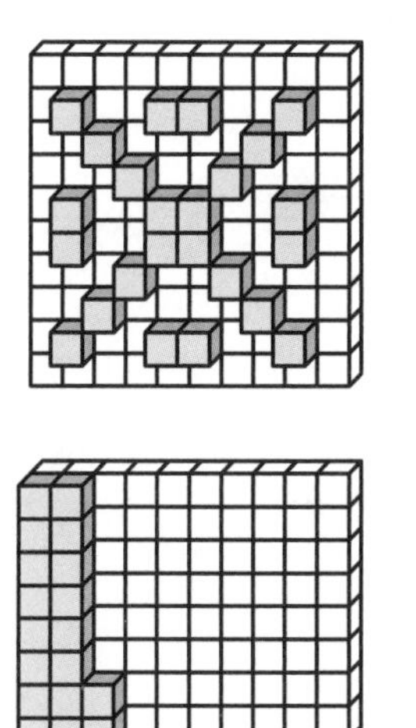

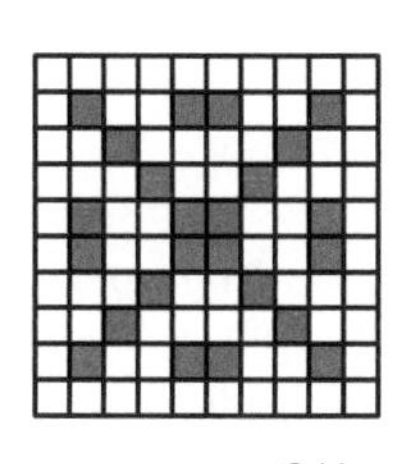

Fraction: $\frac{24}{100}$

Decimal: 0.24

Percent: 24%

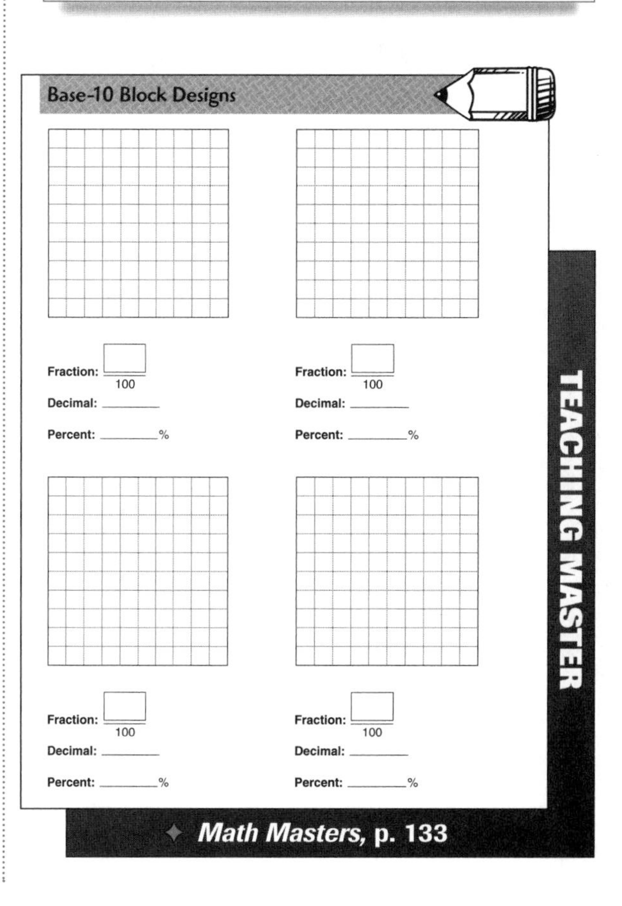
Base-10 Block Designs

Fraction: $\frac{\square}{100}$
Decimal: ______
Percent: ______%

Fraction: $\frac{\square}{100}$
Decimal: ______
Percent: ______%

Fraction: $\frac{\square}{100}$
Decimal: ______
Percent: ______%

Fraction: $\frac{\square}{100}$
Decimal: ______
Percent: ______%

TEACHING MASTER

✦ *Math Masters,* p. 133

9.2 Converting "Easy" Fractions to Decimals and Percents

OBJECTIVES **To rename "easy" fractions (fourths, fifths, and tenths) as decimals and percents; and to solve percent problems by using equivalent fractions.**

summaries	materials
1 Teaching the Lesson	
Students name shaded parts of 10 by 10 grids as fractions, decimals, and percents. The shaded parts are all "easy" fractions: fourths, fifths, and tenths. [Numeration] Students solve percent problems by substituting "easy" equivalent fractions for percents. [Numeration]	☐ *Math Journal 2,* pp. 269, 270, and 356–357 ☐ Study Link 9.1
2 Ongoing Learning & Practice	
Students practice multiplying multidigit whole numbers. [Operations and Computation] Students practice and maintain skills through Math Boxes and Study Link activities.	☐ *Math Journal 2,* pp. 271 and 272 ☐ Teaching Master (*Math Masters,* p. 20 or 80; optional) ☐ Study Link Master (*Math Masters,* p. 344)
3 Options for Individualizing	
Extra Practice Students name a fraction and a percent for the shaded part of a 10 by 10 grid. [Numeration] **Extra Practice** Partners use flash cards to help each other memorize equivalent names for fractions, decimals, and percents. [Numeration] **Language Diversity** Students help classmates who are learning to speak and write in English write and solve "percent-of" number stories. [Numeration]	☐ Teaching Masters (*Math Masters,* pp. 134 and 135) ☐ scissors ***See* Advance Preparation**

Additional Information

Advance Preparation For the first optional Extra Practice activity in Part 3, make one copy of *Math Masters,* page 134. Shade the grids on the copy to create problems for students to solve. Then make one copy of the completed master for each student. For the second optional Extra Practice activity, make one copy of *Math Masters,* page 135 for each partnership.

Getting Started

Mental Math and Reflexes

Draw polygons on the board and have students find their perimeters. *Suggestions:*

rectangle	4 in.
12 in.	
32 in.	

kite: 3 in., 8 in.
22 in.

Math Message

Complete journal page 269.

Study Link 9.1 Follow-Up

Go over the answers. Ask students to explain how they solved Problems 10–12.

1 Teaching the Lesson

✦ Math Message Follow-Up (*Math Journal 2,* p. 269)

WHOLE-CLASS DISCUSSION

Remind students that it is easy to rename a fraction as a percent when the denominator is 100. For example, another name for $\frac{32}{100}$ is 32%.

There are other fractions, such as $\frac{1}{2}$, $\frac{1}{4}$, $\frac{1}{5}$, and $\frac{1}{10}$, which can be renamed as percents fairly easily. One benefit is that knowing such equivalencies often makes percent problems easier to solve. For example, in Problem 1, Alfred missed 50% of 20 problems. To find how many problems he missed, students may think of 50% as $\frac{1}{2}$ and ask themselves, "What is $\frac{1}{2}$ of 20?"

Go over the problems on page 269. Use the shaded 10 by 10 squares to help you illustrate equivalent fraction, decimal, and percent names. Point out the following:

- ▷ The whole is the 20-problem test—100% of the test.
- ▷ The whole test is represented by the 10 by 10 square.
- ▷ Each 10 by 10 square is divided into 20 equal parts (rectangles), each representing 1 problem on the test.

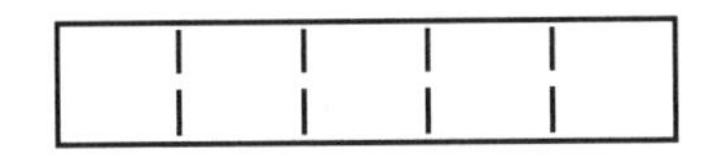

Each rectangle, consisting of 5 small squares, represents 1 problem on the test.

- ▷ Each 10 by 10 square is also divided into 100 small squares; each small square is $\frac{1}{100}$, or 1% of the 10 by 10 square.

"Percent-of" Number Stories

Alfred, Nadine, Kyla, and Jackson each took the same math test. There were 20 problems on the test.

100%
20-problem test

1. Alfred missed $\frac{1}{2}$ of the problems. He missed **0.50** of the problems. That's **50%** of the problems.
   How many problems did he miss? 10 problems
   $\frac{1}{2}$ of 20 = 10
   50% of 20 = 10
   $\frac{1}{2}$, or 50% is shaded.

2. Nadine missed $\frac{1}{4}$ of the problems. She missed **0.25** of the problems. That's **25%** of the problems.
   How many problems did she miss? 5 problems
   $\frac{1}{4}$ of 20 = 5
   25% of 20 = 5
   $\frac{1}{4}$, or 25% is shaded.

3. Kyla missed $\frac{1}{10}$ of the problems. She missed **0.10** of the problems. That's **10%** of the problems.
   How many problems did she miss? 2 problems
   $\frac{1}{10}$ of 20 = 2
   10% of 20 = 2
   $\frac{1}{10}$, or 10% is shaded.

4. Jackson missed $\frac{1}{5}$ of the problems. He missed **0.20** of the problems. That's **20%** of the problems.
   How many problems did he miss? 4 problems
   $\frac{1}{5}$ of 20 = 4
   20% of 20 = 4
   $\frac{1}{5}$, or 20% is shaded.

STUDENT PAGE

✧ *Math Journal 2,* p. 269

NOTE: Being able to use fractions and percents interchangeably will also prove useful in later grades, when students learn to estimate with percents that are not equivalent to "easy" fractions. For example, by the end of sixth grade, most students should be able to apply the following kind of reasoning: The population of Colombia is about 40 million. About 27% of the population lives in rural areas. Since 27% is equivalent to a little more than $\frac{1}{4}$, and $\frac{1}{4}$ of 40 million is 10 million, about 10 million Colombians live in rural areas.

STUDENT PAGE

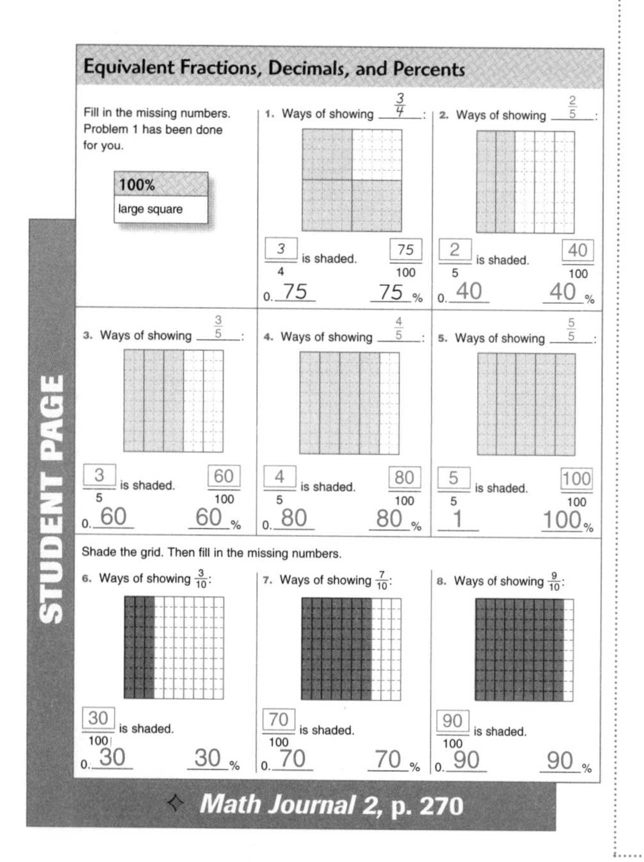
Equivalent Fractions, Decimals, and Percents

Fill in the missing numbers. Problem 1 has been done for you.

100%
large square

1. Ways of showing $\frac{3}{4}$: $\frac{3}{4}$ is shaded. $\frac{75}{100}$ 0.75 75%

2. Ways of showing $\frac{2}{5}$: $\frac{2}{5}$ is shaded. $\frac{40}{100}$ 0.40 40%

3. Ways of showing $\frac{3}{5}$: $\frac{3}{5}$ is shaded. $\frac{60}{100}$ 0.60 60%

4. Ways of showing $\frac{4}{5}$: $\frac{4}{5}$ is shaded. $\frac{80}{100}$ 0.80 80%

5. Ways of showing $\frac{5}{5}$: $\frac{5}{5}$ is shaded. $\frac{100}{100}$ 1 100%

Shade the grid. Then fill in the missing numbers.

6. Ways of showing $\frac{3}{10}$: $\frac{30}{100}$ is shaded. 0.30 30%

7. Ways of showing $\frac{7}{10}$: $\frac{70}{100}$ is shaded. 0.70 70%

8. Ways of showing $\frac{9}{10}$: $\frac{90}{100}$ is shaded. 0.90 90%

Math Journal 2, p. 270

In Problem 1, $\frac{1}{2}$ of the 10 by 10 square is shaded. That's 50 small squares, or $\frac{50}{100}$, or 0.50, or 50% of the 10 by 10 square. 50% of 20 is the same as $\frac{1}{2}$ of 20, or 10.

In Problem 2, $\frac{1}{4}$ of the 10 by 10 square is shaded. That's 25 small squares, or $\frac{25}{100}$, or 0.25, or 25% of the 10 by 10 square. 25% of 20 is the same as $\frac{1}{4}$ of 20, or 5.

In Problem 3, $\frac{1}{10}$ of the 10 by 10 square is shaded. That's 10 small squares, or $\frac{10}{100}$, or 0.10, or 10% of the 10 by 10 square. 10% of 20 is the same as $\frac{1}{10}$ of 20, or 2.

In Problem 4, $\frac{1}{5}$ of the 10 by 10 square is shaded. That's 20 small squares, or $\frac{20}{100}$, or 0.20, or 20% of the 10 by 10 square. 20% of 20 is the same as $\frac{1}{5}$ of 20, or 4.

✦ Finding Equivalent Names for Other "Easy" Fractions (*Math Journal 2*, pp. 269, 270, and 356–357)

PARTNER ACTIVITY

Students work with partners to find equivalent names for several more "easy" fractions on journal page 270. Circulate and assist as needed. After a few minutes, bring the class together and go over the answers.

In Unit 7, students began a table of equivalent names for fractions on journal pages 356 and 357. Ask students to copy the decimal and percent names for the fractions on pages 269 and 270 to this table.

NOTE: Because the table appears many pages after pages 269 and 270, copying the decimal and percent names may be awkward. To make the task easier, you might have one partner open the journal to pages 269 and 270 and the other partner to the table on pages 356 and 357. The first partner then reads the decimal and percent equivalents while the second partner copies them to the table. Then the first partner copies them to his or her table.

When students have completed this activity, they should have recorded the equivalencies shown on the next page.

NOTE: Students may want to check their answers against the chart inside the front cover of their journals.

"Easy" Fractions	Decimals	Percents
$\frac{1}{2}$	0.50	50%
$\frac{1}{4}$	0.25	25%
$\frac{3}{4}$	0.75	75%
$\frac{1}{5}$	0.20	20%
$\frac{2}{5}$	0.40	40%
$\frac{3}{5}$	0.60	60%
$\frac{4}{5}$	0.80	80%
$\frac{1}{10}$	0.10	10%
$\frac{3}{10}$	0.30	30%
$\frac{7}{10}$	0.70	70%
$\frac{9}{10}$	0.90	90%

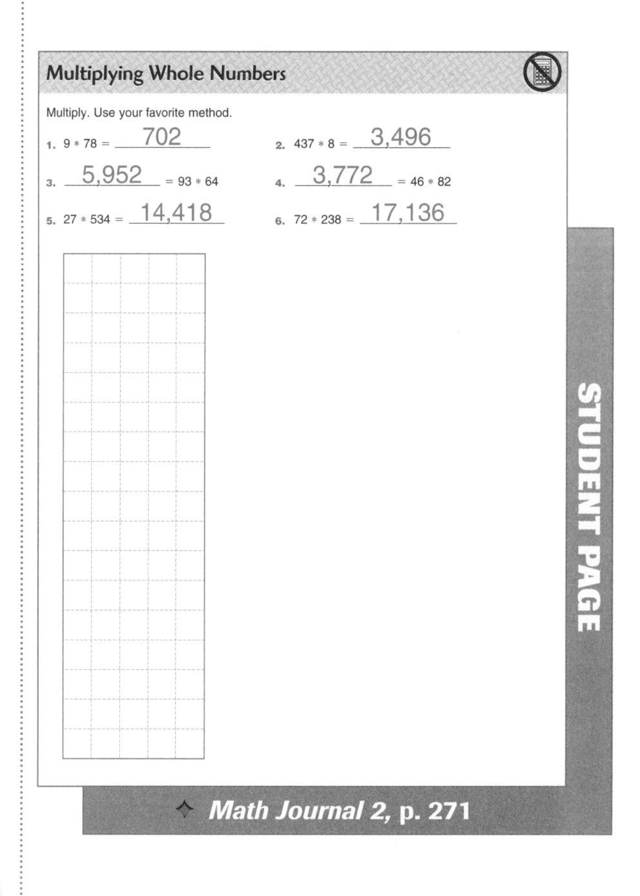

STUDENT PAGE

Multiplying Whole Numbers

Multiply. Use your favorite method.

1. 9 * 78 = 702
2. 437 * 8 = 3,496
3. 5,952 = 93 * 64
4. 3,772 = 46 * 82
5. 27 * 534 = 14,418
6. 72 * 238 = 17,136

✦ *Math Journal 2*, p. 271

2 Ongoing Learning & Practice

✦ Multiplying Whole Numbers (*Math Journal 2*, p. 271; *Math Masters*, p. 20 or 80)

INDEPENDENT ACTIVITY 

Students solve whole number multiplication problems. Have copies of *Math Masters*, page 20 or 80 available for students who need additional grid paper to do their computations.

ONGOING ASSESSMENT

In Lesson 9.8, students will use an estimation strategy to multiply decimals by whole numbers. They will be expected to use the partial-products or lattice algorithm to solve whole number multiplication problems. Use journal page 271 to assess students' skill levels.

✦ Math Boxes 9.2 (*Math Journal 2*, p. 272)

INDEPENDENT ACTIVITY 

Mixed Review Math Boxes in this lesson are paired with Math Boxes in Lesson 9.4. The skill in Problem 1 is a prerequisite for Unit 10.

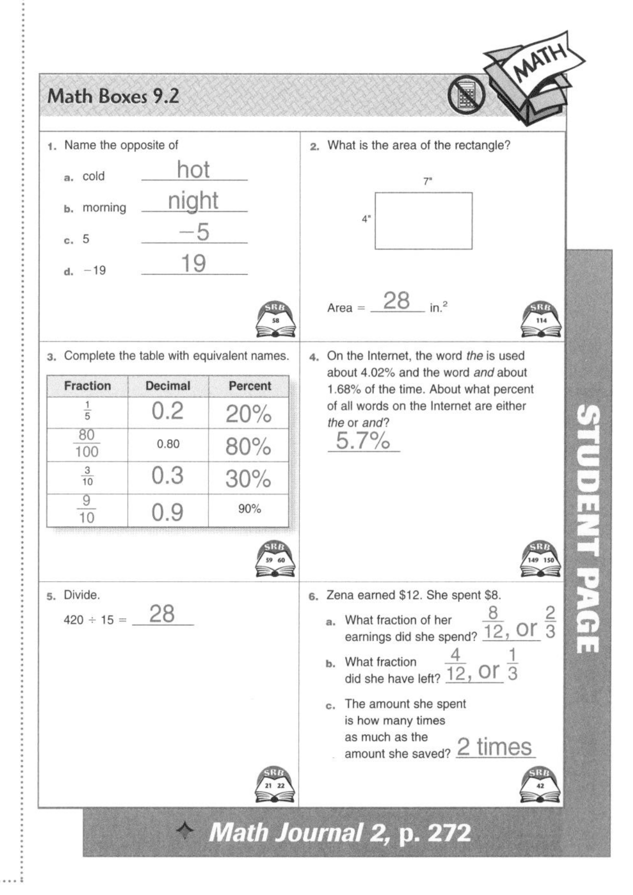

STUDENT PAGE

Math Boxes 9.2

1. Name the opposite of
   a. cold hot
   b. morning night
   c. 5 −5
   d. −19 19

2. What is the area of the rectangle? (7", 4")
   Area = 28 in.²

3. Complete the table with equivalent names.

Fraction	Decimal	Percent
$\frac{1}{5}$	0.2	20%
$\frac{80}{100}$	0.80	80%
$\frac{3}{10}$	0.3	30%
$\frac{9}{10}$	0.9	90%

4. On the Internet, the word *the* is used about 4.02% and the word *and* about 1.68% of the time. About what percent of all words on the Internet are either *the* or *and*? 5.7%

5. Divide.
   420 ÷ 15 = 28

6. Zena earned $12. She spent $8.
   a. What fraction of her earnings did she spend? $\frac{8}{12}$, or $\frac{2}{3}$
   b. What fraction did she have left? $\frac{4}{12}$, or $\frac{1}{3}$
   c. The amount she spent is how many times as much as the amount she saved? 2 times

✦ *Math Journal 2*, p. 272

Coins as Percents of $1 — Study Link 9.2

1. How many pennies in $1? 100
   What fraction of $1 is 1 penny? $\frac{1}{100}$
   Write the decimal that shows what part of $1 is 1 penny. 0.01
   What percent of $1 is 1 penny? 1 %
2. How many nickels in $1? 20 What fraction of $1 is 1 nickel? $\frac{1}{20}$
   Write the decimal that shows what part of $1 is 1 nickel. 0.05
   What percent of $1 is 1 nickel? 5 %
3. How many dimes in $1? 10 What fraction of $1 is 1 dime? $\frac{1}{10}$
   Write the decimal that shows what part of $1 is 1 dime. 0.10
   What percent of $1 is 1 dime? 10 %
4. How many quarters in $1? 4 What fraction of $1 is 1 quarter? $\frac{1}{4}$
   Write the decimal that shows what part of $1 is 1 quarter. 0.25
   What percent of $1 is 1 quarter? 25 %
5. How many half-dollars in $1? 2 What fraction of $1 is 1 half-dollar? $\frac{1}{2}$
   Write the decimal that shows what part of $1 is 1 half-dollar. 0.50
   What percent of $1 is 1 half-dollar? 50 %
6. Three quarters (75¢) is $\frac{3}{4}$ of $1.
   Write the decimal. 0.75
   What percent of $1 is 3 quarters? 75 %
7. Two dimes (20¢) is $\frac{2}{10}$ of $1.
   Write the decimal. 0.20
   What percent of $1 is 2 dimes? 20 %

STUDY LINK MASTER

✦ *Math Masters,* p. 344

✦ Study Link 9.2 (*Math Masters,* p. 344)

Home Connection For each of several coins, students identify what fraction of $1, decimal part of $1, and percent of $1 that coin represents. Point out that they should look carefully at each question to see if it is asking for a fraction, decimal, or percent.

3 Options for Individualizing

✦ EXTRA PRACTICE Finding Equivalent Names for "Easy" Fractions (*Math Masters,* p. 134)

INDEPENDENT ACTIVITY  **15–30 min** 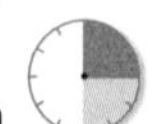

Use *Math Masters,* page 134 to give students additional practice finding equivalent decimals and percents for the "easy" fractions: fourths, fifths, and tenths. The exercises are like those on journal page 270, except that the grids are unshaded. Shade the grids as you wish to create a new set of problems for students each time they use the master.

Fractions, Decimals, and Percents

Fill in the missing numbers. If the grid is not shaded, then shade the grid.

100%
large square

1. Ways of showing ___: [ ] is shaded. $\frac{[\ ]}{4}$ $\frac{[\ ]}{100}$ 0.___ ___%
2. Ways of showing ___: [ ] is shaded. $\frac{[\ ]}{5}$ $\frac{[\ ]}{100}$ 0.___ ___%
3. Ways of showing ___: [ ] is shaded. $\frac{[\ ]}{5}$ $\frac{[\ ]}{100}$ 0.___ ___%
4. Ways of showing ___: [ ] is shaded. $\frac{[\ ]}{5}$ $\frac{[\ ]}{100}$ 0.___ ___%
5. Ways of showing ___: [ ] is shaded. $\frac{[\ ]}{5}$ $\frac{[\ ]}{100}$ 0.___ ___%
6. Ways of showing ___: [ ] is shaded. $\frac{[\ ]}{10}$ $\frac{[\ ]}{100}$ 0.___ ___%
7. Ways of showing ___: [ ] is shaded. $\frac{[\ ]}{10}$ $\frac{[\ ]}{100}$ 0.___ ___%
8. Ways of showing ___: [ ] is shaded. $\frac{[\ ]}{10}$ $\frac{[\ ]}{100}$ 0.___ ___%

TEACHING MASTER

✦ *Math Masters,* p. 134

✦ EXTRA PRACTICE Memorizing Equivalent Names for "Easy" Fractions
(*Math Masters,* p. 135)

PARTNER ACTIVITY **15–30 min**

Students cut out the rectangles on *Math Masters,* page 135. They place the rectangles facedown in a pile between them. Partners take turns. One student picks up a rectangle and covers one of the equivalent names with a thumb. The other student must identify the hidden number.

✦ LANGUAGE DIVERSITY Writing and Solving "Percent-of" Number Stories

PARTNER ACTIVITY **15–30 min**

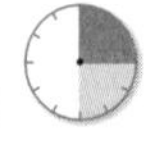

Pair a student proficient in the English language with a student who is learning to speak and write in English. Students work together to write, illustrate, and solve "percent-of" number stories. One example is given below:

Allison and I baked 50 cookies for the bake sale. 40% of the cookies were chocolate chip. How many chocolate chip cookies did we bake? 20 cookies

"Easy" Equivalents

$\frac{1}{2}$	0.50	50%	$\frac{1}{4}$	0.25	25%
$\frac{3}{4}$	0.75	75%	$\frac{1}{5}$	0.20	20%
$\frac{2}{5}$	0.40	40%	$\frac{3}{5}$	0.60	60%
$\frac{4}{5}$	0.80	80%	$\frac{1}{10}$	0.10	10%
$\frac{3}{10}$	0.30	30%	$\frac{7}{10}$	0.70	70%
$\frac{9}{10}$	0.90	90%	$\frac{2}{2}$	1	100%

TEACHING MASTER

✦ *Math Masters,* p. 135

9.3 Using a Calculator to Convert Fractions to Decimals

OBJECTIVES **To rename any fraction as a decimal by using a calculator; and to memorize fraction/percent equivalencies for "easy" fractions (fourths, fifths, and tenths).**

summaries	materials
1 Teaching the Lesson	
Students rename fractions as decimals by dividing on their calculators. [Numeration] Students observe that the decimal for a fraction is either a terminating decimal or repeating decimal. [Numeration]	□ *Math Journal 2,* pp. 356 and 357; Activity Sheet 7 □ Study Link 9.2 □ envelope or small plastic bag □ calculator ***See*** **Advance Preparation**
2 Ongoing Learning & Practice	
Students play *Fraction/Percent Concentration* to help them memorize the "easy" fraction/percent equivalencies. [Numeration] Students practice and maintain skills through Math Boxes and Study Link activities.	□ *Math Journal 2,* p. 273; Activity Sheet 7; and Activity Sheet 8 (optional) □ *Student Reference Book,* p. 196 □ Study Link Master (*Math Masters,* p. 345) □ calculator ***See*** **Advance Preparation**
3 Options for Individualizing	
Reteaching Students read books about fractions and name decimals and percents equivalent to the fractions mentioned in the books. [Numeration] **Extra Practice** Students name shaded regions as fractions, decimals, and percents. They order and compare fractions, decimals, and percents. [Numeration] **Enrichment** Students play *Getting to One* to practice the trial-and-error method in simple problem situations. [Patterns, Functions, and Algebra]	□ Teaching Masters (*Math Masters,* pp. 136 and 137) □ *Gator Pie* □ *Eating Fractions* □ *Student Reference Book,* p. 198 ***See*** **Advance Preparation**

Additional Information

Background Information For additional information on key sequences of calculators, see the *Teacher's Reference Manual.*

Advance Preparation For the Math Message, have students cut out the Fraction/Percent Tiles on Activity Sheet 7 in the back of *Math Journal 2.* For students who need extra practice with fraction/decimal equivalencies, have them also cut out the Decimal Tiles found on Activity Sheet 8. Give them small envelopes or plastic bags to store the tiles.

For the optional Reteaching activity in Part 3, you will need a copy of *Gator Pie* by Louise Mathews (Sundance, 1995) and/or *Eating Fractions* by Bruce McMillan (Scholastic, 1991).

Vocabulary **(teacher) • terminating decimal • repeating decimal**

Getting Started

Mental Math and Reflexes

Pose problems like the following:

- Write each hundredths-fraction as a percent.
  $\frac{15}{100}$ 15% $\frac{55}{100}$ 55% $\frac{8}{100}$ 8%
- Write each tenths-fraction as a hundredths-fraction and then as a percent.
  $\frac{3}{10}$ $\frac{30}{100}$; 30% $\frac{9}{10}$ $\frac{90}{100}$; 90% $\frac{5}{10}$ $\frac{50}{100}$; 50%

Math Message

- *Take 1 envelope (or plastic bag).*
- *Find Activity Sheet 7 in the back of your journal. Cut out the Fraction/Percent Tiles and place them in the envelope (or plastic bag).*

Study Link 9.2 Follow-Up

Briefly go over the answers.

1 Teaching the Lesson

✦ Math Message Follow-Up (*Math Journal 2,* Activity Sheet 7)

WHOLE-CLASS ACTIVITY

Check that students have cut out the Fraction/Percent Tiles on Activity Sheet 7 and have stored them in their envelopes (or plastic bags). They will use the tiles for the activity in Part 2 of this lesson.

✦ Using a Calculator to Rename "Easy" Fractions as Decimals (*Math Journal 2,* pp. 356 and 357)

WHOLE-CLASS ACTIVITY

Ask students to turn to the table of Equivalent Names for Fractions on journal pages 356 and 357. Try the following experiment:

Name several "easy" fractions, such as $\frac{1}{2}$, $\frac{3}{4}$, $\frac{4}{5}$, and $\frac{6}{10}$, and say the following:

- Use your calculator to divide the numerator of the fraction by its denominator.
- What do you observe? The number on the calculator display is the decimal name for the fraction. For example, 1 divided by 2 = 0.5. This is the decimal name for $\frac{1}{2}$.

Help students summarize: One way to rename a fraction as a decimal is to divide its numerator by its denominator.

STUDENT PAGE

Fraction/Percent Tiles

10%	20%	25%	30%
40%	50%	60%	70%
75%	80%	90%	100%
$\frac{1}{2}$	$\frac{1}{4}$	$\frac{3}{4}$	$\frac{1}{5}$
$\frac{2}{5}$	$\frac{3}{5}$	$\frac{4}{5}$	$\frac{1}{10}$
$\frac{3}{10}$	$\frac{7}{10}$	$\frac{9}{10}$	$\frac{2}{2}$

◇ *Math Journal 2,* Activity Sheet 7

STUDENT PAGE

Equivalent Names for Fractions

Fraction	Equivalent Fractions	Decimal	Percent
$\frac{0}{2}$		0	0%
$\frac{1}{2}$	$\frac{2}{4}$, $\frac{3}{6}$		
$\frac{2}{2}$		1	100%
$\frac{1}{3}$			
$\frac{2}{3}$			
$\frac{1}{4}$			
$\frac{3}{4}$			
$\frac{1}{5}$			
$\frac{2}{5}$			
$\frac{3}{5}$			
$\frac{4}{5}$			
$\frac{1}{6}$			
$\frac{5}{6}$			
$\frac{1}{8}$			
$\frac{3}{8}$			
$\frac{5}{8}$			
$\frac{7}{8}$			

✧ ***Math Journal 2,* p. 356**

STUDENT PAGE

Equivalent Names for Fractions *(cont.)*

Fraction	Equivalent Fractions	Decimal	Percent
$\frac{1}{9}$			
$\frac{2}{9}$			
$\frac{4}{9}$			
$\frac{5}{9}$			
$\frac{7}{9}$			
$\frac{8}{9}$			
$\frac{1}{10}$			
$\frac{3}{10}$			
$\frac{7}{10}$			
$\frac{9}{10}$			
$\frac{1}{12}$			
$\frac{5}{12}$			
$\frac{7}{12}$			
$\frac{11}{12}$			

✧ ***Math Journal 2,* p. 357**

✦Using a Calculator to Rename Any Fraction as a Decimal (*Math Journal 2,* pp. 356 and 357)

INDEPENDENT ACTIVITY 

Ask students to rename each fraction on journal pages 356 and 357 as a decimal by using division. (Students should already have filled in the decimal names for "easy" fractions in Lesson 9.2.) Tell them to write each digit shown in the calculator display, up to 6 digits following the decimal point.

When they have finished, ask students to look for patterns in the results. Your discussion should cover the following:

- Some of the fractions have short decimal names with 1, 2, or 3 digits after the decimal point, and no other digits beyond that. What do these fractions with short decimal names have in common? They are fractions whose denominators are 2, 4, 5, 8, and 10.
- The other fractions have long decimal names that look like they could go on forever if the calculator display could show an endless number of digits. Do you see any patterns in these longer decimal names? If you read the digits from left to right, you come to a digit that seems to repeat forever. For example, $\frac{7}{12}$ has the decimal name 0.5833333333; if you could see more decimal places, they would all be 3s.

NOTE: When a fraction is renamed as a decimal, it will be either a **terminating decimal** or a **repeating decimal.** A repeating decimal is one in which a digit or group of digits is repeated endlessly. It is not necessary to use this "terminating" and "repeating" vocabulary with students. The topic of terminating and repeating decimals will be discussed in later grades. The activity here should be viewed as an exploration—an initial exposure to a topic that will be treated formally later.

Ongoing Learning & Practice

✦ Playing *Fraction/Percent Concentration*

(*Student Reference Book,* p. 196; Activity Sheets 7 and 8)

PARTNER ACTIVITY 

The purpose of this game is to help students memorize the "easy" fraction/percent equivalencies. Explain the rules of the game or have students read the rules in the *Student Reference Book.* To play the game, students use the Fraction/Percent Tiles shown on Activity Sheet 7.

Adjusting the Activity If students are having difficulty with the memory aspect of *Fraction/Percent Concentration,* play with fewer fraction/percent pairs or play with the cards faceup.

Some students may benefit from additional practice with fraction/decimal equivalencies. If so, have students use the Decimal Tiles on Activity Sheet 8, found at the back of *Math Journal 2.* Have students play the game using the Fraction Tiles and the Decimal Tiles.

Games

Fraction/Percent Concentration

Materials ☐ 1 set of Fraction/Percent Tiles (*Math Journal 2,* Activity Sheets 7 and 8)
☐ calculator

Players 2 or 3

Object of the game To match equivalent fraction tiles and percent tiles.

Directions

1. Spread out the tiles facedown on the playing surface. Create two separate piles—a fraction pile and a percent pile. Mix up the tiles in each pile. The backs of the 12 fraction tiles should have the letter *F* showing. The backs of the 12 percent tiles should have the letter *P* showing.
2. Players take turns. At each turn, a player turns over a fraction tile and a percent tile. If the fraction and percent are equivalent, the player keeps the tiles. If the tiles do not match, the player turns the tiles facedown.
3. Players may use a calculator to check each other's matches.
4. The game ends when all tiles have been taken. The player with the most tiles wins.

Fraction/Percent Tiles

10%	20%	25%	30%
40%	50%	60%	70%
75%	80%	90%	100%
$\frac{1}{2}$	$\frac{1}{4}$	$\frac{3}{4}$	$\frac{1}{5}$
$\frac{2}{5}$	$\frac{3}{5}$	$\frac{4}{5}$	$\frac{1}{10}$
$\frac{3}{10}$	$\frac{7}{10}$	$\frac{9}{10}$	$\frac{2}{2}$

one hundred ninety-six

STUDENT PAGE

✧ *Student Reference Book,* p. 196

Decimal Tiles

0.10	0.20	0.25	0.30
0.40	0.50	0.60	0.70
0.75	0.80	0.90	1

STUDENT PAGE

✧ *Math Journal 2,* Activity Sheet 8

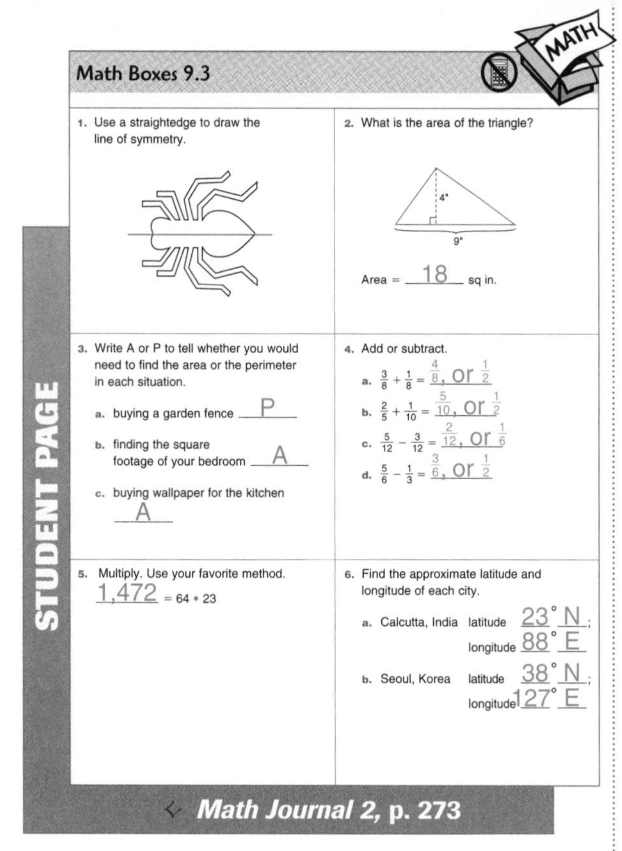
Math Boxes 9.3

1. Use a straightedge to draw the line of symmetry.

2. What is the area of the triangle?

4"
9"
Area = 18 sq in.

3. Write A or P to tell whether you would need to find the area or the perimeter in each situation.

a. buying a garden fence P

b. finding the square footage of your bedroom A

c. buying wallpaper for the kitchen A

4. Add or subtract.

a. $\frac{3}{8} + \frac{1}{8} = \frac{4}{8}$, or $\frac{1}{2}$

b. $\frac{2}{5} + \frac{1}{10} = \frac{5}{10}$, or $\frac{1}{2}$

c. $\frac{5}{12} - \frac{3}{12} = \frac{2}{12}$, or $\frac{1}{6}$

d. $\frac{5}{6} - \frac{1}{3} = \frac{3}{6}$, or $\frac{1}{2}$

5. Multiply. Use your favorite method.

1,472 = 64 * 23

6. Find the approximate latitude and longitude of each city.

a. Calcutta, India latitude 23° N; longitude 88° E

b. Seoul, Korea latitude 38° N; longitude 127° E

STUDENT PAGE

Math Journal 2, p. 273

✦ Math Boxes 9.3 (*Math Journal 2*, p. 273)

INDEPENDENT ACTIVITY 

Mixed Review Math Boxes in this lesson are paired with Math Boxes in Lesson 9.1. The skill in Problem 1 is a prerequisite for Unit 10.

✦ Study Link 9.3 (*Math Masters*, p. 345)

Home Connection Students use a calculator to convert fractions to decimals and make up some conversion problems of their own.

3 Options for Individualizing

✦ RETEACHING Finding Fraction Equivalencies in Literature

SMALL-GROUP ACTIVITY  **15–30 min** 

Literature Link Share the following books with students. Each time a fraction is mentioned, have students name the equivalent decimal and percent. If necessary, have students use a calculator to convert the fractions to decimals.

Gator Pie

Summary: Three alligators decide to share a pie. Before they can cut it, additional alligators arrive. They need to determine how to cut the pie into thirds, fourths, eighths, and finally hundredths.

Eating Fractions

Summary: Wholes, halves, thirds, and fourths are reviewed through color photographs of food, such as bananas and muffins.

NOTE: These books were also recommended in Lesson 7.1, which focused on fractions as equal parts of a whole.

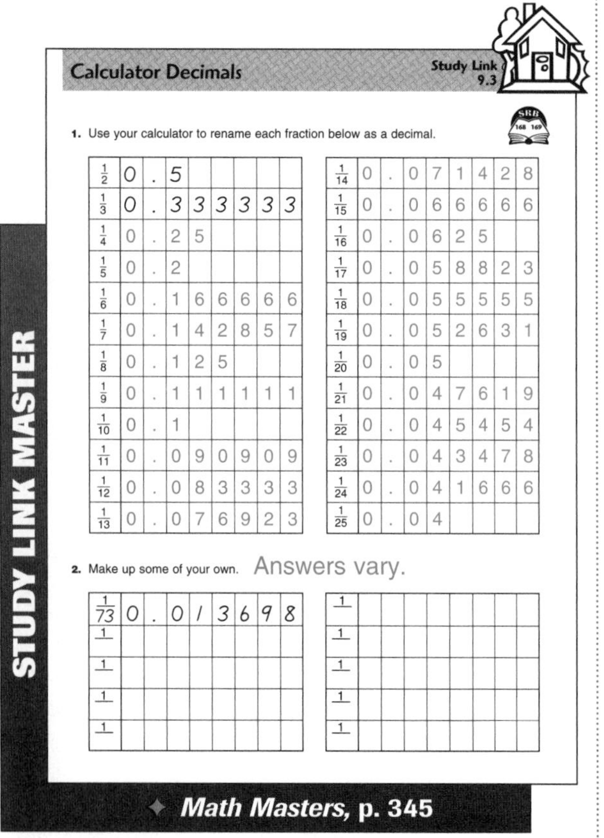
Calculator Decimals

Study Link 9.3

1. Use your calculator to rename each fraction below as a decimal.

Fraction	Decimal	Fraction	Decimal
$\frac{1}{2}$	0.5	$\frac{1}{14}$	0.071428
$\frac{1}{3}$	0.333333	$\frac{1}{15}$	0.066666
$\frac{1}{4}$	0.25	$\frac{1}{16}$	0.0625
$\frac{1}{5}$	0.2	$\frac{1}{17}$	0.058823
$\frac{1}{6}$	0.16666	$\frac{1}{18}$	0.05555
$\frac{1}{7}$	0.142857	$\frac{1}{19}$	0.05263
$\frac{1}{8}$	0.125	$\frac{1}{20}$	0.05
$\frac{1}{9}$	0.111111	$\frac{1}{21}$	0.04761
$\frac{1}{10}$	0.1	$\frac{1}{22}$	0.04545
$\frac{1}{11}$	0.090909	$\frac{1}{23}$	0.04347
$\frac{1}{12}$	0.083333	$\frac{1}{24}$	0.04166
$\frac{1}{13}$	0.076923	$\frac{1}{25}$	0.04

2. Make up some of your own. Answers vary.

Fraction	Decimal	Fraction	Decimal
$\frac{1}{73}$	0.013698	$\frac{1}{}$	
$\frac{1}{}$		$\frac{1}{}$	
$\frac{1}{}$		$\frac{1}{}$	
$\frac{1}{}$		$\frac{1}{}$	
$\frac{1}{}$		$\frac{1}{}$	

STUDY LINK MASTER

Math Masters, p. 345

✦ EXTRA PRACTICE Finding Fraction, Decimal, Percent Equivalencies (*Math Masters*, pp. 136 and 137)

INDEPENDENT ACTIVITY  **30+ min** 

Students name shaded regions as fractions, decimals, and percents. They also rename, order, and compare fractions, decimals, and percents.

✦ ENRICHMENT Playing *Getting to One* (*Student Reference Book*, p. 198)

PARTNER ACTIVITY **5-15 min** 

Students play this game to practice using trial-and-error for guessing mystery numbers. This game also helps strengthen proportional reasoning skills.

Fraction, Decimal, Percent Equivalencies

TEACHING MASTER

1. Write 3 equivalent fractions for each of the following fractions.

a. $\frac{5}{6}$ $\frac{10}{12}$, $\frac{15}{18}$, $\frac{20}{24}$

b. $\frac{15}{25}$ $\frac{3}{5}$, $\frac{30}{50}$, $\frac{150}{250}$

c. $\frac{1}{10}$ $\frac{2}{20}$, $\frac{3}{30}$, $\frac{10}{100}$

d. $\frac{18}{20}$ $\frac{9}{10}$, $\frac{90}{100}$, $\frac{36}{40}$

Sample answers

2. Complete.

	Fraction	Decimal	Percent
a.	$\frac{9}{10}$	0.9	90%
b.	$\frac{75}{100}$	0.75	75%
c.	$\frac{30}{100}$	0.30	30%

3. Shade more than $\frac{2}{5}$, but less than $\frac{1}{2}$ of the square.

Write the value of the shaded part as a fraction, decimal, and percent.

Fraction: $\frac{45}{100}$

Decimal: 0.45

Percent: 45%

Sample answers

4. Name a percent value

a. greater than $\frac{1}{5}$ and less than $\frac{1}{2}$. 40%

b. less than $\frac{8}{10}$ and greater than $\frac{3}{4}$. 76%

Sample answers

5. Insert >, <, or = to make each number sentence true.

a. $\frac{1}{2}$ < 55%

b. 0.63 < $\frac{4}{5}$

c. $\frac{5}{6}$ < $\frac{9}{10}$

d. 27% > $\frac{3}{12}$

e. 80% < 0.92

✦ *Math Masters*, p. 136

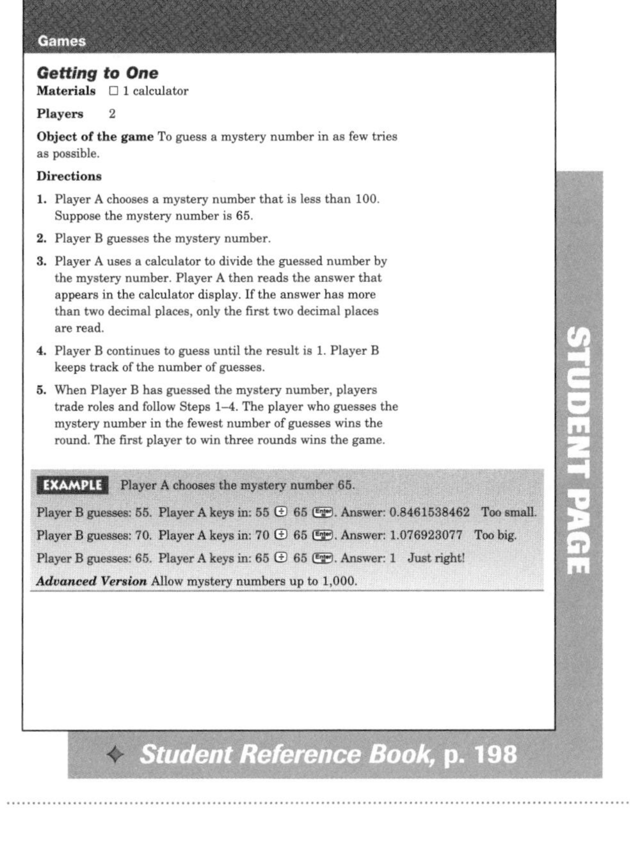

Games

Getting to One

Materials □ 1 calculator

Players 2

Object of the game To guess a mystery number in as few tries as possible.

Directions

1. Player A chooses a mystery number that is less than 100. Suppose the mystery number is 65.
2. Player B guesses the mystery number.
3. Player A uses a calculator to divide the guessed number by the mystery number. Player A then reads the answer that appears in the calculator display. If the answer has more than two decimal places, only the first two decimal places are read.
4. Player B continues to guess until the result is 1. Player B keeps track of the number of guesses.
5. When Player B has guessed the mystery number, players trade roles and follow Steps 1–4. The player who guesses the mystery number in the fewest number of guesses wins the round. The first player to win three rounds wins the game.

EXAMPLE Player A chooses the mystery number 65.

Player B guesses: 55. Player A keys in: 55 ÷ 65 Enter. Answer: 0.8461538462 Too small.

Player B guesses: 70. Player A keys in: 70 ÷ 65 Enter. Answer: 1.076923077 Too big.

Player B guesses: 65. Player A keys in: 65 ÷ 65 Enter. Answer: 1 Just right!

Advanced Version Allow mystery numbers up to 1,000.

STUDENT PAGE

✦ *Student Reference Book*, p. 198

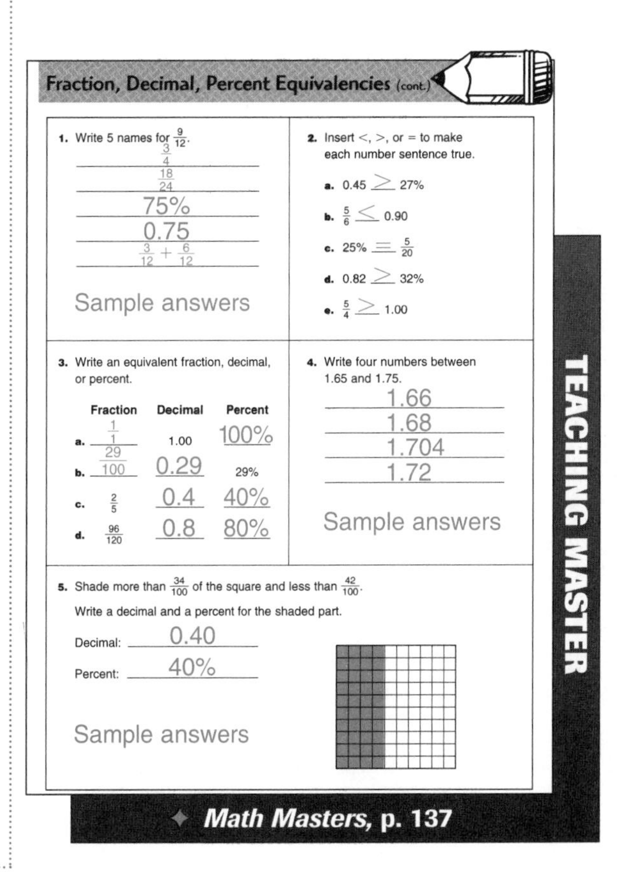

Fraction, Decimal, Percent Equivalencies (cont.)

TEACHING MASTER

1. Write 5 names for $\frac{9}{12}$.

$\frac{3}{4}$

$\frac{18}{24}$

75%

0.75

$\frac{3}{12} + \frac{6}{12}$

Sample answers

2. Insert <, >, or = to make each number sentence true.

a. 0.45 > 27%

b. $\frac{5}{6}$ < 0.90

c. 25% = $\frac{5}{20}$

d. 0.82 > 32%

e. $\frac{5}{4}$ > 1.00

3. Write an equivalent fraction, decimal, or percent.

	Fraction	Decimal	Percent
a.	$\frac{1}{1}$	1.00	100%
b.	$\frac{29}{100}$	0.29	29%
c.	$\frac{2}{5}$	0.4	40%
d.	$\frac{96}{120}$	0.8	80%

4. Write four numbers between 1.65 and 1.75.

1.66

1.68

1.704

1.72

Sample answers

5. Shade more than $\frac{34}{100}$ of the square and less than $\frac{42}{100}$.

Write a decimal and a percent for the shaded part.

Decimal: 0.40

Percent: 40%

Sample answers

✦ *Math Masters*, p. 137

9.4 Using a Calculator to Convert Fractions to Percents

OBJECTIVES **To rename fractions as percents using a calculator; and to solve number stories involving discounts expressed as percents.**

summaries	materials
1 Teaching the Lesson	
Students use the percent key on a calculator to rename fractions as percents. They rename fractions as decimals by dividing, and they are shown that a decimal can be easily renamed as a percent by multiplying it by 100. [Numeration] Students solve number stories involving discounts expressed as percents. [Operations and Computation]	□ *Math Journal 2,* p. 274 □ Study Link 9.3 □ calculator ***See* Advance Preparation**
2 Ongoing Learning & Practice	
Students play *Fraction/Percent Concentration* to help them memorize the "easy" fraction/percent equivalencies. [Numeration] Students practice and maintain skills through Math Boxes and Study Link activities.	□ *Math Journal 2,* p. 275 □ *Student Reference Book,* p. 196 □ Study Link Master (*Math Masters,* p. 346) □ Fraction/Percent Tiles (see Lesson 9.3) □ calculator ***See* Advance Preparation**
3 Options for Individualizing	
Enrichment Students solve more difficult number stories in which they compare the discounts for two items. [Operations and Computation] **Enrichment** Students use circle graphs to estimate the loss of forest land in various countries. [Numeration; Data and Chance] **Language Diversity** Students discuss the definitions of vocabulary words used in this lesson. [multiple strands]	□ Teaching Masters (*Math Masters,* pp. 138 and 139) □ *Inside the Amazing Amazon* □ *The Brazilian Rain Forest* □ *Rain Forest* ***See* Advance Preparation**

Additional Information

Advance Preparation For Parts 1 and 2, find out which type of calculator your students are using before the start of class and experiment with the percent key. The percent key does not work the same way on all calculators.

For the second optional Enrichment activity in Part 3, obtain one or more of the following books:

- *Inside the Amazing Amazon* by Don Lessem and Michael Rothman (Crown Publishing Group, 1995)
- *The Brazilian Rain Forest* by Alexandra Siy (Dillon Press, 1992)
- *Rain Forest* by Barbara Taylor (Dorling Kindersley, Inc., 1992)

Vocabulary • **regular price or list price** • **discount** • **percent or fraction of discount** • **sale price**

Getting Started

Mental Math and Reflexes

Pose pairs of problems, such as these:

- 10 * 9 90 and $\frac{1}{10}$ of 90 9
- 10 * 90 900 and $\frac{1}{10}$ of 900 90
- 10 * 900 9,000 and $\frac{1}{10}$ of 9,000 900
- 6 * 100 600 and $\frac{1}{100}$ of 600 6
- 60 * 100 6,000 and $\frac{1}{100}$ of 6,000 60

Math Message

Experiment with the percent key on your calculator. Find a way to rename $\frac{1}{4}$ as a percent. Write down your method on a half-sheet of paper.

Study Link 9.3 Follow-Up

Review answers. Have students share some of the problems they made up on their own.

1 Teaching the Lesson

✦ Math Message Follow-Up

WHOLE-CLASS ACTIVITY

Ask a volunteer to demonstrate how to use the percent key to rename fractions as percents. Demonstrate the procedure yourself, if no one has discovered how to do it. Then have students practice with a few "easy" fractions.

To convert $\frac{1}{4}$ to a percent, press

1 (÷) 4 (%) (Enter) Display: 25

The percent key does not work the same way on all calculators. The key sequence shown above works on many calculators, including the TI-15.

The percent key does NOT have to be used to rename fractions as percents. Remind students that they can convert any fraction to a decimal by dividing the numerator by the denominator (Lesson 9.3). Once they have the decimal name, it is easy to write the percent name. *For example:*

▷ To rename $\frac{1}{4}$ as a percent, divide 1 by 4 to get 0.25. This is $\frac{25}{100}$, or 25%.

▷ To rename $\frac{33}{75}$ as a percent, divide 33 by 75 to get 0.44. This is $\frac{44}{100}$, or 44%.

You can use this rule to rename any decimal as a percent:

Rule: To convert a decimal to a percent, multiply the decimal by 100. *For example:*

decimal	100 * decimal	percent
0.67	67	67%
0.375	37.5	37.5%
0.1666	16.66	16.66%

NOTE: In Lesson 9.5, students will complete the percent column on journal pages 356 and 357. They will use the percent key to find some answers, and they will use the rule stated at the left to find the remaining answers. Some students may discover that one way to multiply by 100 is to move the decimal point two places to the right.

Discount Number Stories

1. A store is offering a **discount** of 10% on all items. This means that you save $\frac{1}{10}$ of the **regular price.** Find the sale price of each item below. The **sale price** is the amount you pay after subtracting the discount from the regular price.

Item	Regular Price	Discount (10% of regular price)	Sale Price (Subtract: regular price - discount)
CD player	$140	$14	$126
Giant screen TV	$1,200	$120	$1,080
Radio	$80	$8	$72
Cassette player	$30	$3	$27

2. An airline offers a 25% discount on the regular airfare for tickets purchased at least 1 month in advance. Find the sale price of each ticket below.

Regular Airfare	Discount (25% of regular airfare)	Sale Price (Subtract: regular airfare - discount)
$400	$100	$300
$240	$60	$180
$300	$75	$225

3. A swing set can be purchased at a 30% discount if it is ordered before April 1. On April 1, the regular price of $400 will be charged. If you order the swing set before April 1,

   a. how much will you save? $120

   b. how much will you pay? $280

Challenge

4. You can pay for a refrigerator by making 12 payments of $50 each. But you can save 25% if you pay for it all at once.

   How much will the refrigerator cost if you pay for it all at once? $450

STUDENT PAGE

✧ *Math Journal 2,* **p. 274**

✦Solving Number Stories Involving Discounts
(*Math Journal 2,* p. 274)

PARTNER ACTIVITY

Consumer Link Spend a few minutes introducing the problems on journal page 274. Then students solve the problems as you circulate and assist. Those who finish early can try to solve the Challenge problem.

NOTE: The percent key may be used to find discounts and sale prices, but all story problems can be solved without using a calculator.

Adjusting the Activity Some students may have trouble solving the last row in Problems 1 and 2. It may be helpful to rephrase the problems as follows:

Problem 1: If $3 is $\frac{1}{10}$ of the whole, what is the whole? The whole is $\frac{10}{10}$, which is 10 times as much as $\frac{1}{10}$. So $10 * \$3 = \$30$.

Problem 2: If $75 is 25%, or $\frac{1}{4}$ of the whole, what is the whole? The whole is $\frac{4}{4}$, which is 4 times as much as $\frac{1}{4}$. So $4 * \$75 = \$300$.

Bring the class together to go over the answers. If students have trouble with Problem 3, suggest the following approach:

Problem 3: Suppose the discount had been 10% ($\frac{1}{10}$). One-tenth of $400 is $40. A 30% discount is 3 times as much as a 10% discount. So a 30% discount on $400 will be $3 * \$40$, or $120.

Adjusting the Activity As an extension, use Problem 3 to demonstrate how to use the percent key to find the discount and the sale price.

Discount: 400 (×) 30 (%) (Enter) Display: 120

Sale price: 400 (−) 400 (×) 30 (%) (Enter)
Display: 280

The key sequences above work on many calculators, including the TI-15.

2 Ongoing Learning & Practice

✦ Playing *Fraction/Percent Concentration* (*Student Reference Book,* p. 196; Fraction/Percent Tiles)

PARTNER ACTIVITY 

This game will help students memorize some of the "easy" fraction/percent equivalencies. See page 196 in the *Student Reference Book* for instructions on how to play the game.

✦ Math Boxes (*Math Journal 2,* p. 275)

INDEPENDENT ACTIVITY 

Mixed Review Math Boxes in this lesson are paired with Math Boxes in Lesson 9.2. The skill in Problem 1 is a prerequisite for Unit 10.

✦ Study Link 9.4 (*Math Masters,* p. 346)

Home Connection Students rename fractions as percents, with and without a calculator. Note that in Problems 9, 12, and 17, students will have to write the percent using a decimal.

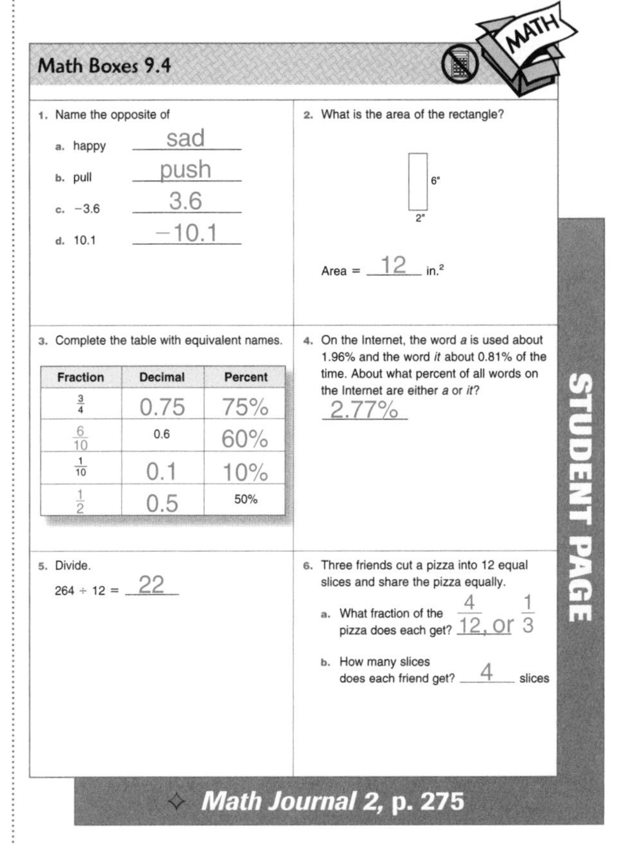

Math Boxes 9.4

1. Name the opposite of
   a. happy sad
   b. pull push
   c. −3.6 3.6
   d. 10.1 −10.1

2. What is the area of the rectangle? (6", 2")
   Area = 12 in.^{2}

3. Complete the table with equivalent names.

Fraction	Decimal	Percent
$\frac{3}{4}$	0.75	75%
$\frac{6}{10}$	0.6	60%
$\frac{1}{10}$	0.1	10%
$\frac{1}{2}$	0.5	50%

4. On the Internet, the word *a* is used about 1.96% and the word *it* about 0.81% of the time. About what percent of all words on the Internet are either *a* or *it*?
   2.77%

5. Divide.
   264 ÷ 12 = 22

6. Three friends cut a pizza into 12 equal slices and share the pizza equally.
   a. What fraction of the pizza does each get? $\frac{4}{12}$, or $\frac{1}{3}$
   b. How many slices does each friend get? 4 slices

STUDENT PAGE

✧ *Math Journal 2,* p. 275

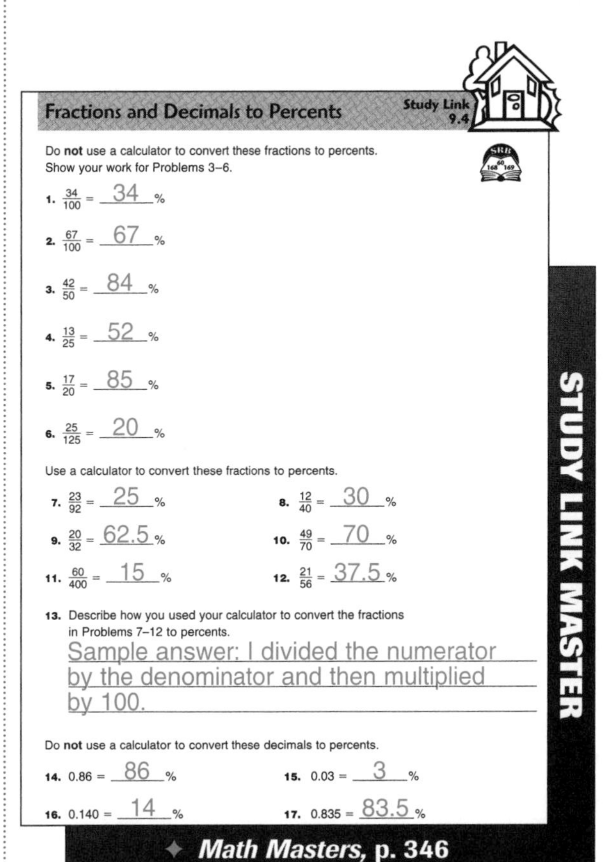

Fractions and Decimals to Percents — Study Link 9.4

Do **not** use a calculator to convert these fractions to percents. Show your work for Problems 3–6.

1. $\frac{34}{100}$ = 34 %
2. $\frac{67}{100}$ = 67 %
3. $\frac{42}{50}$ = 84 %
4. $\frac{13}{25}$ = 52 %
5. $\frac{17}{20}$ = 85 %
6. $\frac{25}{125}$ = 20 %

Use a calculator to convert these fractions to percents.

7. $\frac{23}{92}$ = 25 %
8. $\frac{12}{40}$ = 30 %
9. $\frac{20}{32}$ = 62.5 %
10. $\frac{49}{70}$ = 70 %
11. $\frac{60}{400}$ = 15 %
12. $\frac{21}{56}$ = 37.5 %

13. Describe how you used your calculator to convert the fractions in Problems 7–12 to percents.
    Sample answer: I divided the numerator by the denominator and then multiplied by 100.

Do **not** use a calculator to convert these decimals to percents.

14. 0.86 = 86 %
15. 0.03 = 3 %
16. 0.140 = 14 %
17. 0.835 = 83.5 %

STUDY LINK MASTER

✧ *Math Masters,* p. 346

Discount Number Stories 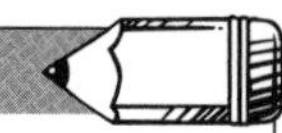

1. A store is having a sale on gym shoes.
   - The regular price of the High Flyers is $50. Now they are on sale for $38.
   - The Zingers are $15 off the regular price. When not on sale, the Zingers cost $75 a pair.

   Which pair has the greater percent of discount? Explain your answer.

   High Flyers has the greater percent of discount.
   High Flyers: You save $\frac{12}{50} = \frac{24}{100} = 24\%$.
   Zingers: You save $\frac{15}{75} = \frac{1}{5} = 0.2 = 20\%$.

2. The same store is also having a sale on tennis rackets.
   - The regular price of the Smasher is $54.00. It is on sale for 25% off the regular price.
   - The regular price of the Fast Flight is $75.00. It is on sale for 20% off the regular price.

   For which tennis racket are you getting more money taken off the regular price? Explain your answer.

   Fast Flight has the greater discount (money taken off).
   Smasher: 25% of $54 = $13.50
   Fast Flight: 20% of $75 = $15.00

TEACHING MASTER

✦ *Math Masters,* p. 138

Deforestation 

Deforestation, the clearing of forest land, is taking place in many parts of the world. Each circle below represents all the forest land that was left in that country in 1990. The shaded part shows the percent of forest land that was cleared between 1990 and the year 2000.

Brazil

Costa Rica

Ghana

Honduras

Indonesia

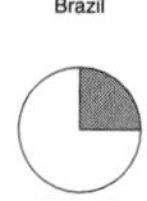
Malaysia

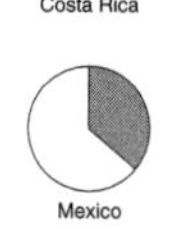
Mexico

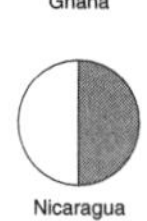
Nicaragua

Philippines

Thailand

Which countries lost

1. 50% of their forests? Honduras, Nicaragua
2. 25% of their forests? Ghana, Malaysia
3. less than 25% of their forests? Indonesia, Philippines
4. more than 25% but less than 50% of their forests? Brazil, Mexico
5. more than 50% but less than 75% of their forests? Thailand
6. more than 75% but less than 100% of their forests? Costa Rica

TEACHING MASTER

✦ *Math Masters,* p. 139

3 Options for Individualizing

✦ ENRICHMENT Solving Challenging Discount Number Stories (*Math Masters,* p. 138)

PARTNER ACTIVITY  **15–30 min** 

Students solve number stories for which they compare the discounts of two items. In one story students compare the discount percents; in a second story they compare the actual discounts.

✦ ENRICHMENT Estimating What Percent of a Circle Graph Is Shaded (*Math Masters,* p. 139)

INDEPENDENT ACTIVITY  **30+ min** 

Science Link The circle graphs on *Math Masters,* page 139 show what fractional part of the rain forest in each of 10 countries was cleared between 1990 and 2000. The activity provides practice in estimating parts of wholes as percents.

To review fractions, have students identify or estimate what fraction of each circle graph is shaded on *Math Masters,* page 139. You might also have students restate each of the questions using fractions instead of percents.

Some students may be interested in learning more about rain forests. Suggest the following books:

Inside the Amazing Amazon

Summary: A beautifully illustrated tour is given of the Amazon rain forest ecosystem.

The Brazilian Rain Forest

Summary: This book offers an exploration of the Brazilian rain forests and the economic and ecological importance of the animals and plants that live there.

Rain Forest

Summary: Readers meet the flying gecko, poison dart frog, curly-haired tarantula, and many other creatures that live in the rain forest.

✦ LANGUAGE DIVERSITY Building Background for Mathematics Words

SMALL-GROUP ACTIVITY  **15–30 min** 

Include a student learning English in a group of proficient English speakers and have them discuss the terms used in some of the "percent-of" problems in this lesson.

- ▷ The **regular price** (sometimes called the **list price**) of an item is the price without a discount.
- ▷ The **discount** is the amount you save. It is given in dollars and cents.
- ▷ The **percent of discount** or the **fraction of discount** is a percent or fraction that tells what part of the regular price you save.
- ▷ The **sale price** (or discounted price) is the amount you pay after subtracting the discount from the regular price.

Illustrate the use of these words with an example, such as the following:

> The regular price of a bird feeder is $15. It is on sale at a 20% discount. What is the sale price?

The *percent of discount* is 20% of the *regular price*. 20% is $\frac{20}{100}$, or $\frac{1}{5}$. You save $\frac{1}{5}$ of the regular price if you buy the bird feeder on sale. One-fifth of $15 is $3; that is, you save $3. This is the *discount*. To find the *sale price,* subtract $3 from $15. The sale price is $12.

9.5 Conversions among Fractions, Decimals, and Percents

OBJECTIVES **To look up and record numerical data; to rename fractions as percents using a calculator; and to rename decimals as percents.**

summaries	materials
1 Teaching the Lesson	
Students continue their World Tour by traveling from Brasília, Brazil, to Beijing, China. They look up a population and a land area and convert these to percents of the world population and land area. [Data and Chance; Operations and Computation] Students complete the percent column of the Equivalent Names for Fractions table on journal pages 356 and 357. [Numeration] Students use the percent key on the calculator to rename fractions as percents. [Numeration] Students rename decimals as percents by multiplying by 100. [Operations and Computation]	□ *Math Journal 2,* pp. 356 and 357 □ *Student Reference Book,* pp. 214 and 225 □ Study Link 9.4 □ calculator
2 Ongoing Learning & Practice	
Students update their Route Map and complete the Country Notes for China. Students who are keeping a Route Log update the log. [multiple strands] Students practice and maintain skills through Math Boxes and Study Link activities.	□ *Math Journal 2,* pp. 276, 345–347, and 350–351 □ *Student Reference Book* □ Teaching Masters (*Math Masters,* pp. 36–38; optional) □ Study Link Master (*Math Masters,* p. 347) □ calculator
3 Options for Individualizing	
Extra Practice Students use data about cats to practice renaming fractions as percents. [Operations and Computation]	□ Teaching Master (*Math Masters,* p. 140) □ calculator

Getting Started

Mental Math and Reflexes

Pose "percent-of" problems. *Suggestions:*

- 10% of 60? 6
- 40% of 25? 10
- 25% of 32? 8
- 75% of 80? 60

Math Message

Use your calculator to rename these fractions as percents: $\frac{1}{8}, \frac{3}{8}, \frac{5}{8}, \frac{7}{8}$.

Study Link 9.4 Follow-Up

Review answers. Have students share the strategies they used to solve Problems 3–6. *For example:*

- Problem 3: $\frac{42}{50} = \frac{84}{100}$ (multiply numerator and denominator by 2); $\frac{84}{100} = 84\%$
- Problem 6: $\frac{25}{125} = \frac{1}{5}$ (divide numerator and denominator by 25); $\frac{1}{5} = 20\%$

Ask if any student can describe a solution strategy to solve Problems 7 and 8 without a calculator.

- Problem 7: $\frac{23}{92} = \frac{1}{4}$ (divide numerator and denominator by 23); $\frac{1}{4} = 25\%$
- Problem 8: $\frac{12}{40} = \frac{3}{10}$ (divide numerator and denominator by 4); $\frac{3}{10} = 30\%$

1 Teaching the Lesson

✦ Math Message Follow-Up

WHOLE-CLASS ACTIVITY

Go over the answers: $\frac{1}{8} = 12.5\%$; $\frac{3}{8} = 37.5\%$; $\frac{5}{8} = 62.5\%$; $\frac{7}{8} = 87.5\%$. Students may have renamed the fractions as percents in one of two ways. They may use whichever method they like better, but they should be able to use both of these methods:

▷ Use the percent key:
For example, to rename $\frac{3}{8}$ as a percent, press:

3 (÷) 8 (%) (Enter) Display: 37.5

▷ Divide numerator by denominator, and multiply by 100:
For example, divide 3 by 8 (= 0.375) and multiply by 100 (= 37.5). Remind students that multiplying a decimal by 100 can be done by moving the decimal point two digits to the right.

Adjusting the Activity Challenge students to explain how $\frac{1}{8}$, $\frac{3}{8}$, $\frac{5}{8}$, and $\frac{7}{8}$ could be renamed as percents without using a calculator. $\frac{1}{8}$ is half of $\frac{1}{4}$. Since $\frac{1}{4}$ = 25%, and half of 25% is 12.5%, $\frac{1}{8}$ = 12.5%. $\frac{3}{8}$ equals $\frac{1}{4} + \frac{1}{8}$, which is 25% + 12.5%, or 37.5%. $\frac{5}{8}$ and $\frac{7}{8}$ are renamed in the same way.

✦ Flying to Beijing, China
(*Student Reference Book*, pp. 214 and 225)

WHOLE-CLASS ACTIVITY

Social Studies Link Tell students that it's time to leave South America and fly to Region 4, which includes Asia and Australia. Their destination is Beijing, the capital of China. Use the classroom world map to identify Russia and China. Russia has the largest land area of any country in the world. China has the largest population of any country in the world.

Ask students to use the *Student Reference Book* to find the population of China and the total world population. Give them several minutes to search; do not reveal the page sources.

Write these populations on the board. Point out that the world population has been rounded to the nearest million.

- ▷ Ask students to round China's population to the nearest million and record this estimate on the board.
- ▷ Ask students what fraction of the world's population lives in China, and write this fraction on the board.

	Population	Population Rounded	Fraction
China	1,246,872,000	1,247,000,000	$\frac{1,247,000,000}{6,071,000,000}$
World	6,071,000,000	6,071,000,000	

Have students use their calculators to rename this fraction as a percent. They should use both methods and get the same answer:

- ▷ Use the percent key:

  1247000000 (÷) 6071000000 (%) (Enter) Display will show 20.54027343.

- ▷ Divide numerator by denominator, and multiply by 100:

  1247000000 (÷) 6071000000 (Enter) Display will show 0.2054027343.

  0.2054027343 (×) 100 (Enter) Display will show 20.54027343.

ONGOING ASSESSMENT

Praise students who notice that, since both numbers are in "millions," it is sufficient to divide 1,247 by 6,071.

STUDENT PAGE

World Tour

Facts about the World

Continents are large land masses. There are seven continents on the Earth, although Europe and Asia are sometimes thought of as one continent. Most continents contain many countries, but there are no countries at all in Antarctica.

A **country** is a territory and the people who live there under one government. The number of countries in the world often changes as countries split apart or join with other countries. At this time, there are about 200 countries in the world.

Population is the number of people who live in a certain region. Population growth is the change in the population every year after all births and deaths are accounted for. The **population growth rate** is the percent of change in the population.

The world's population is now increasing by about 210,000 people per day, or about 77 million people per year. Over the last 40 years, the world's population has about doubled. It reached the 6 billion mark in 1999. World population is expected to reach about 9 billion people by the year 2050.

Dimensions of the Earth

Equatorial circumference*: about 24,900 miles (40,000 kilometers)

Equatorial diameter:** about 7,930 miles (12,760 kilometers)

Volume: 2.6×10^{11} cubic miles (1.1×10^{12} cubic kilometers)

Weight (mass): 6.6×10^{21} tons (6.0×10^{21} metric tons)

Total world water area: about 139,433,000 square miles (361,129,000 square kilometers)

*Circumference is the distance around a circle or sphere.

**Diameter is the distance measured by a straight line passing from one side of a circle or sphere, through the center, to the other side.

The Continents

Continent	Population*	Percent of World Population	Area (sq miles)	Percent of Land Area
North America	482,000,000	7.9%	9,400,000	16.2%
South America	347,000,000	5.7	6,900,000	11.9
Europe	736,000,000	12.1	3,800,000	6.6
Asia	3,688,000,000	60.7	17,400,000	30.1
Africa	788,000,000	13.0	11,700,000	20.2
Australia	30,000,000	0.5	3,300,000	5.7
Antarctica	0	0.0	5,400,000	9.3
World Totals	**6,071,000,000 (about 6.1 billion)**	**100.0%**	**57,900,000**	**100.0%**

*Data are for the year 2000.
World population growth rate for the year 2000: about 1.3% per year

214 two hundred fourteen

✦ *Student Reference Book*, p. 214

STUDENT PAGE

World Tour

REGION 4 Asia and Australia

Australia
Area: 2,967,900 sq mi
Population: 18,784,000
Capital: Canberra (**Pop.** 325,000)
Languages: English, aboriginal languages
Monetary unit: Dollar

Bangladesh
Area: 55,600 sq mi
Population: 127,118,000
Capital: Dhaka (**Pop.** 8,545,000)
Languages: Bangla, English
Monetary unit: Taka

China
Area: 3,705,400 sq mi
Population: 1,246,872,000
Capital: Beijing (**Pop.** 11,299,000)
Languages: Mandarin, Gan, Wu, Haka, Yue, Minbei, Xiang, Minnan
Monetary unit: Renminbi (Yuan)

India
Area: 1,269,300 sq mi
Population: 1,000,849,000
Capital: New Delhi (**Pop.** 9,948,000)
Languages: Hindi, English, 14 regional languages
Monetary unit: Rupee

Iran
Area: 636,000 sq mi
Population: 65,180,000
Capital: Tehran (**Pop.** 6,750,000)
Languages: Farsi, Kurdish, Turkic, Luri
Monetary unit: Rial

Japan
Area: 145,900 sq mi
Population: 126,182,000
Capital: Tokyo (**Pop.** 7,968,000)
Language: Japanese
Monetary unit: Yen

Russia
Area: 6,592,800 sq mi
Population: 146,394,000
Capital: Moscow (**Pop.** 8,368,000)
Languages: Russian, many others
Monetary unit: Ruble

Thailand
Area: 198,500 sq mi
Population: 60,609,000
Capital: Bangkok (**Pop.** 6,547,000)
Languages: Thai, English
Monetary unit: Baht

Turkey
Area: 301,400 sq mi
Population: 65,599,000
Capital: Ankara (**Pop.** 2,938,000)
Languages: Turkish, Arabic, Kurdish
Monetary unit: Lira

Vietnam
Area: 127,200 sq mi
Population: 77,311,000
Capital: Hanoi (**Pop.** 1,236,000)
Languages: Vietnamese, Chinese, French, English
Monetary unit: Dong

REGION 5 North America

Canada
Area: 3,851,800 sq mi
Population: 31,006,000
Capital: Ottawa (**Pop.** 1,000,000)
Languages: English, French
Monetary unit: Dollar

Costa Rica
Area: 19,700 sq mi
Population: 3,674,000
Capital: San José (**Pop.** 324,000)
Language: Spanish
Monetary unit: Colon

Cuba
Area: 42,800 sq mi
Population: 11,096,000
Capital: Havana (**Pop.** 2,185,000)
Language: Spanish
Monetary unit: Peso

El Salvador
Area: 8,100 sq mi
Population: 5,839,000
Capital: San Salvador (**Pop.** 1,214,000)
Language: Spanish
Monetary unit: Colon

Guatemala
Area: 42,000 sq mi
Population: 12,336,000
Capital: Guatemala City (**Pop.** 2,205,000)
Languages: Spanish, Mayan languages
Monetary unit: Quetzal

Haiti
Area: 10,700 sq mi
Population: 6,884,000
Capital: Port-au-Prince (**Pop.** 844,000)
Languages: French, Haitian Creole
Monetary unit: Gourde

Jamaica
Area: 4,200 sq mi
Population: 2,652,000
Capital: Kingston (**Pop.** 104,000)
Languages: English, Jamaican Creole
Monetary unit: Dollar

Mexico
Area: 761,600 sq mi
Population: 100,294,000
Capital: Mexico City (**Pop.** 8,489,000)
Languages: Spanish, Mayan dialects
Monetary unit: New Peso

Panama
Area: 30,200 sq mi
Population: 2,779,000
Capital: Panama City (**Pop.** 465,000)
Languages: Spanish, English
Monetary unit: Balboa

United States of America
Area: 3,717,800 sq mi
Population: 272,640,000
Capital: Washington, D.C. (**Pop.** 523,000)
Languages: English, Spanish
Monetary unit: Dollar

two hundred twenty-five SRB 225

✦ *Student Reference Book*, p. 225

Help students summarize. Round percent answers to the nearest whole-number percent. The digit in the tenths place in 20.54027343% is greater than or equal to 5, so the number is rounded up to 21%. About 21 of every 100 people in the world live in China. Since 21% is close to 20%, and 20% equals $\frac{1}{5}$, about 1 of every 5 people in the world live in China.

Repeat this last routine to calculate the percent of the world's land area that is in Russia. Russia's area is about 6,592,800 square miles. The world's land area is about 57,900,000 square miles. The fraction of the world's area that belongs to Russia is about 6,593,000 ÷ 57,900,000 = 0.1138687392. So about 11% of the world's area belongs to Russia.

✦ Completing the Equivalent Names for Fractions Table (*Math Journal 2*, pp. 356 and 357)

INDEPENDENT ACTIVITY 

Students should already have filled in the equivalent fractions and decimals columns of the table on journal pages 356 and 357. Now they will fill in the percents column.

- ▷ On the first page of the table, students find the percents by using the percent key. If the calculator display shows an answer with more than 3 digits, they record only the first 3 digits. For example, for the fraction $\frac{5}{6}$, the percent answer will be displayed on the calculator as 83.33333333, but only 83.3 should be recorded in the table.
- ▷ On the second page of the table, students can find the percents without using a calculator and without making any actual computations. The decimal names are already recorded in the table. Students need only multiply the decimal by 100 (move the decimal point two digits to the right) to rename the decimal as a percent. As before, ask students to record only the first 3 digits for any percent name.

NOTE: If students were absent or unable to complete the equivalent fractions and decimals columns of the pages, have them work with a partner to complete the rest of the page.

2 Ongoing Learning & Practice

✦ Updating the World Tour (*Math Journal 2,* pp. 345–347 and 350–351; *Student Reference Book; Math Masters,* pp. 36–38)

INDEPENDENT ACTIVITY 

Social Studies Link Students follow the established World Tour routine.

▷ They update the Route Map by drawing a line segment to connect Brasília, Brazil, and Beijing, China.

▷ They use the World Tour section of the *Student Reference Book* to locate facts about China and Beijing, and they fill in the Country Notes pages for this country and capital.

▷ Students who are also keeping a Route Log will update that as well.

Allow students a week or more to complete the Country Notes pages. The second page of Country Notes provides space for students to record interesting facts about the country they are visiting. Discourage rote copying of facts. Encourage students to use classroom and library resources to discover facts about the country that are genuinely interesting to them.

Adjusting the Activity For those students who came from China or Russia, you might suggest that they share with the class any information about their country, such as the population of the city they came from, where it is located, the approximate size or land area of that city, and any trips they may have taken to the capital.

✦ Math Boxes 9.5 (*Math Journal 2,* p. 276)

INDEPENDENT ACTIVITY 

Mixed Review Math Boxes in this lesson are paired with Math Boxes in Lessons 9.7 and 9.9. The skill in Problem 1 is a prerequisite for Unit 10.

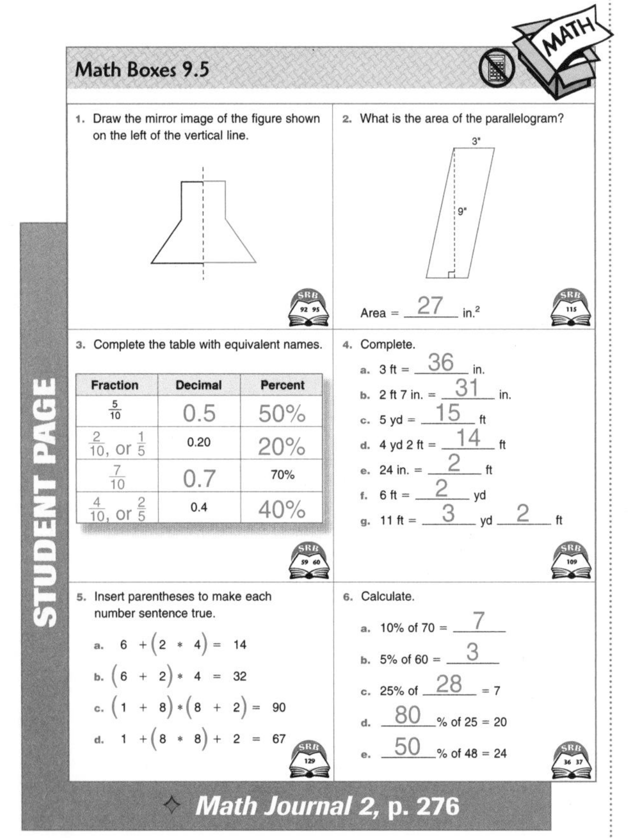

STUDENT PAGE

Math Boxes 9.5

1. Draw the mirror image of the figure shown on the left of the vertical line.

2. What is the area of the parallelogram?

3"

9"

Area = 27 in.^{2}

3. Complete the table with equivalent names.

Fraction	Decimal	Percent
$\frac{5}{10}$	0.5	50%
$\frac{2}{10}$, or $\frac{1}{5}$	0.20	20%
$\frac{7}{10}$	0.7	70%
$\frac{4}{10}$, or $\frac{2}{5}$	0.4	40%

4. Complete.

a. 3 ft = 36 in.

b. 2 ft 7 in. = 31 in.

c. 5 yd = 15 ft

d. 4 yd 2 ft = 14 ft

e. 24 in. = 2 ft

f. 6 ft = 2 yd

g. 11 ft = 3 yd 2 ft

5. Insert parentheses to make each number sentence true.

a. $6 + (2 * 4) = 14$

b. $(6 + 2) * 4 = 32$

c. $(1 + 8) * (8 + 2) = 90$

d. $1 + (8 * 8) + 2 = 67$

6. Calculate.

a. 10% of 70 = 7

b. 5% of 60 = 3

c. 25% of 28 = 7

d. 80 % of 25 = 20

e. 50 % of 48 = 24

✧ Math Journal 2, p. 276

✦ Study Link 9.5 (*Math Masters,* p. 347)

Home Connection Students use a table of data to calculate the approximate percentage of marriages that occurred each month in 1996.

Options for Individualizing

✦ EXTRA PRACTICE Using a Calculator to Rename Fractions as Percents (*Math Masters,* p. 140)

INDEPENDENT ACTIVITY  **15–30 min** 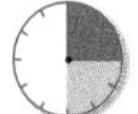

Students use a table of data to calculate the approximate percent of the top ten breeds of cats that were registered with the Cat Fancier's Association in 1997.

PLANNING AHEAD

Remind students to bring to school the second page of Study Link 9.1 (Trivia Survey). Their survey results will be used in Lesson 9.6.

Renaming Fractions as Percents

Study Link 9.5

In 1996, there were about 2,342,000 marriages in the United States. The table below shows the approximate number of marriages each month.

SRB 60 169

1. Use a calculator to find the percent of the total number of marriages that occurred each month. Round the answers to the nearest whole percent.

Month	Approximate Number of Marriages	Approximate Percent of Total Marriages
January	100,000	4%
February	155,000	7%
March	147,000	6%
April	172,000	7%
May	241,000	10%
June	242,000	10%
July	235,000	10%
August	239,000	10%
September	225,000	10%
October	231,000	10%
November	171,000	7%
December	184,000	8%

Source: *The Top 10 of Everything 1999*

2. Describe how you used your calculator to calculate the percent for each month.
Sample answer: I divided the first three digits of the number by 2,342 and multiplied the answer by 100. Then I rounded to the nearest percent.

3. Do the percents in the table add up to 100%? no Explain why or why not.
Sample answer: Because each percentage was rounded to the nearest whole percent

STUDY LINK MASTER

✦ *Math Masters,* p. 347

Renaming Fractions as Percents

According to the Cat Fancier's Association, 65,183 cats were registered in the United States in 1997. Of the 36 breeds registered, the table below shows the top ten.

1. Use a calculator to find what percent of 65,183 registered cats belongs to each breed. Round the percents to the nearest whole percent.

Breed	Number of Cats Registered	Percent of Total Number of Cats Registered
Persian	39,119	60%
Maine coon	4,819	7%
Siamese	2,657	4%
Abyssinian	2,308	4%
Exotic	2,037	3%
Oriental	1,337	2%
Scottish fold	1,202	2%
American shorthair	1,072	2%
Birman	1,007	2%
Burmese	939	1%

Source: *The Top 10 of Everything 1999*

2. Describe the procedure that you used to round the percents to the nearest whole percent.
Sample answer: I looked at the digit in the tenths place to see if I should round up or down. If this digit was less than 5, I rounded down. If it was 5 or more, I rounded up.

3. Explain why the percents do not add up to 100%.
Sample answer: The chart only shows the top ten breeds of cats, so all the cats registered are not listed; also, each number was rounded to the nearest whole percent.

TEACHING MASTER

✦ *Math Masters,* p. 140

9.6 Comparing the Results of a Survey

OBJECTIVES **To organize and tabulate survey data; and to use percents to compare quantities expressed as fractions with unlike denominators.**

summaries	materials
1 Teaching the Lesson	
Students tabulate the results from the trivia survey distributed in Lesson 9.1. For each survey question, they write a fraction to express the number of "Yes" answers as a part of the total number of answers. Then they convert each fraction to a percent. [Data and Chance]	☐ *Math Journal 2,* p. 277 ☐ Study Links 9.1 (Trivia Survey) and 9.5 ☐ Transparency (*Math Masters,* p. 141; optional) ☐ calculator ***See* Advance Preparation**
2 Ongoing Learning & Practice	
Students solve whole-number division problems and write the remainders as fractions. [Operations and Computation] Students practice and maintain skills through Math Boxes and Study Link activities.	☐ *Math Journal 2,* pp. 278 and 279 ☐ Teaching Master (*Math Masters,* p. 20 or 80; optional) ☐ Study Link Master (*Math Masters,* p. 348)
3 Options for Individualizing	
Enrichment Students make a bar graph of the class survey results. [Data and Chance] **Enrichment** Students read a book to learn how scale drawings and other models are used to compare data. [Data and Chance]	☐ *Incredible Comparisons* ***See* Advance Preparation**

Additional Information

Advance Preparation For Part 1, copy the chart on *Math Masters,* page 141 onto the board or make a transparency.

For the second optional Enrichment activity in Part 3, you will need a copy of *Incredible Comparisons* by Russell Ash (Dorling Kindersley, Inc., 1996).

Getting Started

Mental Math and Reflexes

Write "easy" fractions on the board. For each fraction, students write the equivalent decimal and percent.
Suggestions

- $\frac{1}{2}$ 0.50, 50%
- $\frac{1}{4}$ 0.25, 25%
- $\frac{3}{4}$ 0.75, 75%
- $\frac{2}{5}$ 0.40, 40%
- $\frac{3}{5}$ 0.60, 60%
- $\frac{4}{5}$ 0.80, 80%
- $\frac{3}{10}$ 0.30, 30%
- $\frac{7}{10}$ 0.70, 70%
- $\frac{9}{10}$ 0.90, 90%

Math Message

Use your calculator to rename the following fractions as percents to the nearest whole percent:

$\frac{18}{63}$ $\frac{57}{78}$ $\frac{42}{59}$ $\frac{2}{47}$

Study Link 9.5 Follow-Up

Go over the answers. Students should note that because of rounding, the percents may not add up to 100%.

1 Teaching the Lesson

Math Message Follow-Up

WHOLE-CLASS DISCUSSION

Go over the answers. 29%, 73%, 71%, 4% Ask volunteers to show what they did to rename the fractions as percents. Make sure that both methods are presented:

▷ Using the percent key on a calculator

▷ Dividing the numerator by the denominator, and multiplying by 100

Making a Prediction Based on Individual Survey Data (Study Link 9.1, Trivia Survey)

WHOLE-CLASS DISCUSSION

Have students make some rough guesses about people's behavior based on the survey results for the people they interviewed. Ask the following questions:

Do you think it is more likely that a person will

- read a book or go to a movie?
- eat breakfast or eat at a fast-food restaurant?
- like liver or like Mondays?

Take a vote and record the results on the board.

Trivia Survey — Study Link 9.1

Conduct the survey below. The results won't be needed until Lesson 9.6.

Ask at least 5 people the following questions. You can ask family members, relatives, neighbors, and friends. You can ask the questions in person or by telephone.

Record each answer with a tally mark in the "Yes" or "No" column.

BE CAREFUL! You will not ask everyone every question. Pay attention to the instructions that go with each question. Answers vary.

Question	Yes	No
1. Is Monday your favorite day? (Ask everyone younger than 20.)		
2. Have you gone to the movies in the last month? (Ask everyone older than 8.)		
3. Did you eat breakfast today? (Ask everyone over 25.)		
4. Do you keep a map in your car? (Ask everyone who owns a car.)		
5. Did you eat at a fast-food restaurant yesterday? (Ask everyone.)		
6. Did you read a book during the last month? (Ask everyone over 20.)		
7. Are you more than 1 meter tall? (Ask everyone over 20.)		
8. Do you like liver? (Ask everyone.)		

STUDY LINK MASTER

Math Masters, p. 343

STUDENT PAGE

Trivia Survey Results

1. The chart below will show the results of the trivia survey for the whole class. Wait for your teacher to explain how to fill in the chart.

Class Results for the Trivia Survey

Question	Yes	No	Total	$\frac{\text{Yes}}{\text{Total}}$	% Yes
1. Is Monday your favorite day?					
2. Have you gone to the movies in the last month?					
3. Did you eat breakfast today?					
4. Do you keep a map in your car?					
5. Did you eat at a fast-food restaurant yesterday?					
6. Did you read a book during the last month?					
7. Are you more than 1 meter tall?					
8. Do you like liver?					

2. On the basis of the survey results, is it more likely that a person will
   a. read a book or go to a movie? ______
   b. eat breakfast or eat at a fast-food restaurant? ______
   c. like liver or like Mondays? ______

Math Journal 2, p. 277

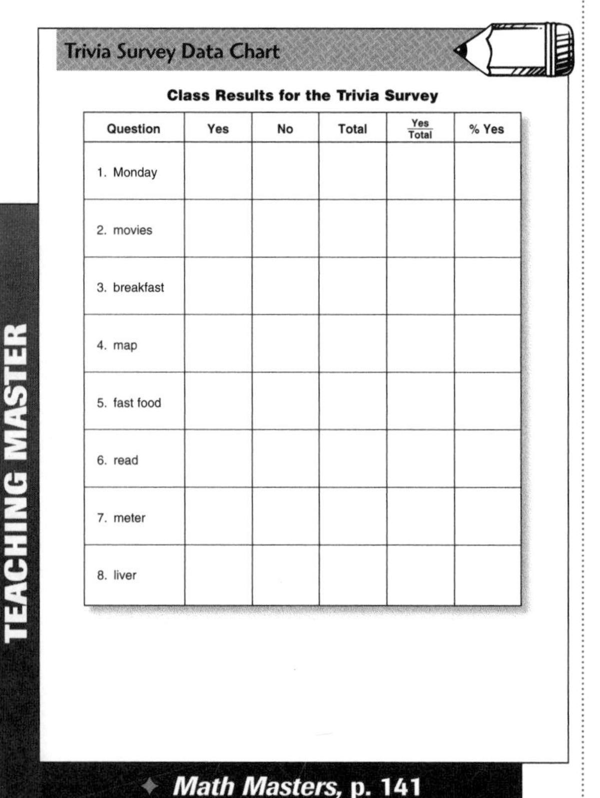
TEACHING MASTER

Trivia Survey Data Chart

Class Results for the Trivia Survey

Question	Yes	No	Total	$\frac{\text{Yes}}{\text{Total}}$	% Yes
1. Monday					
2. movies					
3. breakfast					
4. map					
5. fast food					
6. read					
7. meter					
8. liver					

Math Masters, p. 141

✦ Tabulating Survey Results for the Whole Class (*Math Journal 2,* p. 277; Study Link 9.1, Trivia Survey; *Math Masters,* p. 141)

WHOLE-CLASS ACTIVITY

Tell students that they will use the results of *all* the surveys to check their guesses. The first step is to combine the results from all of the surveys. The goal is to create a chart that shows the total number of "Yes" and "No" answers to each question for the whole class.

Ask for suggestions on how to do this most efficiently. Use whatever practical suggestions are made.

One possibility is to divide the class into small groups of 4 or 5. For each question on the survey, have the students in each group find the total number of "Yes" answers and the total number of "No" answers for their group. Each group can then report its totals. You or a student volunteer can add these as they are reported. Finally, record the total number of "Yes" and the total number of "No" answers to each question on the chart on the board (or overhead transparency of *Math Masters,* page 141).

Students copy the results in the "Yes" and "No" columns on page 277 in their journals. They add the "Yes" and "No" results and record the sums in the "Total" column. These are the total numbers of people who answered the survey questions.

Next, students record the "Yes" answers as a fraction of the total number of answers in the $\frac{\text{Yes}}{\text{Total}}$ column. If necessary, help them complete the $\frac{\text{Yes}}{\text{Total}}$ column for the first two rows of the chart. At this point, your classroom chart or overhead transparency might look as follows:

Question	Yes	No	Total	$\frac{\text{Yes}}{\text{Total}}$	% Yes
1. Monday	18	45	63	$\frac{18}{63}$	
2. movies	57	21	78	$\frac{57}{78}$	

✦ Analyzing the Survey Results
(*Math Journal 2,* p. 277)

WHOLE-CLASS DISCUSSION 

Ask students if they can tell from the results so far whether it is more likely that a person will

▷ read a book or go to a movie.

▷ eat breakfast or eat at a fast-food restaurant.

▷ like liver or like Mondays.

Some students might argue that you need to simply compare the "Yes" answers. For example, suppose that 45 out of 50 people interviewed had read a book and that 57 out of 78 people had seen a movie last month. On the basis of these results, is it correct to conclude that since more people had seen a movie than had read a book, people are more likely to go to the movies than to read a book? Or does the total number of people interviewed need to be taken into account?

This discussion is *crucial* to understanding why percents are useful. Students should see that it is difficult to compare quantities that are expressed as fractions with unlike denominators. Explain that this is why we rename fractions with unlike denominators as fractions that have the same denominator. The denominator 100—used in percents—is especially useful, because in our base-ten system, it is easy to rename such fractions as decimals and percents.

Once students understand why it is helpful to rename the fraction of "Yes" answers to a percent of "Yes" answers, have them use their calculators to fill in the "% Yes" column. Ask them to round the answers to the nearest whole percent. Students' completed charts should resemble your classroom chart or overhead transparency, which might look like this:

Question	Yes	No	Total	$\frac{\text{Yes}}{\text{Total}}$	% Yes
1. Monday	18	45	63	$\frac{18}{63}$	29%
2. movies	57	21	78	$\frac{57}{78}$	73%

Working together, have partners use their completed table to answer Problem 2 at the bottom of journal page 277.

Adjusting the Activity Challenge students to combine the trivia survey data from all of the fourth grade classes in the school. Discuss why "% Yes" estimates based on the combined data are more reliable than estimates based on the data collected by any single classroom.

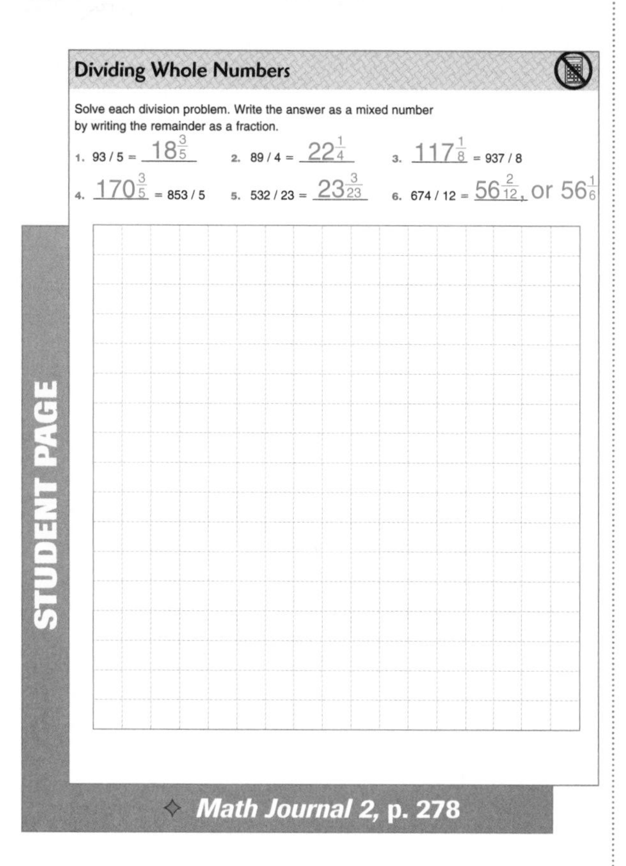
STUDENT PAGE

Dividing Whole Numbers

Solve each division problem. Write the answer as a mixed number by writing the remainder as a fraction.

1. 93 / 5 = $18\frac{3}{5}$
2. 89 / 4 = $22\frac{1}{4}$
3. $117\frac{1}{8}$ = 937 / 8
4. $170\frac{3}{5}$ = 853 / 5
5. 532 / 23 = $23\frac{3}{23}$
6. 674 / 12 = $56\frac{2}{12}$, or $56\frac{1}{6}$

✧ *Math Journal 2*, p. 278

2 Ongoing Learning & Practice

✦ Dividing Whole Numbers (*Math Journal 2*, p. 278; *Math Masters*, p. 20 or 80)

INDEPENDENT ACTIVITY 

Students solve whole-number division problems and write the remainders as fractions. Have copies of *Math Masters*, page 20 or 80 available for students who need additional grid paper to do their computations.

ONGOING ASSESSMENT

In Lesson 9.9, students will use an estimation strategy to divide decimals by whole numbers. In preparation for this activity, it is expected that students are able to use the partial-quotients algorithm to solve whole-number division problems. Use journal page 278 to assess students' skill levels.

✦ Math Boxes 9.6 (*Math Journal 2*, p. 279)

INDEPENDENT ACTIVITY 

Mixed Review Math Boxes in this lesson are paired with Math Boxes in Lesson 9.8. The skill in Problem 1 is a prerequisite for Unit 10.

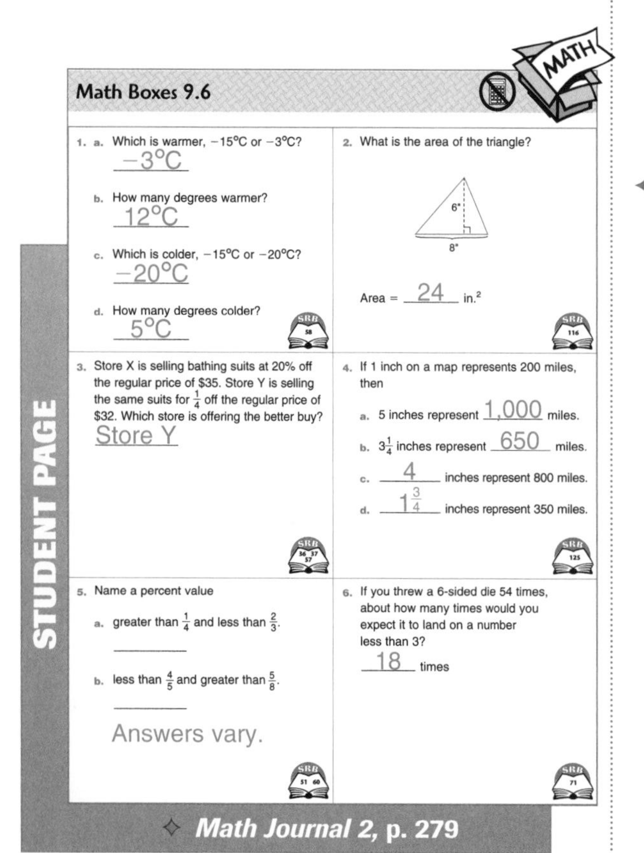
STUDENT PAGE

Math Boxes 9.6

1. a. Which is warmer, −15°C or −3°C? −3°C
   b. How many degrees warmer? 12°C
   c. Which is colder, −15°C or −20°C? −20°C
   d. How many degrees colder? 5°C
2. What is the area of the triangle? (6", 8")
   Area = 24 in.^{2}
3. Store X is selling bathing suits at 20% off the regular price of $35. Store Y is selling the same suits for $\frac{1}{4}$ off the regular price of $32. Which store is offering the better buy? Store Y
4. If 1 inch on a map represents 200 miles, then
   a. 5 inches represent 1,000 miles.
   b. $3\frac{1}{4}$ inches represent 650 miles.
   c. 4 inches represent 800 miles.
   d. $1\frac{3}{4}$ inches represent 350 miles.
5. Name a percent value
   a. greater than $\frac{1}{4}$ and less than $\frac{2}{3}$. ______
   b. less than $\frac{4}{5}$ and greater than $\frac{5}{8}$. ______
   Answers vary.
6. If you threw a 6-sided die 54 times, about how many times would you expect it to land on a number less than 3? 18 times

✧ *Math Journal 2*, p. 279

✦ Study Link 9.6 (*Math Masters*, p. 348)

Home Connection Students use percents to compare quantities expressed as fractions with unlike denominators.

Options for Individualizing

✦ ENRICHMENT Graphing Survey Results

PARTNER ACTIVITY **15–30 min**

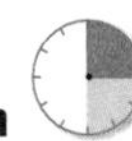

Students graph the results of the class survey. You might suggest that students use a side-by-side bar graph.

Example

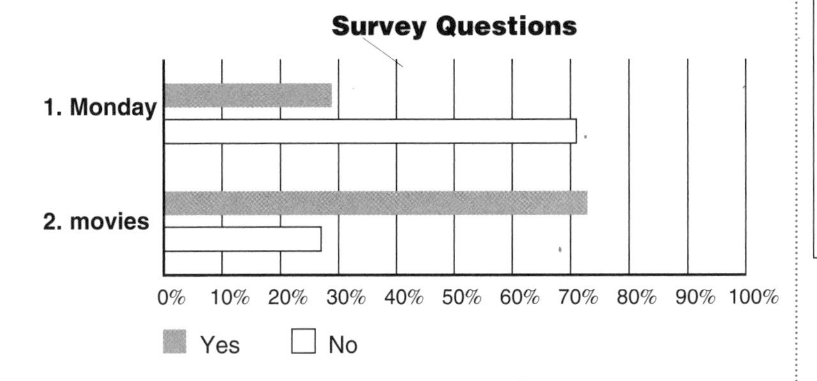

✦ ENRICHMENT Reading about Comparisons

INDEPENDENT ACTIVITY **15–30 min**

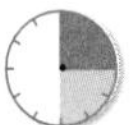

Literature Link Lesson 9.6 focuses on using percents to compare quantities expressed as fractions with unlike denominators. Encourage students to read the following book to learn about other ways that data can be compared:

Incredible Comparisons

Summary: Students will enjoy the scale drawings and other models that are used to compare facts about topics such as the surface of Earth, rain forests, big buildings, animal speeds, growth and age, light and heavy, great and small, population, land and water speed, and the solar system.

Using Percents to Compare Fractions — Study Link 9.6

1. The girls' varsity basketball team won 8 of the 10 games it played. The junior varsity team won 6 of 8 games. Which team has the better record? Explain your reasoning. Sample answer: The varsity team has a better record. It won $\frac{8}{10}$ = 80% of its games. The junior varsity team won $\frac{6}{8}$ = 75% of its games.

SRB 60 169

2. The record keeper for the varsity team kept a record of the shots taken by each player (not including free throws) during the most recent game. Complete the table. Calculate the percent of shots made to the nearest whole percent.

Player	Shots Made	Shots Missed	Total Shots	Shots Made / Total Shots	% of Shots Made
#1	5	12	17	$\frac{5}{17}$	29%
#2	5	6	11	$\frac{5}{11}$	45%
#3	3	0	3	$\frac{3}{3}$	100%
#4	9	2	11	$\frac{9}{11}$	82%
#5	4	3	7	$\frac{4}{7}$	57%
#6	11	5	16	$\frac{11}{16}$	69%
#7	6	4	10	$\frac{6}{10}$	60%
#8	1	1	2	$\frac{1}{2}$	50%

3. The basketball game is tied. Your team has the ball. There is only enough time for one more shot. Based only on the information in the table, which player would you choose to take the shot? Why? Sample answer: I would choose Player #4, who has taken 11 shots and made 82% of her shots. Player #3 has a higher percent of shots made (100%), but she has only taken 3 shots.

STUDY LINK MASTER

✦ Math Masters, p. 348

9.7 Comparing Population Data

OBJECTIVES To rank and compare data that are reported as percents; and to display ranked data by coloring maps.

summaries	materials
1 Teaching the Lesson	
Students rank the countries in Region 4 (Asia and Australia) according to the percent of the population that is rural and the percent of the population that is 14 years old or younger. [Data and Chance] Students color maps to display the ranked data and interpret the maps. [Data and Chance]	☐ *Math Journal 2,* p. 280 ☐ *Student Reference Book,* p. 245 ☐ Study Link 9.6 ☐ Teaching Master (*Math Masters,* p. 142) ☐ red, green, and blue pencils or markers per partnership ☐ slate ***See* Advance Preparation**
2 Ongoing Learning & Practice	
Students practice and maintain skills through Math Boxes and Study Link activities.	☐ *Math Journal 2,* p. 281 ☐ Study Link Master (*Math Masters,* p. 349)
3 Options for Individualizing	
Enrichment Students rank the countries in Region 4 according to the percent of the population that is literate. They color a map to display the ranked data and compare it to the maps created earlier to display the percent of the population ages 0–14 and the percent that is rural. [Data and Chance]	☐ *Student Reference Book,* p. 243 ☐ Teaching Masters (*Math Masters,* pp. 142 and 143) ☐ red, green, and blue pencils or markers per partnership ***See* Advance Preparation**

Additional Information

Advance Preparation For Part 1, make two copies of *Math Masters,* page 142 for each student. For the optional Enrichment activity in Part 3, make one additional copy of *Math Masters,* page 142 for each student.

Vocabulary • **urban** • **rural** • **life expectancy** • **rank** • **literate and illiterate** • **percent of literacy**

Getting Started

Mental Math and Reflexes

Write pairs of expressions with fractions and percents on the board. Students write >, <, or = on their slates. *Suggestions:*

- $\frac{1}{3}$ of 9 < 50% of 10
- 75% of 16 = 100% of 12
- 20% of 40 > $\frac{1}{6}$ of 30
- 10% of 100 = $\frac{2}{5}$ of 25
- $\frac{1}{4}$ of 20 < $\frac{1}{3}$ of 21
- 10% of 10 > 1% of 50

Math Message

Look up the following words in a dictionary:

urban
rural
life expectancy

Study Link 9.6 Follow-Up

Review answers. Note that for Problem 3, there is not a single correct answer. Some students may choose Player #3 because she hit 100% of her shots. Some students may choose Player #4 because she hit a high percentage of her shots. Because Player #4 took more shots than Player #3, she may be more capable of taking a shot in a pressure situation. Praise students who mention that in making a decision such as this, a coach would need to consider many different variables.

1 Teaching the Lesson

✦ Math Message Follow-Up

WHOLE-CLASS DISCUSSION

The meaning of each of these words will be discussed in the course of the lesson.

✦ Discussing a Table of Population Data (*Student Reference Book,* p. 245)

WHOLE-CLASS DISCUSSION

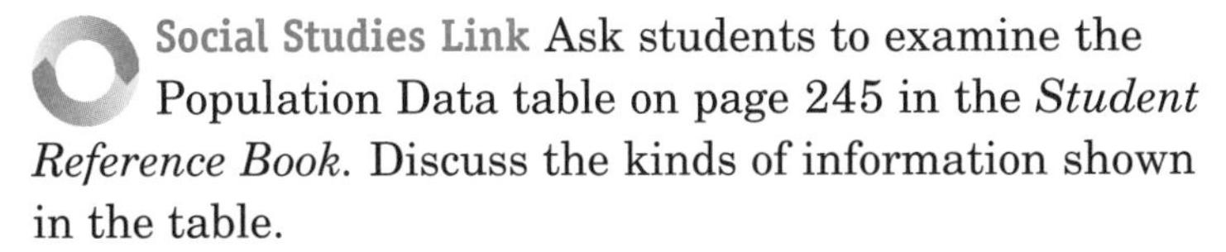

Social Studies Link Ask students to examine the Population Data table on page 245 in the *Student Reference Book.* Discuss the kinds of information shown in the table.

- According to the table, 22% of the population in the U.S. is 14 years old or younger (Column 1). What does this mean? 22 out of 100 people in the U.S. are 14 or younger.
- Which country has the largest (smallest) number in Column 1, and what does the number mean? The largest number is 48, for Senegal; in Senegal, 48%, or 48 out of 100 people, are 14 or younger. The smallest number is 14, for Italy; in Italy, 14%, or 14 out of 100 people, are 14 or younger.

STUDENT PAGE

World Tour

Population Data

Region	Country	Percent of Population Ages 0–14	Life Expectancy: Males	Life Expectancy: Females	Percent Population Growth in 1 Year	Percent Urban	Percent Rural
Region 1	Algeria	37	68	70	2.1	56	44
	Egypt	36	60	64	1.9	45	55
	Ethiopia	46	39	42	2.3	16	84
	Ghana	42	55	59	2.1	36	64
	Kenya	43	47	47	1.6	30	70
	Liberia	45	57	63	3.0	46	54
	Morocco	36	67	71	2.0	53	47
	Senegal	48	55	61	3.3	44	56
	South Africa	34	53	57	1.3	50	50
	Zimbabwe	43	39	39	1.0	33	67
Region 2	France	19	75	83	0.2	74	26
	Greece	16	76	81	0.1	59	41
	Hungary	17	67	76	−0.2	65	35
	Iceland	23	77	81	0.8	92	8
	Italy	14	75	82	−0.1	67	33
	Netherlands	18	75	81	0.3	89	11
	Norway	20	76	81	0.2	73	27
	Poland	20	69	77	0.1	64	36
	Spain	15	74	82	0	77	23
	United Kingdom	19	75	80	0.1	89	11
Region 3	Argentina	27	71	79	1.2	88	12
	Bolivia	39	59	65	2.1	61	39
	Brazil	30	59	69	1.2	79	21
	Chile	28	72	79	1.2	84	16
	Colombia	33	67	75	1.9	73	27
	Ecuador	35	70	75	1.7	60	40
	Paraguay	39	70	75	2.7	53	47
	Peru	35	68	73	2.0	71	29
	Uruguay	24	73	79	0.8	91	9
	Venezuela	33	70	76	1.7	86	14
Region 4	Australia	21	77	83	0.6	85	15
	Bangladesh	38	61	60	1.7	19	81
	China	26	69	71	0.8	29	71
	India	34	63	64	1.7	27	73
	Iran	36	68	71	1.5	60	40
	Japan	15	77	83	0.2	78	22
	Russia	19	59	72	−0.5	76	24
	Thailand	24	66	73	0.9	20	80
	Turkey	30	71	76	1.6	71	29
	Vietnam	33	66	71	1.4	19	81
Region 5	Canada	20	76	83	0.5	77	23
	Costa Rica	33	74	79	1.8	50	50
	Cuba	22	73	78	0.6	76	24
	El Salvador	37	67	74	2.0	45	55
	Guatemala	43	64	69	2.9	39	61
	Haiti	42	50	54	1.9	32	68
	Jamaica	31	73	78	1.5	54	46
	Mexico	35	69	75	2.0	74	26
	Panama	32	72	78	1.7	56	44
	United States	22	73	80	0.6	76	24

two hundred forty-five SRB 245

✦ *Student Reference Book,* p. 245

STUDENT PAGE

Color-Coded Population Maps

1. List the countries in Region 4 from *smallest to largest* according to the **percent of population, ages 0–14.** Take one copy of *Math Masters,* page 142 and write a title for your first map. Color these countries using the color code shown below.

Rank	Country	Percent of Population Ages 0–14	Color Code
1	Japan	15%	blue
2	Russia	19%	blue
3	Australia	21%	blue
4	Thailand	24%	green
5	China	26%	green
6	Turkey	30%	green
7	Vietnam	33%	green
8	India	34%	red
9	Iran	36%	red
10	Bangladesh	38%	red

2. List the countries in Region 4 from *smallest to largest* according to the **percent of population that is rural.** Take another copy of *Math Masters,* page 142 and write a title for your second map. Color these countries using the color code shown below.

Rank	Country	Percent of Rural Population	Color Code
1	Australia	15%	blue
2	Japan	22%	blue
3	Russia	24%	blue
4	Turkey	29%	green
5	Iran	40%	green
6	China	71%	green
7	India	73%	green
8	Thailand	80%	red
9	Vietnam	81%	red
10	Bangladesh	81%	red

✦ *Math Journal 2,* p. 280

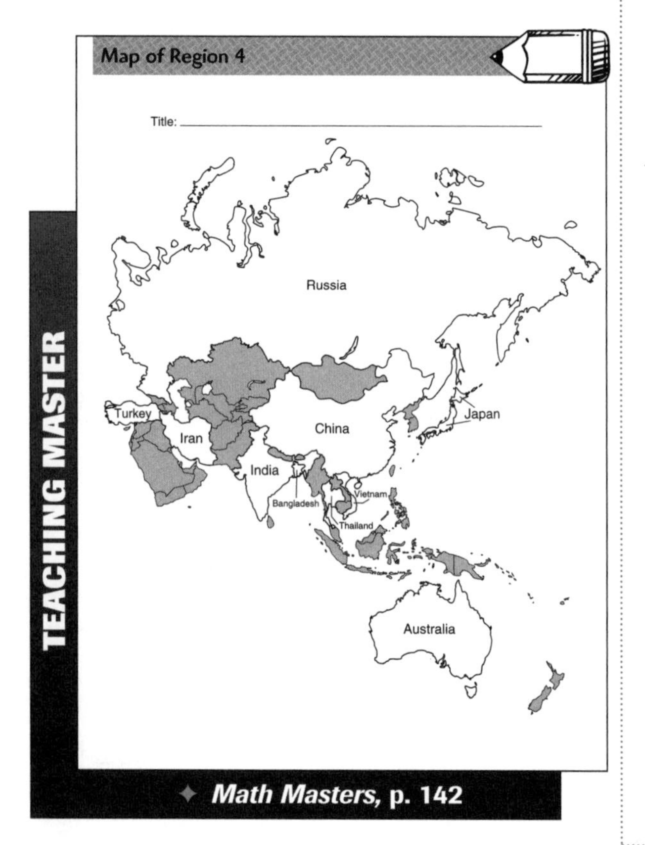

✦ *Math Masters,* p. 142

Review the meanings of the words **urban** and **rural** as they refer to a town or city and a country area.

- According to the last two columns of the table, 76% of the U.S. population lives in towns or cities, and 24% of the U.S. population lives in the country. The two percents add up to 100% because the urban and rural groups together include everyone.
- Which country has the largest (smallest) percent of its population living in the country? 84% of Ethiopia's population is rural. 8% of Iceland's population is rural.

The table includes **life expectancy** data, the average number of years a person can expect to live. Data for males and females are given separately. In every country, except Bangladesh, the average lifetime is longer for females than for males. Zimbabwe has the shortest average lifetime: about 39 years for both males and females.

The table includes population growth data, expressed as percent growth for 1 year. Explain this column by giving several examples:

▷ Liberia's growth is 3.0% in one year. For every 100 people in Liberia at the beginning of the year, there will be 100 + 3, or 103 people at the end of the year.

▷ Russia's growth is −0.5% in one year. A negative percent growth means the population is getting smaller. For every 100 people in Russia at the beginning of the year, there will be $100 - \frac{1}{2}$, or 99.5 people at the end of the year. That is, for every 200 people at the beginning of the year, there will be 199 people at the end of the year.

✦ Ranking Countries and Coloring Maps to Display Population Data (*Math Journal 2,* p. 280; *Student Reference Book,* p. 245; *Math Masters,* p. 142)

PARTNER ACTIVITY

Tell students they are going to focus on the data for Region 4—Asia and Australia. Students work with partners. They use the top part of journal page 280 to **rank** and display the countries in Region 4 according to the data in Column 1 of the Population Data table (percent of population, ages 0–14). They use the bottom part of journal page 280 to rank and display the countries according to the data in Column 6 of the table (percent rural).

Show students how to rank the countries in Region 4 according to the percent of population, ages 0–14. Make a list numbered from 1 to 10 on the board.

▷ Ask which country in Region 4 has the smallest percent in Column 1. Japan, 15% Write Japan as the first country on your list.

▷ Ask which country has the next smallest percent in column 1. Russia, 19% Write Russia as the second country on your list.

▷ Continue in the same way until all 10 countries in Region 4 have been listed (*see margin*).

We rank data when we list it in order, from smallest to largest or from largest to smallest. The list just created ranks Region 4 countries from smallest to largest percent of population, ages 0–14.

Tell students to title each copy of the map on *Math Masters,* page 142. Explain how to color the maps, using the color code shown on journal page 280. For example, since Japan is ranked first on the chart for percent of population, ages 0–14, and the color code for line 1 is blue, Japan should be colored blue on the map for that subject. On this same map, Vietnam should be colored green, and India colored red.

When finished, each student will have two tables of country rankings and two colored maps—for percent of population, ages 0–14, and for percent rural.

NOTE: Suggest that students compare their rankings of the countries with those of other students and come to an agreement *before* coloring the maps on their two copies of *Math Masters,* page 142.

✦ Interpreting the Maps (*Math Masters,* p. 142)

WHOLE-CLASS DISCUSSION 

Discuss the students' colored maps.

- What do the map colors blue, green, and red indicate? Blue identifies countries that have the lowest percents of young people and of rural people; these are the countries that rank 1st, 2nd, or 3rd. Red identifies countries that have the highest percents; countries that rank 8th, 9th, or 10th. Green identifies countries that have middle value percents; they rank 4th, 5th, 6th, or 7th.
- Which countries are colored blue on both maps? Japan, Russia, and Australia What does this tell you about these countries? They have smaller fractions of young people in their countries than the other countries of Region 4. They also have smaller fractions of people living in rural areas than the other countries of Region 4.

Countries Ranked from Smallest to Largest Percent of Population, Ages 0–14

1	Japan	15%
2	Russia	19%
3	Australia	21%
4	Thailand	24%
5	China	26%
6	Turkey	30%
7	Vietnam	33%
8	India	34%
9	Iran	36%
10	Bangladesh	38%

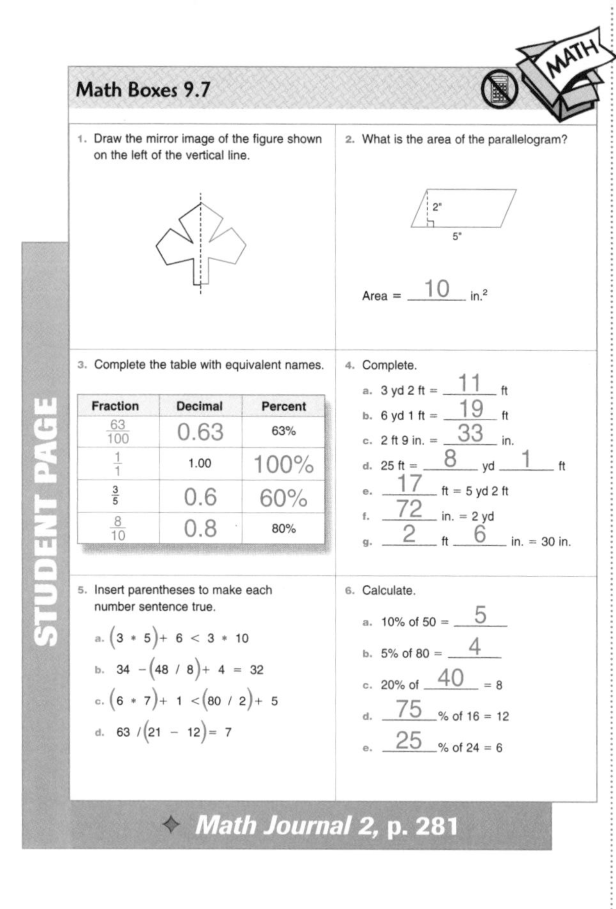

Math Boxes 9.7

1. Draw the mirror image of the figure shown on the left of the vertical line.

2. What is the area of the parallelogram?

2" 5"

Area = 10 in.^{2}

3. Complete the table with equivalent names.

Fraction	Decimal	Percent
$\frac{63}{100}$	0.63	63%
$\frac{1}{1}$	1.00	100%
$\frac{3}{5}$	0.6	60%
$\frac{8}{10}$	0.8	80%

4. Complete.

a. 3 yd 2 ft = 11 ft
b. 6 yd 1 ft = 19 ft
c. 2 ft 9 in. = 33 in.
d. 25 ft = 8 yd 1 ft
e. 17 ft = 5 yd 2 ft
f. 72 in. = 2 yd
g. 2 ft 6 in. = 30 in.

5. Insert parentheses to make each number sentence true.

a. $(3 * 5) + 6 < 3 * 10$
b. $34 - (48 / 8) + 4 = 32$
c. $(6 * 7) + 1 < (80 / 2) + 5$
d. $63 / (21 - 12) = 7$

6. Calculate.

a. 10% of 50 = 5
b. 5% of 80 = 4
c. 20% of 40 = 8
d. 75 % of 16 = 12
e. 25 % of 24 = 6

STUDENT PAGE

✦ Math Journal 2, p. 281

- Which country is colored red on both maps? Bangladesh What does this tell you about this country? Its population includes a large fraction of young people; about 40 out of 100 people are 14 years old or younger. It also has a very large fraction of people that live in the country; about 80 out of 100 people live in rural areas.
- Six of the ten countries are the same color on both maps. The other four countries are just one color apart. What conclusion can you draw from these observations? There seems to be a strong connection between the fraction of young people and the fraction that live in rural areas.
- What are some advantages and disadvantages of displaying data by coloring maps? It is easier to compare data about countries and groups of countries at a glance on the map. However, the map does not give you as accurate a picture as a table of data. For example, Turkey and India have the same color on the percent-rural map. This tells us that both countries are in the middle group for the fraction of population that is rural. But we know from the table that India has more than double the percent of population living in rural areas than Turkey does.

Least Populated Countries — Study Link 9.7

The table below shows the approximate population for the 10 least populated countries in the world.

Country	Approximate Population
Vatican City	860
Nauru	11,000
Tuvalu	11,000
San Marino	25,000
Monaco	32,000
Liechtenstein	32,000
Dominica	65,000
Marshall Islands	66,000
Seychelles	79,000
Kiribati	86,000

Use the data in the table to complete the statements.

1. There are about 54,000 more people living in Kiribati than Monaco.
2. The difference in population between Vatican City and Dominica is about 64,140 people.
3. The population of San Marino is about $\frac{1}{3}$ the population of Seychelles.
4. The combined population of Monaco and Liechtenstein is about 64,000 people.
5. The population of Liechtenstein is about 50 % of the population of Dominica.
6. The combined population of Kiribati and the Marshall Islands is about 152,000 people.
7. The population of Tuvalu is about 17 % of the population of the Marshall Islands.

STUDY LINK MASTER

✦ Math Masters, p. 349

2 Ongoing Learning & Practice

✦ Math Boxes 9.7 (*Math Journal 2*, p. 281)

INDEPENDENT ACTIVITY 

Mixed Review Math Boxes in this lesson are paired with Math Boxes in Lessons 9.5 and 9.9. The skill in Problem 1 is a prerequisite for Unit 10.

✦ Study Link 9.7 (*Math Masters*, p. 349)

Home Connection Students use population data from the 10 least populated countries in the world to complete statements involving addition, subtraction, fractions, and percents.

3 Options for Individualizing

✦ ENRICHMENT Ranking Countries and Coloring a Map to Show Literacy Data

(*Student Reference Book,* p. 243; *Math Masters,* pp. 142 and 143)

PARTNER ACTIVITY **30+ min**

Portfolio Ideas

Discuss the information in the last column in the Literacy and Standard of Living table on page 243 of the *Student Reference Book.* It tells something about the population's level of education in each country.

- Who is a **literate** person? A person who can read and write People who cannot read and write are said to be **illiterate.**
- What is the **percent of literacy**? The fraction of the total population that is literate; the number of people out of 100 who are literate. For example, 90% of the population in Mexico is literate—this means that 90 out of every 100 people can read and write. Point out that young children are not counted until they reach an age at which they are expected to be able to read and write.
- Which region, overall, seems to have the most literate population? Region 2—Europe Which region seems to have the least literate population? Region 1—Africa

Distribute copies of *Math Masters,* pages 142 and 143 to each student. Have students rank the countries in Region 4 according to percent of literacy. Point out the instruction on the *Math Masters* page to *rank from largest to smallest* percent. Australia and Japan have 100% literacy; they both rank first and are written on lines 1 and 2 in either order. Bangladesh has 38% literacy, ranks last, and is written on the tenth line.

Then ask students to give the map a title and to color the map using the color codes indicated. Ask them to compare this map with the maps they made in Part 1 of the lesson and to record their observations.

NOTE: As on the first two maps, Australia, Japan, and Russia will rank as the top three. Bangladesh, India, and Iran will rank as the bottom three.

World Tour

Literacy and Standard of Living Data

Region	Country	Televisions (Per 1,000 People)	Radios (Per 1,000 People)	Telephones (Per 1,000 People)	Cars (Per 1,000 People)	Percent Literate*
Region 1	Algeria	71	122	51	16	62
	Egypt	110	312	59	19	51
	Ethiopia	4	153	3	1	35
	Ghana	15	249	6	5	64
	Kenya	18	103	9	9	78
	Liberia	20	263	2	6	38
	Morocco	93	222	51	37	44
	Senegal	7	93	13	11	33
	South Africa	84	268	107	100	82
	Zimbabwe	12	113	19	22	85
Region 2	France	579	869	576	432	99
	Greece	442	402	517	219	95
	Hungary	444	590	304	224	99
	Iceland	285	733	615	486	100
	Italy	436	790	458	546	97
	Netherlands	495	877	591	368	100
	Norway	459	763	616	397	100
	Poland	250	263	228	195	99
	Spain	490	306	416	391	97
	United Kingdom	612	1,194	539	433	100
Region 3	Argentina	347	614	199	130	96
	Bolivia	202	560	67	25	83
	Brazil	193	348	116	81	85
	Chile	280	305	176	60	95
	Colombia	188	151	164	29	91
	Ecuador	79	277	80	20	90
	Paraguay	144	141	40	13	92
	Peru	85	221	62	19	89
	Uruguay	191	586	249	144	97
	Venezuela	183	372	117	65	91
Region 4	Australia	641	1,148	513	463	100
	Bangladesh	5	65	2	1	38
	China	189	177	68	4	82
	India	21	117	18	4	52
	Iran	117	213	100	25	79
	Japan	619	799	479	370	100
	Russia	379	341	184	94	99
	Thailand	56	167	80	26	94
	Turkey	171	141	259	50	82
	Vietnam	43	106	26	1	94
Region 5	Canada	647	919	621	429	97
	Costa Rica	102	224	159	13	95
	Cuba	200	327	33	1	96
	El Salvador	91	373	83	6	71
	Guatemala	45	52	35	8	56
	Haiti	4	41	9	5	45
	Jamaica	306	739	158	16	85
	Mexico	192	227	99	82	90
	Panama	13	5	132	52	91
	United States	776	2,122	633	476	97

* Data are hard to measure and may vary greatly.

two hundred forty-three SRB 243

STUDENT PAGE

✦ *Student Reference Book,* p. 243

Color-Coded Map for Percent of Literacy

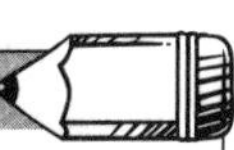

List the countries in Region 4 from *largest* to *smallest* according to the **percent of the population that is literate.** On *Math Masters,* page 142, write a title for the map. Then color these countries using the color code shown below.

Rank	Country	Percent of Literacy	Color Code
1	Australia	100%	blue
2	Japan	100%	blue
3	Russia	99%	blue
4	Thailand	94%	green
5	Vietnam	94%	green
6	China	82%	green
7	Turkey	82%	green
8	Iran	79%	red
9	India	52%	red
10	Bangladesh	38%	red

TEACHING MASTER

✦ *Math Masters,* p. 143

9.8 Multiplication of Decimals

OBJECTIVES **To multiply decimals by whole numbers; and to practice the partial-products and lattice methods for multiplication.**

summaries	materials
1 Teaching the Lesson	
Students use an estimation strategy for multiplying decimals. They solve a set of decimal multiplication problems that offers review and practice of the partial-products and lattice algorithms. [Operations and Computation]	☐ *Math Journal 2,* pp. 282 and 283 ☐ Study Link 9.7 ☐ Teaching Master (*Math Masters,* p. 20 or 80; optional)
2 Ongoing Learning & Practice	
Students play *Fraction/Percent Concentration.* [Numeration] Students practice and maintain skills through Math Boxes and Study Link activities.	☐ *Math Journal 2,* p. 284 ☐ *Student Reference Book,* p. 196 ☐ Study Link Master (*Math Masters,* p. 350) ☐ Fraction/Percent Tiles (see Lesson 9.3)
3 Options for Individualizing	
Reteaching Students use the lattice method of multiplication to multiply decimals. [Operations and Computation] **Reteaching** Students practice multiplying whole numbers. [Operations and Computation]	☐ *Math Journal 2,* p. 283 ☐ Teaching Master (*Math Masters,* p. 144)

Additional Information

Background Information For additional information on the following topics, see the *Teacher's Reference Manual:* partial-products algorithm; and lattice method.

Getting Started

Mental Math and Reflexes

Write hundredths-fractions on the board. Students write each as a percent. *Suggestions:*

- $\frac{9}{100}$ 9%
- $\frac{46}{100}$ 46%

Write tenths-fractions on the board. Students write each as a hundredths-fraction and as a percent. *Suggestions:*

- $\frac{4}{10}$ $\frac{40}{100}$, 40%
- $\frac{7}{10}$ $\frac{70}{100}$, 70%

Math Message

Solve the problem at the top of journal page 282.

Study Link 9.7 Follow-Up

Students share their answers and solution strategies. Some may have noticed that nine of the populations are in the ten-thousands and that when working with these numbers, it is necessary to focus only on the first two digits.

Teaching the Lesson

Math Message Follow-Up
(*Math Journal 2,* p. 282)

WHOLE-CLASS DISCUSSION

Encourage students to read a decimal such as 0.2 as "two tenths" rather than "point two" or "zero point two."

Have students share their solution strategies. Some students may approach the problem as repeated addition: $0.2 + 0.2 + ... + 0.2 = 1.6$.

Others may approach it as a multiplication problem. Have those students explain how they decided where to place the decimal point. Ask: *Why are 16 and 0.16 not reasonable answers?* Because 0.2 is less than 1, the answer must be less than 8, so 16 is not a reasonable answer. Since 0.2 is greater than 0.16, 0.16 is too small, so the answer must be 1.6.

Estimating Products of Decimals

WHOLE-CLASS ACTIVITY

In this lesson, students learn to find the product of decimals by multiplying the numbers as if they were whole numbers and then using estimation to place the decimal point in the answer.

To practice estimating products, write the following problems on the board:

11 * 2.8 110 * 2.8 11 * 0.28

Ask students to estimate each product. Write some of their responses next to the problems, and discuss their estimates. For example, some students may round 11 * 2.8 to 11 * 3 and estimate 33. Others may multiply 10 * 3 = 30 or 10 * 2 = 20. Since the purpose of this estimate is to help them place the decimal point, any of these estimates is satisfactory.

- Which problem is most likely to have the answer 30.8? 11 * 2.8
- How do you know? The estimates made for this problem were about 20 or 30. The estimates for the other problems were much larger or smaller.

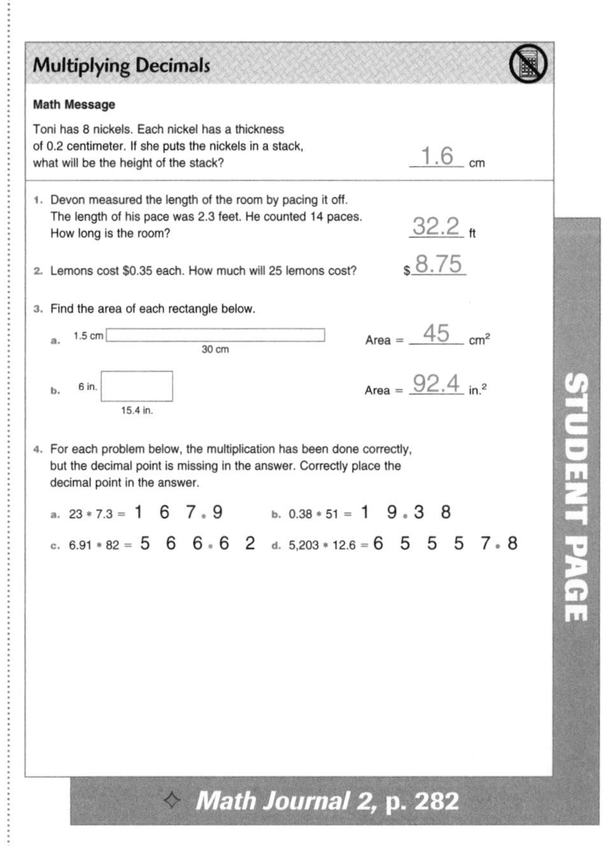

Multiplying Decimals

Math Message

Toni has 8 nickels. Each nickel has a thickness of 0.2 centimeter. If she puts the nickels in a stack, what will be the height of the stack? 1.6 cm

1. Devon measured the length of the room by pacing it off. The length of his pace was 2.3 feet. He counted 14 paces. How long is the room? 32.2 ft

2. Lemons cost $0.35 each. How much will 25 lemons cost? $8.75

3. Find the area of each rectangle below.

 a. 1.5 cm, 30 cm Area = 45 cm²

 b. 6 in., 15.4 in. Area = 92.4 in.²

4. For each problem below, the multiplication has been done correctly, but the decimal point is missing in the answer. Correctly place the decimal point in the answer.

 a. 23 * 7.3 = 1 6 7 . 9 b. 0.38 * 51 = 1 9 . 3 8

 c. 6.91 * 82 = 5 6 6 . 6 2 d. 5,203 * 12.6 = 6 5 5 5 7 . 8

STUDENT PAGE

Math Journal 2, p. 282

Write the number 308 next to the second problem, $110 * 2.8$.

- Where would you place the decimal point? After the 8
- How do you know? One strategy: The answer must be larger than $110 * 1$.

Write the number 308 next to the third problem, $11 * 0.28$.

- Where would you place the decimal point? Between the 3 and 0
- How do you know? One strategy: The answer is less than $11 * 1 = 11$; so 308 and 30.8 are too large. The answer is much larger than $1 * 0.28$; so 0.308 is too small. That leaves 3.08 as the only possible answer.

Now write the following problem on the board:

> Calculators are on sale for $9.29 each. How much will 5 of them cost?

Ask students to estimate the cost of 5 calculators. 5 * \$9 = \$45 and 5 * \$10 = \$50, so they will cost between 45 and 50 dollars.

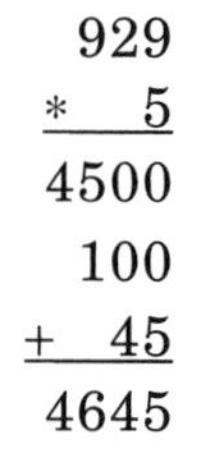

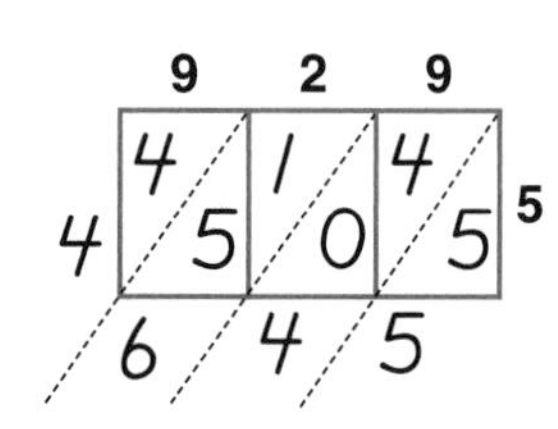

Have volunteers come to the board and multiply $5 * 929$ (9.29 without the decimal point). Ask some students to use the partial-products method and others to use the lattice method (*see margin*).

Finally, have students use their initial estimates of the total cost to place the decimal. $5 * 929 = 4645$, and the estimate was about \$50. So place the decimal point between the 6 and the following 4; the total cost is \$46.45.

Help students summarize the use of estimation to place the decimal point in the answer when multiplying decimals. *For example:*

$6 * 3.7 = ?$

1. Estimate the product.	$6 * 3.7$ is about $6 * 4$, or 24.
2. Multiply the factors as though they were whole numbers.	$6 * 37 = 222$
3. Use the estimate to place the decimal point in the answer.	22.2 is close to the estimate of 24.

ONGOING ASSESSMENT

Use this time to check students' skill in multidigit multiplication. Give additional problems if students need more review and practice.

✦ Multiplying Decimals (*Math Journal 2,* pp. 282 and 283; *Math Masters,* p. 20 or 80)

PARTNER ACTIVITY 

Students complete journal pages 282 and 283. Circulate and assist as needed. Have *Math Masters,* page 20 or 80 available for students who need additional grid paper for their computations. When most of the students have completed the pages, briefly go over the answers.

2 Ongoing Learning & Practice

✦ Playing *Fraction/Percent Concentration* (*Student Reference Book,* p. 196; Fraction/Percent Tiles)

PARTNER ACTIVITY 

This game will help students memorize the "easy" fraction/percent equivalencies.

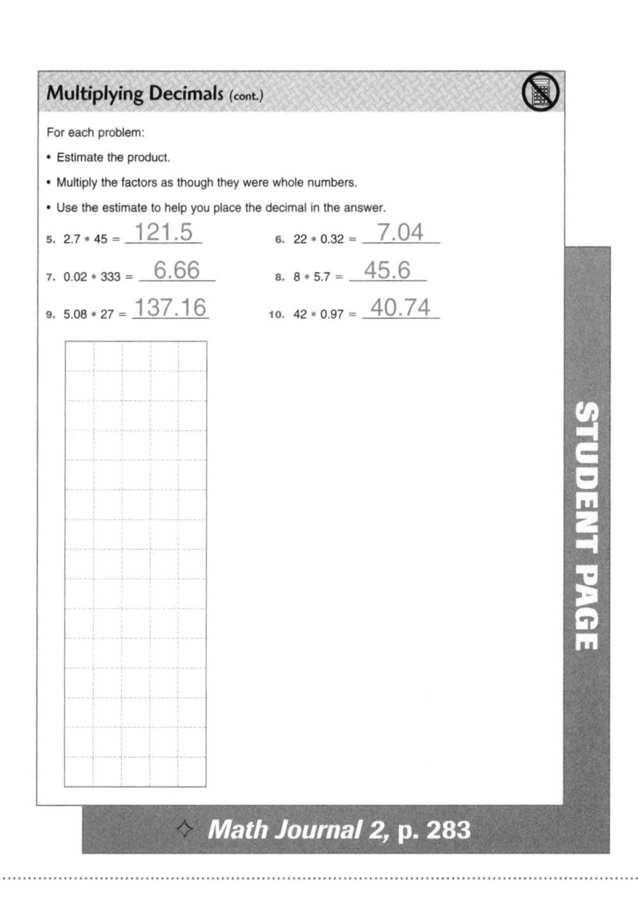

Multiplying Decimals (cont.)

For each problem:

- Estimate the product.
- Multiply the factors as though they were whole numbers.
- Use the estimate to help you place the decimal in the answer.

5. 2.7 * 45 = 121.5
6. 22 * 0.32 = 7.04
7. 0.02 * 333 = 6.66
8. 8 * 5.7 = 45.6
9. 5.08 * 27 = 137.16
10. 42 * 0.97 = 40.74

STUDENT PAGE

✧ *Math Journal 2,* p. 283

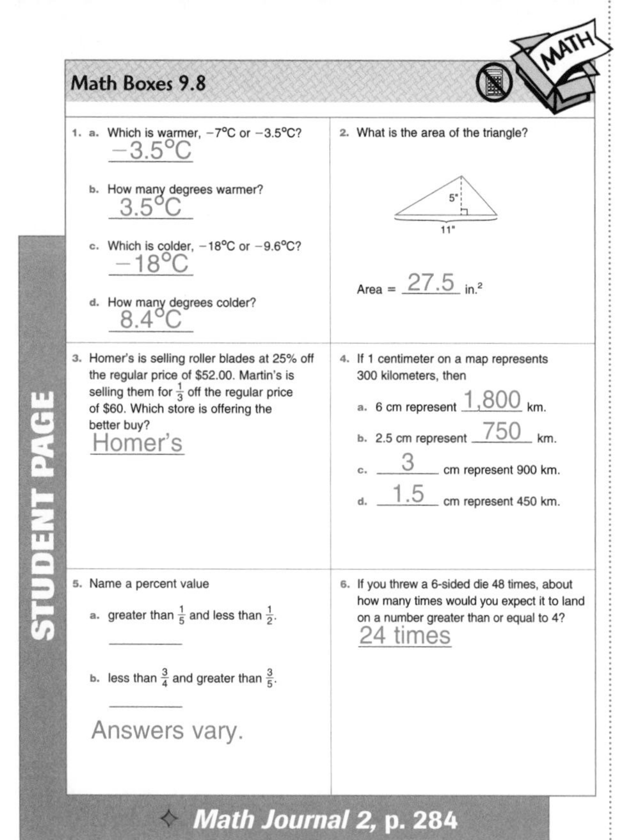
Math Boxes 9.8

1. a. Which is warmer, −7°C or −3.5°C? −3.5°C
b. How many degrees warmer? 3.5°C
c. Which is colder, −18°C or −9.6°C? −18°C
d. How many degrees colder? 8.4°C

2. What is the area of the triangle?
5"
11"
Area = 27.5 in.²

3. Homer's is selling roller blades at 25% off the regular price of $52.00. Martin's is selling them for $\frac{1}{3}$ off the regular price of $60. Which store is offering the better buy?
Homer's

4. If 1 centimeter on a map represents 300 kilometers, then
a. 6 cm represent 1,800 km.
b. 2.5 cm represent 750 km.
c. 3 cm represent 900 km.
d. 1.5 cm represent 450 km.

5. Name a percent value
a. greater than $\frac{1}{5}$ and less than $\frac{1}{2}$. ________
b. less than $\frac{3}{4}$ and greater than $\frac{3}{5}$. ________
Answers vary.

6. If you threw a 6-sided die 48 times, about how many times would you expect it to land on a number greater than or equal to 4?
24 times

STUDENT PAGE
Math Journal 2, p. 284

Multiplying Decimals

Study Link 9.8

For each problem below, the multiplication has been done correctly, but the decimal point is missing in the answer. Correctly place the decimal point in the answer.

1. 6 ∗ 4.3 = 2 5.8
2. 72 ∗ 6.8 = 4 8 9.6
3. 0.96 ∗ 47 = 4 5.1 2
4. 5.12 ∗ 22 = 1 1 2.6 4
5. 8,457 ∗ 9.8 = 8 2 8 7 8.6
6. 0.04 ∗ 140 = 5.6

7. Explain how you decided where to place the decimal point in Problem 4.
Sample answer: I estimated that the answer should be about 5 ∗ 20 = 100.

Multiply. Show your work.

8. 5.9 ∗ 36 = 212.4	9. 0.46 ∗ 84 = 38.64	10. 382.13 = 7.21 ∗ 53

STUDY LINK MASTER
Math Masters, p. 350

✦ Math Boxes 9.8 (*Math Journal 2,* p. 284)

INDEPENDENT ACTIVITY 

Mixed Review Math Boxes in this lesson are paired with Math Boxes in Lesson 9.6. The skill in Problem 1 is a prerequisite for Unit 10.

✦ Study Link 9.8 (*Math Masters,* p. 350)

Home Connection Students estimate products of decimals and whole numbers. They multiply decimals and whole numbers.

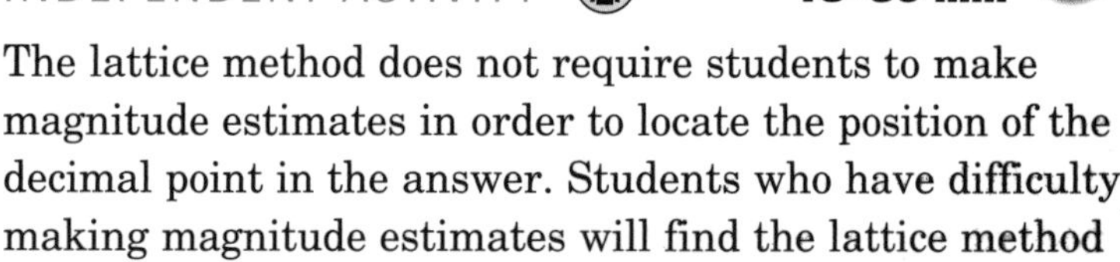

3 Options for Individualizing

✦ RETEACHING Using the Lattice Method to Position Decimal Points (*Math Journal 2,* p. 283)

INDEPENDENT ACTIVITY  **15–30 min**

The lattice method does not require students to make magnitude estimates in order to locate the position of the decimal point in the answer. Students who have difficulty making magnitude estimates will find the lattice method ideal, because it can automatically locate the position of the decimal point in the final answer.

▷ When writing the factors above and on the right side of the lattice, include the decimal points. In the factor above the grid, the decimal point should be above the column line. In the factor on the right side of the grid, the decimal point should be to the right of the row line.

▷ Locate the decimal point in the answer as follows: Slide the decimal point in the factor above the grid down. Slide the decimal point in the factor on the right side of the grid across. The decimal points will intersect on a diagonal line. Slide the decimal point down along that diagonal line. Write a decimal point at the end of the diagonal line.

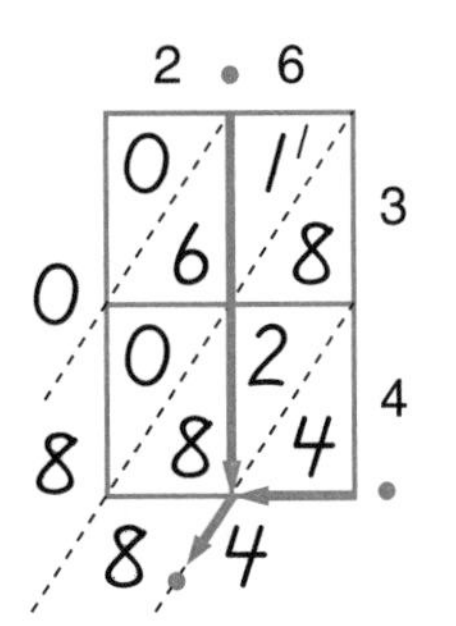

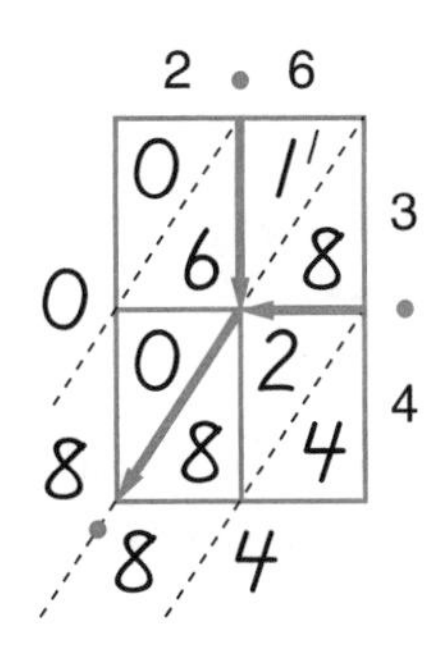

Decimal multiplied by whole number   Decimal multiplied by decimal

NOTE: Students who are able to make magnitude estimates should, of course, always do so. Even if they use the lattice method to find a product, the magnitude estimate can be used to check their answer.

If they have not already done so, ask students to solve Problems 5–10 on journal page 283 using the lattice method.

✦ RETEACHING Multiplying Whole Numbers (*Math Masters,* p. 144)

INDEPENDENT ACTIVITY  **15–30 min**

Some students may need to refresh their skills at multiplying whole numbers before working on multiplication of decimals.

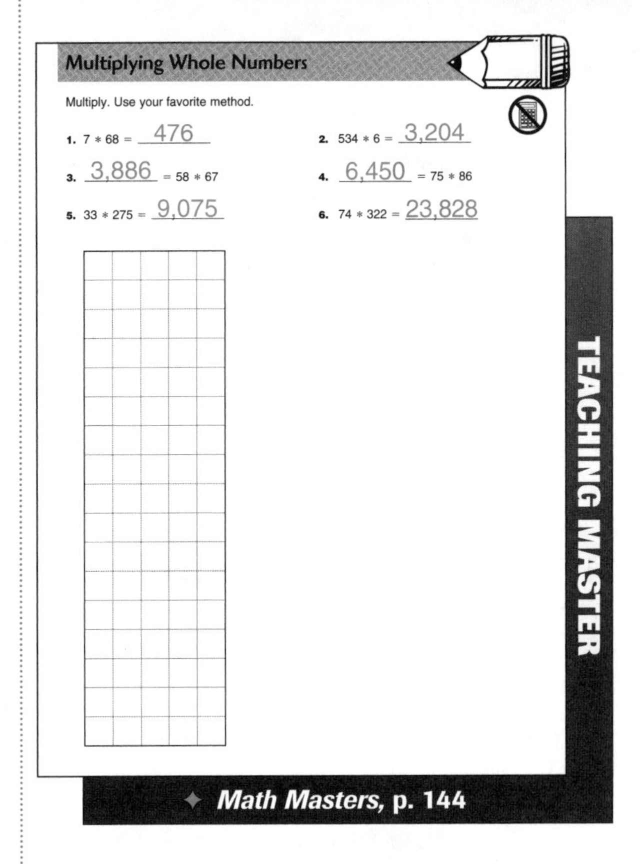

Multiplying Whole Numbers

Multiply. Use your favorite method.

1. 7 * 68 = 476
2. 534 * 6 = 3,204
3. 3,886 = 58 * 67
4. 6,450 = 75 * 86
5. 33 * 275 = 9,075
6. 74 * 322 = 23,828

TEACHING MASTER

✦ *Math Masters,* p. 144

9.9 Division of Decimals

OBJECTIVES **To divide decimals by whole numbers; and to practice the partial-quotients division algorithm introduced in Unit 6.**

summaries	materials
1 Teaching the Lesson	
Students use an estimation strategy for dividing decimals. They solve decimal division problems that offer review and practice of the partial-quotients division algorithm. [Operations and Computation]	☐ *Math Journal 2,* pp. 285 and 286 ☐ Study Link 9.8 ☐ Teaching Master (*Math Masters,* p. 20 or 80; optional)
2 Ongoing Learning & Practice	
Students review some of the main concepts in this unit. [multiple strands] Students practice and maintain skills through Math Boxes and Study Link activities.	☐ *Math Journal 2,* pp. 287 and 288 ☐ Study Link Master (*Math Masters,* p. 351)
3 Options for Individualizing	
Enrichment Students write and solve number stories involving decimals. [Operations and Computation] **Reteaching** Students divide whole numbers by whole numbers. [Operations and Computation]	☐ Teaching Masters (*Math Masters*, p. 145; p. 20 or 80, optional)

Additional Information

Background Information For additional information on the partial-quotients division algorithm, see the *Teacher's Reference Manual.*

Getting Started

Mental Math and Reflexes

Write multiplication number sentences on the board in which one factor is a whole number and the other factor a decimal. Students use estimation to place the decimal point in the product. *Suggestions:*

- 12 ∗ 4.85 = 5 8 2 58.2
- 0.93 ∗ 15 = 1 3 9 5 13.95
- 0.04 ∗ 36 = 1 4 4 1.44
- 1,987 ∗ 5.1 = 1 0 1 3 3 7 10,133.7

Math Message

Think of a number story that could be solved by dividing 4.2 by 7. Be prepared to discuss your answer.

Study Link 9.8 Follow-Up

Review answers. Students share the strategies they used to determine where to place the decimal point in the products.

1 Teaching the Lesson

✦ Math Message Follow-Up

WHOLE-CLASS DISCUSSION

Discuss students' answers. Suggest examples like the following, which illustrate different uses for division:

▷ Partitioning into equal parts: A ribbon is 4.2 meters long. It must be cut into 7 pieces of the same length.

▷ Money and equal sharing: Think of 4.2 as $4.20, which is to be shared equally among 7 students.

▷ Calculating an average: Tom watched TV for a total of 4.2 hours in one week. His average viewing time per day was $4.2 \div 7$ hours.

▷ Calculating a fraction or a percent: Alice and Dave took a 7-hour trip, and Alice drove for 4.2 hours. So $4.2 \div 7$ is the fraction of time that Alice drove. And $[(4.2 \div 7) * 100]\%$ is the percent of time that Alice drove.

NOTE: The goal of the Math Message and follow-up activity is to increase students' awareness of how decimal division problems are based on real-life problems.

✦ Estimating Quotients of Decimals

WHOLE-CLASS ACTIVITY

As they did with multiplication of decimals, students will use estimation to place decimal points in the answers to problems involving division of decimals.

Write the following problems on the board. Write the 4-digit quotient shown for each problem, but do not include any decimal point.

$$3\overline{)40.5} = 1350 \qquad 6\overline{)2.52} = 4200 \qquad 7\overline{)1.54} = 2200 \qquad 4\overline{)150.88} = 3772$$

Tell students that each problem shows the solution, but the decimal point is missing in the quotient. Ask students to decide where the decimal points should go by estimating each quotient.

Discuss students' estimates and answers. Here are some possible responses:

$\begin{array}{r} 1350 \\ 3\overline{)40.5} \end{array}$ 10 threes equals 30; this is less than 40.5, but not by much. So the quotient is somewhat larger than 10. The number 135.0 is too large, so the only possible answer that is close to 10 is 13.50.

$\begin{array}{r} 4200 \\ 6\overline{)2.52} \end{array}$ $2.52 \div 6$ is about $3 \div 6$, which is $\frac{1}{2}$, or 0.5. So the quotient must be 0.4200. The numbers 4.200, 42.00, 420.0, and 4,200 are all greater than 1 and therefore cannot be the quotient.

$\begin{array}{r} 2200 \\ 7\overline{)1.54} \end{array}$ There are many possible ways to round the numbers to create easy estimates: $2 \div 10$, $1 \div 10$, $2 \div 5$, and $1 \div 5$; all of these have answers between 0.1 and 0.4. Or, think of this problem as sharing $1.54 among 7 people: each share will be less than $1.00 and more than $0.10. All estimates are between 0.1 and 1.0, so the answer must be 0.2200. Since the purpose of this estimate is to help students place the decimal point, any of these estimates is satisfactory.

$\begin{array}{r} 3\ 7\ 7\ 2 \\ 4\overline{)150.88} \end{array}$ There are at least 30 fours in 150 ($30 * 4 = 120$). There are not 40 fours in 150 ($40 * 4 = 160$). The quotient must be between 30 and 40. So 37.72 is the answer.

Now write the following problem on the board:

> Bill paid $5.52 for 8 ballpoint pens. How much did 1 pen cost?

Ask students to estimate the cost of 1 pen. Round $5.52 to $5 or to $6, and round 8 to 10. $5 ÷ 10 = $0.50, or $6 ÷ 10 = $0.60; so the cost of 1 pen is about 50 or 60 cents.

Adjusting the Activity If students are having trouble estimating quotients involving amounts in dollars and cents, have them rename each amount as cents. Use the amount in cents to estimate and then rename the estimate as a dollars-and-cents amount. For example, in the above problem, think of $5.52 as 552 cents. Then 1 pen costs between 50 cents and 60 cents, or between $0.50 and $0.60.

Have volunteers come to the board and divide 552 by 8 (ignoring the decimal point). Remind students about the division algorithm they have used before. If students are having difficulty getting started, remind them that either of the estimates they just made (50 or 60) would be a good estimate to start with.

```
 8)552 |            8)552 |
 - 400 |  50        - 480 |  60
   152 |               72 |
 -  80 |  10         - 72 |___9
    72 |                0    69
 -  72 |___9
     0    69
```

Finally, have students use their initial estimates of the total cost to place the decimal point in the answer. $552 \div 8 = 69$, and the estimate was about \$0.50 or \$0.60. So place the decimal point before the 6; the cost for 1 pen is \$0.69.

Help students summarize the use of estimation to place the decimal point when dividing decimals. *For example:*

$3.66 \div 6 = ?$

1. **Estimate the quotient.** — $3.66 \div 6$ is about $3 \div 6$, or 0.5.
2. **Divide the numbers as though they were whole numbers.** — $366 \div 6 = 61$
3. **Use the estimate to place the decimal point.** — 0.61 is close to the estimate of 0.5.

ONGOING ASSESSMENT

Use this time to check students' skill in using the partial-quotients division algorithm. Give additional problems if students need more review and practice.

◆ Dividing Decimals (*Math Journal 2,* pp. 285 and 286; *Math Masters,* p. 20 or 80)

PARTNER ACTIVITY

Students complete journal pages 285 and 286. Have copies of *Math Masters,* page 20 or 80 available for students who need additional grid paper for their computations. Circulate and assist as needed. When most of the students have finished, briefly go over the answers.

Dividing Decimals 

1. Janine is building a bookshelf. She has a board that is 3.75 meters long. She wants to cut it into 5 pieces of equal length. What will be the length of each piece? 0.75 meter
2. Three sisters set up a lemonade stand. On Wednesday they made \$8.46. If they shared the money equally, how much did each girl get? \$2.82
3. Alex and his three friends went out to lunch. The total bill, including tax and tip, was \$42.52. They decided that each would pay the same amount. How much did each person pay? \$10.63
4. Victor divides a 98.4 cm piece of string into 3 equal pieces. What is the length of each piece? 32.8 cm

For each problem below, the division has been done correctly, but the decimal point is missing in the answer. Correctly place the decimal point in the answer.

5. 3)43.8 → 14.6
6. 5)4.35 → .8700
7. 4)6.46 → 1.615
8. 6)298.92 → 49.820

STUDENT PAGE

◆ *Math Journal 2,* p. 285

Dividing Decimals (cont.) 

For each problem:
- Estimate the quotient.
- Divide the numbers as though they were whole numbers.
- Use the estimate to place the decimal point in the answer.

9. 89.6 / 4 = 22.4
10. 2.96 / 8 = 0.37
11. 0.73 = 3.65 ÷ 5
12. 2.36 = 9.44 / 4
13. 253.8 / 6 = 42.3
14. 46.8 ÷ 12 = 3.9

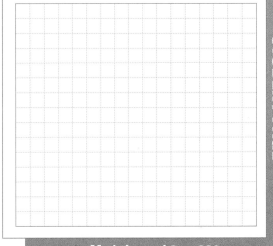

STUDENT PAGE

◆ *Math Journal 2,* p. 286

STUDENT PAGE

Review: Fractions, Decimals, and Percents

1. Fill in the missing numbers in the table of equivalent fractions, decimals, and percents.

Fraction	Decimal	Percent
$\frac{4}{10}$	0.4	40%
$\frac{6}{10}$	0.6	60%
$\frac{75}{100}$	0.75	75%

2. Kendra set a goal of saving $50 in 8 weeks. During the first 2 weeks, she was able to save $10.
   a. What fraction of the $50 did she save in the first 2 weeks? $\frac{1}{5}$
   b. What percent of the $50 did she save? 20%
   c. At this rate, how long will it take her to reach her goal? 10 weeks

3. Shade 80% of the square.
   a. What fraction of the square did you shade? $\frac{80}{100}$, or $\frac{8}{10}$
   b. Write this fraction as a decimal. 0.80, or 0.8
   c. What percent of the square is *not* shaded? 20%

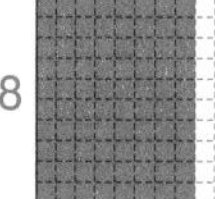

4. Tanara's new skirt was on sale at 15% off the original price. The original price of the skirt was $60.
   a. How much money did Tanara save with the discount? $9.00
   b. How much did she pay for the skirt? $51.00

5. Star Video and Vic's Video Mart sell videos at about the same regular prices. Both stores are having sales. Star Video is selling its videos at $\frac{1}{3}$ off the regular price. Vic's Video Mart is selling its videos at 25% off the regular price. Which store has the better sale? Explain your answer.
   Sample answer: Star Video has the better sale, because $\frac{1}{3}$ is $33\frac{1}{3}$%, and $33\frac{1}{3}$% off is more than 25% off.

◇ *Math Journal 2,* p. 287

2 Ongoing Learning & Practice

✦ Reviewing Unit 9 (*Math Journal 2,* p. 287)

INDEPENDENT ACTIVITY 

Students review some of the main concepts in this unit, including equivalent fractions, decimals, percents, and "percent-off" problems.

✦ Math Boxes 9.9 (*Math Journal 2,* p. 288)

INDEPENDENT ACTIVITY 

Mixed Review Math Boxes in this lesson are paired with Math Boxes in Lessons 9.5 and 9.7. The skill in Problem 1 is a prerequisite for Unit 10.

✦ Study Link 9.9 (*Math Masters,* p. 351)

Home Connection Students use estimation to place decimal points in the quotients of division problems. They divide decimals by whole numbers.

STUDENT PAGE

Math Boxes 9.9

1. Study the figure. Draw the other half along the vertical line of symmetry.

2. What is the area of the parallelogram?
   8" 2"
   Area = 16 sq in.

3. Complete the table with equivalent names.

Fraction	Decimal	Percent
$\frac{7}{10}$	0.7	70%
$\frac{3}{4}$	0.75	75%
$\frac{3}{5}$	0.6	60%
$\frac{72}{100}$	0.72	72%

4. Complete.
   a. 6 yd 8 ft = 26 ft
   b. 5 yd 3 ft = 18 ft
   c. 4 ft 7 in. = 55 in.
   d. 35 ft = 11 yd 2 ft
   e. 30 ft = 7 yd 9 ft
   f. 216 in. = 6 yd
   g. 3 ft 9 in. = 45 in.

5. Insert parentheses to make each number sentence true.
   a. $4 * (6 + 3) > 3 * 10$
   b. $17 - (24 / 6) + 6 = 19$
   c. $(40 * 30) + 60 < 100 * 20$
   d. $56 / (7 - 3) = 14$

6. Calculate.
   a. 10% of 90 = 9
   b. 5% of 140 = 7
   c. 20% of 45 = 9
   d. 80 % of 30 = 24
   e. 75 % of 48 = 36

◇ *Math Journal 2,* p. 288

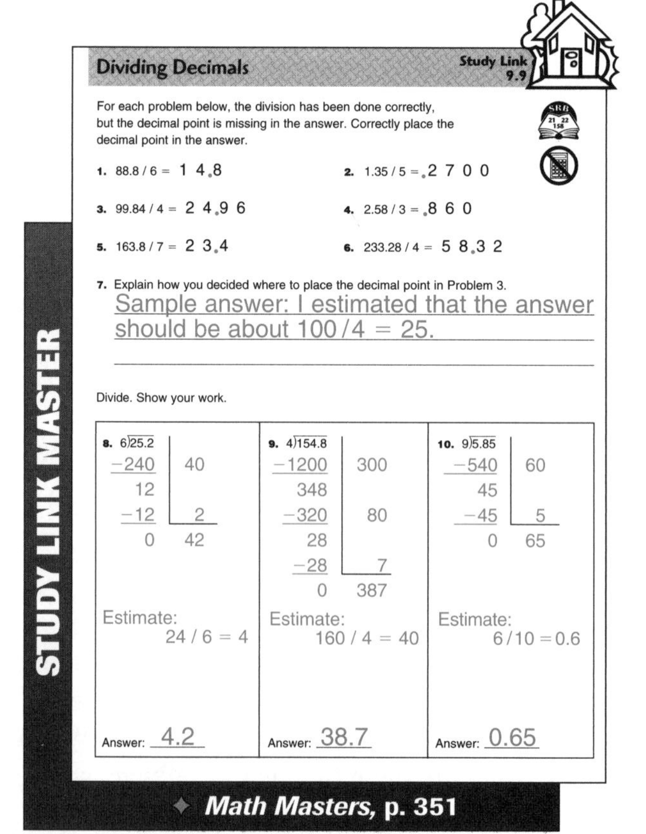

STUDY LINK MASTER

Dividing Decimals

Study Link 9.9

For each problem below, the division has been done correctly, but the decimal point is missing in the answer. Correctly place the decimal point in the answer.

1. 88.8 / 6 = 14.8
2. 1.35 / 5 = .2700
3. 99.84 / 4 = 24.96
4. 2.58 / 3 = .860
5. 163.8 / 7 = 23.4
6. 233.28 / 4 = 58.32

7. Explain how you decided where to place the decimal point in Problem 3.
   Sample answer: I estimated that the answer should be about 100 / 4 = 25.

Divide. Show your work.

8. $6\overline{)25.2}$
   −240 | 40
   12
   −12 | 2
   0 | 42
   Estimate: 24 / 6 = 4
   Answer: 4.2

9. $4\overline{)154.8}$
   −1200 | 300
   348
   −320 | 80
   28
   −28 | 7
   0 | 387
   Estimate: 160 / 4 = 40
   Answer: 38.7

10. $9\overline{)5.85}$
   −540 | 60
   45
   −45 | 5
   0 | 65
   Estimate: 6 / 10 = 0.6
   Answer: 0.65

◇ *Math Masters,* p. 351

3 Options for Individualizing

✦ ENRICHMENT Writing and Solving Division Number Stories with Decimals

PARTNER ACTIVITY  **15–30 min** 

Students write number stories involving the division of a decimal by a whole number. They solve each other's stories. Suggest that students write one of each of the following types of division number stories. See the Math Message Follow-Up for examples.

- ▷ partitioning into equal parts
- ▷ money and equal sharing
- ▷ calculating an average
- ▷ calculating a fraction or a percent

✦ RETEACHING Dividing Whole Numbers (*Math Masters,* p. 20 or 80; p. 145)

INDEPENDENT ACTIVITY  **15–30 min** 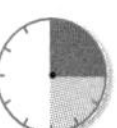

Some students may need to freshen their skills in dividing whole numbers before working on division of decimals by whole numbers. In these problems, they write the remainders as fractions. Have copies of *Math Masters,* page 20 or 80 available for students who need additional grid paper for their computations.

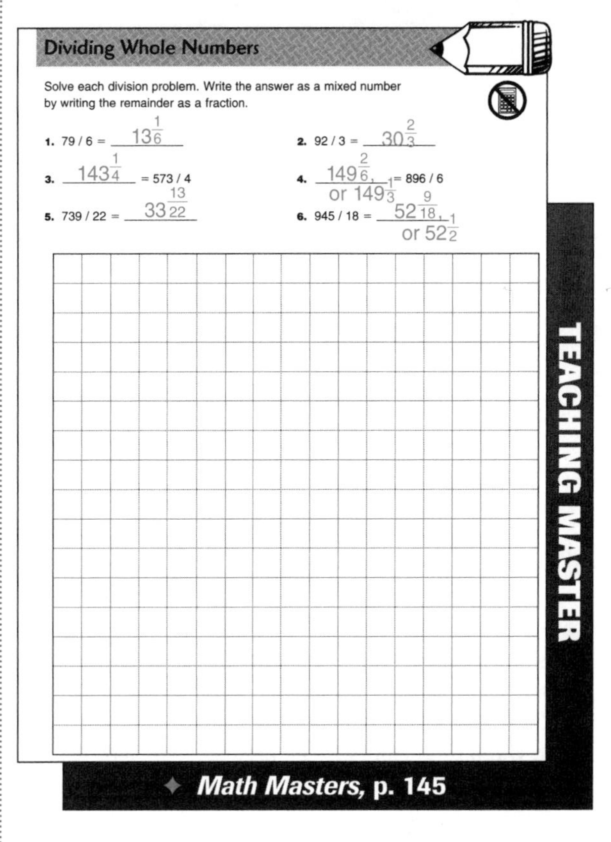

Dividing Whole Numbers

Solve each division problem. Write the answer as a mixed number by writing the remainder as a fraction.

1. 79 / 6 = $13\frac{1}{6}$
2. 92 / 3 = $30\frac{2}{3}$
3. $143\frac{1}{4}$ = 573 / 4
4. $149\frac{2}{6}$, or $149\frac{1}{3}$ = 896 / 6
5. 739 / 22 = $33\frac{13}{22}$
6. 945 / 18 = $52\frac{9}{18}$, or $52\frac{1}{2}$

TEACHING MASTER

✦ *Math Masters,* p. 145

9.10 Unit 9 Review and Assessment

OBJECTIVE **To review and assess students' progress on the material covered in Unit 9.**

1 Assess Progress

learning goals	activities
9a **Beginning Goal** Use an estimation strategy to divide decimals by whole numbers. **(Lesson 9.9)**	❑ Oral Assessment, Problem 1 ❑ Written Assessment, Problems 12–14 ❑ Alternative Assessment Option
9b **Beginning Goal** Use an estimation strategy to multiply decimals by whole numbers. **(Lesson 9.8)**	❑ Oral Assessment, Problem 2 ❑ Written Assessment, Problems 9–11 ❑ Alternative Assessment Option
9c **Developing Goal** Find a percent or a fraction of a number. **(Lessons 9.1–9.3 and 9.6)**	❑ Slate Assessment, Problem 1 ❑ Written Assessment, Problems 6–8 ❑ Alternative Assessment Option
9d **Developing Goal** Convert between "easy" fractions (fourths, fifths, and tenths), decimals, and percents. **(Lessons 9.1–9.3)**	❑ Slate Assessment, Problem 2 ❑ Written Assessment, Problems 1, 3, and 6
9e **Secure Goal** Convert between hundredths-fractions, decimals, and percents. **(Lessons 9.1 and 9.2)**	❑ Slate Assessment, Problem 3 ❑ Written Assessment, Problem 2
9f **Secure Goal** Use a calculator to rename any fraction as a decimal or percent. **(Lessons 9.3–9.5 and 9.7)**	❑ Written Assessment, Problems 4 and 5

materials

- □ *Math Journal 2,* p. 289
- □ Teaching Masters (*Math Masters,* pp. 146–148)
- □ markers or crayons
- □ Study Link 9.9
- □ Assessment Masters (*Math Masters,* pp. 406–408)
- □ calculator

2 Build Background for Unit 10

summaries	materials
Students practice and maintain skills through Math Boxes and Study Link activities.	□ *Math Journal 2,* p. 290 □ Study Link Masters (*Math Masters,* pp. 352–355)

Each **learning goal** listed above indicates a level of performance that might be expected at this point in the *Everyday Mathematics* K–6 curriculum. For a variety of reasons, the levels indicated may not accurately portray your class's performance.

Additional Information

Advance Preparation For additional information on assessment for Unit 9, see the *Assessment Handbook,* pages 63–65. For assessment checklists, see *Math Masters,* pages 442, 443, and 465–467.

Getting Started

Math Message

Complete the Time to Reflect *questions on journal page 289.*

Study Link 9.9 Follow-Up

Review answers. Students share the strategies they used to determine the location of the decimal point in the quotients.

1 Assess Progress

✦ Math Message Follow-Up (*Math Journal 2,* p. 289)

WHOLE-CLASS DISCUSSION

Students share their answers. Problems 1 and 3 provide students with an opportunity to demonstrate awareness of uses of fractions, decimals, and percents in everyday life. Problem 2 allows students to evaluate their own skill level at identifying "easy" fraction, decimal, and percent equivalencies. If students did not find the game useful, suggest the "flash cards" found in the second Extra Practice activity in Lesson 9.2. Problem 4 assesses students' understanding of the purpose of a survey.

✦ Oral and Slate Assessments

WHOLE-CLASS ACTIVITY

If the suggested problems are not appropriate for your class's level of performance, adjust the numbers or the problems themselves to better assess your students' abilities.

Oral Assessment Suggestions

1. On the board, write division number sentences in which a decimal is divided by a whole number. Students explain the strategy that they used to locate the position of the decimal point in the quotient. **Goal 9a**

   Suggestions

   - 98.5 / 5 = 1 9 7 19.7
   - 1.96 / 4 = 4 9 0 0 0.49
   - 407.82 / 8 = 5 0 9 7 7 5 50.9775

Time to Reflect

1. Think of some numbers you have seen in the past week in a grocery store or in a magazine. Do you think you have seen more decimals, more percents, or more fractions? Try to explain why.

2. Did *Fraction/Percent Concentration* help you learn some of the easy fraction/percent equivalencies? If not, what strategy do you think would help you learn them?

3. Give two examples of uses of percents.

4. Suppose you are conducting a survey. You want to know what 9-year-olds like best about living in the country. Would you ask people over 20 years old any questions? Explain your answer.

STUDENT PAGE

✧ *Math Journal 2,* p. 289

Unit 9 Checking Progress

1. Gloria made 15 out of 20 shots in the school basketball free-throw contest.
   a. What fraction of the shots did she make? $\frac{15}{20}$, or $\frac{3}{4}$
   b. What percent of the shots did she make? 75%
   c. At this rate, how many shots would she make if she took 100 shots? 75 shots
2. Jimmy set a goal of jogging a total of 100 miles over the summer. He filled in the square at the right to keep track of the miles he ran. During the first two weeks of June, he jogged 20 miles.
   a. What fraction of 100 miles did he jog in 2 weeks? $\frac{20}{100}$, $\frac{2}{10}$, or $\frac{1}{5}$
   b. What percent of 100 miles did he jog? 20%
   c. At this rate, how many weeks will it take him to jog 100 miles? 10 weeks
3. Fill in the table of equivalent fractions, decimals, and percents.

Fraction	Decimal	Percent
$\frac{3}{10}$	0.30	30%
$\frac{1}{2}$	0.50	50%
$\frac{1}{4}$	0.25	25%
$\frac{3}{4}$	0.75	75%
$\frac{4}{5}$	0.80	80%
$\frac{5}{5}$	1.00	100%

ASSESSMENT MASTER

✦ *Math Masters*, p. 406

Unit 9 Checking Progress (cont.)

4. Use a calculator to rename each fraction as a decimal.
   a. $\frac{7}{16}$ = 0.4375 b. $\frac{3}{25}$ = 0.12 c. $\frac{6}{32}$ = 0.1875
5. Use a calculator to rename each fraction as a percent.
   a. $\frac{3}{8}$ = 37.5 % b. $\frac{15}{16}$ = 93.75 % c. $\frac{3}{96}$ = 3.125 %
6. Shade 40% of the square at the right.
   a. What fraction of the square did you shade? $\frac{40}{100}$, $\frac{4}{10}$, or $\frac{2}{5}$
   b. Write this fraction as a decimal. 0.4
   c. What percent of the square is *not* shaded? 60%
7. Susan bought a coat that sold for $150. She had a coupon for a 10% discount.
   a. How much money did she save with the discount? $15
   b. How much did she pay for the coat? $135
8. Randy is buying a color television. The television he wants costs $200 at both L-Mart and Al's Department Store. After Christmas, L-Mart put it on sale at a savings of $\frac{1}{4}$ off the regular price. Al's Department Store offered a 30% discount on all items.

   At which store should Randy buy the television? Al's Department Store

   Why? Sample answer: Al's: A 30% discount on $200 is $60. L-Mart: $\frac{1}{4}$ = 25%. A 25% discount on $200 is $50.

ASSESSMENT MASTER

✦ *Math Masters*, p. 407

2. On the board, write multiplication number sentences in which one factor is a whole number and the other factor a decimal. Students explain the strategy that they used to locate the position of the decimal point in the product. **Goal 9b**

   Suggestions
   - 15 * 2.08 = 3 1 2 31.2
   - 0.89 * 475 = 4 2 2 7 5 422.75
   - 14 * 0.9 = 1 2 6 12.6

Slate Assessment Suggestions

1. Pose "percent-of" and "fraction-of" problems. **Goal 9c**

   Suggestions
   - 25% of 24 6
   - 60% of 35 21
   - $\frac{2}{3}$ of 90 60
   - $\frac{4}{5}$ of 20 16
2. Write "easy" fractions on the board. Students write the equivalent decimal and percent. **Goal 9d**

   Suggestions
   - $\frac{1}{2}$ 0.50, 50% $\frac{1}{4}$ 0.25, 25% $\frac{3}{4}$ 0.75, 75%
   - $\frac{2}{5}$ 0.40, 40% $\frac{3}{5}$ 0.60, 60% $\frac{4}{5}$ 0.80, 80%
   - $\frac{3}{10}$ 0.3, 30% $\frac{7}{10}$ 0.7, 70% $\frac{9}{10}$ 0.9, 90%
3. Write hundredths-fractions on the board. Students write them as percents. **Goal 9e**

   Suggestions
   - $\frac{3}{100}$ 3% • $\frac{57}{100}$ 57%

   Write tenths-fractions on the board. Students write them as hundredths-fractions and then as percents.

   Suggestions
   - $\frac{9}{10}$ $\frac{90}{100}$, 90% • $\frac{3}{10}$ $\frac{30}{100}$, 30%

✦ Written Assessment
(*Math Masters,* pp. 406–408)

INDEPENDENT ACTIVITY 

Depending on the needs of students, you may want to work through an example together, reading a problem aloud, discussing it, and providing additional examples as necessary before students work the problem independently.

Each of the problems is listed on the next page and paired with one or more of this unit's learning goals.

- Write a ratio as a fraction and a percent. Interpret a percent. (Problems 1 and 2) **Goals 9d and 9e**
- Fill in the table of equivalent fractions, decimals, and percents. (Problem 3) **Goal 9d**
- Use a calculator to rename fractions as decimals. (Problem 4) **Goal 9f**
- Use a calculator to rename fractions as percents. (Problem 5) **Goal 9f**
- Shade a percent of a region. Write the percent as a fraction and a decimal. (Problem 6) **Goals 9c and 9d**
- Use the percent of discount to calculate the discount and sale price of an item. Compare a fraction of discount and percent of discount. (Problems 7 and 8) **Goal 9c**
- Use an estimation strategy to multiply decimals by whole numbers. (Problems 9–11) **Goal 9b**
- Use an estimation strategy to divide decimals by whole numbers. (Problems 12–14) **Goal 9a**

NOTE: Problems 9–14 on *Math Masters,* page 408 assess learning goals 9a and 9b, which are considered beginning skills. Students should complete this page. However, if they do poorly, do not count it against their final score on the written assessment. Consider *Math Masters,* page 408 as a tool to assess your students' level of proficiency with these skills at this time.

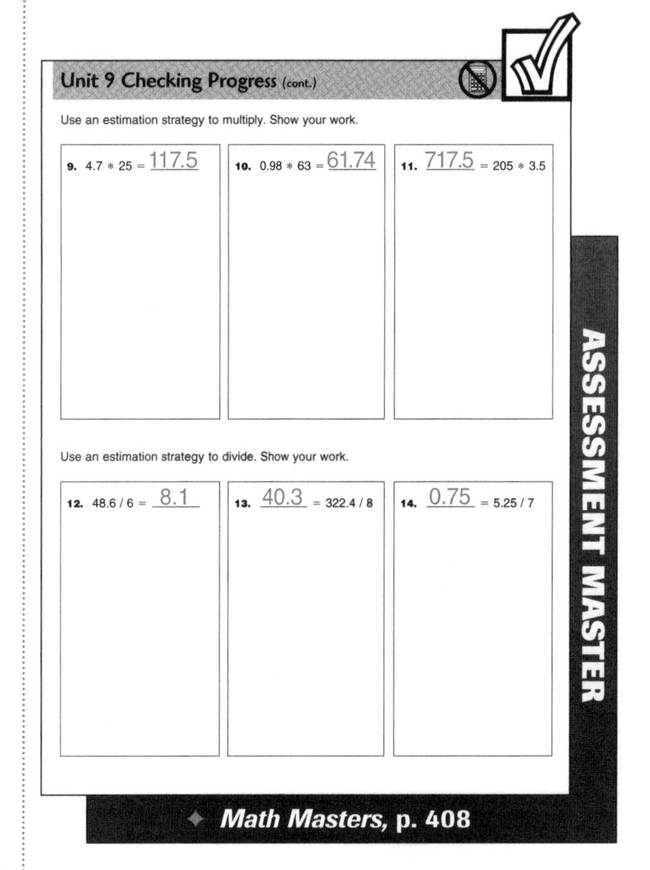

Math Masters, p. 408

ALTERNATIVE ASSESSMENT OPTION

Find the "Fraction-of" and "Percent-of" a Design (*Math Masters,* p. 146)

INDEPENDENT ACTIVITY 

Students color a design on grid paper. They make a tally chart to show the colors used in their design and what fraction or percent of the total is represented by each color. Tell students to round the percents to the nearest whole number. See the next page for an example.

Portfolio Ideas

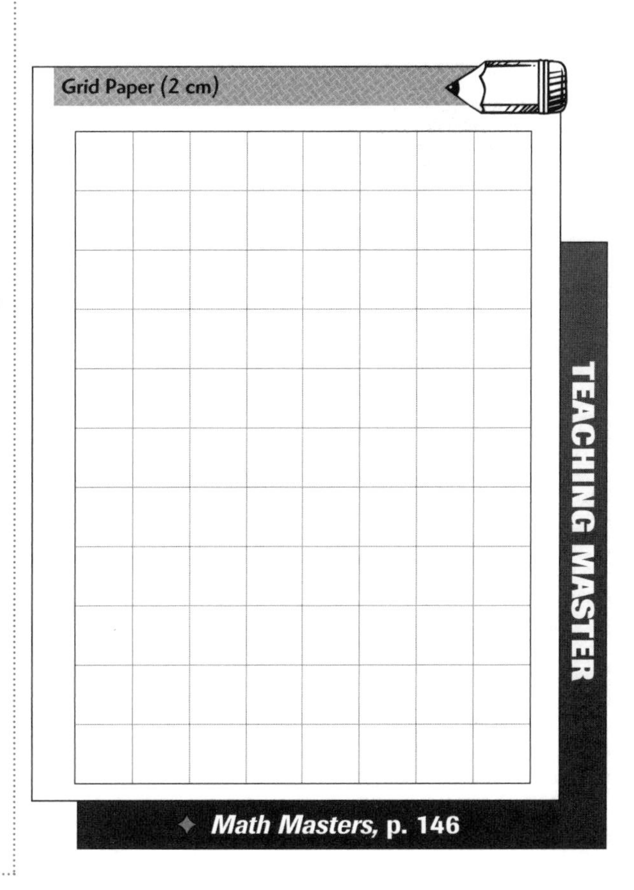

Math Masters, p. 146

My Decimal Division Strategy

1. Solve the problem below. Show your work.

2. Tell how you solved this problem.

TEACHING MASTER

✦ *Math Masters,* p. 147

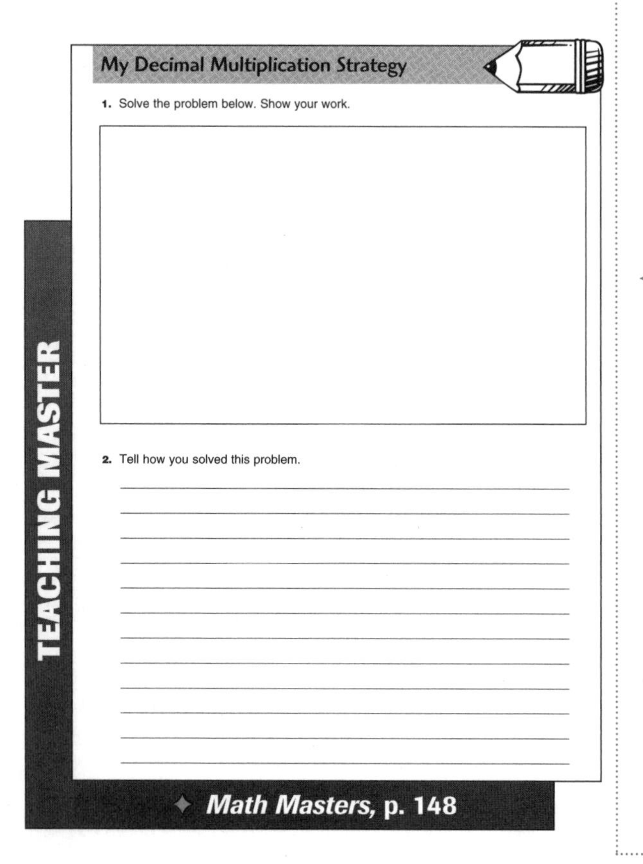
My Decimal Multiplication Strategy

1. Solve the problem below. Show your work.

2. Tell how you solved this problem.

TEACHING MASTER

✦ *Math Masters,* p. 148

P	P	P	P	P	P	P	P
B		Y	Y	Y	Y		B
	B		O	O		B	
G		B	O	O	B		G
O	G		R	R		G	O
O		R	Y	Y	R		O
O	G		R	R		G	O
G		B	O	O	B		G
	B		O	O		B	
B		Y	Y	Y	Y		B
P	P	P	P	P	P	P	P

Color	Tally	Fraction of Total Design	Percent of Total Design
white	~~IIII~~ ~~IIII~~ ~~IIII~~ ~~IIII~~ II	$\frac{22}{88}$	25%
red	~~IIII~~ I	$\frac{6}{88}$	7%
yellow	~~IIII~~ ~~IIII~~	$\frac{10}{88}$	11%
orange	~~IIII~~ ~~IIII~~ IIII	$\frac{14}{88}$	16%
purple	~~IIII~~ ~~IIII~~ ~~IIII~~ I	$\frac{16}{88}$	18%
green	~~IIII~~ III	$\frac{8}{88}$	9%
blue	~~IIII~~ ~~IIII~~ II	$\frac{12}{88}$	14%

Students write summary statements about their design such as the following:

▷ 45% of the design is made up of the colors white, yellow, and green.

▷ 41% of the design is made up of *cool* colors.

▷ 34% of the design is made up of *warm* colors.

Have students check that their percentages add up to 100%.

ALTERNATIVE ASSESSMENT OPTION

Describe a Decimal Division Strategy (*Math Masters,* p. 147)

INDEPENDENT ACTIVITY

Pose a division problem in which a decimal is divided by a whole number. Create problems to suit the ability levels of individual students. Ask students to first solve the problem and then describe the strategy that they used.

ALTERNATIVE ASSESSMENT OPTION

Describe a Decimal Multiplication Strategy
(*Math Masters,* p. 148)

INDEPENDENT ACTIVITY 

Pose a multiplication problem in which a decimal is multiplied by a whole number. Create problems to suit the ability levels of individual students. Ask students to first solve the problem and then describe the strategy that they used.

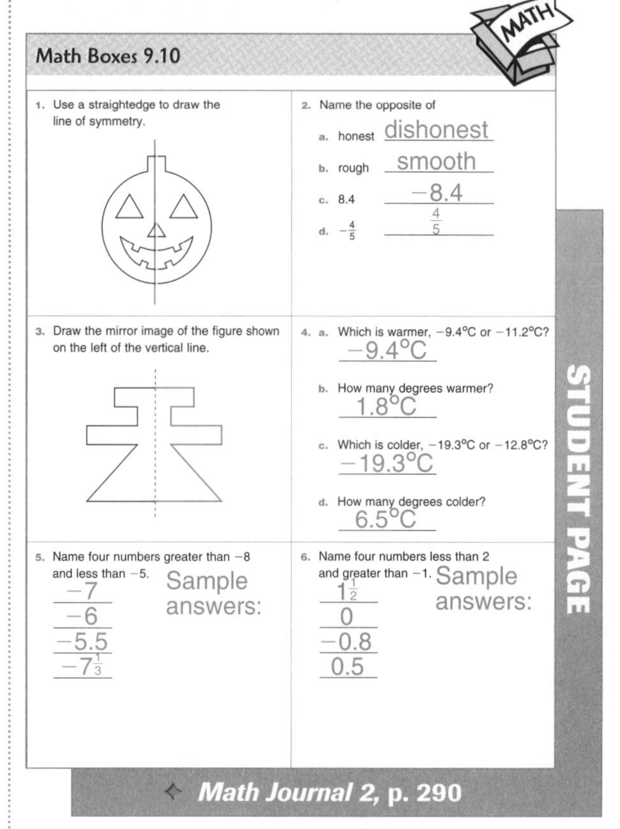

Math Boxes 9.10

1. Use a straightedge to draw the line of symmetry.

2. Name the opposite of
   a. honest dishonest
   b. rough smooth
   c. 8.4 −8.4
   d. $-\frac{4}{5}$ $\frac{4}{5}$

3. Draw the mirror image of the figure shown on the left of the vertical line.

4. a. Which is warmer, −9.4°C or −11.2°C? −9.4°C
   b. How many degrees warmer? 1.8°C
   c. Which is colder, −19.3°C or −12.8°C? −19.3°C
   d. How many degrees colder? 6.5°C

5. Name four numbers greater than −8 and less than −5. Sample answers: −7, −6, −5.5, $-7\frac{1}{3}$

6. Name four numbers less than 2 and greater than −1. Sample answers: $1\frac{1}{2}$, 0, −0.8, 0.5

STUDENT PAGE

Math Journal 2, p. 290

2 Build Background for Unit 10

Math Boxes 9.10 (*Math Journal 2,* p. 290)

INDEPENDENT ACTIVITY 

Mixed Review The skills in Problems 1–6 are prerequisites for Unit 10.

Study Link 9.10: Unit 10 Family Letter
(*Math Masters,* pp. 352–355)

Home Connection This Study Link is a four-page newsletter that introduces parents and guardians to Unit 10's topics and terms. The letter also offers ideas for mathematics activities that are supportive of classroom work and can be done at home.

Family Letter — Study Link 9.10

Unit 10: Reflections and Symmetry

In this unit, your child will take another look at geometry, with an emphasis on symmetry. Many objects in nature are symmetric: flowers, insects, and the human body, to name just a few. Symmetry is all around—in buildings, furniture, clothing, paintings, and so on.

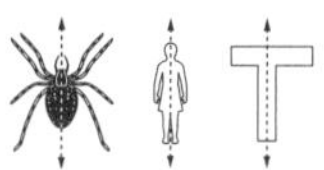

The class will focus on **reflectional symmetry,** also called **line symmetry** or **mirror symmetry,** in which half of a figure is the mirror image of the other half. Encourage your child to look for symmetric objects, and if possible, to collect pictures of symmetric objects from magazines and newspapers. For example, the right half of the printed letter T is the mirror image of the left half. If you have a small hand mirror, have your child check letters, numbers, and other objects to see whether they have line symmetry. The class will use a device called a **transparent mirror,** which is pictured below. Students will use it to see and trace the mirror image of an object.

Geometry is not only the study of figures (such as lines, rectangles, and circles), but also the study of transformations or "motions" of figures. These motions include **reflections** (flips), **rotations** (turns), and **translations** (slides). Your child will use these motions to create pictures like the ones below, called **frieze patterns.**

Students will also work with positive and negative numbers, looking at them as reflections of each other across zero on a number line. They will develop skills of adding positive and negative numbers by thinking in terms of credits and debits for a new company, and they will practice these skills in the *Credits/Debits Game.*

Please keep this Family Letter for reference as your child works through Unit 10.

STUDY LINK MASTERS

Math Masters, pp. 352–355

Unit 10 Reflections and Symmetry

overview

Unit 10 returns to geometry, now from the point of view of *transformations* or "motions" of geometric figures. The approach is informal and intended for exposure and development of spatial intuition, not for mastery. Four transformations are usually discussed in school geometry:

Informal Name	Formal Name
flip	reflection
turn	rotation
slide	translation
stretcher/shrinker	similarity

A Zebra butterfly exhibits line symmetry.

In this unit, most of the attention is on reflections and the related topic of symmetry. Students will also work with rotations and translations.

Lesson 10.6 introduces formal operations with positive and negative numbers. Unit 11 will extend this introduction to include both addition and subtraction of integers.

contents

Lesson	Objective	Page
10.1	**Explorations with a Transparent Mirror** *To explore reflections of 2-dimensional figures.*	730
10.2	**Finding Lines of Reflection** *To explore reflections; and to identify lines of reflection.*	735
10.3	**Properties of Reflections** *To discover basic properties of reflections.*	741
10.4	**Line Symmetry** *To explore the connection between reflections and line symmetry.*	746
10.5	**Frieze Patterns** *To explore an application of reflections, rotations, and translations.*	752
10.6	**Positive and Negative Numbers** *To explore addition of integers.*	757
10.7	**Unit 10 Review and Assessment** *To review and assess students' progress on the material covered in Unit 10.*	763

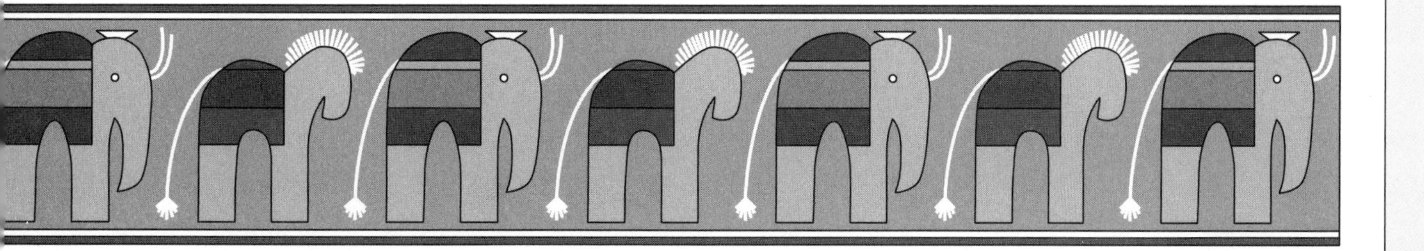

learning goals in perspective

learning goals	links to the past	links to the future
10a **Beginning Goal** Add integers. **(Lesson 10.6)**	Grade 3: Review uses of positive and negative numbers to relate numbers to a zero point, as in temperatures and elevations, and to record change. Solve number stories about positive and negative numbers.	Grade 4: Play the *Credits/Debits Game* to practice addition of positive and negative integers (Units 11 and 12). Grade 5: Solve addition/subtraction stories with positive and negative numbers. Grade 6: Add and subtract positive and negative numbers on a number line; develop a rule for adding and subtracting positive and negative numbers; practice adding and subtracting positive and negative numbers.
10b **Beginning Goal** Rotate figures. **(Lessons 10.4 and 10.5)**	Grades 1–3: Use straws, geoboards, and body turns to demonstrate rotations and angles. Grade 4: Make turns and fractions of turns; relate turns and angles (Unit 6).	Grade 5: Applications and maintenance. Grade 6: Study rotations, rotational symmetry, and point symmetry.
10c **Developing Goal** Translate figures. **(Lesson 10.5)**	Grade 3: Model polygons; change the shapes of constructed polygons; perform polygon calisthenics to form polygons and explore their properties. Grade 4: Investigate how transformations of number pairs change figures plotted on a coordinate grid (Unit 9).	Grade 5: Transform ordered number pairs and explore the resulting transformations of geometric figures. Explore regular tessellations. Grade 6: Review regular tessellations; introduce notation for tessellations; find semiregular tessellations. Create Escher-type translation tessellations. Explore topological transformations.
10d **Secure Goal** Use a transparent mirror to draw the reflection of a figure. **(Lessons 10.1–10.3)**	Grade 3: Explore symmetry with geoboards and pattern blocks; complete symmetric figures; identify symmetric shapes and draw lines of symmetry.	Grade 6: Study rotations, rotational symmetry, and point symmetry.
10e **Secure Goal** Identify lines of symmetry, lines of reflection, reflected figures, and figures with line symmetry. **(Lessons 10.2–10.6)**	See Goal 10d.	See Goal 10d.

assessment

ongoing • product • periodic

Informal Assessment

Math Boxes These *Math Journal* pages provide opportunities for cumulative review or assessment of concepts and skills.

Ongoing Assessment: Kid Watching Use the Ongoing Assessment suggestions in the following lessons to make quick, on-the-spot observations about students' understanding of:
- Geometry **(Lesson 10.2, Part 1; Lesson 10.5, Part 1)**
- Measurement and Reference Frames **(Lesson 10.3, Part 2)**
- Operations and Computation **(Lesson 10.6, Part 1)**

Portfolio Ideas Samples of students' work may be obtained from the following assignments:
- Creating a Paint Reflection **(Lesson 10.2)**
- Displaying Pictures of Symmetric Objects **(Lesson 10.4)**
- Exploring Turn Symmetry **(Lesson 10.4)**
- Creating Frieze Patterns **(Lesson 10.5)**
- Interpret a Cartoon **(Lesson 10.7)**

Unit 10 Review and Assessment

Math Message Use the Time to Reflect questions in Lesson 10.7 to assess students' progress toward the following learning goals: **Goals 10a and 10e**

Oral and Slate Assessments Use oral or slate assessments during Lesson 10.7 to assess students' progress toward the following learning goals: **Goals 10a, 10b, and 10e**

Written Assessment Use a written review during Lesson 10.7 to assess students' progress toward the following learning goals: **Goals 10a–10e**

Alternative Assessment Options Use alternative assessments in Lesson 10.7 to assess students' progress toward the following learning goal: **Goal 10e**

assessmenthandbook

For more information on how to use different types of assessment in Unit 10, see the Assessment Overview on pages 66–68 in the *Assessment Handbook.* The following Assessment Masters can be found in the *Math Masters* book:
- Unit 10 Checking Progress, pp. 409 and 410
- Unit 10 Class Checklist, p. 444
- Unit 10 Individual Profile of Progress, p. 445
- Class Progress Indicator, p. 467
- Interest Inventories, pp. 468 and 469
- Math Logs, pp. 470–472
- Self-Assessment Forms, pp. 473 and 474

problem solving

A process of modeling everyday situations using tools from mathematics

Encourage students to use a variety of strategies when attacking a given problem—and to explain those strategies. *Strategies students might use in this unit:*

- Drawing a picture
- Acting out the problem
- Using data in a table
- Using a pattern
- Using computation

Four Problem-Solving REPRESENTATIONS

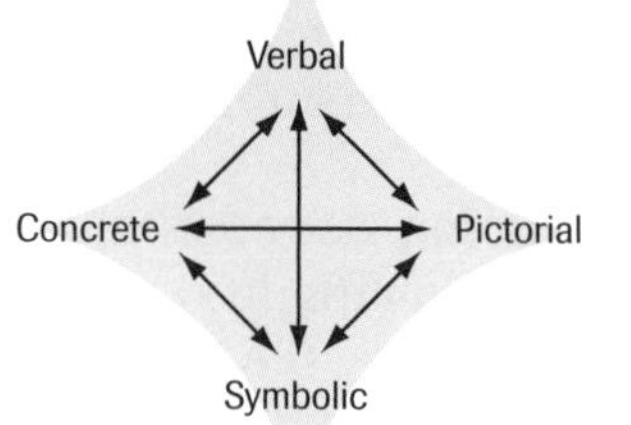

Lessons that teach *through* problem solving, not just *about* problem solving

Lesson	Activity	Lesson	Activity
10.1, 10.2	Using a transparent mirror to draw reflected images of shapes and to find lines of reflection	**10.5**	Continuing frieze patterns made of geometric shapes
10.2	Solving problems based on data about recent United States presidents	**10.6**	Maintaining the "bottom line" for a business by using credits and debits
10.3, 10.4	Folding paper to draw reflected images and to find lines of symmetry of pictures, shapes, and the alphabet		

For more information about problem solving in *Everyday Mathematics,* see the *Teacher's Reference Manual.*

cross-curricular links

art

- Students paint a paper and fold it to create a paint reflection. **(Lesson 10.2)**
- Students copy patterns from home or around school. **(Lesson 10.5)**
- Students create frieze patterns. **(Lesson 10.5)**

language arts

- Students discuss the meanings of the words *image* and *preimage* in the context of reflected images. **(Lesson 10.1)**

literature

- Students examine books about reflected images and symmetry. **(Lesson 10.1)**
- Students read and discuss books about money and other consumer topics. **(Lesson 10.6)**

science

- Students solve a temperature number story. **(Lesson 10.6)**

social studies

- Students solve problems based on data about twelve recent U.S. Presidents. **(Lesson 10.2)**
- Students explore additional countries on the World Tour. **(Lesson 10.3)**
- Students research and report on the Reflecting Pool in the Washington, D.C. Mall. **(Lesson 10.3)**

meeting INDIVIDUAL needs

UNIVERSAL ACCESS

✦ RETEACHING

The following features provide additional instructional support:

Adjusting the Activity	Options for Individualizing
• **Lesson 10.4, Part 1** • **Lesson 10.5, Part 1**	• **Lesson 10.1** Reviewing Polygons • **Lesson 10.2** Creating a Paint Reflection • **Lesson 10.6** Using a Number Line to Add Positive and Negative Numbers

✦ ENRICHMENT

The following features suggest some enrichment and extension activities found in this unit:

Adjusting the Activity	Options for Individualizing
• **Lesson 10.2, Part 1**	• **Lesson 10.1** Exploring Reflected Images and Symmetry in Literature • **Lesson 10.3** Exploring Reflections of 3-Dimensional Figures • **Lesson 10.3** Researching the Reflecting Pool in Washington, D.C. • **Lesson 10.4** Exploring Turn Symmetry • **Lesson 10.5** Creating Frieze Patterns • **Lesson 10.6** Solving a Temperature Number Story

✦ LANGUAGE DIVERSITY

The following features suggest some ways to support students who are acquiring proficiency in English:

Adjusting the Activity	Options for Individualizing
• **Lesson 10.4, Part 1**	• **Lesson 10.2** Building Background for Mathematics Words • **Lesson 10.6** Building Background for Mathematics Words

✦ MULTIAGE CLASSROOM

The following chart lists related lessons from Grades 3 and 5 that can help you meet your instructional needs:

Grade 3	6.3 6.9	6.9	6.3 6.9	6.3 6.9	1.11 6.3	
Grade 4	10.1	10.2	10.3	10.4	10.5	10.6
Grade 5				3.8	3.8	7.6–7.8 7.10

materials

lesson	math masters pages	manipulative kit items	other items
10.1	Study Link Master, p. 356 Teaching Masters, pp. 149–151	1 transparent mirror per partnership (Geo Reflector, if available)	Geometry Template *The Mirror Puzzle Book, Reflections, Round Trip,* and *Shadows and Reflections* ***See* Advance Preparation, p. 730**
10.2	Study Link Master, p. 357 Teaching Masters, pp. 152–154	1 transparent mirror per partnership (Geo Reflector, if available)	ruler Geometry Template large sheet of paper paints, brushes, and dark marker ***See* Advance Preparation, p. 735**
10.3	Study Link Master, p. 358 transparency of Study Link Master, p. 357 (optional) Teaching Masters, pp. 36–38 (optional); and p. 155	1 transparent mirror per partnership (Geo Reflector, if available) centimeter cubes	ruler blank sheet of paper dark, wide-point marker Geometry Template
10.4	Study Link Master, p. 359 transparency of Study Link Master, p. 358 (optional) Teaching Masters, pp. 156–160	1 transparent mirror per partnership (Geo Reflector, if available)	scissors magazines and newspapers tape Geometry Template pattern blocks ***See* Advance Preparation, p. 746**
10.5	Study Link Master, p. 360 Teaching Masters, pp. 162 and 163 transparency of Teaching Master, p. 161 (optional)	1 transparent mirror per partnership (Geo Reflector, if available) overhead or regular pattern blocks (optional)	straightedge index cards scissors
10.6	Study Link Master, p. 361 transparency of Study Link Master, p. 360 (optional) Teaching Masters, p. 164; p. 166 (optional) transparency of Teaching Master, p. 165 (optional) ***See* Advance Preparation, p. 757**	1 deck of number cards per partnership (Everything Math Deck, if available) 1 transparent mirror per partnership (Geo Reflector, if available)	Geometry Template *The Monster Money Book* *How the Second Grade Got $8205.50 to Visit the Statue of Liberty*
10.7	Study Link Masters, pp. 362–365 Teaching Masters, p. 20 (optional); and p. 167 Assessment Masters, pp. 409 and 410	transparent mirror (Geo Reflector, if available) pattern blocks or centimeter cubes	slate Geometry Template

planningtips

Pacing

Pacing depends on a number of factors, such as students' individual needs and how long your school has been using *Everyday Mathematics.* At the beginning of Unit 10, review your Content by Strand Poster to help you set a monthly pace.

MARCH	APRIL (MOST CLASSROOMS)	MAY

Using the Projects

Use Project 4, Making a Quilt, after Unit 10 to explore and apply ideas of pattern, symmetry, rotation, and reflection in the context of quilts. Use Project 7, Numbers, Maya Style, during or after Unit 10 to learn about the Maya numeration system and to convert between Maya numerals and base-ten numerals. The Projects can be found at the back of this book.

Home Communication

Share Study Links 10.1–10.6 with families to help them understand the content and procedures in this unit. At the end of the unit, use Study Link 10.7 to introduce Unit 11. Supplemental information can be found in the *Home Connection Handbook.*

NCTM Standards

Standard	1	2	3	4	5	6	7	8	9	10
Unit 10 Lessons	1, 3, 6	5, 6	1–5	3, 6	2, 3	1–7	1–7	1–7	1–7	1–7

Content Standards
1 Number and Operations
2 Algebra
3 Geometry
4 Measurement
5 Data Analysis and Probability

Process Standards
6 Problem Solving
7 Reasoning and Proof
8 Communication
9 Connections
10 Representation

PRACTICE *through* Games

Everyday Mathematics uses games to help students develop good fact power and other math skills.

- *Dart Game* to experiment with reflections and practice finding lines of reflection **(Lesson 10.2)**
- *Pocket-Billiards Game* to experiment with reflections and practice finding lines of reflection **(Lesson 10.2)**
- *Credits/Debits Game* to practice addition of positive and negative integers **(Lesson 10.6)**

unit 10 content highlights

The discussion below highlights the major content ideas presented in Unit 10 and may help you establish instructional priorities.

Types of Geometry (Lessons 10.1 and following)

You may remember your high school geometry course as dealing with definitions, axioms, theorems ("Given ..., To Prove ..."), and perhaps straightedge-and-compass constructions. This form of **synthetic geometry** was first developed by Euclid about 300 B.C. and has been the model for teaching geometry ever since.

However, there are two modern geometries that cover the same topics:

Analytic geometry The study of figures in a coordinate plane.

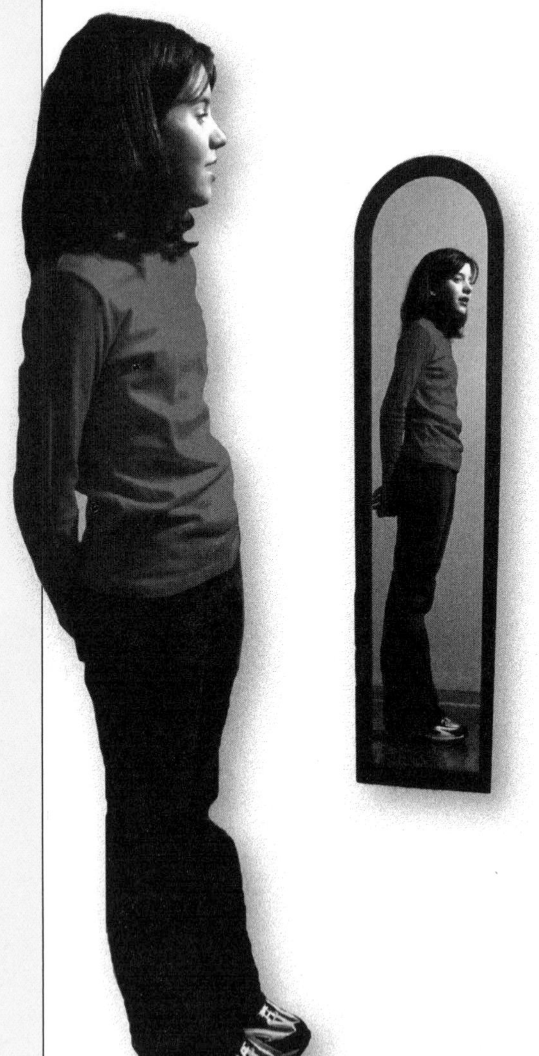

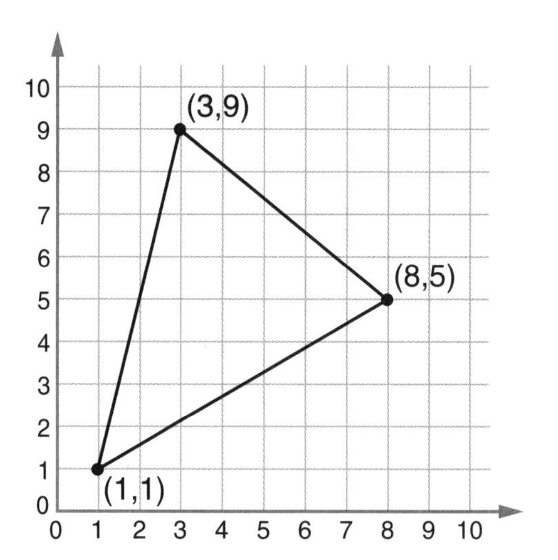

Figure in a coordinate plane

Transformation geometry The study of certain operations on figures. These operations, or "transformations," produce figures that are the same shape as (similar to) the original figures, or the same size and shape as (congruent to) the original figures.

These two geometries are probably more useful than synthetic geometry. Both are featured in Grades 4–6 of *Everyday Mathematics,* with Unit 10 introducing the transformation approach.

"Isometric" or "Congruence" Transformations
(Lessons 10.1 and following)

You may remember from your high school geometry course the emphasis on **congruent** figures, especially on proving triangles congruent by theorems called "side-angle-side" or "SAS," and so on.

This topic is handled in transformation geometry by **rigid motions** or **isometric transformations,** which do not change the size or shape of figures. These transformations—**translations** (slides), **reflections** (flips), and **rotations** (turns)—can duplicate any figure. (SAS and similar theorems of synthetic geometry apply only to triangles.)

Reflections (Flips) and Symmetry with Transparent Mirrors (Lessons 10.1–10.4)

Everyone is familiar with mirrors and the exact—but reversed—images one sees in them. The device used in this unit, the **transparent mirror,** has an advantage over a regular mirror: It allows students to look through a mirror and reach behind it to touch or trace the mirror image (almost like Alice going "through the looking glass").

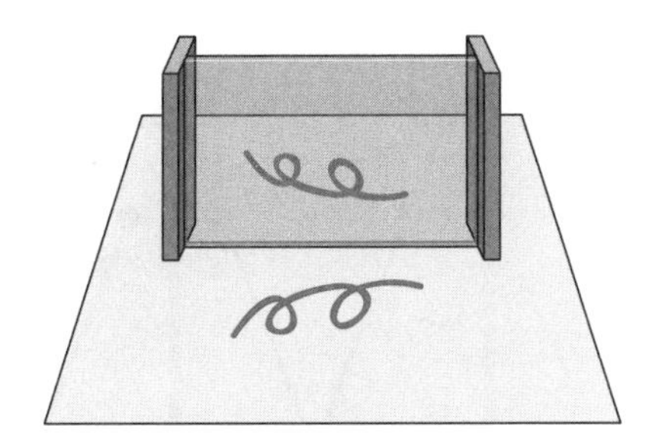

Transparent mirror

As with any new tool, developing the skills for its use takes time, practice, and patience. For accurate placement of images, have students practice these skills:

- ▹ Lean down and look directly through the transparent mirror.
- ▹ Use the ends of the transparent mirror to keep it perpendicular to the paper.
- ▹ Use the inner part of the recessed edge to place the transparent mirror on points or lines or to draw mirror lines.
- ▹ Hold the transparent mirror firmly in position with one hand while drawing behind it or along its recessed edge. (This is one of the main skills to be learned.)

It is probably a good idea to acquire or practice these skills yourself before teaching the lessons. Do the mirror exercises on journal pages and masters until you feel comfortable using the transparent mirror.

Transformations as Design Tools (Lesson 10.5)

Geometric patterns are part of many designs—in arts and crafts from around the world, in architecture and engineering, and in paintings and other works of art (sometimes in disguised forms). Lesson 10.5, on **frieze patterns,** encourages students to explore reflections, symmetry, rotations, and translations in order to analyze and create designs. The authors believe that fourth graders will find these design tasks enjoyable. Some of their creations may be quite elegant.

An interesting property of transformations is that two successive reflections across parallel mirror lines are equivalent to one translation. (The original image is reversed in the first reflection, but the mirror image of the first reflection can be a translated image.) Hence one can make friezes either by translating and tracing or by using transparent mirrors twice for each frieze copy.

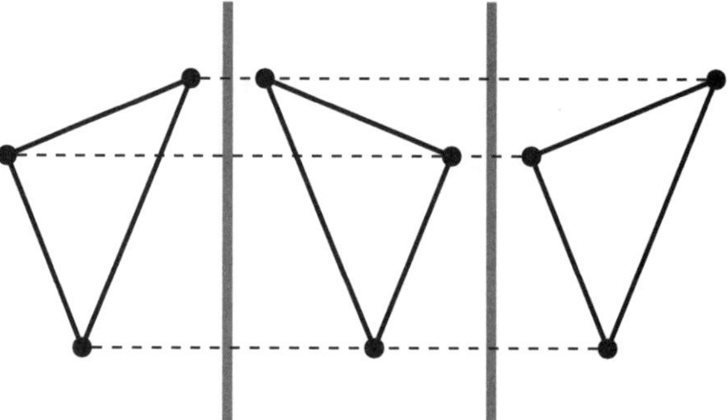

Two reflections equivalent to one translation

The authors hope that the principles learned here can be linked to teaching visual arts in your school. Geometry that is useful in both art and practical matters will be applied many times throughout *Everyday Mathematics.*

Operations with Positive and Negative Numbers (Lesson 10.6)

Since Kindergarten, *Everyday Mathematics* students have been using positive and negative numbers to identify locations on timelines, number lines, number grids, and thermometers. Since first grade, students have informally used addition and subtraction in going from one place to another and in finding distances. But Lesson 10.6 may be students' first exposure to *operations* with positive and negative numbers. In this lesson, the numbers are limited to integers—whole numbers and their (negative) opposites.

"Credits and debits" number stories are used to help make addition concrete. Single-digit numbers ensure that most problems can be done mentally. It is important in these "accounting" situations to name both the operation and the number.

- "Add +$3" is read "Add positive 3 dollars" (a credit transaction).
- "Add −$5" is read "Add negative 5 dollars" (a debit transaction).
  This distinguishes the addition operation from the numbers involved.

Later lessons in Grade 4 will introduce subtraction of positive and negative numbers and will teach the use of the "change sign" key, which enables calculators to work with negative as well as positive numbers. Many practice and review exercises will be included. Other operations with positive and negative numbers, as well as applications using them, will be featured in Grades 5 and 6.

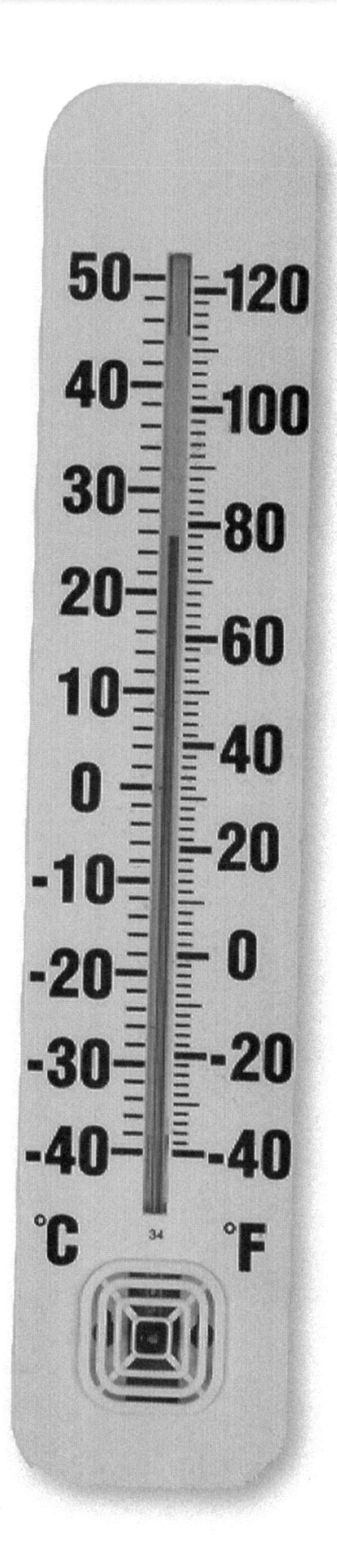

Confusing Notation for Positive and Negative Numbers (Lesson 10.6)

The use of the same notation with several meanings can be confusing. This is true of the symbol "$-$":

- ▷ The symbol "$-$" attached to a numeral, as in -3, -0.5, or -37, is read **"negative"** and is used in naming numbers on the number line ("negative three," "negative five-tenths," "negative thirty-seven").
- ▷ The symbol "$-$" in a number model, preceding a positive or negative number, as in $-(+3)$ or $-(-17)$, is read **"opposite of."** The opposite of a negative number is a positive number; the opposite of a positive number is a negative number. For example, the "opposite of positive 3" is negative 3, and the "opposite of negative 17" is positive 17.

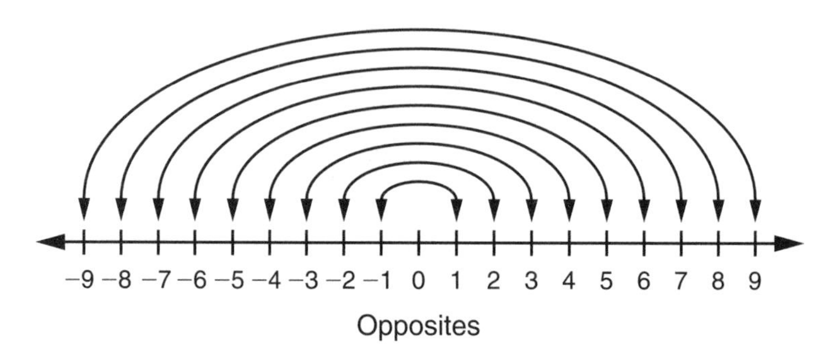

Opposites

- ▷ The symbol "$-$" in a number model, as in $17 - 3 = 14$, is read **"minus," "subtract,"** or **"take away"** and indicates the familiar subtraction operation.

Examples

$17 - 3 = 14$ is read "17 minus 3 equals 14."
$17 - (+3) = 14$ is read "17 minus 3 equals 14."
$-(-17) - 3 = 14$ is read "the opposite of negative 17 minus 3 equals 14."
$17 + (-3) = 14$ is read "17 plus negative 3 equals 14."
$17 - (-3) = 20$ is read "17 minus negative 3 equals 20."

The meanings of the symbol "$-$" can get quite tangled in number models like $-17 - 3 = -20$ ("Negative 17 minus 3 equals negative 20") or $12 - -(-4) = 8$ ("12 take away the opposite of negative 4 equals 8").

Some mathematics programs of the past tried to reduce confusion by using "$-$" only for subtraction. Positive and negative numbers were designated with small raised symbols (for example, $^{-}3$, $^{-}17$, $^{+}17$), and opposites were indicated by "opp." But everyday usage and nearly all algebra books continued to use the traditional notation, so students eventually had to reconcile the two notations.

Given the problems associated with both notations, the authors have decided to use the traditional system. Help students sort it out when you read expressions by consistently saying "plus" or "minus" for addition or subtraction, and "positive," "negative," or "opposite" for numbers, as indicated by the context. Encourage students to do likewise when they eventually read expressions to each other and to themselves.

NOTE: Public or private speech is very helpful in dealing with complexities of meanings. It is verifiable and observable common sense for students to use speech, as well as sight, to sort out complicated symbolic expressions. (This is a key tenet of the learning theory of Lev S. Vygotsky. An excellent article on Vygotskian learning theory is "Why Children Talk to Themselves," by Laura E. Berk, in the November 1994 issue of *Scientific American*.)

Review and Assessment (Lesson 10.7)

The Unit 10 assessment in Lesson 10.7 includes oral, slate, and written assessments of the following concepts and skills:

- using a transparent mirror to draw the reflection of a figure
- identifying reflected and symmetric figures
- identifying lines of reflection and lines of symmetry
- rotating figures
- translating figures
- adding integers

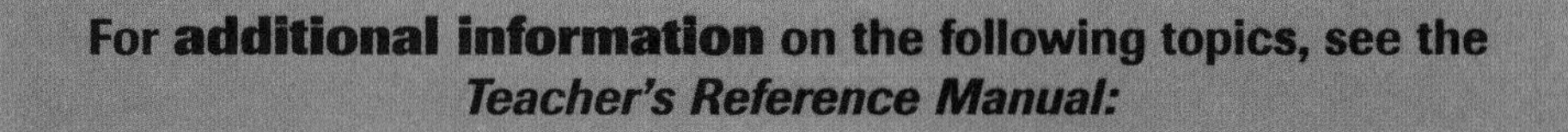

For **additional information** on the following topics, see the *Teacher's Reference Manual:*

- patterns
- positive and negative numbers
- symmetry
- transformations
- transparent mirrors

10.1 Explorations with a Transparent Mirror

OBJECTIVE **To explore reflections of 2-dimensional figures.**

summaries	materials
1 Teaching the Lesson	
Students experiment with reflections, using a transparent mirror to move and draw reflected images. [Geometry]	☐ *Math Journal 2,* p. 291 ☐ Teaching Masters (*Math Masters,* pp. 149 and 150) ☐ 1 transparent mirror per partnership ***See*** **Advance Preparation**
2 Ongoing Learning & Practice	
Students multiply and divide with decimals. [Operations and Computation] Students practice and maintain skills through Math Boxes and Study Link activities.	☐ *Math Journal 2,* pp. 292 and 293 ☐ Study Link Master (*Math Masters,* p. 356) ☐ Geometry Template
3 Options for Individualizing	
Reteaching Students review polygons by matching pictures of polygons with the names of the polygons. [Geometry] **Enrichment** Students explore reflected images and symmetry in literature. [Geometry]	☐ Teaching Master (*Math Masters,* p. 151) ☐ *The Mirror Puzzle Book, Reflections, Round Trip,* and *Shadows and Reflections* ***See*** **Advance Preparation**

Additional Information

Background Information The transparent mirror is a special kind of perpendicular "mirror." By looking through the mirror, a student can see and trace the mirror image of an object. You should experiment with the transparent mirror, using *Math Masters,* pages 149 and 150, before teaching the lesson.

Advance Preparation For Part 1, put a box of transparent mirrors near the Math Message. Label the box "Transparent Mirrors."

For the optional Enrichment activity in Part 3, obtain as many of the following books as possible: *The Mirror Puzzle Book* by Marion Walter (Parkwest, 1985); *Reflections* by Ann Jonas (Greenwillow, 1987); *Round Trip* by Ann Jonas (Greenwillow, 1983); and *Shadows and Reflections* by Tana Hoban (Greenwillow, 1990).

Vocabulary • **transparent mirror** • **recessed** • **image** • **preimage**

Getting Started

Mental Math and Reflexes

Pose "fraction-of" and "percent-of" problems. *Suggestions:*

What is

- $\frac{1}{3}$ of 18? 6
- $\frac{1}{9}$ of 36? 4
- $\frac{1}{8}$ of 40? 5
- 20% of 25? 5
- 25% of 28? 7
- 75% of 36? 27

Math Message

Work with a partner. Take one transparent mirror for your partnership. Read journal page 291. Then experiment with the mirror.

Teaching the Lesson

✦ Math Message Follow-Up
(*Math Journal 2,* p. 291)

WHOLE-CLASS DISCUSSION

Discuss journal page 291. Have students examine the top and bottom edges of the **transparent mirror.** Point out that one side of one edge is **recessed.** (On some transparent mirrors, both edges have a recessed side.) The recessed side can be used as a straightedge.

✦ Using a Transparent Mirror to "Move" Shapes

WHOLE-CLASS ACTIVITY

Have students follow this procedure:

1. Draw a squiggle on a sheet of paper.
2. Place the transparent mirror so that the squiggle is between the mirror and your eyes.
3. Look through the mirror.
4. Tell what you see when you look through the transparent mirror. Another squiggle that has the same shape as the original squiggle

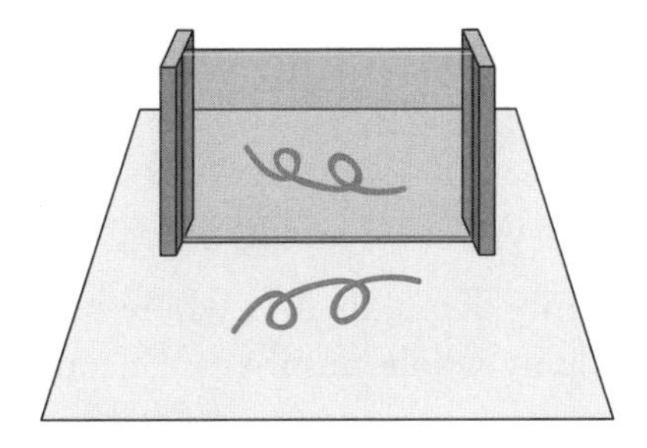

This transparent mirror has two endpieces.
Some may have only one endpiece.

Basic Use of a Transparent Mirror

A **transparent mirror** is shown at the right.

Notice that the mirror has a **recessed** drawing edge, along which lines are drawn. Some transparent mirrors have a drawing edge both on the top and on the bottom.

Place your transparent mirror on this page so that its drawing edge lies along line *MK* below. Then look through the transparent mirror to read the "backward" message.

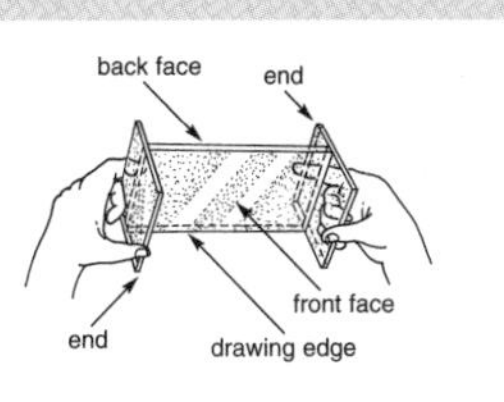

If you have followed the directions correctly, you are now able to read this message. Here are a few things to remember when using your transparent mirror:
- Always look into the front of the transparent mirror. In this position, the drawing edge will be facing you.
- Use your transparent mirror on flat surfaces like your desk or a tabletop.
- Use a sharp pencil when tracing along the drawing edge.
- Experiment and have fun!

M K

If you have followed the directions correctly, you are now able to read this message. Here are a few things to remember when using your transparent mirror:
- Always look into the front of the transparent mirror. In this position, the drawing edge will be facing you.
- Use your transparent mirror on flat surfaces like your desk or a tabletop.
- Use a sharp pencil when tracing along the drawing edge.
- Experiment and have fun!

STUDENT PAGE

Math Journal 2, p. 291

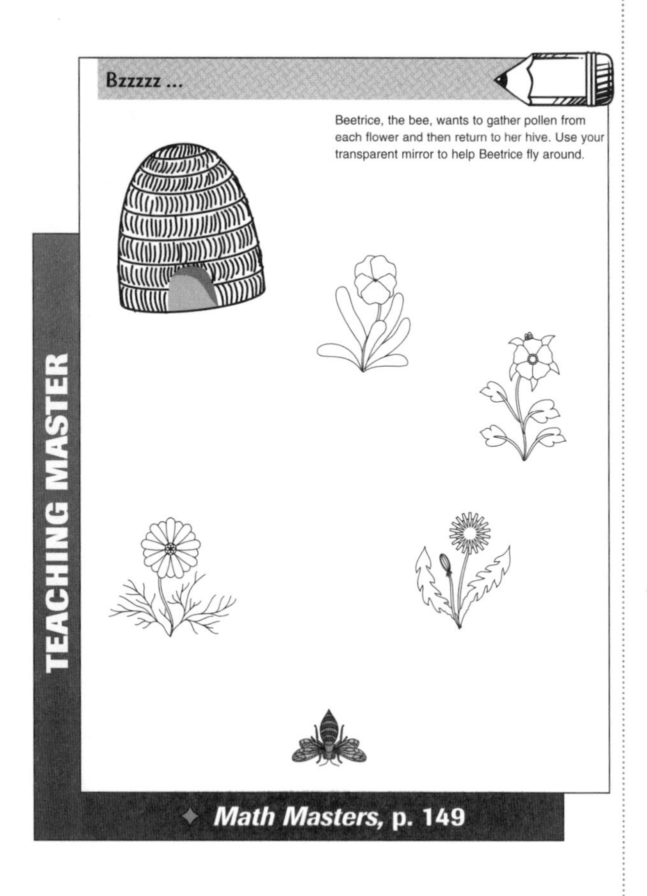

✦ *Math Masters,* p. 149

✦ *Math Masters,* p. 150

Language Arts Link The squiggle on the other side of the transparent mirror is called the **image** of the original squiggle. The original squiggle is known as the **preimage.** Discuss the use of the prefix *pre-* to mean "before." The preimage is the image before it has been reflected in the transparent mirror. Ask students to think of other words that have the prefix *pre-*. Possible responses include *prehistoric, premature,* and *preschool.*

Ask students to move the transparent mirror around and observe what happens to the image of the squiggle. Then suggest that students experiment with their mirrors—they can "move" small objects around on their desks.

✦ Using the Transparent Mirror to "Move" Reflected Images (*Math Masters,* p. 149)

PARTNER ACTIVITY 

Partners do the activity on *Math Masters,* page 149. They should have no difficulty moving the bee around the page.

✦ Using the Transparent Mirror to Draw Images of Shapes (*Math Masters,* p. 150)

PARTNER ACTIVITY

Students use their transparent mirrors to move a hat, a nose, and a mouth to their appropriate places on the clown face on *Math Masters,* page 150. When each part, as seen through the mirror, is in its desired place, students trace it to complete the picture of the clown. They may want to color and cut out their completed clowns.

2 Ongoing Learning & Practice

✦ Multiplying and Dividing with Decimals (*Math Journal 2,* p. 292)

INDEPENDENT ACTIVITY 

Students multiply decimals and whole numbers and divide decimals by whole numbers. Encourage students to use an estimation strategy to place the decimal point in the answers.

✦ Math Boxes 10.1 (*Math Journal 2,* p. 293)

INDEPENDENT ACTIVITY 

Mixed Review Math Boxes in this lesson are paired with Math Boxes in Lesson 10.4. The skill in Problem 1 is a prerequisite for Unit 11.

✦ Study Link 10.1 (*Math Masters,* p. 356)

Home Connection Students use a mirror to draw the image of a design. They will need a blank piece of paper to complete the activity.

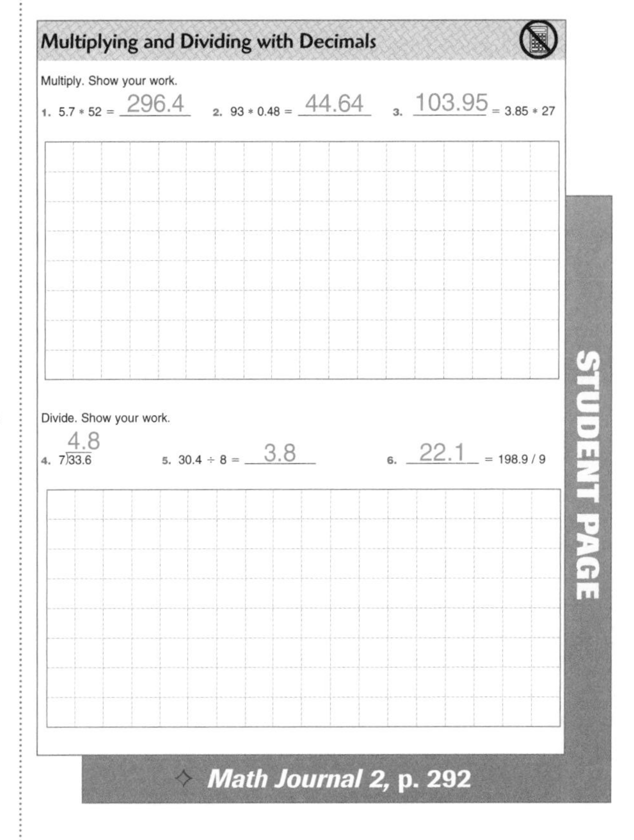

Multiplying and Dividing with Decimals

Multiply. Show your work.

1. 5.7 * 52 = 296.4
2. 93 * 0.48 = 44.64
3. 103.95 = 3.85 * 27

Divide. Show your work.

4. $7\overline{)33.6}$ = 4.8
5. 30.4 ÷ 8 = 3.8
6. 22.1 = 198.9 / 9

STUDENT PAGE

✧ *Math Journal 2,* p. 292

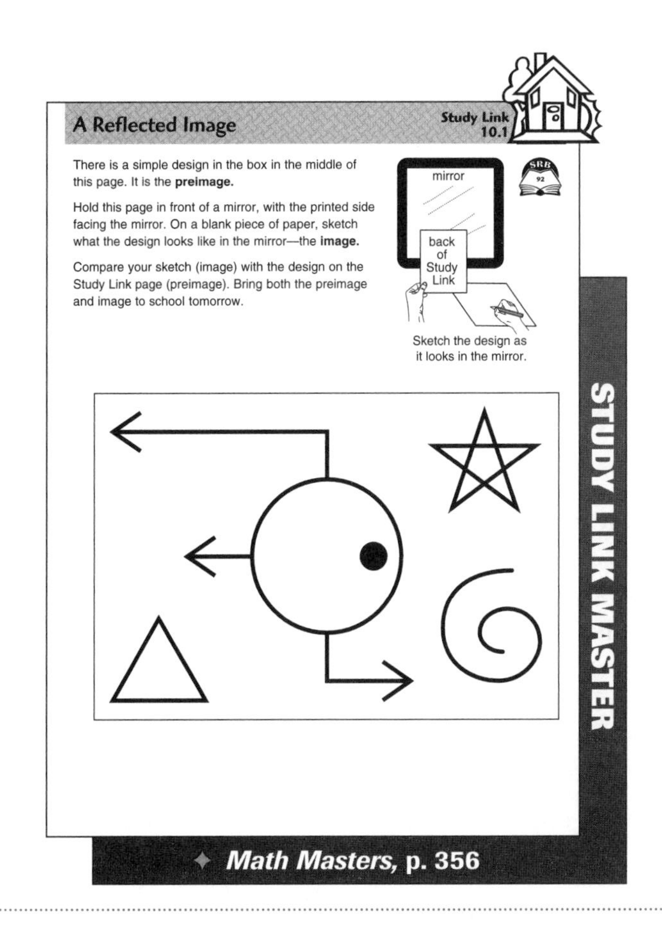

A Reflected Image Study Link 10.1

There is a simple design in the box in the middle of this page. It is the **preimage.**

Hold this page in front of a mirror, with the printed side facing the mirror. On a blank piece of paper, sketch what the design looks like in the mirror—the **image.**

Compare your sketch (image) with the design on the Study Link page (preimage). Bring both the preimage and image to school tomorrow.

Sketch the design as it looks in the mirror.

STUDY LINK MASTER

✦ *Math Masters,* p. 356

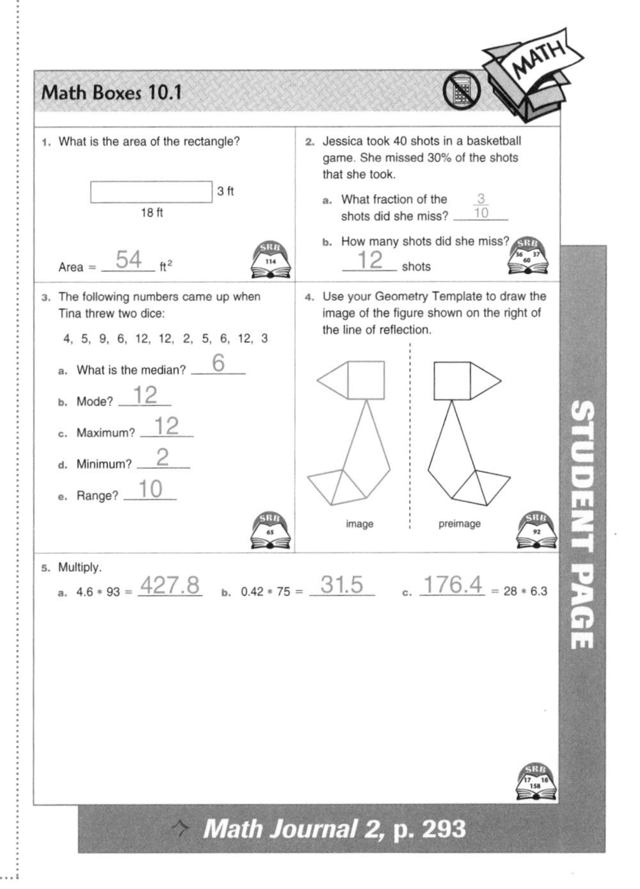

Math Boxes 10.1

1. What is the area of the rectangle?

Area = 54 ft^2

2. Jessica took 40 shots in a basketball game. She missed 30% of the shots that she took.
   a. What fraction of the shots did she miss? $\frac{3}{10}$
   b. How many shots did she miss? 12 shots

3. The following numbers came up when Tina threw two dice:
   4, 5, 9, 6, 12, 12, 2, 5, 6, 12, 3
   a. What is the median? 6
   b. Mode? 12
   c. Maximum? 12
   d. Minimum? 2
   e. Range? 10

4. Use your Geometry Template to draw the image of the figure shown on the right of the line of reflection.

5. Multiply.
   a. 4.6 * 93 = 427.8
   b. 0.42 * 75 = 31.5
   c. 176.4 = 28 * 6.3

STUDENT PAGE

✧ *Math Journal 2,* p. 293

TEACHING MASTER

Polygon Review

1. Match each polygon below with its name. Place the correct letter on the line next to the polygon.

Three of the polygons have more than one name. The square, for example, is also a parallelogram. For these three polygons, write the letters for all the names they can have.

Answer	Names
c	a. kite
e, i	b. hexagon
f	c. equilateral triangle
k	d. rectangle
j, i, d, e	e. rhombus
a	f. pentagon
i	g. right triangle
b	h. octagon
d, i	i. parallelogram
g	j. square
h	k. trapezoid

2. Which of the polygons above are regular polygons?
Equilateral triangle, square, hexagon, octagon

✦ *Math Masters,* p. 151

3 Options for Individualizing

✦ RETEACHING Reviewing Polygons (*Math Masters,* p. 151)

INDEPENDENT ACTIVITY  **5–15 min** 

At the beginning of the school year, students studied 2-dimensional shapes. During the next few lessons, they will investigate what happens when 2-dimensional shapes are moved to different positions.

Some students may benefit from a review of different shapes. On *Math Masters,* page 151 they match pictures of polygons with the names of the polygons.

✦ ENRICHMENT Exploring Reflected Images and Symmetry in Literature

INDEPENDENT ACTIVITY  **30+ min** 

Literature Link The following books provide opportunities to explore reflections, shadows, distortions, symmetry, and perspective. Have the books available for students to look through during free moments.

The Mirror Puzzle Book

Summary: A mirror is attached to the inner cover so that the reader can create symmetric designs.

Shadows and Reflections

Summary: Photographs are used to show that when shapes are reflected in mirrors, windows, puddles, or ponds, distortions may appear, but certain attributes are unchanged. Changes that occur in shadows are also explored.

Reflections

Summary: This book can be read from front to back and then turned over and read from back to front. The reader follows a child's day and studies the illustrations to see how different images appear when the perspective is changed.

Round Trip

Summary: This book is similar in format to *Reflections.* A family's trip to the city and return home are followed.

10.2 Finding Lines of Reflection

OBJECTIVES **To explore reflections; and to identify lines of reflection.**

summaries	materials
1 Teaching the Lesson	
Students play games that involve reflections, such as the *Dart Game* and the *Pocket-Billiards Game*. They explore finding the line of reflection of a reflected image. [Geometry]	□ Study Link 10.1 □ Teaching Masters (*Math Masters,* pp. 152–154) □ 1 transparent mirror per partnership □ ruler
2 Ongoing Learning & Practice	
Students solve problems based on data about recent U.S. presidents. [Data and Chance] Students practice and maintain skills through Math Boxes and Study Link activities.	□ *Math Journal 2,* pp. 294 and 295 □ Study Link Master (*Math Masters,* p. 357) □ Geometry Template
3 Options for Individualizing	
Language Diversity Students build background for mathematics words by thinking of ways to use the word *reflect.* [Geometry] **Reteaching** Students create a reflection by painting on half a sheet of paper and then folding the paper. [Geometry]	□ large sheet of paper □ paints, brushes, and dark marker ***See* Advance Preparation**

Additional Information

Advance Preparation For the optional Reteaching activity in Part 3, students will need supplies and space for painting.

Vocabulary • **reflection** • **line of reflection**

Getting Started

Mental Math and Reflexes

On the board, write whole-number times decimal multiplication number sentences like the following. Students insert the decimal point in each product.

- 8 ∗ 9.6 = 7 6 8 76.8
- 83 ∗ 0.02 = 1 6 6 1.66
- 19 ∗ 4.96 = 9 4 2 4 94.24
- 14 ∗ 0.53 = 7 4 2 7.42

Math Message

Have you ever played darts or pocket billiards? Discuss the object of each game and some of the rules with a friend.

Study Link 10.1 Follow-Up

Students place Study Link 10.1 and their sketch side by side on their desks. They compare the preimage and the image. Students should note that the image is the opposite or reverse of the preimage.

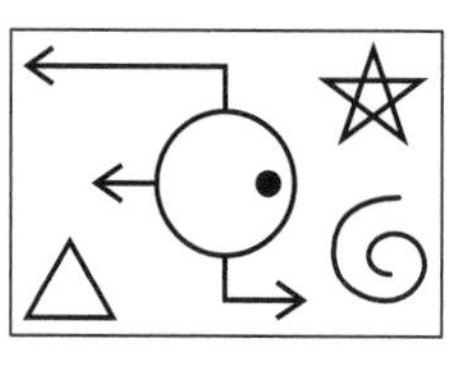

preimage

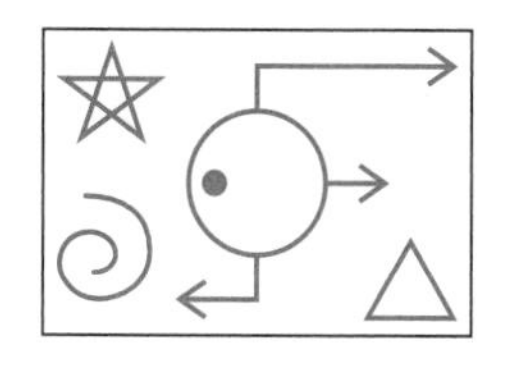

image

1 Teaching the Lesson

✦ Math Message Follow-Up

WHOLE-CLASS DISCUSSION 

Students briefly share the object and some of the rules of each game with the class. Some students may mention that another name for pocket billiards is *pool*.

NOTE: It isn't essential that students know the rules or have played these games in order to understand the activities in this lesson. However, if you are able, displaying a dartboard or a picture of a pool table would be helpful to students who are unfamiliar with the games.

✦ Playing Games that Involve Reflections
(*Math Masters,* pp. 152–154)

PARTNER ACTIVITY 

Directions for the following games are on *Math Masters,* page 152. The purpose of the games is to experiment with reflections.

TEACHING MASTER

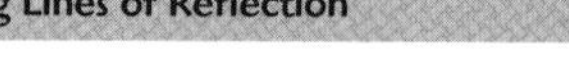

Finding Lines of Reflection

Dart Game

Practice before you play the game on *Math Masters,* page 153. One partner chooses Dart A and the other partner Dart B. Try to hit the target with your own dart, using the transparent mirror. **Do not practice with your partner's dart.**

Now play the game with your partner.

Directions Take turns. When it is your turn, use the other dart — the one you did not use for practice. Try to hit the target by placing the transparent mirror on the page, but **do not look through the mirror.** Then both you and your partner look through the mirror to see where the dart hit the target. Keep score.

Pocket-Billiards Game

Practice before you play the game on *Math Masters,* page 154. Choose a ball (1, 2, 3, or 4) and a pocket (A, B, C, D, E, or F). Try to get the ball into the pocket, using the transparent mirror.

Now play the game with a partner.

Directions Take turns. When it is your turn, say which ball and which pocket you have picked: for example, "Ball 2 to go into Pocket D." Try to get the ball into the pocket by placing the transparent mirror on the billiard table, **but do not look through the mirror.** Then both you and your partner look through the mirror to check whether the ball has gone into the pocket.

✦ ***Math Masters,* p. 152**

Dart Game

Math Masters, page 153 contains two darts, labeled A and B, and a target. The idea is to “hit” the target by reflecting one of the darts in the transparent mirror.

Students first practice hitting the target. One partner uses Dart A; the other uses Dart B. Students look through the mirror and move it around on the master until the image of the dart hits the target.

After a little practice, students should be ready to play the game. Players now use the dart they didn’t use in practice—that is, if they practiced with Dart A, they play the game with Dart B (or vice versa).

The actual game varies from the practice game in one important respect: When trying to hit the target, students must place the mirror on the master *without looking through the mirror.* (There would not be much of a game if they could look through the mirror—it would be easy to hit the bull’s-eye every time.) Only after a player has placed the mirror on the master may the player look through it in order to find the score.

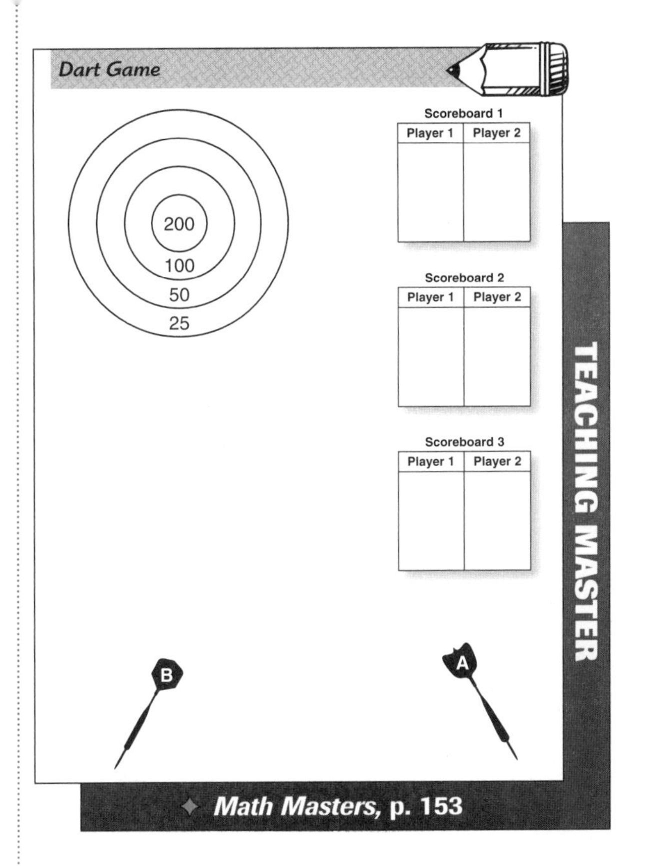

Math Masters, p. 153

Pocket-Billiards Game

The *Pocket-Billiards Game* is similar to the *Dart Game.*

Math Masters, page 154 shows the top of a pocket-billiards table. There are six pockets, labeled A–F, and four billiard balls, labeled 1–4. The idea is to “sink” a ball into one of the pockets by reflecting the ball in the transparent mirror.

As with the *Dart Game,* students practice by looking at the image of a billiard ball through the mirror. Then partners play the game, *without looking through the mirror.* Players should look through the mirror only to check results.

Adjusting the Activity Challenge partners to devise their own scoring system for the game. It might be as simple as scoring 1 point for each time a ball is sunk into a pocket. Or perhaps each partner gets three tries at sinking a ball into a designated pocket, scoring 5 points if the ball goes in on the first try, 3 points if it goes in on the second try, or 1 point if it goes in on the last try.

ONGOING ASSESSMENT

After students have played the game several times, pose the following question: *How could measuring distances with a ruler help you decide where to place the mirror so that the ball will go into the pocket?* (For example: *Exactly where can you put the mirror so that Ball 2 will go into Pocket D?*)

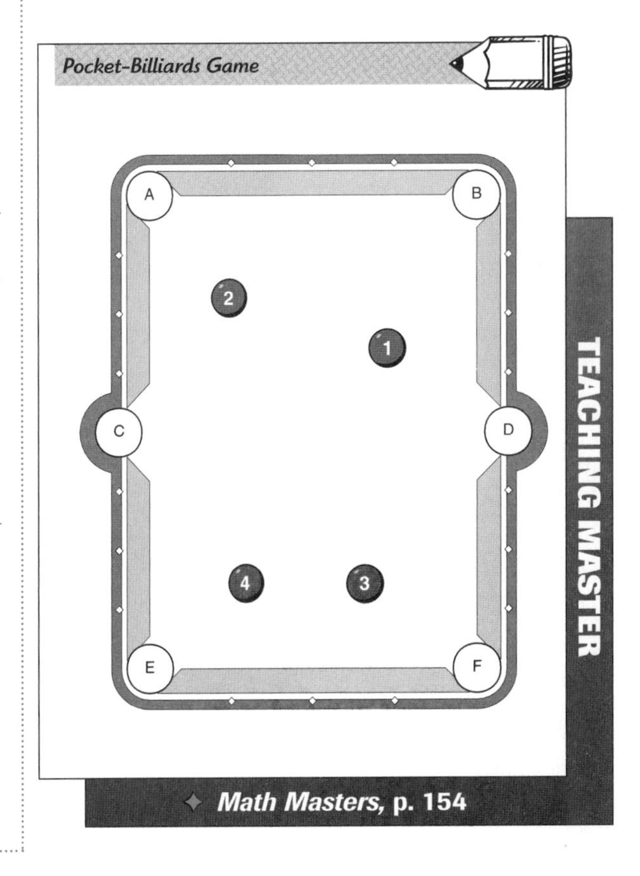

Math Masters, p. 154

✦ Introducing the Concept of Reflection

WHOLE-CLASS DISCUSSION

Start the discussion by asking the following question:

- In Lesson 10.1, the clown hats were drawn upside down. What would have happened if they had been drawn right-side up? The hats, after being moved to the clown's head, would be upside down.

Introduce the word **reflection**—a flipping motion that makes the image appear to be the "opposite" of the original object. Point out that in a reflection in a mirror, everything is reversed. Explain that the line along the recessed edge of a transparent mirror is called the **line of reflection.**

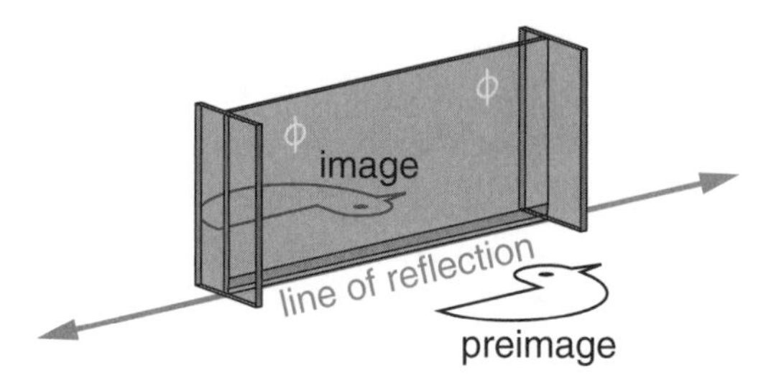

Have students share their strategies for locating the line of reflection on the pocket-billiards table. Help them see that the mirror must be placed about halfway between the ball and the pocket, and that it should be perpendicular (at right angles) to the invisible line connecting the ball and the pocket. This method works because a reflected object is the same distance from the line of reflection as the original object.

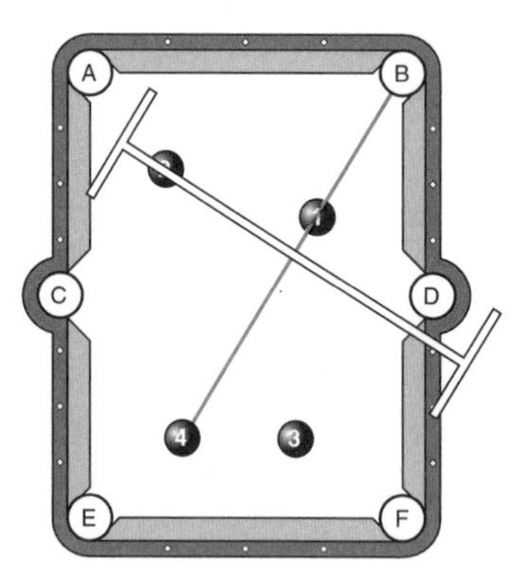

NOTE: This is as far as you need to go with this topic for now. With additional experience, students will learn that when an object is reflected, corresponding points on the object and on its reflection are the same distance from the line of reflection.

Ongoing Learning & Practice

Interpreting a Data Table
(*Math Journal 2,* p. 294)

INDEPENDENT ACTIVITY 

Social Studies Link Students solve problems based on data about the twelve most recent United States presidents. Problem 4 is tricky. If you look only at the years of Ford's and Kennedy's terms, it appears that Kennedy was president for the shortest time. Actually, Kennedy was president for a little more than 2 years and 10 months, Ford for less than 2 years and 6 months.

Presidential Information

The following table shows the dates on which the most recent presidents of the United States were sworn in and their ages at the time they were sworn in.

President	Date Sworn In	Age
F.D. Roosevelt	March 4, 1933	51
Truman	April 12, 1945	60
Eisenhower	January 20, 1953	62
Kennedy	January 20, 1961	43
Johnson	November 22, 1963	55
Nixon	January 20, 1969	56
Ford	August 9, 1974	61
Carter	January 20, 1977	52
Reagan	January 20, 1981	69
G.H. Bush	January 20, 1989	64
Clinton	January 20, 1993	46
G.W. Bush	January 20, 2001	54

1. What is the median age (the middle age) of the presidents at the time they were sworn in? $55\frac{1}{2}$ years
2. What is the range of their ages (the difference between the ages of the oldest and the youngest)? 26 years
3. Who was president for the longest time? Roosevelt
4. Who was president for the shortest time before 2001? Ford
5. Presidents are elected to serve for 1 term. A term lasts 4 years. Which presidents served only 1 term or less than 1 term? Kennedy, Ford, Carter, G.H. Bush
6. Which president was sworn in 28 years after Roosevelt? Kennedy
7. Roosevelt was born on January 30, 1882. If he were alive today, how old would he be? As of January 30, 2001: 119 years old

STUDENT PAGE

Math Journal 2, p. 294

Math Boxes 10.2 (*Math Journal 2,* p. 295)

INDEPENDENT ACTIVITY 

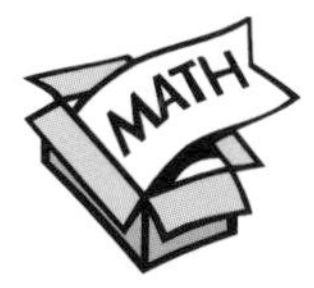

Mixed Review Math Boxes in this lesson are paired with Math Boxes in Lesson 10.5. The skill in Problem 1 is a prerequisite for Unit 11.

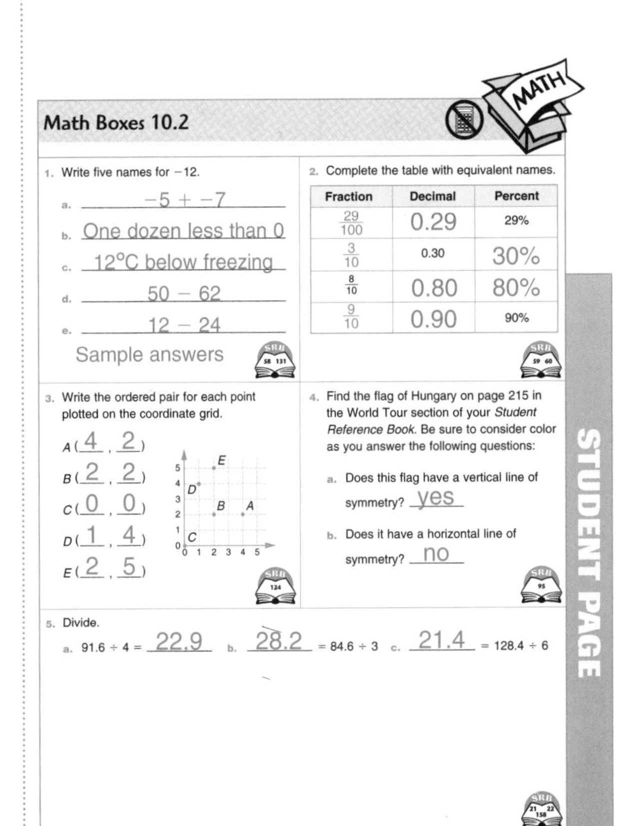

Math Boxes 10.2

1. Write five names for −12.
   a. −5 + −7
   b. One dozen less than 0
   c. 12°C below freezing
   d. 50 − 62
   e. 12 − 24
   Sample answers

2. Complete the table with equivalent names.

Fraction	Decimal	Percent
$\frac{29}{100}$	0.29	29%
$\frac{3}{10}$	0.30	30%
$\frac{8}{10}$	0.80	80%
$\frac{9}{10}$	0.90	90%

3. Write the ordered pair for each point plotted on the coordinate grid.
   A(4, 2)
   B(2, 2)
   C(0, 0)
   D(1, 4)
   E(2, 5)

4. Find the flag of Hungary on page 215 in the World Tour section of your *Student Reference Book.* Be sure to consider color as you answer the following questions:
   a. Does this flag have a vertical line of symmetry? yes
   b. Does it have a horizontal line of symmetry? no

5. Divide.
   a. 91.6 ÷ 4 = 22.9
   b. 28.2 = 84.6 ÷ 3
   c. 21.4 = 128.4 ÷ 6

STUDENT PAGE

Math Journal 2, p. 295

Study Link 10.2 (*Math Masters,* p. 357)

Home Connection Students draw lines of reflection between preimages and images. For given preimages, they use the Geometry Template to draw the image on the other side of the line of reflection.

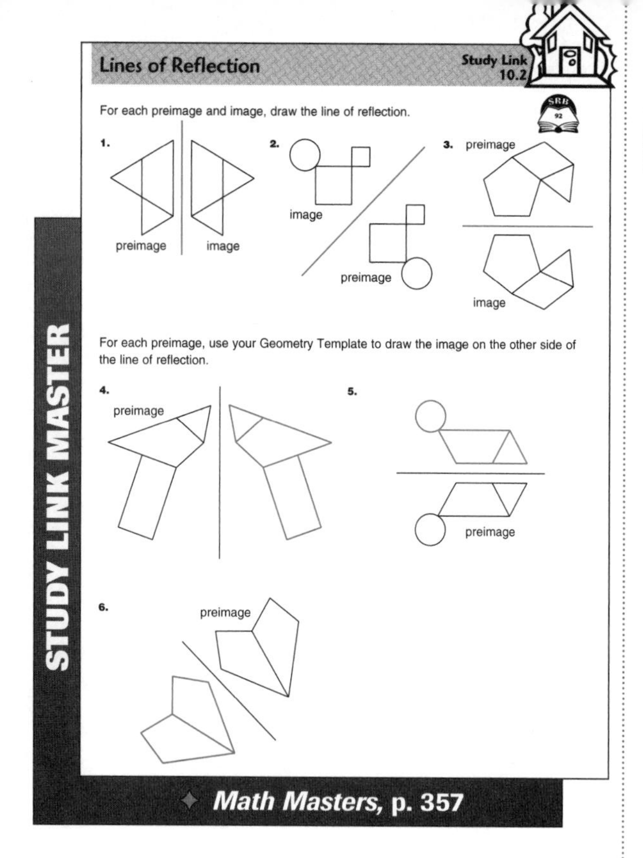
STUDY LINK MASTER

Lines of Reflection — Study Link 10.2

For each preimage and image, draw the line of reflection.

1. preimage, image
2. image, preimage
3. preimage, image

For each preimage, use your Geometry Template to draw the image on the other side of the line of reflection.

4. preimage
5. preimage
6. preimage

✦ *Math Masters,* p. 357

3 Options for Individualizing

✦ LANGUAGE DIVERSITY Building Background for Mathematics Words

PARTNER ACTIVITY  **5–15 min** 

Pair a student learning English with a proficient English speaker. Have them think of as many ways of using the word *reflect* in a sentence as they can.

Examples

▷ At the end of each unit in math, we think about the work we have done throughout the unit. Then we answer a page of questions called "Time to *Reflect.*"

▷ Anna missed two free throws at the end of the basketball game. She was worried that this would *reflect* poorly on her ability to perform under pressure.

▷ An object *reflected* in a mirror appears to be the reverse of the original image.

✦ RETEACHING Creating a Paint Reflection

INDEPENDENT ACTIVITY  **15–30 min**

Art Link Students fold a large sheet of paper in half and then unfold it. They paint a simple design, using several colors if they wish, on half of the sheet without touching the fold line. Before the paint has dried, students refold the paper and unfold it again. The result will be a reflection of the painted design on the other half of the paper.

Have students use a dark marker to highlight the fold line and label it as the *line of reflection.* In addition, have students label the *preimage* and *image.*

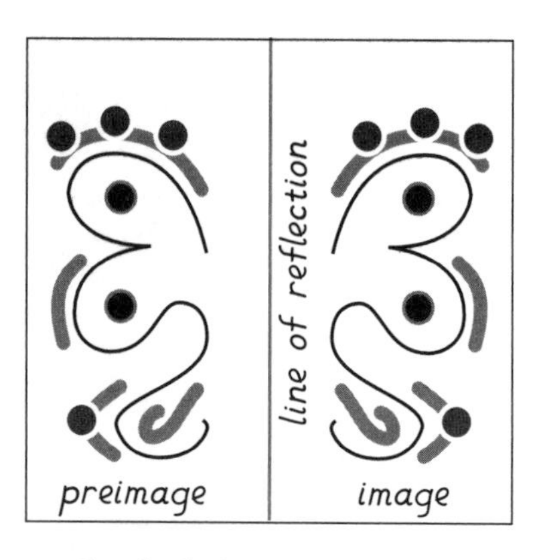

Simple design with reflection

PLANNING AHEAD

Begin collecting pictures of symmetric objects, such as the front view of an automobile, a table, a window, and a fork. These will be used in an optional Extra Practice activity in Lesson 10.4 to start individual booklets or a bulletin-board display of symmetric objects.

10.3 Properties of Reflections

OBJECTIVE **To discover basic properties of reflections.**

summaries	materials
1 Teaching the Lesson	
Students use a transparent mirror to discover basic properties of reflections. They draw reflected images by folding paper. [Geometry]	☐ Study Link 10.2 ☐ Transparency (*Math Masters,* p. 357; optional) ☐ Teaching Master (*Math Masters,* p. 155) ☐ 1 transparent mirror per partnership ☐ ruler ☐ blank sheet of paper ☐ dark, wide-point marker
2 Ongoing Learning & Practice	
Students travel on the World Tour to a second country in Region 4. [multiple strands] Students practice and maintain skills through Math Boxes and Study Link activities.	☐ *Math Journal 2,* p. 296; pp. 345–347 and 352–353 (optional) ☐ *Student Reference Book* ☐ Teaching Masters (*Math Masters,* pp. 36–38; optional) ☐ Study Link Master (*Math Masters,* p. 358) ☐ Geometry Template ***See* Advance Preparation**
3 Options for Individualizing	
Enrichment Students use centimeter cubes to construct 3-dimensional buildings and their reflections. [Geometry] **Enrichment** Students research the Reflecting Pool in Washington, D.C. [Geometry]	☐ *Student Reference Book,* p. 213 ☐ centimeter cubes

Additional Information

Advance Preparation The World Tour activity in Part 2 is optional.

Vocabulary • **line of reflection** • **preimage** • **image**

Getting Started

Mental Math and Reflexes

On the board, write problems involving decimals divided by whole numbers. Students use an estimation strategy to locate the decimal point for each quotient. *Suggestions:*

- 35.2 ÷ 16 = 2.2
- 33.3 / 9 = 3.7
- $6\overline{)262.8}$ 43.8

Math Message

Stand facing a partner. One partner poses. The other partner positions his or her body to be the mirror image of the partner. Then switch roles.

Study Link 10.2 Follow-Up

Go over the answers. An overhead transparency of Study Link 10.2 will be helpful.

1 Teaching the Lesson

✦Math Message Follow-Up

WHOLE-CLASS ACTIVITY

Have partners show their mirror-image poses to the class. Strike your own pose. Have students show the mirror image. Slowly change your pose and challenge students to mirror your changes.

✦Examining Relationships between an Object and Its Reflected Image

(*Math Masters,* p. 155)

WHOLE-CLASS ACTIVITY

Divide the class into partnerships so that pairs of students can share a transparent mirror. Distribute a copy of *Math Masters,* page 155 to each student.

Tell students to put the recessed edge of the mirror on the line next to the dog's head. When they look directly through the mirror, they will see the image of the dog's head. (It is best to look through the mirror at the same level as the mirror.) Ask students to carefully draw the image of the dog's head on the paper where they see it through the mirror.

When all students have completed the drawings, bring the class together and lead them in the following exploration:

▷ Point out that the picture of the dog's head to the left of the **line of reflection** is the **preimage.** Remind students that *pre-* means *before,* so they can think of this picture as the "before image."

▷ Ask: *How are the two drawings alike? How are they different?* The drawings are the same size and shape. They look exactly alike, except that the heads are facing in opposite directions. Also, everything is reversed—for example, the preimage shows a right eye and ear; the image shows a left eye and ear.

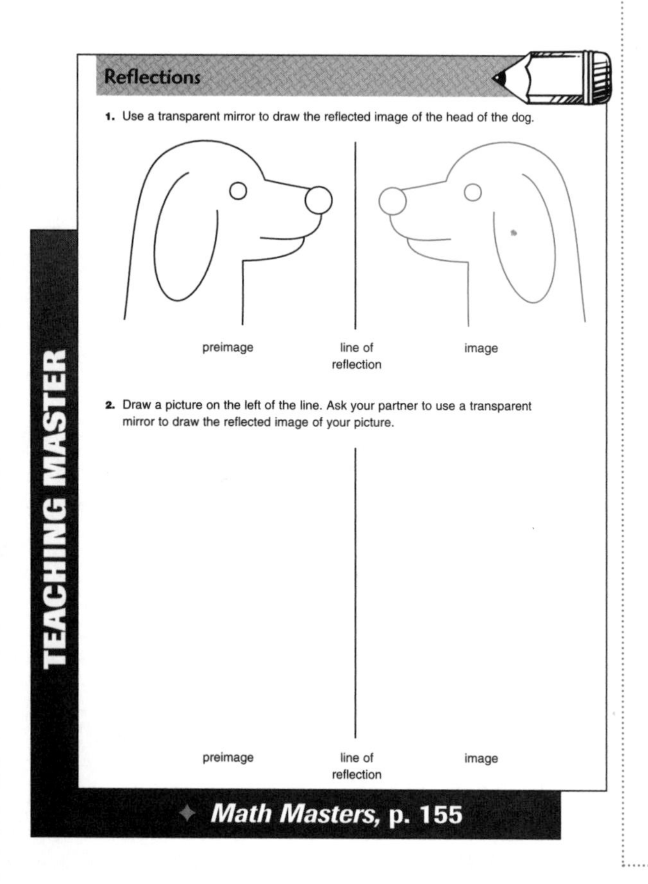

TEACHING MASTER
Reflections
1. Use a transparent mirror to draw the reflected image of the head of the dog.
preimage
line of reflection
image
2. Draw a picture on the left of the line. Ask your partner to use a transparent mirror to draw the reflected image of your picture.
preimage
line of reflection
image

✦ *Math Masters,* p. 155

▷ Have students mark a point A anywhere on the preimage. Then ask them to look through the mirror, mark the **image** of point A, and label the image A' ("A prime"). If necessary, write A' on the board and explain that the little mark by the A is read "prime." The prime mark shows that A and A' are different, but related, points.

Check that all students have labeled the corresponding points A and A' on the dogs. The points may be anywhere, but they must be in the same place on the image as on the preimage.

▷ Have students use a ruler to measure the distance from point A to the line of reflection and from point A' to the line of reflection. Ask: *What did you find out about the distances?* They are the same.

▷ Have students mark and label several other points (B, C, ...) on the preimage; use the mirror to mark and label the corresponding points (B', C', ...) on the image; and check with a ruler that corresponding points are the same distance from the line of reflection.

▷ Remind students of the *Pocket-Billiards Game.* Ask: *Where did you place the mirror in order to get the ball in the pocket?* Halfway between the ball and the pocket

▷ Finally, have each student draw a picture on the left side of the reflection line in the bottom half of the page. Then ask partners to exchange papers and draw the image of their partner's picture.

✦Folding Paper to Draw Reflected Images

PARTNER ACTIVITY 

Lead the class through the following procedure. Steps 1–3 are illustrated in the margin.

1. Each student folds a blank sheet of paper in half lengthwise and draws a picture in the upper-left half of the sheet, using a dark, wide-point marker.
2. Partners exchange sheets and draw the reflected image of their partner's picture by placing the edge of the transparent mirror on the fold.
3. Students fold the sheet again. They hold the folded sheet up to the light to check that the picture and its image match.
4. Students draw a picture in the lower-left half of the sheet and exchange sheets again.
5. Students draw the image of the picture *without using the transparent mirror.* (*Hint:* Fold the paper.)
6. Students use the mirror to check the result.

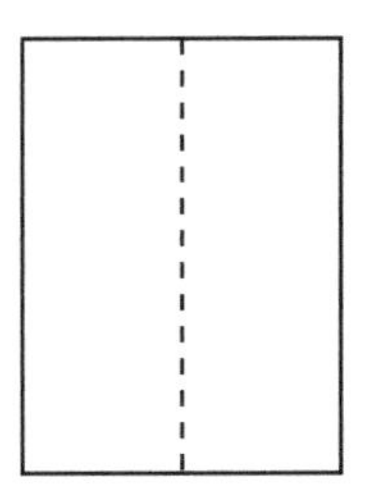

Step 1

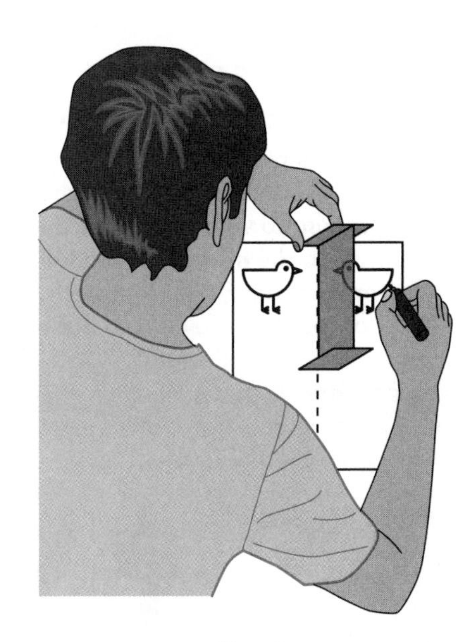

Step 2

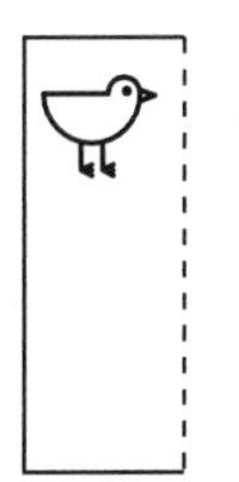

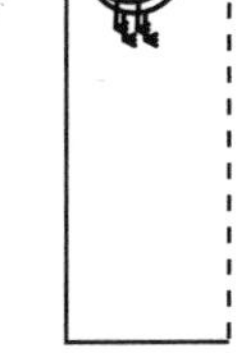

Right—the image and preimage line up when the paper is folded.

Wrong—the image and preimage do not line up.

Step 3

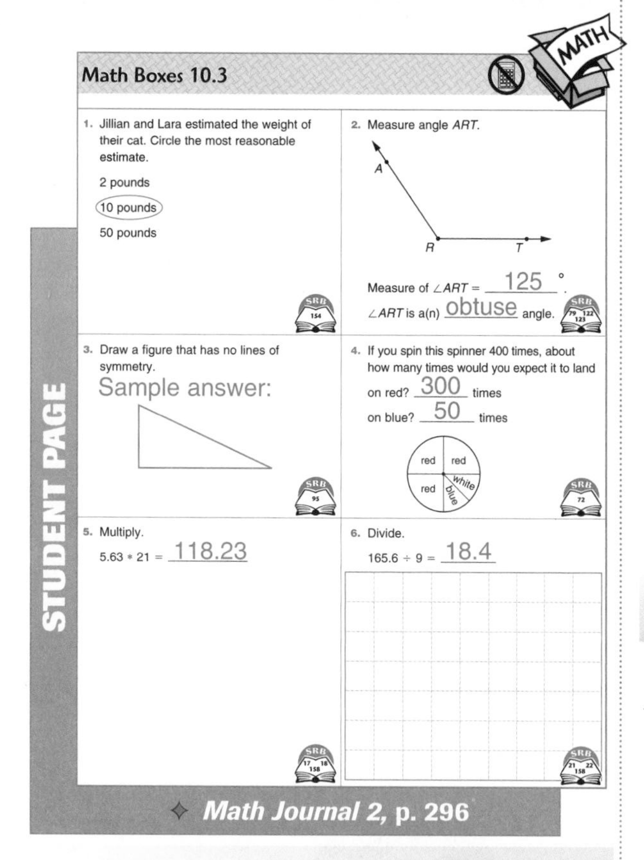

Math Boxes 10.3
1. Jillian and Lara estimated the weight of their cat. Circle the most reasonable estimate.
2 pounds
10 pounds
50 pounds
2. Measure angle ART.
Measure of ∠ART = 125 °.
∠ART is a(n) obtuse angle.
3. Draw a figure that has no lines of symmetry.
Sample answer:
4. If you spin this spinner 400 times, about how many times would you expect it to land
on red? 300 times
on blue? 50 times
5. Multiply.
5.63 * 21 = 118.23
6. Divide.
165.6 ÷ 9 = 18.4
STUDENT PAGE

◆ *Math Journal 2,* p. 296

ONGOING ASSESSMENT

Have students find the latitude and longitude of the capital city of the country they choose to visit. Encourage them to estimate to the nearest degree. Allow a 5-degree variance in their answers, but most of the time they should not be off by more than 1 or 2 degrees.

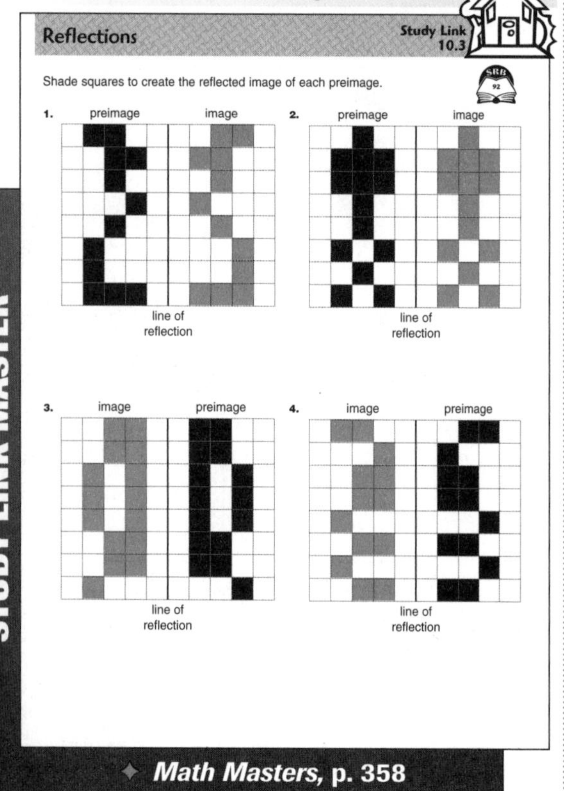

◆ *Math Masters,* p. 358

Bring the class together to discuss how partners drew the image without using the transparent mirror. If the picture was drawn in dark, wide lines, they should be able to see it through the folded paper. Some students might have used the following approach:

1. Turn the paper over and trace the original picture (the preimage) on the blank side of the paper.
2. Fold the sheet backwards along the fold line so that the original picture is on the outside.
3. Trace the picture on the blank side of the fold.

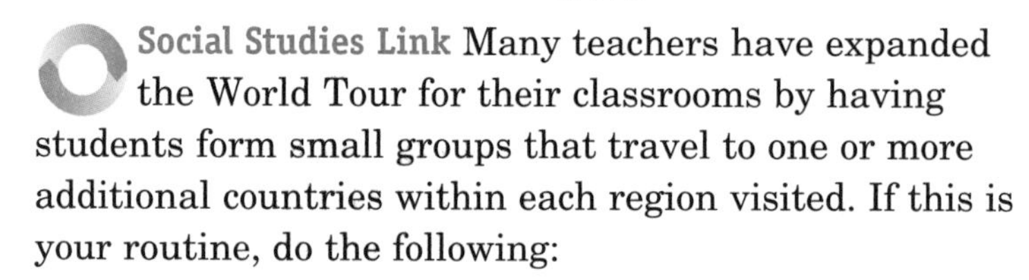

2 Ongoing Learning & Practice

◆ World Tour Option: Traveling to a Second Country in Region 4 (*Math Journal 2,* pp. 345–347 and 352–353; *Student Reference Book; Math Masters,* pp. 36–38)

SMALL-GROUP ACTIVITY 

Social Studies Link Many teachers have expanded the World Tour for their classrooms by having students form small groups that travel to one or more additional countries within each region visited. If this is your routine, do the following:

1. Divide the class into groups of 4 or 5. Each group selects one of the remaining countries in Region 4 to visit. Or you may assign a country to each group. Make sure that no two groups visit the same country.
2. Have each student complete Country Notes pages for the country he or she visits. If you are using the Route Log, students should update it for their new country.

◆ Math Boxes 10.3 (*Math Journal 2,* p. 296)

INDEPENDENT ACTIVITY

Mixed Review Math Boxes in this lesson are paired with Math Boxes in Lesson 10.6. The skill in Problem 1 is a prerequisite for Unit 11.

✦ Study Link 10.3 (*Math Masters,* p. 358)

Home Connection Students shade grid squares to create images of given preimages. A transparent mirror is not required to do this page.

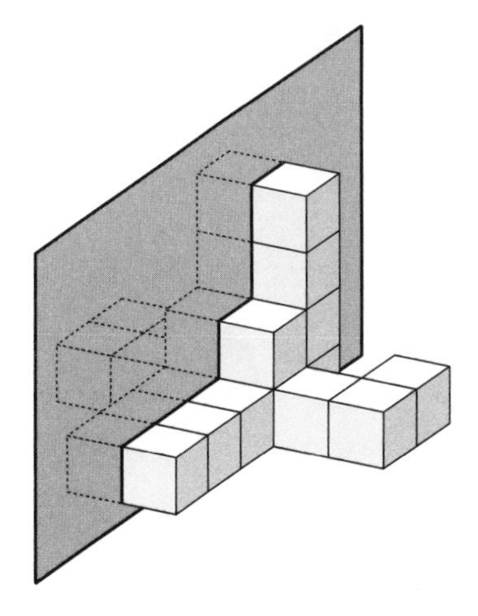

Cube structure with reflection

3 Options for Individualizing

✦ ENRICHMENT Exploring Reflections of 3-Dimensional Figures

PARTNER ACTIVITY  **15–30 min** 

Each partner uses centimeter cubes to construct a 3-dimensional building. Partners then trade buildings and construct the reflections. Each point in the first building should correspond to a point in the reflected building.

✦ ENRICHMENT Researching the Reflecting Pool in Washington, D.C.
(*Student Reference Book,* p. 213)

INDEPENDENT ACTIVITY **30+ min** 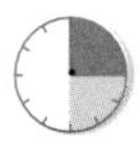

Social Studies Link Students locate the Reflecting Pool on the map of the Washington, D.C., Mall on page 213 of the *Student Reference Book.* They research the Reflecting Pool and report their findings to the class. Encourage students to find a picture that shows how the Reflecting Pool works. Reports might include the following:

- ▷ The Reflecting Pool is in Constitution Gardens between the Washington Monument and the Lincoln Memorial.
- ▷ It was inspired by the Taj Mahal and designed by Henry Bacon.
- ▷ Construction began in November 1919 and was completed in December 1922.
- ▷ The Reflecting Pool is 3 feet deep, 2,318 feet long, and 160 feet wide.
- ▷ Its capacity is 6,750,000 gallons. It takes 24 hours to drain or fill.

The Washington Monument reflected in the pool

10.4 Line Symmetry

OBJECTIVE To explore the connection between reflections and line symmetry.

summaries	materials
1 Teaching the Lesson	
Students use a transparent mirror to complete symmetric pictures and to find lines of symmetry in symmetric objects. They fold paper to sort polygons by the number of lines of symmetry. [Geometry]	☐ *Math Journal 2,* p. 297 ☐ *Student Reference Book,* p. 95 (optional) ☐ Study Link 10.3 ☐ Transparency (*Math Masters,* p. 358; optional) ☐ Teaching Masters (*Math Masters,* pp. 156–159) ☐ 1 transparent mirror per partnership ☐ scissors
2 Ongoing Learning & Practice	
Students practice and maintain skills through Math Boxes and Study Link activities.	☐ *Math Journal 2,* p. 298 ☐ Study Link Master (*Math Masters,* p. 359) ☐ Geometry Template
3 Options for Individualizing	
Extra Practice Students cut out pictures of symmetric objects and use them to create a bulletin-board display or individual booklets. [Geometry] **Enrichment** Students explore turn symmetry. [Geometry]	☐ Teaching Master (*Math Masters,* p. 160) ☐ magazines and newspapers ☐ scissors ☐ pattern blocks ☐ tape ☐ Geometry Template ***See* Advance Preparation**

Word Wall
Vocabulary
(make strips)

...tional Extra Practice activity in Part 3, you may want to begin a bulletin-board display of the ... have been collecting. For the optional Enrichment activity in Part 3, use pattern blocks and ... n symmetry but not line symmetry. *Suggestions:*

...urn symmetry

$\frac{1}{3}$-turn symmetry

Vocabulary • line of symmetry • symmetric • turn symmetry

Getting Started

Mental Math and Reflexes

Write fractions on the board. Students write an equivalent decimal and percent for each. If necessary, students may use a calculator. *Suggestions:*

- $\frac{1}{4}$ 0.25; 25%
- $\frac{4}{5}$ 0.80; 80%
- $\frac{5}{8}$ 0.625; 62.5%
- $\frac{7}{9}$ 0.777..., or $0.\overline{7}$; $77.\overline{7}$%, or 77.8%

Math Message

What is symmetry? Name an object in the classroom that has line symmetry.

Study Link 10.3 Follow-Up

Go over the answers. An overhead transparency of Study Link 10.3 will be helpful.

Prior Knowledge

1 Teaching the Lesson

✦ Math Message Follow-Up

WHOLE-CLASS DISCUSSION

Students studied line symmetry previously in *Everyday Mathematics.* Use students' responses to the Math Message to assess what they remember about the topic.

✦ Completing Symmetric Pictures
(*Math Journal 2,* p. 297; *Math Masters,* p. 156)

PARTNER ACTIVITY 

Distribute *Math Masters,* pages 156–159. Ask students to turn to journal page 297. Partners share a transparent mirror while working on the activities.

Tell the class that each drawing on *Math Masters,* page 156, is only half a picture. Students are to figure out what each picture would look like if it were complete and then use their transparent mirrors to complete each picture. Remind them to use the recessed edge to draw the line of reflection. Bring the class together to discuss results. Ask the following questions:

- How are these drawings like the dog picture in Lesson 10.3? How are they different? As in the dog picture, there are two sides that look exactly alike but are facing in opposite directions. Here, however, the end results are single drawings instead of pairs of drawings.

Line Symmetry

You will need *Math Masters,* pages 156–159.

1. The drawings on *Math Masters,* page 156 are only half-pictures. Figure out what each whole picture would show. Then use a transparent mirror to complete each picture. Use the recessed side of the mirror to draw the line of reflection.
2. The pictures on *Math Masters,* page 157 are symmetric.
   a. Use the transparent mirror to draw the line of symmetry for the bat and the turtle.
   b. Cut out the other three pictures and find their lines of symmetry by folding.
   c. Which picture has two lines of symmetry? The bow
3. Cut out each polygon on *Math Masters,* pages 158 and 159. Find all the lines of symmetry for each polygon. Record the results below.

Polygon	Number of Lines of Symmetry
A	3
B	1
C	4
D	2
E	2

Polygon	Number of Lines of Symmetry
F	0
G	1
H	0
I	5
J	6

4. Study the results in the tables above.
   a. How many lines of symmetry are in a regular pentagon (Polygon I)? 5 lines
   b. How many lines of symmetry are in a regular hexagon (Polygon J)? 6 lines
   c. How many lines of symmetry are in a regular octagon? (An octagon has 8 sides.) 8 lines

STUDENT PAGE

✦ *Math Journal 2,* p. 297

✦ *Math Masters,* p. 156

Point out that here the lines of reflection are in the middle of the pictures or objects—not outside, as in the dog picture. When a line of reflection is in the middle of a picture or object, it is called a **line of symmetry.** The pictures or objects are said to be **symmetric.**

Adjusting the Activity Students learning English may find it helpful if you use page 95 in the *Student Reference Book* to summarize the discussion of line symmetry.

NOTE: Students may be familiar with line symmetry from previous work but may not have made a connection between line symmetry and reflections. Thinking about line symmetry in terms of reflections is a more powerful approach because it can be generalized to other kinds of symmetry. Rotational symmetry, for example, can be thought of in terms of turns.

✦ Finding Lines of Symmetry
(*Math Journal 2,* p. 297; *Math Masters,* p. 157)

PARTNER ACTIVITY 

Students use their transparent mirrors to draw lines of symmetry in the pictures of a bat and a turtle on *Math Masters,* page 157. Then they cut out the other three pictures on the page and find their lines of symmetry by folding. Point out that a picture may have more than one line of symmetry. Have students answer the question in Problem 2c on journal page 297.

Bring the class together to discuss results. Ask:

- Which picture has more than one line of symmetry? The bow

Adjusting the Activity This activity works best if the pictures are carefully cut out. If there are students in your class who have difficulty with scissors, consider having a volunteer cut their shapes out for them ahead of time. The same is true for polygons A–J on *Math Masters,* pages 158 and 159 in the activity that follows.

Symmetric Pictures

TEACHING MASTER

✦ *Math Masters,* p. 157

✦ Exploring Lines of Symmetry of Polygons (*Math Journal 2*, p. 297; *Math Masters*, pp. 158 and 159)

PARTNER ACTIVITY 

Students cut out the polygons on *Math Masters*, pages 158 and 159. They find all lines of symmetry for each polygon by folding and then record the results in the tables and answer the related questions on journal page 297. Circulate and assist as needed.

Bring the class together to share results. Students should have found that a regular polygon has the same number of lines of symmetry as it has sides. For example, a regular octagon has 8 lines of symmetry.

NOTE: Although Polygon F, the parallelogram, has no lines of symmetry, many people think it does. The reason is that Polygon F does have symmetry, but a different kind of symmetry. Polygon F cannot be folded (or reflected) so that the two halves match, but it can be turned so that it matches. See the optional Enrichment activity in Part 3 for a discussion of turn symmetry.

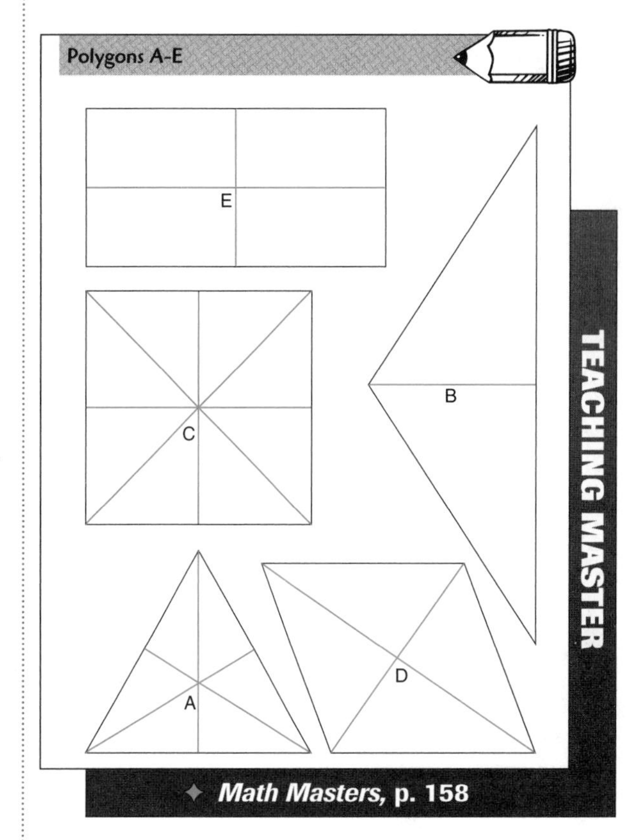

✦ *Math Masters*, p. 158

2 Ongoing Learning & Practice

✦ Math Boxes 10.4 (*Math Journal 2*, p. 298)

INDEPENDENT ACTIVITY 

Mixed Review Math Boxes in this lesson are paired with Math Boxes in Lesson 10.1. The skill in Problem 1 is a prerequisite for Unit 11.

✦ Study Link 10.4 (*Math Masters*, p. 359)

Home Connection Students identify capital letters of the alphabet that have horizontal and/or vertical line symmetry. They list words with horizontal or vertical line symmetry.

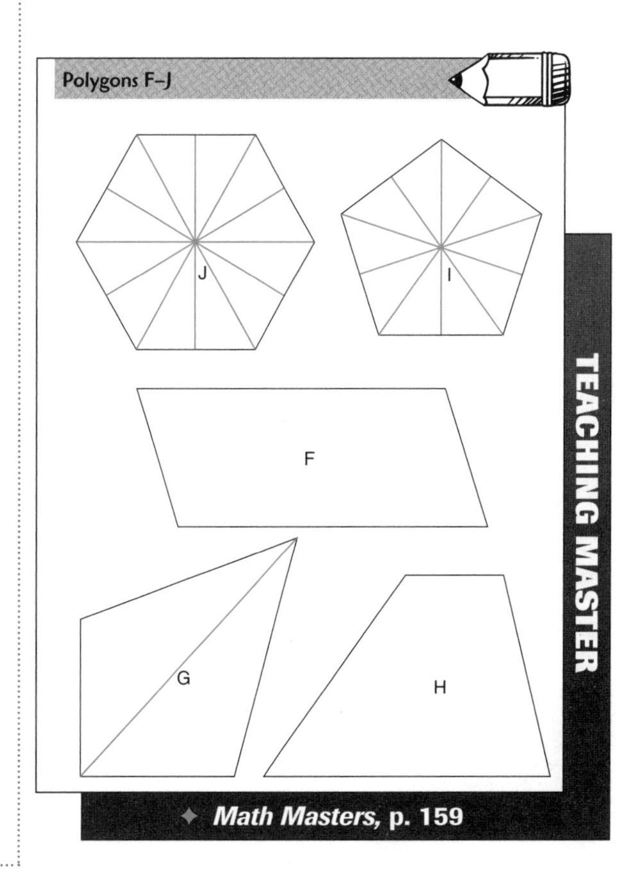

✦ *Math Masters*, p. 159

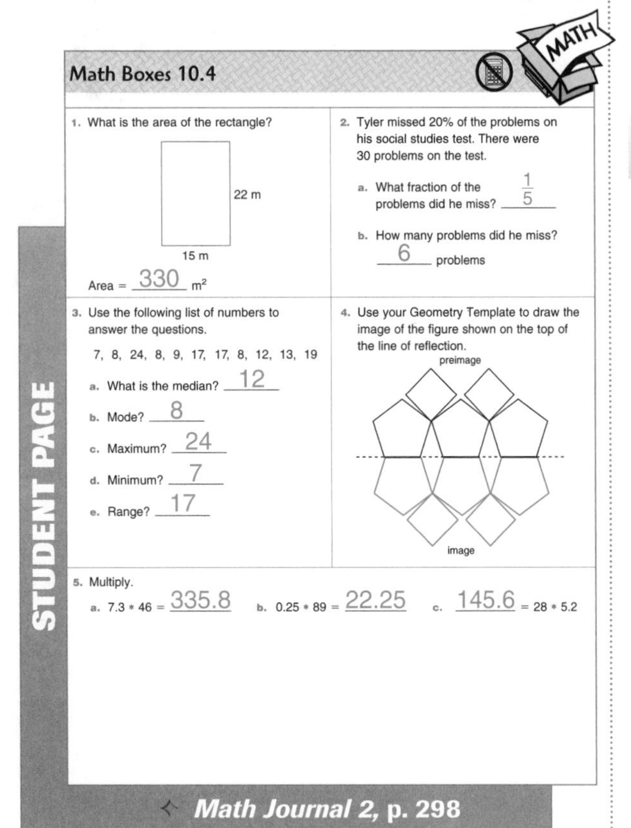

Math Boxes 10.4

1. What is the area of the rectangle?

22 m

15 m

Area = 330 m²

2. Tyler missed 20% of the problems on his social studies test. There were 30 problems on the test.

a. What fraction of the problems did he miss? $\frac{1}{5}$

b. How many problems did he miss? 6 problems

3. Use the following list of numbers to answer the questions.

7, 8, 24, 8, 9, 17, 17, 8, 12, 13, 19

a. What is the median? 12

b. Mode? 8

c. Maximum? 24

d. Minimum? 7

e. Range? 17

4. Use your Geometry Template to draw the image of the figure shown on the top of the line of reflection.

preimage

image

5. Multiply.

a. 7.3 * 46 = 335.8 b. 0.25 * 89 = 22.25 c. 145.6 = 28 * 5.2

STUDENT PAGE

Math Journal 2, p. 298

3 Options for Individualizing

✦ EXTRA PRACTICE Displaying Pictures of Symmetric Objects

INDEPENDENT ACTIVITY  **15–30 min**

Students cut pictures of symmetric objects from magazines and newspapers and use them to create a bulletin-board display or individual booklets. For each picture, students record the number of lines of symmetry or draw the lines of symmetry directly on the picture.

Since some of the pictures that students collect will probably not be perfectly symmetric, you may want to have a section of the bulletin board or booklets labeled *Almost Symmetric.* Discuss how these pictures fail to be completely symmetric.

NOTE: If students do the optional Enrichment activity on turn symmetry below, have them also indicate which of the pictures have turn symmetry as well as line symmetry.

✦ ENRICHMENT Exploring Turn Symmetry (*Math Masters,* p. 160)

SMALL-GROUP ACTIVITY  **15–30 min**

Use an overhead projector to display a parallelogram formed by taping together a trapezoid and an equilateral triangle. (See Advance Preparation.) Help students see that it has turn symmetry but not line symmetry. Ask the following questions:

- Will the parallelogram look exactly the same if it is flipped over? No. If it slanted to the right before the flip, then it will slant to the left after the flip.
- Does the parallelogram have line symmetry? No. Students have already tried folding a parallelogram to find a line of symmetry and know that it does not have one.
- Will the parallelogram look exactly the same if it is turned through a $\frac{1}{2}$-turn? Yes. Trace the parallelogram and show that after a $\frac{1}{2}$-turn, the tracing matches the original figure.

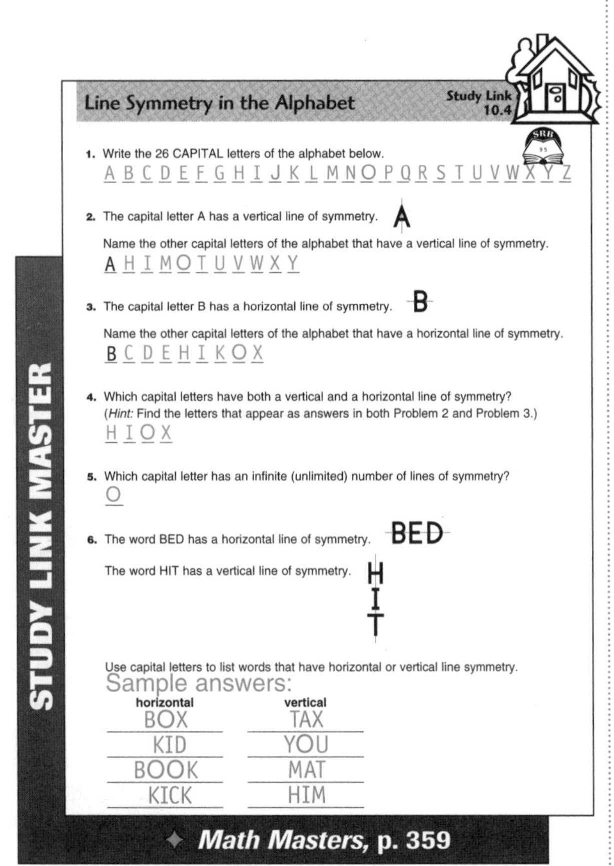

Line Symmetry in the Alphabet

Study Link 10.4

1. Write the 26 CAPITAL letters of the alphabet below.
A B C D E F G H I J K L M N O P Q R S T U V W X Y Z

2. The capital letter A has a vertical line of symmetry. A
Name the other capital letters of the alphabet that have a vertical line of symmetry.
A H I M O T U V W X Y

3. The capital letter B has a horizontal line of symmetry. B
Name the other capital letters of the alphabet that have a horizontal line of symmetry.
B C D E H I K O X

4. Which capital letters have both a vertical and a horizontal line of symmetry? (*Hint:* Find the letters that appear as answers in both Problem 2 and Problem 3.)
H I O X

5. Which capital letter has an infinite (unlimited) number of lines of symmetry?
O

6. The word BED has a horizontal line of symmetry. BED
The word HIT has a vertical line of symmetry. H I T

Use capital letters to list words that have horizontal or vertical line symmetry.
Sample answers:

horizontal	vertical
BOX	TAX
KID	YOU
BOOK	MAT
KICK	HIM

STUDY LINK MASTER

Math Masters, p. 359

Say that shapes that look the same after they have been turned less than a full turn have **turn symmetry.** Many shapes that have line symmetry also have turn symmetry—for example, any regular polygon has line symmetry and turn symmetry. Some shapes, such as parallelograms without right angles, have turn symmetry but not line symmetry.

Display the other turn-symmetric shapes you prepared. Help students see that each will look the same after a $\frac{1}{2}$-turn or a $\frac{1}{3}$-turn. Ask:

- Are there shapes that would look the same after a $\frac{1}{4}$-turn? Yes—for example, a square.

Challenge students to use pattern blocks and tape to make their own turn-symmetric shapes. Have them use their Geometry Templates to draw their shapes on *Math Masters,* page 160.

Students also look through magazines and newspapers for corporate logos that have turn symmetry. They copy or tape them onto the back of *Math Masters,* page 160.

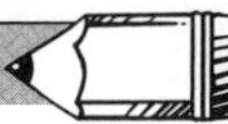

Turn Symmetry

A shape that looks the same after it has been turned by less than a full turn has **turn symmetry.**

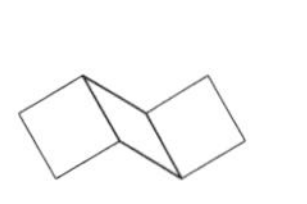

$\frac{1}{2}$-turn symmetry

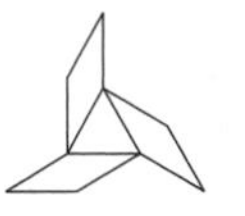

$\frac{1}{3}$-turn symmetry

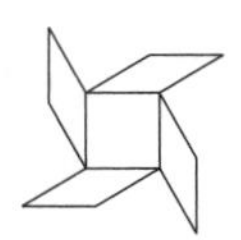

$\frac{1}{4}$-turn symmetry

1. Use tape and pattern blocks to make shapes that have turn symmetry. Use your Geometry Template to draw your shapes below. Underneath each shape, write the smallest turn that leaves the shape looking the same. Answers vary.

2. A corporate logo is a symbol that stands for a company. Look through magazines and newspapers for corporate logos that have turn symmetry. Copy them or cut them out and tape them onto the back of this page. Underneath each logo, write the smallest turn that leaves the logo looking the same. Answers vary.

TEACHING MASTER

✦ *Math Masters,* p. 160

10.5 Frieze Patterns

OBJECTIVE **To explore an application of reflections, rotations, and translations.**

summaries	materials
1 Teaching the Lesson	
Students read about frieze patterns, in which a design is repeatedly reflected, rotated, or translated to produce a pattern. They complete frieze patterns and create their own. [Geometry; Patterns, Functions, and Algebra]	□ *Math Journal 2,* p. 299 □ *Student Reference Book,* p. 94; pp. 92–93 (optional) □ Study Link 10.4 □ Transparency (*Math Masters,* p. 161; optional) □ 1 transparent mirror per partnership □ overhead or regular pattern blocks (optional) □ straightedge
2 Ongoing Learning & Practice	
Students multiply and divide decimals by whole numbers. [Operations and Computation] Students practice and maintain skills through Math Boxes and Study Link activities.	□ *Math Journal 2,* pp. 300 and 301 □ Study Link Master (*Math Masters,* p. 360)
3 Options for Individualizing	
Extra Practice Students find patterns around school and at home and copy several. [Geometry; Patterns, Functions, and Algebra] **Enrichment** Students cut out a template and create frieze patterns. [Geometry; Patterns, Functions, and Algebra]	□ Teaching Masters (*Math Masters,* pp. 162 and 163) □ straightedge □ index cards □ scissors

Additional Information

Vocabulary • **frieze pattern** • **reflection (flip)** • **translation (slide)** • **rotation (turn)**

Getting Started

Mental Math and Reflexes

Pose "fraction-of" and "percent-of" problems. *Suggestions:*

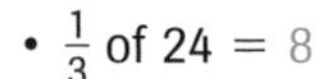

- $\frac{1}{3}$ of 24 = 8
- $\frac{2}{9}$ of 18 = 4
- $\frac{5}{8}$ of 32 = 20
- 25% of 20 = 5
- 75% of 80 = 60
- 40% of 30 = 12

Math Message

Read page 94 in your Student Reference Book. *Be prepared to discuss frieze patterns.*

Study Link 10.4 Follow-Up

Review answers. If you decided to create a bulletin board of symmetric objects, you may want to add students' responses to Problem 6 to the display. For Problem 5, students should note that the letter O has an infinite number of lines of symmetry if it is printed as a circle.

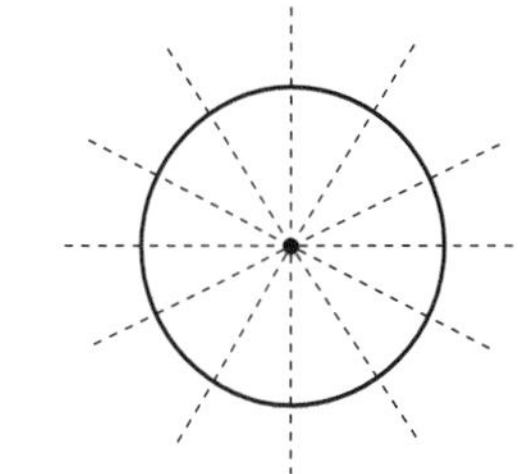

1 Teaching the Lesson

Math Message Follow-Up

WHOLE-CLASS DISCUSSION

Students describe in their own words what they have read about frieze patterns on *Student Reference Book,* page 94.

Introducing Frieze Patterns
(*Student Reference Book,* p. 94; *Math Masters,* p. 161)

WHOLE-CLASS DISCUSSION

The examples of **frieze patterns** on *Student Reference Book,* page 94 provide an initial exposure to "rigid motions," in which objects retain their shape as they are moved in various ways. If possible, use an overhead transparency of *Math Masters,* page 161—the *Student Reference Book* page—to help you explain the various patterns.

Through work in the preceding lessons, students should be familiar with **reflections.** (The top frieze on *Student Reference Book,* page 94 was created by reflecting the horse repeatedly, across vertical lines of reflection.) The second frieze on *Student Reference Book,* page 94 is an example of another rigid motion—a **translation,** or slide, in which a shape is moved without being turned or flipped.

STUDENT PAGE

Geometry and Constructions

Frieze Patterns

A frieze pattern is a design made of shapes that are lined up. Frieze patterns are often found on the walls of buildings, on the borders of rugs and tiled floors, and on clothing.

In many frieze patterns, the same design is reflected over and over. For example, the following frieze pattern was used to decorate a sash worn by a Mazahua woman from San Felipe Santiago in the state of New Mexico. The strange-looking beasts in the frieze are probably meant to be horses.

Some frieze patterns are made by repeating (translating) the same design instead of reflecting it. These patterns look as if they were made by sliding the design along the strip. An example of such a frieze pattern is the elephant and horse design below that was found on a woman's sarong from Sumba, Indonesia. All the elephants and horses are facing in the same direction.

The following frieze pattern is similar to one painted on the front page of a Koran in Egypt about 600 years ago. (The Koran is the sacred book of Islam.) The pattern is more complicated than the two above. It was created with a combination of reflections, rotations, and translations.

ninety-four

Student Reference Book, p. 94

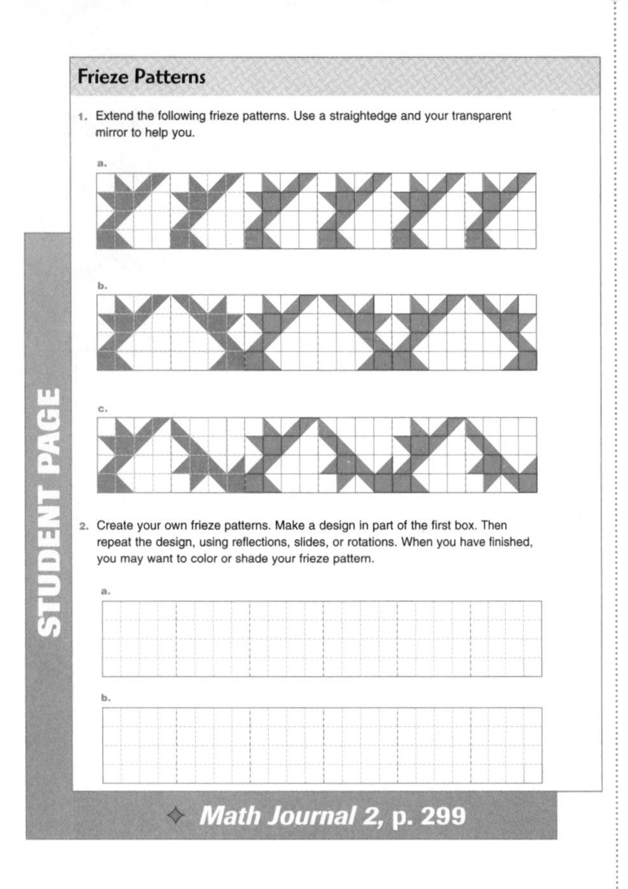
Frieze Patterns

1. Extend the following frieze patterns. Use a straightedge and your transparent mirror to help you.

a.

b.

c.

2. Create your own frieze patterns. Make a design in part of the first box. Then repeat the design, using reflections, slides, or rotations. When you have finished, you may want to color or shade your frieze pattern.

a.

b.

✧ *Math Journal 2*, p. 299

Students should observe a difference between the first and second friezes: In the first frieze, the design is repeated so that alternating designs face in opposite directions. In the second frieze, the designs all face in the same direction.

The third frieze on the *Student Reference Book* page combines slides, flips, and turns in a complex design.

NOTE: You may wish to use the less formal terms **flip, turn,** and **slide** instead of *reflection, rotation,* and *translation.*

Overhead or regular pattern blocks can also be used to illustrate rigid motions. For example, the pattern below was made by a **rotation** of each figure 90° clockwise, followed by a translation of the figure to the right.

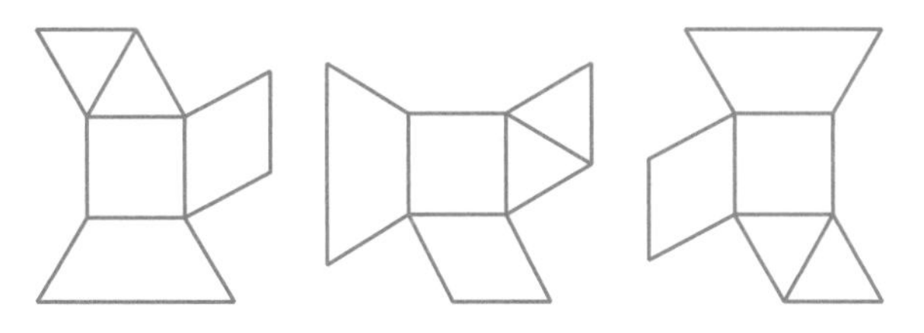

A pattern made by rotations and translations

Adjusting the Activity Some students may find it helpful if you use pages 92 and 93 of the *Student Reference Book* to summarize the discussion of reflections, translations, and rotations.

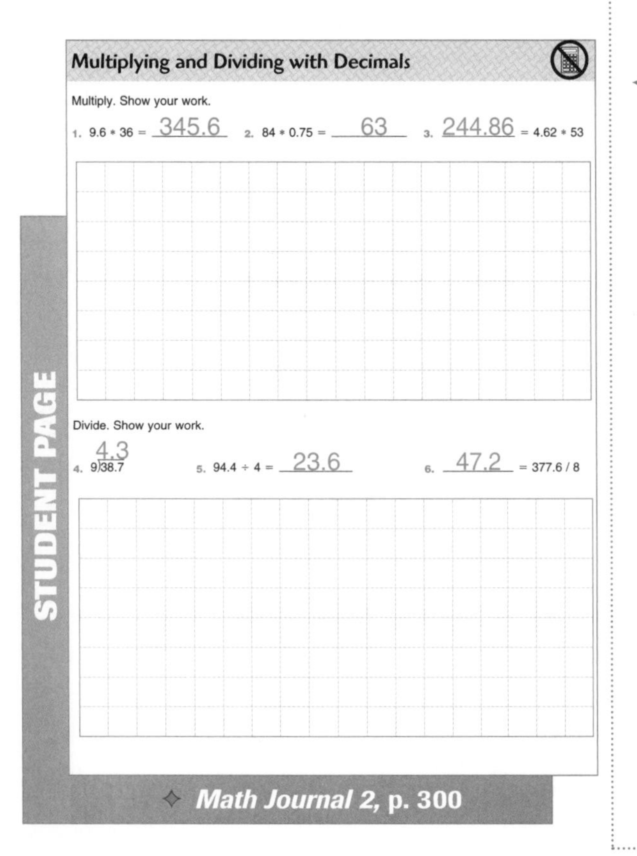
Multiplying and Dividing with Decimals

Multiply. Show your work.

1. 9.6 ∗ 36 = 345.6 2. 84 ∗ 0.75 = 63 3. 244.86 = 4.62 ∗ 53

Divide. Show your work.

4. 9)38.7 = 4.3 5. 94.4 ÷ 4 = 23.6 6. 47.2 = 377.6 / 8

✧ *Math Journal 2*, p. 300

✦ Drawing Frieze Patterns
(*Math Journal 2*, p. 299)

INDEPENDENT ACTIVITY 

Art Link Students complete three frieze patterns on journal page 299 and design two of their own.

ONGOING ASSESSMENT

Problem 2 is open-ended. Some students may just translate simple figures to create their frieze patterns. Other students may create more complex figures and then use a combination of reflections, slides, and rotations. Circulate and ask students to explain how they created their frieze patterns. Encourage students to stretch their abilities, not just create patterns that are easy for them to do.

2 Ongoing Learning & Practice

Multiplying and Dividing with Decimals
(*Math Journal 2,* p. 300)

INDEPENDENT ACTIVITY 

Students multiply decimals and whole numbers and divide decimals by whole numbers. Encourage students to use an estimation strategy to place the decimal point in each answer.

Math Boxes 10.5 (*Math Journal 2,* p. 301)

INDEPENDENT ACTIVITY 

Mixed Review Math Boxes in this lesson are paired with Math Boxes in Lesson 10.2. The skill in Problem 1 is a prerequisite for Unit 11.

Math Boxes 10.5

1. Write five names for −73.
   a. (−35) + (−38)
   b. 73 − 146
   c. (−8 * 9) + (−1)
   d. −10 + −21 + −32 + −10
   e. (−10) + (−7 * 9)
   Sample answers

2. Complete the table with equivalent names.

Fraction	Decimal	Percent
$\frac{31}{100}$	0.31	31%
$\frac{1}{10}$	0.10	10%
$\frac{4}{16}$	0.25	25%
$\frac{1}{20}$	0.05	5%

3. Write the ordered pair for each point plotted on the coordinate grid.
   A (0, 4)
   B (2, 2)
   C (1, 3)
   D (3, 5)
   E (4, 2)

4. Find two flags on page 215 in the World Tour section of your *Student Reference Book* that have both horizontal and vertical symmetry. (Remember that the colors must also be symmetric.)
   a. Bangladesh
   b. Thailand
   Japan, Jamaica — Possible answers

5. Divide.
   a. 74.8 ÷ 4 = 18.7
   b. 29.5 = 88.5 ÷ 3
   c. 24.2 = 193.6 ÷ 8

STUDENT PAGE

Math Journal 2, p. 301

Study Link 10.5 (*Math Masters,* p. 360)

Home Connection Students continue geometric patterns and create patterns of their own. As with the similar activity during class time, encourage students to stretch their abilities, not just create a pattern that is easy for them to do.

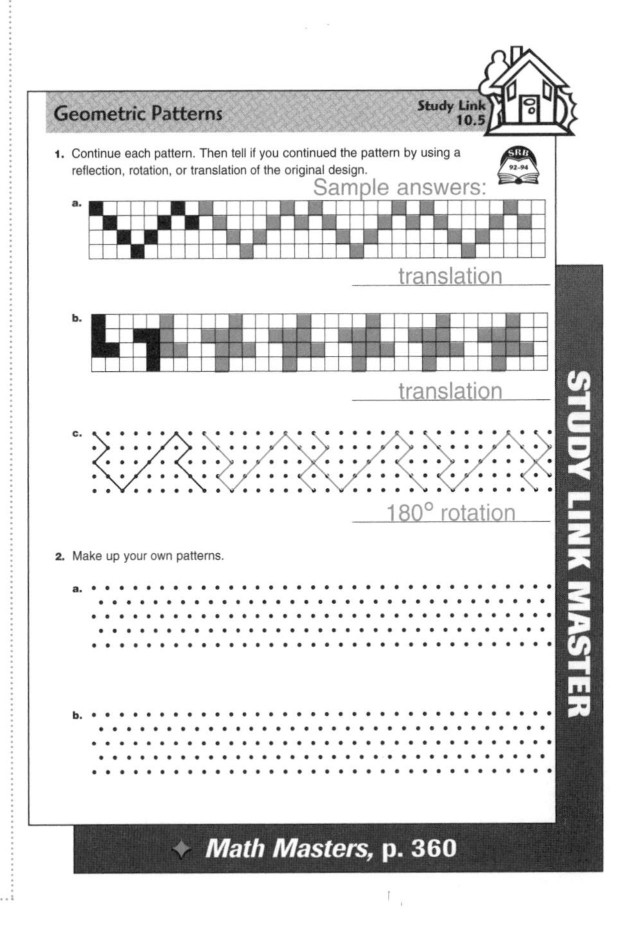
Geometric Patterns — Study Link 10.5

1. Continue each pattern. Then tell if you continued the pattern by using a reflection, rotation, or translation of the original design.
   Sample answers:
   a. translation
   b. translation
   c. 180° rotation

2. Make up your own patterns.
   a.
   b.

STUDY LINK MASTER

Math Masters, p. 360

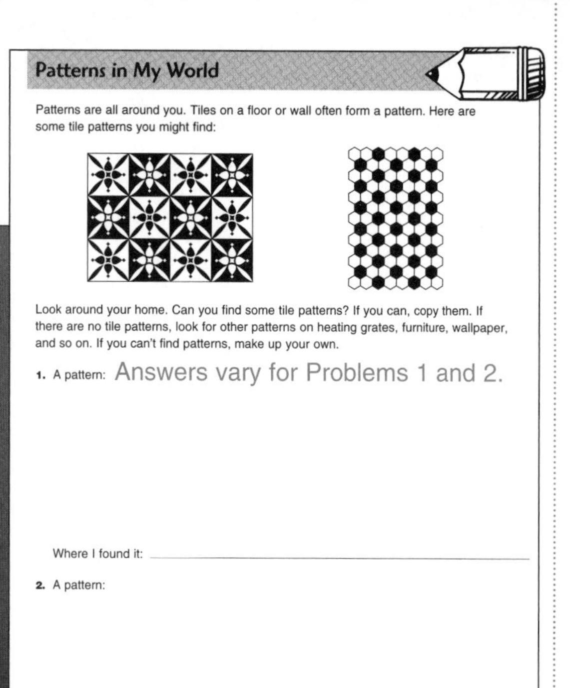
Patterns in My World

Patterns are all around you. Tiles on a floor or wall often form a pattern. Here are some tile patterns you might find:

Look around your home. Can you find some tile patterns? If you can, copy them. If there are no tile patterns, look for other patterns on heating grates, furniture, wallpaper, and so on. If you can't find patterns, make up your own.

1. A pattern: Answers vary for Problems 1 and 2.

Where I found it: ______

2. A pattern:

Where I found it: ______

TEACHING MASTER

✦ *Math Masters,* p. 162

3 Options for Individualizing

✦ EXTRA PRACTICE Finding Patterns
(*Math Masters,* p. 162)

INDEPENDENT ACTIVITY  **15–30 min** 

Art Link Students look around school and home for patterns. They copy the patterns onto *Math Masters,* page 162. Have students present their patterns to the class and describe any reflections, translations, or rotations in the patterns.

✦ ENRICHMENT Creating Frieze Patterns
(*Math Masters,* p. 163)

INDEPENDENT ACTIVITY  **15–30 min**

Art Link Students make frieze patterns by following the directions on *Math Masters,* page 163. You may want to demonstrate the procedure before students begin working.

Be sure to discard the piece cut from the index card so that students do not mistake that piece for the template.

Have students present their completed patterns to the class and describe any reflections, translations, or rotations they used.

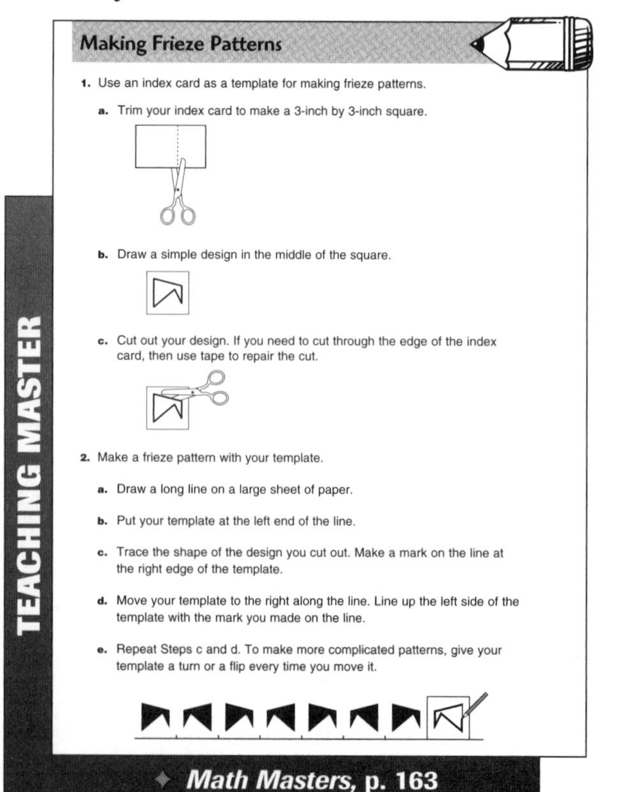
Making Frieze Patterns

1. Use an index card as a template for making frieze patterns.
   a. Trim your index card to make a 3-inch by 3-inch square.
   b. Draw a simple design in the middle of the square.
   c. Cut out your design. If you need to cut through the edge of the index card, then use tape to repair the cut.
2. Make a frieze pattern with your template.
   a. Draw a long line on a large sheet of paper.
   b. Put your template at the left end of the line.
   c. Trace the shape of the design you cut out. Make a mark on the line at the right edge of the template.
   d. Move your template to the right along the line. Line up the left side of the template with the mark you made on the line.
   e. Repeat Steps c and d. To make more complicated patterns, give your template a turn or a flip every time you move it.

TEACHING MASTER

✦ *Math Masters,* p. 163

10.6 Positive and Negative Numbers

OBJECTIVE **To explore addition of integers.**

summaries	materials
1 Teaching the Lesson	
Students review positive and negative numbers on the number line, thinking of them as reflected across the zero point. They discuss and practice addition of positive and negative numbers as accounting problems, keeping track of "credits" and "debits," and they play the *Credits/Debits Game* for additional practice. [Operations and Computation]	☐ *Math Journal 2,* p. 302 ☐ Study Link 10.5 ☐ *Student Reference Book,* pp. 58 and 192 ☐ Teaching Masters (*Math Masters,* p. 164; p. 166 (optional)) ☐ Transparencies (*Math Masters,* pp. 165 and 360; optional) ☐ 1 transparent mirror per partnership ☐ 1 deck of number cards per partnership (Everything Math Deck, if available) ***See* Advance Preparation**
2 Ongoing Learning & Practice	
Students practice and maintain skills through Math Boxes and Study Link activities.	☐ *Math Journal 2,* p. 303 ☐ Study Link Master (*Math Masters,* p. 361) ☐ Geometry Template
3 Options for Individualizing	
Enrichment Students solve a temperature number story. [Operations and Computation; Measurement and Reference Frames] **Language Diversity** The teacher or students read books about money and other consumer topics. [Operations and Computation] **Reteaching** Students use a number line to add positive and negative numbers. [Operations and Computation]	☐ *The Monster Money Book* ☐ *How the Second Grade Got $8205.50 to Visit the Statue of Liberty* ***See* Advance Preparation**

Additional Information

Advance Preparation For Part 1, make one copy of *Math Masters,* page 164 for every 2 students. Cut the copies apart and place them next to the Math Message. Make an overhead transparency of the ledger page on *Math Masters,* page 165 to display and record results for the credits-and-debits activity. Alternatively, draw the ledger on the board, preferably in semipermanent chalk and in a place where it can be kept for a few days.

For the optional Language Diversity activity in Part 3, obtain *The Monster Money Book* by Loreen Leedy (Holiday House, 2000) and *How the Second Grade Got $8205.50 to Visit the Statue of Liberty* by Nathan Zimelman (Albert Whitman, 1992).

Vocabulary • **opposite (of a number)** • **credit** • **debit**

Getting Started

Mental Math and Reflexes

Pose problems about comparisons of integers. *Suggestions:*

- Which is colder?
  −3°C or −10°C? −10°C
  10°C or 3°C? 3°C
- Which is greater?
  −99 or −33? −33
  8 or −10? 8
- Are you better off if you have \$3 or owe \$10? Have \$3
  Owe \$4 or owe \$9? Owe \$4

Math Message

Take a slip of paper.

Follow the directions and answer the questions.

Share 1 transparent mirror with a partner.

Study Link 10.5 Follow-Up

Review answers. Have students share some of the patterns they created on their own. An overhead transparency of Study Link 10.5 will be helpful.

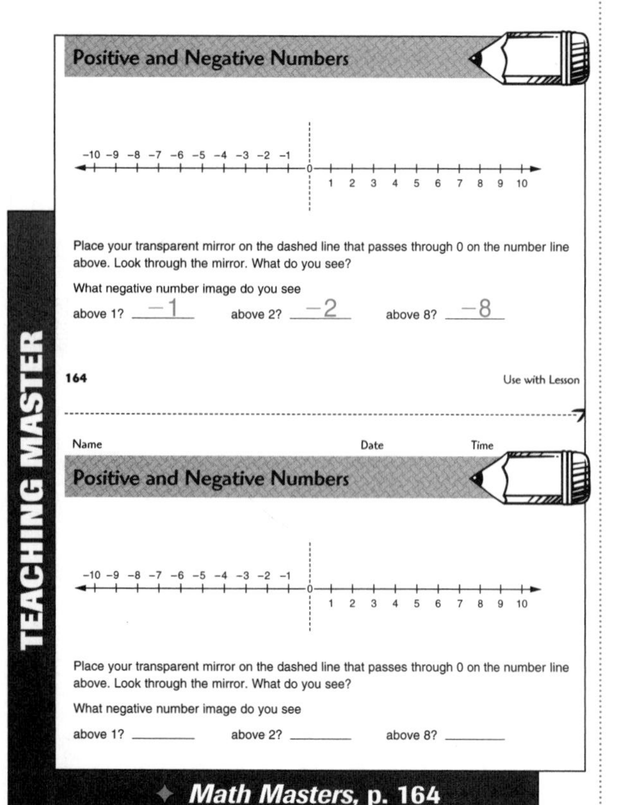

TEACHING MASTER

Positive and Negative Numbers

Place your transparent mirror on the dashed line that passes through 0 on the number line above. Look through the mirror. What do you see?

What negative number image do you see

above 1? −1 above 2? −2 above 8? −8

164 Use with Lesson

Name Date Time

Positive and Negative Numbers

Place your transparent mirror on the dashed line that passes through 0 on the number line above. Look through the mirror. What do you see?

What negative number image do you see

above 1? ______ above 2? ______ above 8? ______

◆ ***Math Masters*, p. 164**

1 Teaching the Lesson

◆ Math Message Follow-Up

(*Student Reference Book*, p. 58; *Math Masters*, p. 164)

WHOLE-CLASS DISCUSSION 

One way to think about a number line is to imagine the whole numbers reflected across the zero point. Each of these positive numbers picks up a negative sign as it crosses to the other side of zero. The **opposite** of a positive number is a negative number.

Conversely, imagine the negative numbers reflected across the zero point. The sign of each number changes from negative to positive as it crosses to the other side of zero. The **opposite** of a negative number is a positive number.

NOTE: In this "flipping" of the number line, the zero point stays motionless, like the fulcrum of a lever. Zero is its own opposite: $+0 = -0$. Zero is the only number that equals its opposite.

When students place the transparent mirror on the line passing through the zero point on *Math Masters,* page 164, the negative numbers appear (reversed) across from the corresponding positive numbers.

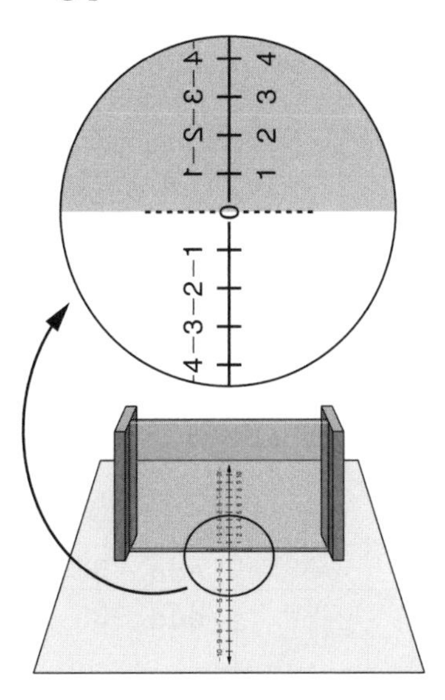

Negative numbers appear (reversed) across from the corresponding positive numbers.

Read and discuss page 58 of the *Student Reference Book* with the class. The diagram on the page is another way of showing that the opposite of every positive number is a negative number, and the opposite of every negative number is a positive number.

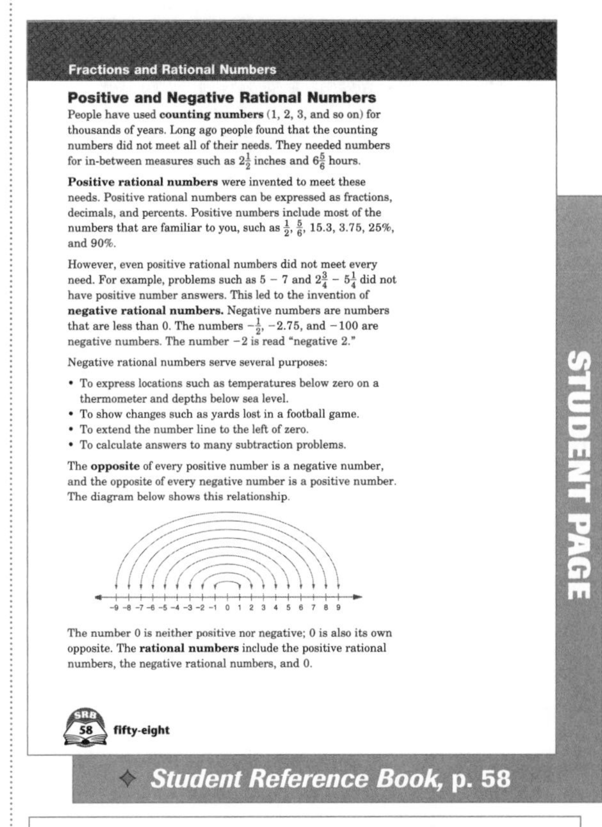

Fractions and Rational Numbers

Positive and Negative Rational Numbers

People have used **counting numbers** (1, 2, 3, and so on) for thousands of years. Long ago people found that the counting numbers did not meet all of their needs. They needed numbers for in-between measures such as $2\frac{1}{2}$ inches and $6\frac{5}{6}$ hours.

Positive rational numbers were invented to meet these needs. Positive rational numbers can be expressed as fractions, decimals, and percents. Positive numbers include most of the numbers that are familiar to you, such as $\frac{1}{2}$, $\frac{5}{6}$, 15.3, 3.75, 25%, and 90%.

However, even positive rational numbers did not meet every need. For example, problems such as $5 - 7$ and $2\frac{3}{4} - 5\frac{1}{4}$ did not have positive number answers. This led to the invention of **negative rational numbers.** Negative numbers are numbers that are less than 0. The numbers $-\frac{1}{2}$, -2.75, and -100 are negative numbers. The number -2 is read "negative 2."

Negative rational numbers serve several purposes:

- To express locations such as temperatures below zero on a thermometer and depths below sea level.
- To show changes such as yards lost in a football game.
- To extend the number line to the left of zero.
- To calculate answers to many subtraction problems.

The **opposite** of every positive number is a negative number, and the opposite of every negative number is a positive number. The diagram below shows this relationship.

-9 -8 -7 -6 -5 -4 -3 -2 -1 0 1 2 3 4 5 6 7 8 9

The number 0 is neither positive nor negative; 0 is also its own opposite. The **rational numbers** include the positive rational numbers, the negative rational numbers, and 0.

SRB 58 fifty-eight

STUDENT PAGE

◆ *Student Reference Book,* p. 58

NOTE: Be consistent throughout this lesson in "adding" credits and debits as positive and negative numbers, because a later lesson uses the same format to show "subtraction" of positive and negative numbers—the effect on the bottom line of "taking away" what were thought to be credits or debits.

◆ Using Credits and Debits to Practice Addition of Positive and Negative Numbers
(*Math Masters,* p. 165)

WHOLE-CLASS ACTIVITY

It is important to examine some relatively difficult aspects of negative numbers now, in order to prepare students for rules about operations with negative numbers that will be introduced later.

Display an overhead transparency of the ledger page on *Math Masters,* page 165, or refer to the ledger you drew on the board. Ask the class to pretend that they are accountants for a new business. They will figure out the "bottom line" as you post transactions.

Discuss **credits** (money received for sales, interest earned, and other income) as *positive additions* to the bottom line, and **debits** (cost of making goods, salaries, and other expenses) as *negative additions* to the bottom line. Explain that you will label credits with a "+" and debits with a "−" to keep track of them as positive and negative numbers (*see margin Note*).

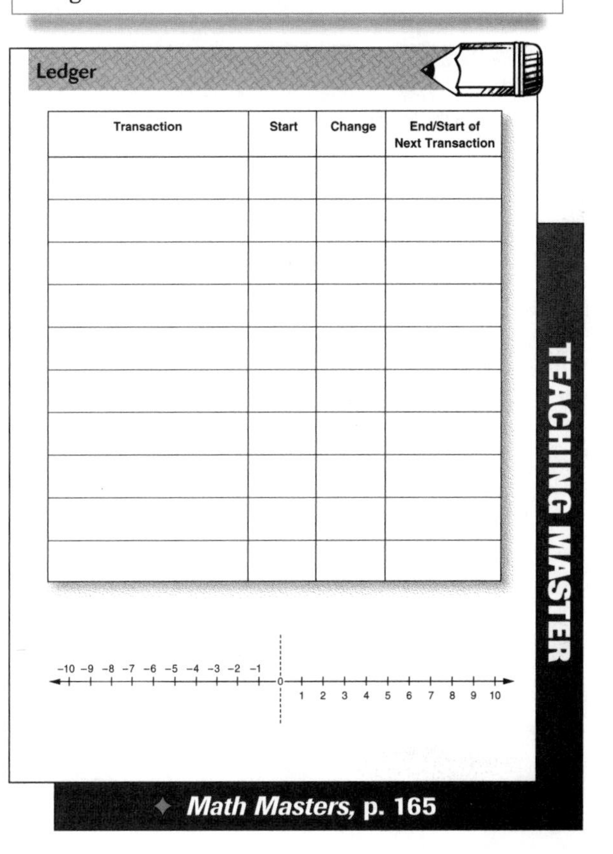

Ledger

Transaction	Start	Change	End/Start of Next Transaction

-10 -9 -8 -7 -6 -5 -4 -3 -2 -1 0 1 2 3 4 5 6 7 8 9 10

TEACHING MASTER

◆ *Math Masters,* p. 165

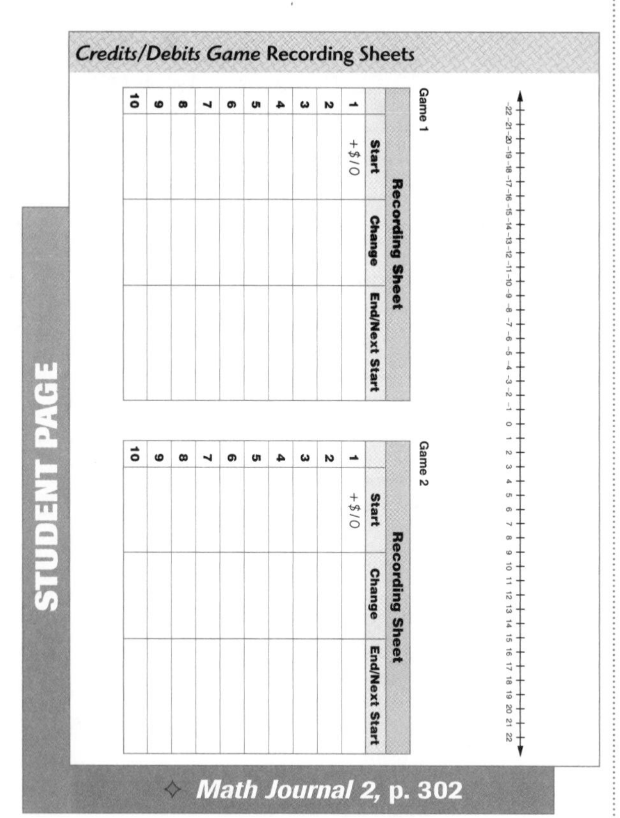
Credits/Debits Game Recording Sheets

Game 1

	Recording Sheet		
	Start	Change	End/Next Start
1	+$10		
2			
3			
4			
5			
6			
7			
8			
9			
10			

Game 2

	Recording Sheet		
	Start	Change	End/Next Start
1	+$10		
2			
3			
4			
5			
6			
7			
8			
9			
10			

STUDENT PAGE

✧ *Math Journal 2,* p. 302

Additional record forms are available on *Math Masters,* page 166.

Games

Credits/Debits Game

Materials ☐ 1 complete deck of number cards
☐ recording sheet for each player (*Math Masters,* p. 166)

Players 2

Directions

	Recording Sheet		
	Start	Change	End/next start
1	+$10		
2			
3			
4			
5			
6			
7			
8			
9			
10			

Pretend that you are an accountant for a business. Your job is to keep track of the company's current balance. The current balance is also called the "bottom line." As credits and debits are reported, you will record them and then adjust the bottom line.

1. Shuffle the deck and lay it facedown between the players.
2. The black-numbered cards are the "credits," and the blue- or red-numbered cards are the "debits."
3. Each player begins with a bottom line of +$10.
4. Players take turns. On your turn, do the following:
   - Draw a card. The card tells you the dollar amount and whether it is a credit or debit to the bottom line. Record the credit or debit in the "Change" column.
   - Use the credit or debit to adjust the bottom line.
   - Record the result in the table.

EXAMPLE Beth has a "Start" balance of +$20. She draws a black 9. This is a credit of $9, so she records +$9 in the "Change" column. She adds $9 to the bottom line: $20 + $9 = $29. Beth then records +$29 in the "End" column. She also records +$29 in the "Start" column on the next line.

Alex has a "Start" balance of +$10. He draws a red 12. this is a debit of $12, so he records −$12 in the "Change" column. He subtracts $12 from the bottom line: $10 − $12 = −$2. Alex then records −$2 in the "End" column. He also records −$2 in the "Start" column on the next line.

Scoring: At the end of 10 draws each, the player with the most money is the winner of the round. If both players have negative dollar amounts, the player whose amount is closest to 0 wins.

SRB 192 one hundred ninety-two

STUDENT PAGE

✧ *Student Reference Book,* p. 192

Following is a suggested series of transactions. Entries in black would be reported to the class; entries in color are appropriate student responses.

Transaction	Start	Change	End/Start of Next Transaction
New business, start at $0	$0	$0	$0
Credit (payment) of $5 comes in	$0	add +$5	+$5
Credit of $3	+$5	add +$3	+$8
Debit of $6	+$8	add −$6	+$2
Debit of $8 (Be sure to share strategies.)	+$2	add −$8	−$6
Debit of $3	−$6	add −$3	−$9
Credit of $5 (At last!)	−$9	add +$5	−$4
Credit of $6	−$4	add +$6	+$2

Continue until most students respond with ease.

✦ Playing the *Credits/Debits Game*

(*Math Journal 2,* p. 302; *Student Reference Book,* p. 192; *Math Masters,* p. 166)

PARTNER ACTIVITY 

Have students read the rules for the *Credits/Debits Game* on page 192 of the *Student Reference Book,* and then play the game. They record their steps on journal page 302.

ONGOING ASSESSMENT

As students play, circulate and assess their strategies to see if some are beginning to devise shortcuts for finding answers. For example, most students will probably count up and back on a number line. Some students may notice that when two positive numbers are added, the result is "more positive"; when two negative numbers are added, the result is "more negative"; and when a positive and a negative number are added, the result is the difference of the two (ignoring the signs) and has the sign of the number that is "bigger" in the sense of being farther from 0.

Bring the class together and ask several students to describe their strategies. Don't try too hard to get explanations; these will evolve over time as students have more experience with positive and negative numbers. Students should continue to play the *Credits/Debits Game* to gain experience before more formal work with subtraction of positive and negative numbers is introduced. Follow up with sessions in which students share their strategies.

2 Ongoing Learning & Practice

✦ Math Boxes 10.6 (*Math Journal 2,* p. 303)

INDEPENDENT ACTIVITY 

Mixed Review Math Boxes in this lesson are paired with Math Boxes in Lesson 10.3. The skill in Problem 1 is a prerequisite for Unit 11.

✦ Study Link 10.6 (*Math Masters,* p. 361)

Home Connection Students compare and order positive and negative numbers, and add positive and negative integers.

3 Options for Individualizing

✦ ENRICHMENT Solving a Temperature Number Story

SMALL-GROUP ACTIVITY  **15–30 min**

Science Link Pose the following temperature number story to students:

One of the most bizarre temperature changes in history occurred in Spearfish, South Dakota, on January 22, 1943. At 7:30 A.M., the temperature was −4°F. By 7:32 A.M., the temperature had risen 49 degrees. By 9:00 A.M., it had climbed to 54°F. Then it plunged 58 degrees in 27 minutes. What was the temperature at 9:27 A.M.? −4°F

Source: National Weather Service

Challenge students to find other interesting statistics that involve temperatures above and below zero.

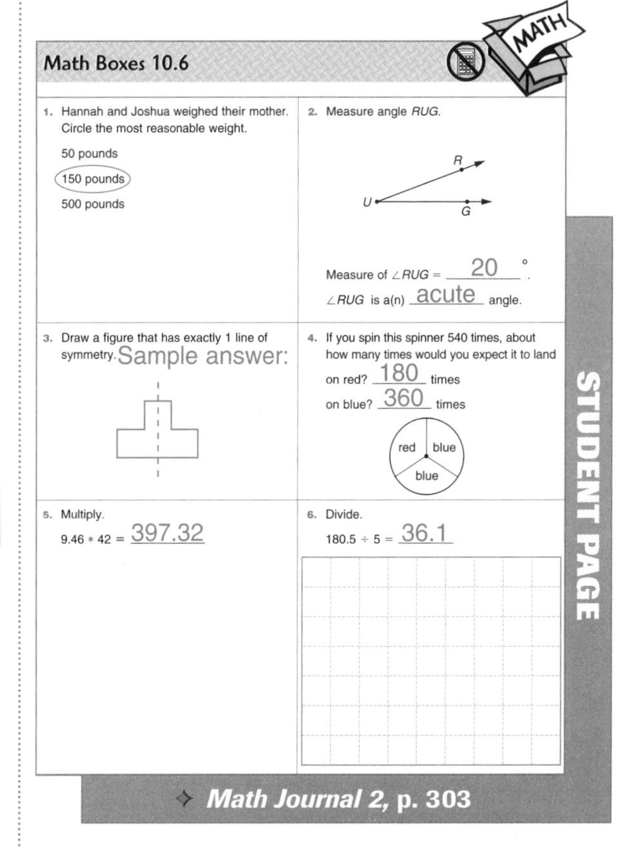

Math Boxes 10.6

1. Hannah and Joshua weighed their mother. Circle the most reasonable weight.
   50 pounds
   (150 pounds)
   500 pounds

2. Measure angle *RUG*.
   Measure of ∠*RUG* = 20°.
   ∠*RUG* is a(n) acute angle.

3. Draw a figure that has exactly 1 line of symmetry. Sample answer:

4. If you spin this spinner 540 times, about how many times would you expect it to land
   on red? 180 times
   on blue? 360 times

5. Multiply.
   9.46 ∗ 42 = 397.32

6. Divide.
   180.5 ÷ 5 = 36.1

✦ *Math Journal 2,* p. 303

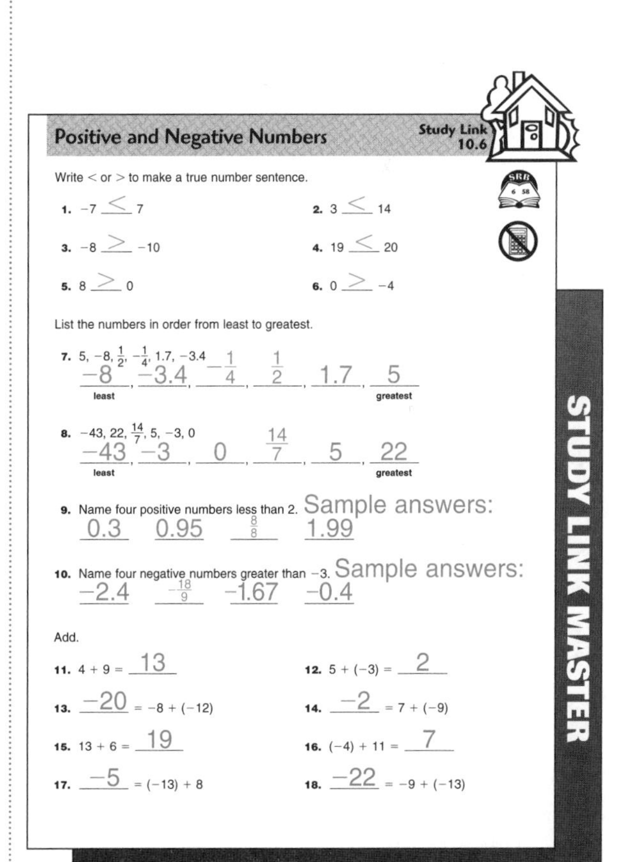

Positive and Negative Numbers Study Link 10.6

Write $<$ or $>$ to make a true number sentence.

1. $-7 < 7$
2. $3 < 14$
3. $-8 > -10$
4. $19 < 20$
5. $8 > 0$
6. $0 > -4$

List the numbers in order from least to greatest.

7. 5, −8, $\frac{1}{2}$, $-\frac{1}{4}$, 1.7, −3.4
   −8 (least), −3.4, $-\frac{1}{4}$, $\frac{1}{2}$, 1.7, 5 (greatest)

8. −43, 22, $\frac{14}{7}$, 5, −3, 0
   −43 (least), −3, 0, $\frac{14}{7}$, 5, 22 (greatest)

9. Name four positive numbers less than 2. Sample answers:
   0.3, 0.95, $\frac{8}{8}$, 1.99

10. Name four negative numbers greater than −3. Sample answers:
    −2.4, $-\frac{18}{9}$, −1.67, −0.4

Add.

11. 4 + 9 = 13
12. 5 + (−3) = 2
13. −20 = −8 + (−12)
14. −2 = 7 + (−9)
15. 13 + 6 = 19
16. (−4) + 11 = 7
17. −5 = (−13) + 8
18. −22 = −9 + (−13)

✦ *Math Masters,* p. 361

✦ LANGUAGE DIVERSITY Building Background for Mathematics Words

SMALL-GROUP ACTIVITY **15–30 min** 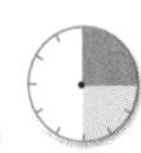

Literature Link Share the following books with students to introduce concepts like investments, profit, expenses, interest, withdrawals, checks, and bank cards. When necessary, assist students learning English by explaining terms in more detail.

The Monster Money Book

Summary: The Monster Club discusses how to spend fifty-four dollars. From this discussion, consumer terms are introduced.

How the Second Grade Got $8205.50 to Visit the Statue of Liberty

Summary: Susan Olson writes a report on the fund-raising projects that her second grade class did to raise money. Readers can keep track of the children's earnings. Due to expenses, the children, at times, will have a negative balance.

✦ RETEACHING Using a Number Line to Add Positive and Negative Numbers

PARTNER ACTIVITY  **15–30 min** 

Some students may find it easier to think about addition of positive and negative numbers in terms of a number line rather than credits and debits. Have students draw a number line from -10 to 10.

Consider the problem $A + B = ?$, where A and B are any integers. Discuss the explanation in the margin. Then provide problems for students to solve.

Suggestions

- $-5 + 2 = ?$ (Start at -5. Face in the positive direction. Move forward 2 steps. End up at -3.)
- $-6 + -3 = ?$ (Start at -6. Face in the positive direction. Move backward 3 steps. End up at -9.)
- $4 + -6 = ?$ (Start at 4. Face in the positive direction. Move backward 6 steps. End up at -2.)

NOTE: Students will subtract positive and negative integers in Lesson 11.6.

Explanation

Explanation for number-line walking to solve $A + B$:

1. The number A tells you where to start on the number line.
2. The addition sign (+) between A and B tells you to face towards the positive end of the number line. (A subtraction sign ($-$) between A and B tells you to face towards the negative end of the number line.)
3. If the number B is negative (has a $-$ sign), then walk backward. Otherwise, walk forward.
4. The number B (ignoring its sign) tells you how many steps to take.
5. The number where you wind up is the answer.

10.7 Unit 10 Review and Assessment

OBJECTIVE **To review and assess students' progress on the material covered in Unit 10.**

1 Assess Progress

learning goals	activities
10a **Beginning Goal** Add integers. **(Lesson 10.6)**	❑ Slate Assessment, Problem 1 ❑ Written Assessment, Problem 10
10b **Beginning Goal** Rotate figures. **(Lessons 10.4 and 10.5)**	❑ Oral Assessment, Problem 1 ❑ Written Assessment, Problem 7
10c **Developing Goal** Translate figures. **(Lesson 10.5)**	❑ Written Assessment, Problem 6
10d **Secure Goal** Use a transparent mirror to draw the reflection of a figure. **(Lessons 10.1–10.3)**	❑ Written Assessment, Problems 8 and 9
10e **Secure Goal** Identify lines of symmetry, lines of reflection, reflected figures, and figures with line symmetry. **(Lessons 10.2–10.6)**	❑ Oral Assessment, Problem 2 ❑ Written Assessment, Problems 1-5 ❑ Alternative Assessment Options

materials

- ☐ *Math Journal 2,* p. 304
- ☐ Study Link 10.6
- ☐ Teaching Masters (*Math Masters,* p. 20, optional; and p. 167)
- ☐ Assessment Masters (*Math Masters,* pp. 409 and 410)
- ☐ slate
- ☐ Geometry Template
- ☐ transparent mirror
- ☐ pattern blocks or centimeter cubes

2 Build Background for Unit 11

summaries	materials
Students practice and maintain skills through Math Boxes and Study Link activities.	☐ *Math Journal 2,* p. 305 ☐ Study Link Masters (*Math Masters,* pp. 362–365)

Each **learning goal** listed above indicates a level of performance that might be expected at this point in the *Everyday Mathematics* K-6 curriculum. For a variety of reasons, the levels indicated may not accurately portray your class's performance.

Additional Information

Advance Preparation For additional information on assessment for Unit 10, see the *Assessment Handbook,* pages 66–68. For assessment checklists, see *Math Masters,* pages 444, 445, and 465–467.

Getting Started

Math Message

Complete the Time to Reflect *questions on journal page 304.*

Study Link 10.6 Follow-Up

Review answers. Use a number line as necessary.

1 Assess Progress

✦ Math Message Follow-Up
(*Math Journal 2,* p. 304)

WHOLE-CLASS DISCUSSION 

Students share answers. Problem 1 provides students with an opportunity to demonstrate their understanding of line symmetry in everyday life. Problem 2 allows students to evaluate their own skill level at working with positive and negative numbers.

NOTE: Some of the slate assessment suggestions relate to learning goals that have been addressed in previous units. Now is a good time to evaluate students' progress toward these goals.

✦ Oral and Slate Assessments

WHOLE-CLASS ACTIVITY 

If the suggested problems below are not appropriate for your class's level of performance, adjust the numbers or the problems themselves to better assess your students' abilities.

Oral Assessment Suggestions

1. Students perform turns and fractions of turns. **Goal 10b**
   - Turn counterclockwise $\frac{1}{2}$ turn.
   - Turn clockwise $\frac{1}{4}$ turn.
   - Make a full turn clockwise.
   - Turn clockwise 180°.
   - Turn counterclockwise 180° and then 90° clockwise.
2. Students identify objects in the classroom that have line symmetry. Look for students to identify 3-dimensional as well as 2-dimensional objects. **Goal 10e**

STUDENT PAGE

Time to Reflect

1. Think of the front of your house or apartment building. Does it have a line of symmetry? Draw a picture of it in the space below. Then explain why it is or is not symmetric.

My Home

____
____
____
____

2. This unit was your first introduction to positive and negative numbers. Did you find them easy or hard to work with? Why?

____
____
____
____
____
____
____

✧ *Math Journal 2,* p. 304

Slate Assessment Suggestions

1. Pose problems that require students to add positive and negative integers. **Goal 10a**
   - 9 + 6 15
   - 8 + (−2) 6
   - −7 + (−6) −13
   - −9 + 4 −5
2. Pose problems that require students to divide decimals by whole numbers.
   - 58.8 ÷ 7 8.4
   - 31.6 ÷ 4 7.9
   - 78.24 ÷ 12 6.52
3. Pose decimal multiplication problems.
   - 9.6 * 32 307.2
   - 45 * 3.4 153
   - 0.85 * 247 209.95

✦ Written Assessment
(*Math Masters,* pp. 409 and 410)

INDEPENDENT ACTIVITY 

Depending on the needs of your students, you may want to work through an example together, reading a problem aloud, discussing it, and providing additional examples as necessary before your students work the problem independently.

Each of the problems is listed below and paired with one or more of this unit's learning goals.

- Use the Geometry Template to draw shapes that have 0, 1, 2, or more than 2 lines of symmetry. (Problems 1–4) **Goal 10e**
- Identify a figure that shows a reflection (flip) of the original figure. (Problem 5) **Goal 10e**
- Identify a figure that shows a translation (slide) of the original figure. (Problem 6) **Goal 10c**
- Identify a figure that shows a rotation (turn) of the original figure. (Problem 7) **Goal 10b**
- Use a transparent mirror to draw the reflection of a given preimage. (Problem 8) **Goal 10d**
- Use a transparent mirror to draw the other half of a given figure across a horizontal line of symmetry. (Problem 9) **Goal 10d**
- Add integers. (Problem 10) **Goal 10a**

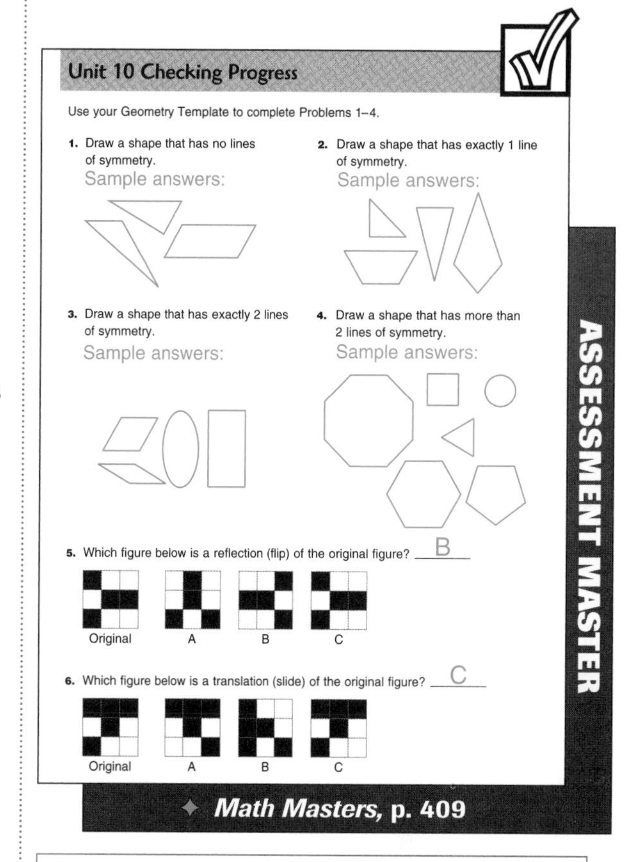

Unit 10 Checking Progress

Use your Geometry Template to complete Problems 1–4.

1. Draw a shape that has no lines of symmetry.
   Sample answers:
2. Draw a shape that has exactly 1 line of symmetry.
   Sample answers:
3. Draw a shape that has exactly 2 lines of symmetry.
   Sample answers:
4. Draw a shape that has more than 2 lines of symmetry.
   Sample answers:
5. Which figure below is a reflection (flip) of the original figure? B
   Original A B C
6. Which figure below is a translation (slide) of the original figure? C
   Original A B C

ASSESSMENT MASTER

✦ *Math Masters,* p. 409

NOTE: Problems 7 and 10 assess learning goals 10a and 10b, which are beginning skills. If students do poorly on these problems, do not count it against their final score on the written assessment. Consider these problems as a tool to assess the level at which students are performing these skills at this time.

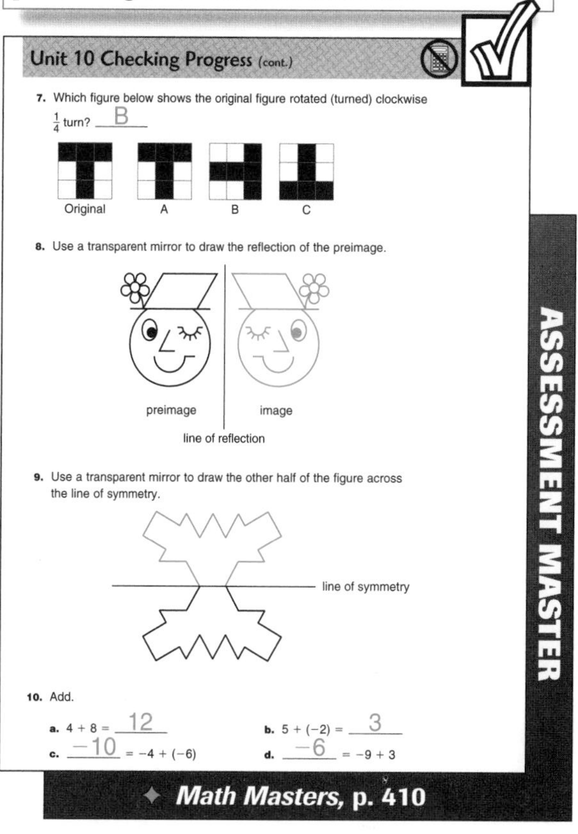

Unit 10 Checking Progress (cont.)

7. Which figure below shows the original figure rotated (turned) clockwise $\frac{1}{4}$ turn? B
   Original A B C
8. Use a transparent mirror to draw the reflection of the preimage.
   preimage image
   line of reflection
9. Use a transparent mirror to draw the other half of the figure across the line of symmetry.
   line of symmetry
10. Add.
    a. 4 + 8 = 12
    b. 5 + (−2) = 3
    c. −10 = −4 + (−6)
    d. −6 = −9 + 3

ASSESSMENT MASTER

✦ *Math Masters,* p. 410

Interpreting a Cartoon

Ruthie's brother doesn't think she understands "fraction-of" problems. He knows that half of eight is four. However, Ruthie does know quite a bit about line symmetry. Can you explain her answers? You may want to draw a picture.

"Up and down, it's three." "Across, it's zero."

TEACHING MASTER

✦ *Math Masters,* p. 167

✦ ALTERNATIVE ASSESSMENT OPTION

Create Reflections with Pattern Blocks or Centimeter Cubes (*Math Masters,* p. 20)

PARTNER ACTIVITY

Each partner folds a blank piece of paper in half to create a line of symmetry. Students use pattern blocks to create a design on one side of the fold. (The blocks may touch the fold.) Partners trade designs and try to build the reflection of the design on the other side of the fold.

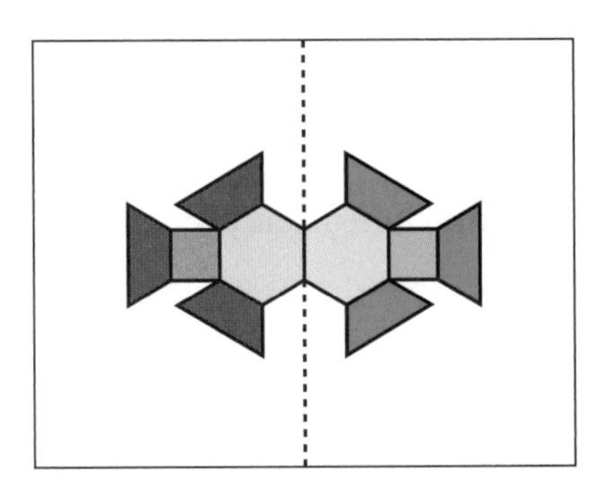

Alternatively, students fold a sheet of centimeter grid paper (*Math Masters,* page 20) in half and use centimeter cubes to create a design on one side of the fold. (Again, the cubes may touch the fold.) Partners trade designs and try to build the reflection of the design on the other side of the fold.

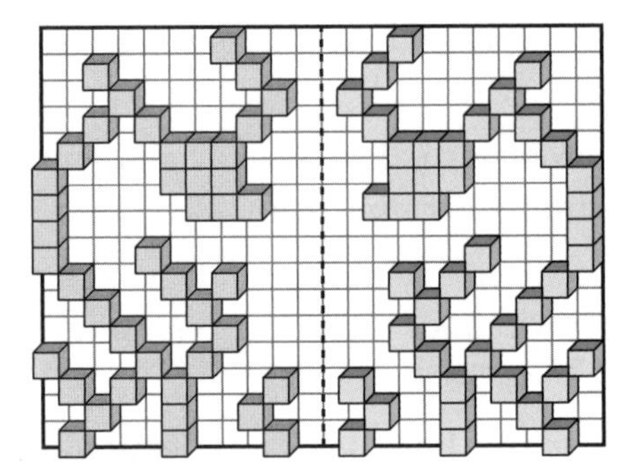

✦ ALTERNATIVE ASSESSMENT OPTION
Interpret a Cartoon (*Math Masters,* p. 167)

INDEPENDENT ACTIVITY 

Students apply their knowledge of line symmetry to explain a cartoon. Look for the following illustrations in students' explanations.

"Up and down, it's three."

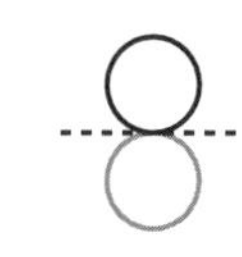

"Across, it's zero."

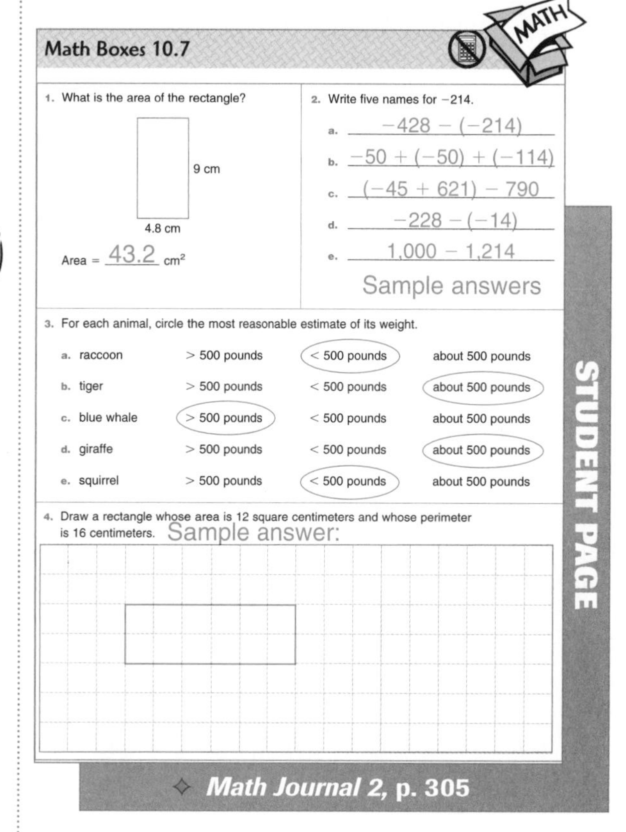

Math Boxes 10.7

1. What is the area of the rectangle?

   9 cm; 4.8 cm

   Area = 43.2 cm^2

2. Write five names for −214.

   a. −428 − (−214)
   b. −50 + (−50) + (−114)
   c. (−45 + 621) − 790
   d. −228 − (−14)
   e. 1,000 − 1,214

   Sample answers

3. For each animal, circle the most reasonable estimate of its weight.

a.	raccoon	> 500 pounds	(< 500 pounds)	about 500 pounds
b.	tiger	> 500 pounds	< 500 pounds	(about 500 pounds)
c.	blue whale	(> 500 pounds)	< 500 pounds	about 500 pounds
d.	giraffe	> 500 pounds	< 500 pounds	(about 500 pounds)
e.	squirrel	> 500 pounds	(< 500 pounds)	about 500 pounds

4. Draw a rectangle whose area is 12 square centimeters and whose perimeter is 16 centimeters. Sample answer:

STUDENT PAGE

✦ *Math Journal 2,* p. 305

2 Build Background for Unit 11

✦ Math Boxes 10.7 (*Math Journal 2,* p. 305)

INDEPENDENT ACTIVITY 

Mixed Review The skills in Problems 1–4 are prerequisites for Unit 11.

✦ Study Link 10.7: Unit 11 Family Letter (*Math Masters,* pp. 362–365)

Home Connection This Study Link is a four-page newsletter that introduces parents and guardians to Unit 11's topics and terms. The letter also offers ideas for mathematics activities that are supportive of classroom work and can be done at home.

Unit 11: 3-Dimensional Shapes, Weight, Volume, and Capacity

Our next unit introduces several new topics, as well as reviewing some of the work with geometric solids from previous grades and some of the main ideas your child has been studying this past year.

We begin with a lesson on weight, focusing on grams and ounces. Students handle and weigh a variety of objects, trying to develop "weight sense" so that they can estimate weights effectively.

As part of a review of the properties of 3-dimensional shapes (prisms, pyramids, cylinders, and cones), your child will construct models of geometric solids using straws and paper patterns. The class will also search for 3-dimensional objects that look like geometric shapes to put into a Shapes Museum. For example, someone might bring a can of soup to represent a cylinder. You might want to help your child find such objects.

By experimenting with cubes, the class will develop and apply a formula for finding the volumes of rectangular prisms (solids that look like boxes).

We will consider familiar units of capacity (cups, pints, quarts, gallons) and the relationships among them.

Your child will also explore subtraction of positive and negative numbers by playing a variation of the *Credits/Debits Game* introduced in Unit 10.

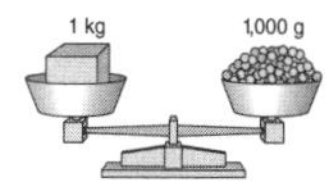

In Lesson 11.1, a pan balance is used to measure weight in grams.

STUDY LINK MASTERS

✦ *Math Masters,* pp. 362–365

Unit 11 Shapes, Weight, Volume, and Capacity

overview

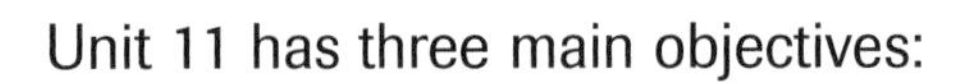

Unit 11 has three main objectives:

- ▷ To review and extend concepts and skills having to do with the properties of 3-dimensional shapes and the volume of a rectangular prism. (Lessons 11.2–11.5)
- ▷ To explore subtraction with positive and negative integers. (Lesson 11.6)
- ▷ To review weight and to relate capacity and weight. (Lessons 11.1 and 11.7)

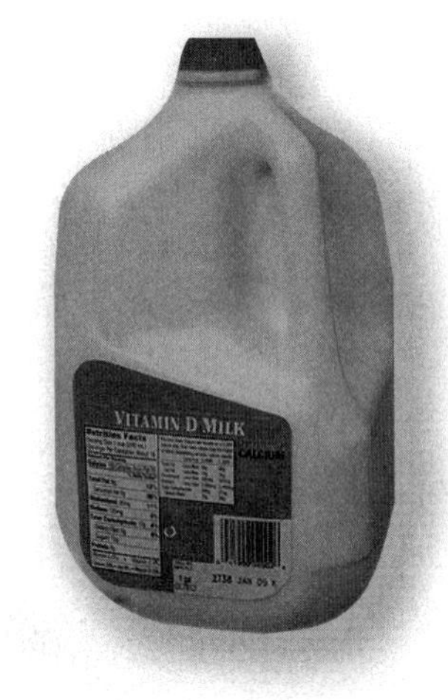

contents

Lesson	Objective	Page
11.1	**Weight** *To review grams and ounces as units of weight; and to estimate and measure weights in grams and ounces.*	782
11.2	**Geometric Solids** *To review properties of common geometric solids.*	788
11.3	**Constructing Geometric Solids** *To identify geometric solids, given their properties; and to construct polyhedrons with straws and twist-ties.*	794
11.4	**A Volume Exploration** *To review concepts and units of volume.*	801
11.5	**A Formula for the Volume of Rectangular Prisms** *To derive and use a formula for the volume of a rectangular prism.*	807
11.6	**Subtraction of Positive and Negative Numbers** *To add and subtract positive and negative integers.*	813
11.7	**Capacity and Weight** *To review customary units of capacity.*	819
11.8	**Unit 11 Review and Assessment** *To review and assess students' progress on the material covered in Unit 11.*	825

UNIT 11

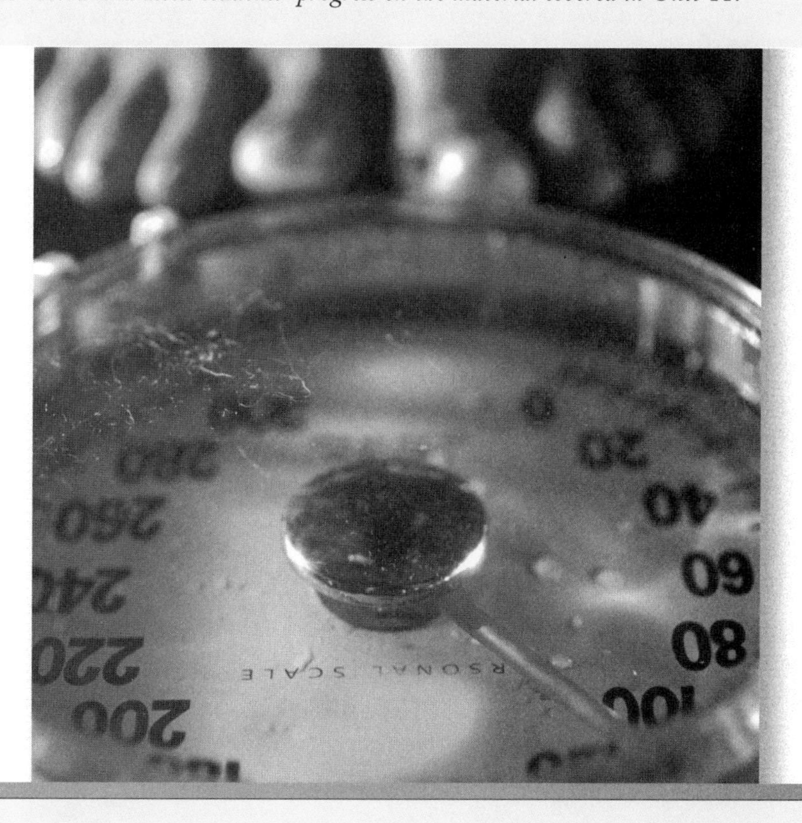

learning goals in perspective

learning goals	links to the past	links to the future
11a **Beginning Goal** Use a formula to calculate volumes of rectangular prisms. **(Lesson 11.5)**	Grade 3: Estimate, then find the volume of boxes by filling them with centimeter cubes. Find the volume of 2-cm, 3-cm, and larger cubes. Find rectangular prisms of a given volume. Use cm cubes to build rectangular prisms with the same volume but different dimensions. Compare the volume of irregular objects by water displacement.	Grade 5: Develop and apply a formula for the volume of a rectangular prism. Build a prism of a given volume. Extend and apply the volume formula to non-rectangular prisms. Find the dimensions of an open box with the greatest possible volume that can be made out of one sheet of grid paper. Grade 6: Solve volume, angle, perimeter, and area problems.
11b **Beginning Goal** Subtract positive and negative integers. **(Lesson 11.6)** 11c **Developing Goal** Add positive and negative integers. **(Lessons 11.5 and 11.6)**	Grade 3: Review uses of positive and negative numbers to relate numbers to a zero point, as in temperatures and elevations, and to record change. Solve number stories about positive and negative numbers.	Grade 5: Solve addition/subtraction stories with positive and negative numbers. Grade 6: Add and subtract positive and negative numbers on a number line; develop a rule for adding and subtracting positive and negative numbers; practice adding and subtracting positive and negative numbers.
11d **Developing Goal** Estimate the weight of objects in ounces or grams; weigh objects in ounces or grams. **(Lessons 11.1 and 11.7)**	Grade 3: Discuss the meaning of weight; review equivalencies between units of weight. Study various kinds of scales with respect to capacity, precision, and use; discuss appropriate scales for weighing different objects; practice reading scales. Guess weights and volumes of objects and check guesses; discuss relationships between weight and volume; order objects by weight and volume.	Grades 5 and 6: Applications and maintenance.
11e **Developing Goal** Solve cube-stacking volume problems. **(Lessons 11.4 and 11.5)**	Grade 3: See Goal 11a.	Grade 5: Build a prism of a given volume. Find the dimensions of an open box with the greatest possible volume that can be made out of 1 sheet of grid paper. Grade 6: Solve volume, angle, perimeter, and area problems.
11f **Developing Goal** Describe properties of geometric solids. **(Lessons 11.2 and 11.3)**	Grade 2: Review names and parts of 3-dimensional objects. Construct and compare pyramids. Grade 3: Identify five basic 3-dimensional shapes (pyramid, prism, cone, cylinder, and sphere) and discuss their characteristics. Construct models of a cube, pyramid, and prism. Classify prisms according to the shapes of their bases. Identify 3-D shapes in the real world.	Grade 5: Review names and properties of geometric solids. Build geometric solids from paper patterns. Identify bases of prisms, pyramids, cylinders, and cones. Compare properties of prisms, pyramids, cylinders, and cones. Sort solids by attributes. Grade 6: Play *3-D Shape Sort* to sort solids by attributes. Explore cross sections of solids.

assessment
ongoing • product • periodic

Informal Assessment

Math Boxes These *Math Journal* pages provide opportunities for cumulative review or assessment of concepts and skills.

Ongoing Assessment: Kid Watching Use the Ongoing Assessment suggestions in the following lessons to make quick, on-the-spot observations about students' understanding of:
- Operations and Computation **(Lesson 11.3, Part 2; Lesson 11.5, Part 2; Lesson 11.6, Part 2)**
- Geometry **(Lesson 11.2, Part 1)**
- Measurement and Reference Frames **(Lesson 11.1, Part 1; Lesson 11.5, Part 1; Lesson 11.6, Part 2)**

Portfolio Ideas Samples of students' work may be obtained from the following assignments:
- Comparing Mammals' Weights **(Lesson 11.1)**
- Writing and Solving "What Am I?" Riddles **(Lesson 11.3)**
- Exploring Volume by Building Prisms **(Lesson 11.5)**
- Estimating the Volume of a Sheet of Paper **(Lesson 11.5)**
- Modeling the Capacity of Annual Rice Consumption **(Lesson 11.7)**
- Solve a Record Rainfall Problem **(Lesson 11.8)**

Unit 11 Review and Assessment

Math Message Use Time to Reflect Problems 1 and 2 in Lesson 11.8 to assess students' progress toward the following learning goals: **Goals 11b, 11c, and 11f**

Oral and Slate Assessments Use oral or slate assessments during Lesson 11.8 to assess students' progress toward the following learning goals: **Goals 11b–11e**

Written Assessment Use a written review during Lesson 11.8 to assess students' progress toward the following learning goals: **Goals 11a–11f**

Alternative Assessment Option Use the small-group alternative assessment in Lesson 11.8 to assess students' progress toward the following learning goal: **Goal 11a**

assessmenthandbook

For more information on how to use different types of assessment in Unit 11, see the Assessment Overview on pages 69–71 in the *Assessment Handbook*. The following Assessment Masters can be found in the *Math Masters* book:
- Unit 11 Checking Progress, pp. 411 and 412
- Unit 11 Class Checklist, p. 446
- Unit 11 Individual Profile of Progress, p. 447
- Class Progress Indicator, p. 467
- Interest Inventories, pp. 468 and 469
- Math Logs, pp. 470–472
- Self-Assessment Forms, pp. 473 and 474

problemsolving

A process of modeling everyday situations using tools from mathematics

Encourage students to use a variety of strategies when attacking a given problem—and to explain those strategies. *Strategies students might use in this unit:*

- Using estimation
- Using a scale (number line)
- Using physical models
- Using logical reasoning
- Using data in a table
- Using computation

Four Problem-Solving **REPRESENTATIONS**

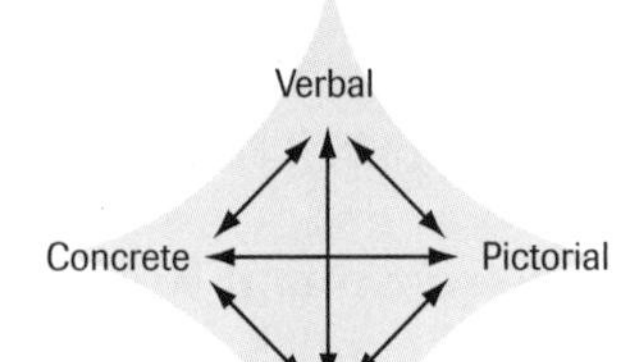

Lessons that teach *through* problem solving, not just *about* problem solving

Lesson	Activity	Lesson	Activity
11.1	Estimating the weight of a variety of objects and using a double-scaled number line to convert between metric and customary weights	11.5	Solving cube-stacking problems to find a formula for the volume of a rectangular prism
11.2	Describing how a given geometric solid is different from other geometric solids	11.6	Keeping track of the "bottom line" of a business by using credits and debits
11.3	Solving riddles about geometric solids	11.7	Solving rice consumption problems involving units of weight and capacity
11.4	Solving problems about the world's largest foods by converting between ounces, pounds, and tons		

For more information about problem solving in *Everyday Mathematics,* see the *Teacher's Reference Manual.*

cross-curricularlinks

art

- Students experiment with different ways to draw a cube after examining the following books: *Ed Emberley's Big Green (Orange, Purple, and Red) Drawing Book.* **(Lesson 11.3)**

science

- Students compare their own weights with those of other mammals. **(Lesson 11.1)**

social studies

- Students continue the World Tour by traveling to Mexico City, Mexico. **(Lesson 11.1)**

language arts

- Students make up and then display riddles about geometric solids. **(Lesson 11.3)**
- Students discuss the similarities and differences among different versions of a mathematical folktale. **(Lesson 11.7)**

literature

- Students read the following books by Robert E. Wells: *Is a Blue Whale the Biggest Thing There Is?* and *What's Smaller than a Pygmy Shrew?* **(Lesson 11.1)**
- Students read books about the power of doubling, such as *The King's Chessboard* by David Birch. **(Lesson 11.7)**

meeting INDIVIDUAL needs

UNIVERSAL ACCESS

✦ RETEACHING

The following features provide additional instructional support:

Adjusting the Activity

- **Lesson 11.1, Part 1**
- **Lesson 11.3, Part 1**
- **Lesson 11.4, Part 1**
- **Lesson 11.5, Part 1**
- **Lesson 11.6, Part 1**

Options for Individualizing

- **Lesson 11.2** Reviewing 2-Dimensional Shapes
- **Lesson 11.5** Exploring Volume by Building Prisms
- **Lesson 11.6** Using a Number Line to Add and Subtract Positive and Negative Numbers

✦ ENRICHMENT

The following features suggest some enrichment and extension activities found in this unit:

Adjusting the Activity

- **Lesson 11.2, Part 1**
- **Lesson 11.3, Part 1**
- **Lesson 11.3, Part 3**
- **Lesson 11.4, Part 1**
- **Lesson 11.4, Part 2**
- **Lesson 11.7, Part 1**

Options for Individualizing

- **Lesson 11.1** Comparing Mammals' Weights
- **Lesson 11.3** Writing and Solving "What Am I?" Riddles
- **Lesson 11.3** Drawing a Cube
- **Lesson 11.3** Making a Model of a Tetrahedron
- **Lesson 11.5** Estimating the Volume of a Sheet of Paper
- **Lesson 11.7** Modeling the Capacity of Annual Rice Consumption
- **Lesson 11.7** Doubling Grains of Rice

✦ LANGUAGE DIVERSITY

The following features suggest some ways to support students who are acquiring proficiency in English:

Adjusting the Activity

- **Lesson 11.3, Part 3**

Options for Individualizing

- **Lesson 11.2** Creating a Word Wall
- **Lesson 11.4** Building Background for Mathematics Words

✦ MULTIAGE CLASSROOM

The following chart lists related lessons from Grades 3 and 5 that can help you meet your instructional needs:

Grade 3	10.4	10.3		10.2	10.3 10.5	10.2 10.3	10.6
Grade 4	11.1	11.2	11.3	11.4	11.5	11.6	11.7
Grade 5	11.6	11.1 11.2		11.5	9.8	7.8	9.10 11.6

materials

lesson	math masters pages	manipulative kit items	other items
11.1	Study Link Master, p. 366 Teaching Masters, pp. 36–38 (optional); and p. 169 transparency of Teaching Master, p. 168 (optional) ***See* Advance Preparation, p. 782**		balance or scale; standard masses nickel (optional); index cards different objects for weighing *Is a Blue Whale the Biggest Thing There Is?* *What's Smaller than a Pygmy Shrew?*
11.2	Study Link Master, p. 367 Teaching Masters, pp. 170–172 (optional); and pp. 173 and 174 ***See* Advance Preparation, p. 788**	straws and twist-ties	models of geometric solids boxes; resealable bags, (optional) balance or scale pennies, nickels, dimes, quarters
11.3	Study Link Master, p. 368 Teaching Masters, p. 166; pp. 175 and 176 (optional); and pp. 179–182 transparencies of Teaching Masters, pp. 177 and 178 (optional) ***See* Advance Preparation, p. 794**	deck of number cards per partnership (from the Everything Math Deck, if available) straws and twist-ties (see Lesson 11.2)	models of geometric solids (see Lesson 11.2) boxes; resealable bags, (optional) (see Lesson 11.2) books by Ed Emberely staples, tape, or glue scissors
11.4	Study Link Master, p. 369 Teaching Masters, pp. 20 and 183	base-10 blocks cm cubes inch cube for demonstration purposes	slate; tape; dictionary; scissors metersticks; cones and string (optional) at least 3 12-inch rulers or 3 yardsticks per group; or 2 brown paper shopping bags; 12-inch ruler and scissors per group ***See* Advance Preparation, p. 801**
11.5	Study Link Master, p. 370 Teaching Masters, pp. 166 and 184–186 ***See* Advance Preparation, p. 807**	cm cubes deck of number cards per partnership (from the Everything Math Deck, if available) 36 cm cubes per partnership	centimeter ruler sheet of notebook paper scissors
11.6	Study Link Master, p. 371 Teaching Masters, p. 187 (optional); and p. 188 transparency of Teaching Master, p. 165 (optional) Assessment Master, p. 471 or 475 (optional) ***See* Advance Preparation, p. 813**	deck of number cards per partnership (from the Everything Math Deck, if available)	1 penny per partnership semipermanent chalk (optional) number line (optional)
11.7	Study Link Master, p. 372		measuring cup, empty milk cartons, rice, pourable substance, such as sand, and scale Per group: empty copy-paper carton, measuring cup, and pourable substance, such as sand *The King's Chessboard* *One Grain of Rice: A Mathematical Folktale* *The Token Gift* *A Grain of Rice* calculator ***See* Advance Preparation, p. 819**
11.8	Study Link Masters, pp. 373–376 Teaching Master, p. 189 Assessment Masters, pp. 411 and 412	cm cubes	slate

planningtips

Pacing

Pacing depends on a number of factors, such as students' individual needs and how long your school has been using *Everyday Mathematics*. At the beginning of Unit 11, review your Content by Strand Poster to help you set a monthly pace.

← MOST CLASSROOMS →

APRIL	MAY	JUNE

Using the Projects

Use Project 6, Building and Viewing Structures, during or after Unit 11 to build structures with cubes, given "blueprints" or side views of the structures; and to represent structures with diagrams. The Projects can be found at the back of this book.

Home Communication

Share Study Links 11.1–11.7 with families to help them understand the content and procedures in this unit. At the end of the unit, use Study Link 11.8 to introduce Unit 12. Supplemental information can be found in the *Home Connection Handbook*.

NCTM Standards

Standard	1	2	3	4	5	6	7	8	9	10
Unit 11 Lessons	3, 5, 6, 7	5	2, 3	1, 2, 4, 5, 6, 7		1–8	1–8	1–8	1–8	1–8

Content Standards
1 Number and Operations
2 Algebra
3 Geometry
4 Measurement
5 Data Analysis and Probability

Process Standards
6 Problem Solving
7 Reasoning and Proof
8 Communication
9 Connections
10 Representation

PRACTICE *through* Games

Everyday Mathematics uses games to help students develop good fact power and other math skills.

- *What's My Weight?* to practice estimating weights **(Lesson 11.1)**
- *Credits/Debits Game* to practice addition of positive and negative integers **(Lessons 11.3 and 11.5)**
- *Credits/Debits Game* (Advanced Version) to practice addition and subtraction of positive and negative integers **(Lesson 11.6)**

unit 11 content highlights

The discussion below highlights the major content ideas presented in Unit 11 and may help you establish instructional priorities.

Weight (Lesson 11.1)

Students review weight as measured in grams and ounces, estimate the weight of objects, and check their estimates by actually weighing the objects. The minimum equipment required is one pan balance and a set of standard masses; however, a variety of scales is desirable. An important activity is setting up a Gram & Ounce Museum, displaying everyday objects labeled with their weights.

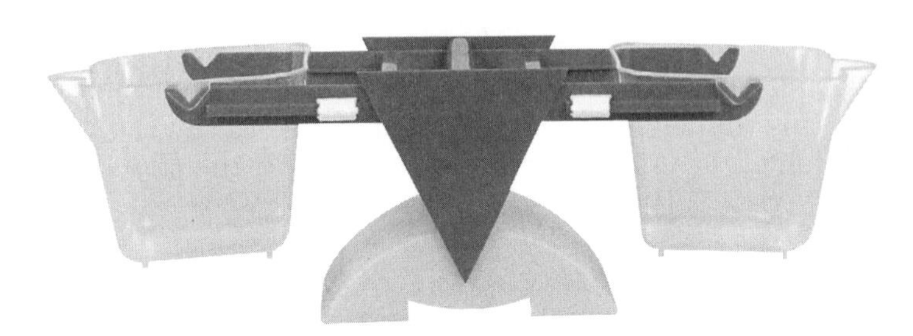

Pan balance

No distinction is made between mass and weight in this unit, and the terms are used interchangeably. See the *Teacher's Reference Manual* for a discussion of the difference between mass and weight.

Geometric Solids (Lessons 11.2 and 11.3)

Work and play with 2-dimensional figures and 3-dimensional shapes are essential at every level of *Everyday Mathematics.* The reviews, reminders, and constructions in Lessons 11.2 and 11.3 are intended for enjoyment, as well as for preparation for the study of volume that begins in Lesson 11.4. In keeping with the program's philosophy, the study of volume continues through *Fifth* and *Sixth Grade Everyday Mathematics.*

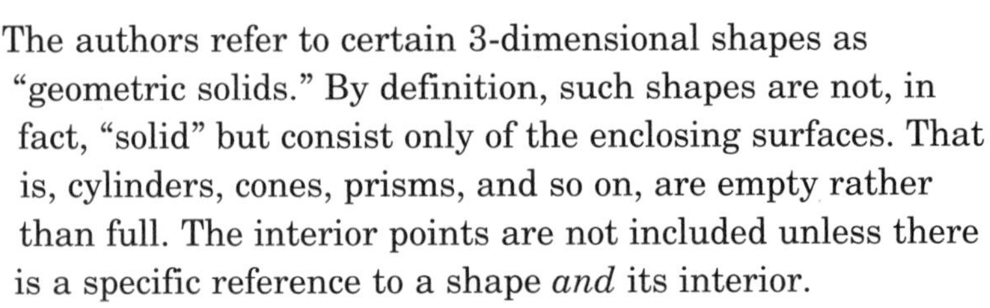

The authors refer to certain 3-dimensional shapes as "geometric solids." By definition, such shapes are not, in fact, "solid" but consist only of the enclosing surfaces. That is, cylinders, cones, prisms, and so on, are empty rather than full. The interior points are not included unless there is a specific reference to a shape *and* its interior.

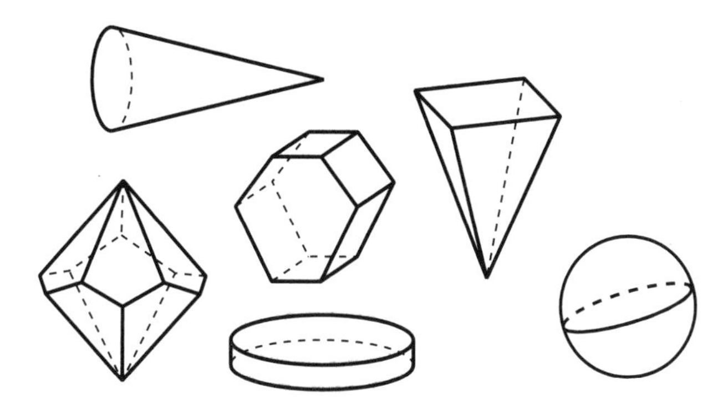

Some geometric solids

Further complication occurs when a straw construction is used to model a geometric solid: Only the *frames* of the surfaces appear, not the surfaces themselves. Such ambiguities are harmless in informal discourse. Periodically remind students that a geometric solid is made up of surfaces; however, it is not necessary to enforce the definition at this time. (*Fifth* and *Sixth Grade Everyday Mathematics* will include work with exact mathematical definitions, especially in geometry.)

Subtraction of Positive and Negative Numbers
(Lesson 11.6)

Throughout *Everyday Mathematics,* students have been using positive and negative numbers to record information from various reference frames (thermometers, timelines, number lines, number-chart arrays). Recording reference-frame information using positive and negative numbers is one of the main applications of such numbers in everyday life, including the areas of science and technology. (Positive and negative numbers are also used as exponents and as positive or negative factors in expressing "slopes" or "rates" in coordinate graphs, equations, and formulas.)

Situations that involve addition, subtraction, multiplication, or division of positive and negative numbers are rare. However, it may be useful to compare what happens when these operations are performed on only positive numbers with what happens when they are performed on both positive and negative numbers. Furthermore, for students who will be taking algebra and more advanced mathematics courses later, operational skills involving the entire set of positive and negative rational numbers are essential.

The approach to subtraction of positive and negative numbers in Lesson 11.6 parallels the approach to addition in Lesson 10.6. Again, the context is bookkeeping for a small business. "Credits" are represented by positive numbers and "debits" by negative numbers. Transactions are recorded in a ledger with the headings "Start," "Change," and "End." There is one new element: Occasionally, mistakes in recording are made and must be corrected. Corrections are done by subtracting (that is, removing or taking away) credits or debits that have been recorded "by mistake."

It should become apparent that taking away a credit (a positive number) leaves a business worse off, and taking away a debit (a negative number) leaves it better off. This is the central idea of the lesson. That is, when you subtract a negative number, your answer is greater than the number you started with. For example, $10 - (-5) = 15$ (not 5). This illustrates the following, very helpful procedure for subtraction:

> To subtract a number (whether positive or negative), add the opposite of the number.

While some students may *discover* this procedure, it would be premature to teach it at this time. This initial exploration of subtraction involving both positive and negative numbers is for fun and familiarization—mastery is not expected.

$$+6 - (+3) = +6 + (-3) = +3$$
$$+8 - (-2) = +8 + (+2) = +10$$
$$-5 - (+2) = -5 + (-2) = -7$$
$$-12 - (-8) = -12 + (+8) = -4$$

$$+7 - (+10) = +7 + (-10) = -3$$
$$+6 - (-11) = +6 + (+11) = +17$$
$$-3 - (+4) = -3 + (-4) = -7$$
$$-5 - (-9) = -5 + (+9) = +4$$

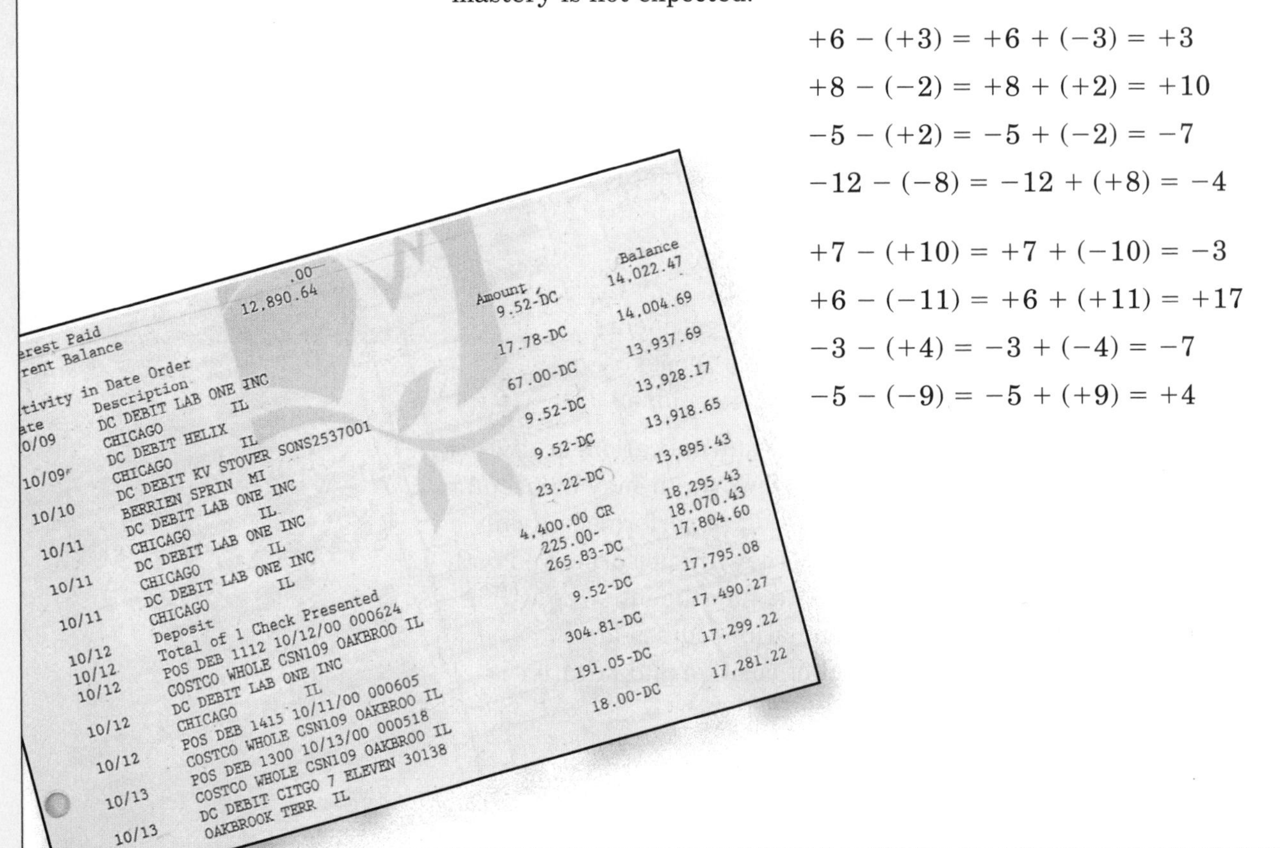

erest Paid .00
rent Balance 12,890.64

tivity in Date Order

ate	Description	Amount	Balance
0/09	DC DEBIT LAB ONE INC CHICAGO IL	9.52-DC	14,022.47
10/09	DC DEBIT HELIX CHICAGO IL	17.78-DC	14,004.69
10/10	DC DEBIT KV STOVER SONS2537001 BERRIEN SPRIN MI	67.00-DC	13,937.69
10/11	DC DEBIT LAB ONE INC CHICAGO IL	9.52-DC	13,928.17
10/11	DC DEBIT LAB ONE INC CHICAGO IL	9.52-DC	13,918.65
10/11	DC DEBIT LAB ONE INC CHICAGO IL	23.22-DC	13,895.43
10/12	Deposit	4,400.00 CR	18,295.43
10/12	Total of 1 Check Presented	225.00-	18,070.43
10/12	POS DEB 1112 10/12/00 000624 COSTCO WHOLE CSN109 OAKBROO IL	265.83-DC	17,804.60
10/12	DC DEBIT LAB ONE INC CHICAGO IL	9.52-DC	17,795.08
10/12	POS DEB 1415 10/11/00 000605 COSTCO WHOLE CSN109 OAKBROO IL	304.81-DC	17,490.27
10/13	POS DEB 1300 10/13/00 000518 COSTCO WHOLE CSN109 OAKBROO IL	191.05-DC	17,299.22
10/13	DC DEBIT CITGO 7 ELEVEN 30138 OAKBROOK TERR IL	18.00-DC	17,281.22

Volume (Lessons 11.4 and 11.5)

Volume is a measure of the amount of space inside a 3-dimensional shape. In Lessons 11.4 and 11.5, students develop the concept of volume by building 3-dimensional structures with identical cubes, or by filling open boxes with such cubes, and then counting the cubes. If the shape is a rectangular prism, a natural strategy is to build one layer of cubes, count the number of cubes in that layer, and then multiply that number by the number of layers needed to fill the prism. Since the number of cubes in one layer corresponds to the area of the base (often represented by the formula $A = l * w$), this process can be linked to the two standard formulas for the volume of a rectangular prism:

$V = l * w * h$ (volume equals the product of the length and width of the rectangular base and the height perpendicular to that base)

$V = B * h$ (volume equals the product of the area of the base and the height perpendicular to that base)

The former is commonly used in textbooks and on standardized tests; the latter is used in many mathematics courses and technical applications. *Everyday Mathematics* uses both formulas, but the authors prefer $V = B * h$ because it can be used for prisms other than rectangular prisms, as well as for cylinders.

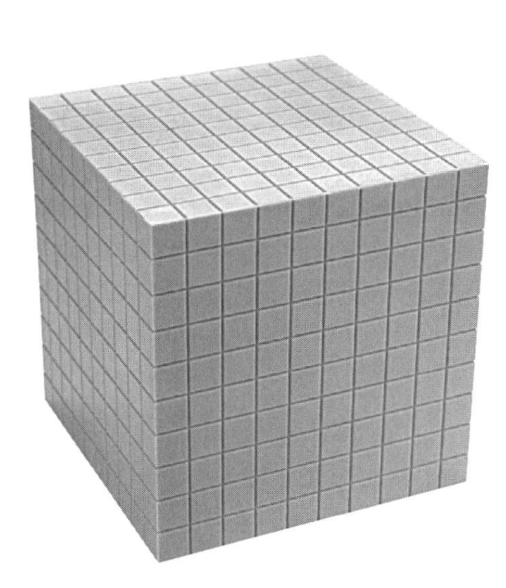

A base-10 block has 10 layers, with $10 * 10 = 100$ cubes in each layer.
$V = 100 \text{ cm}^2 * 10 \text{ cm} = 1{,}000 \text{ cm}^3$

The Content Highlights for Unit 8 suggest that students be encouraged to think of the area of a rectangle in terms of "painting" the surface inside the rectangle. Similarly, students can think of the volume of a prism in terms of the base rising along the "sides" of the prism until the prism is filled to the top. As an illustration of this idea, an optional activity in Lesson 11.8 asks students to imagine a large amount of rain falling into their classroom. Assuming that the classroom floor is rectangular, the rainwater will rise, forming a rectangular prism whose height becomes greater and greater as more rain falls. Students find the volume of the rain and the weight of the water.

Units of Volume and Capacity (Lessons 11.4 and 11.7)

It is important to note that, like other measures, volume and capacity are expressed with both numbers and units. Usually, volume units are *cubic units,* based on some linear measure; for example, cubic centimeters, cubic inches, cubic meters, cubic yards, and so on. In everyday life, it is common to express capacities in units that are not cubic units: teaspoons, cups, pints, U.S. or Imperial gallons, liters, barrels, bushels, and so on. These standards were developed centuries ago to measure things poured into or out of containers, such as liquids, grains, fruits, salt, and so on. Every locality had its own system of measures, and a variety of standards persists even today. For example, in the United States, *pint* has different meanings for dry and liquid measures and still another meaning in England. *Ounce* can refer to *fluid ounce* (a unit of capacity, about 1.8 cubic inches), *avoirdupois ounce* (a familiar unit of weight, about 28 grams), or *troy ounce* (a specialized unit of weight, about 31 grams).

In spite of these kinds of ambiguities, traditional units for capacity continue to be used in everyday life. Along with the *liter,* they have been the main focus of the discussion of capacity since *Kindergarten Everyday Mathematics.* The authors assume that by now, most students using *Everyday Mathematics* will have mastered these units and their relationships. However, some students may need to refer to tables of equivalent measures in cookbooks or their journals.

In Lesson 11.7, students examine the relationship between various quantities of rice and their weights. In an optional activity, they try to visualize the amount of rice a typical Thai family of four eats in a year by estimating how many empty cartons of copy paper would be needed to hold that amount of rice.

Continuation of the World Tour (Lesson 11.1)

Students return to North America by flying to Mexico City, Mexico. North America is the final region on the World Tour.

Review and Assessment (Lesson 11.8)

Lesson 11.8 includes oral, slate, and written assessments of students' progress on the following concepts and skills:

- using a formula to calculate volumes of rectangular prisms
- adding and subtracting signed numbers
- estimating weights and weighing objects
- solving cube-stacking volume problems
- describing properties of geometric solids

For additional information on the following topics, see the *Teacher's Reference Manual:*

- balance scale
- capacity
- converting between measures
- integers
- mass and weight
- volume
- World Tour Project

11.1 Weight

OBJECTIVES **To review grams and ounces as units of weight; and to estimate and measure weights in grams and ounces.**

summaries	materials
1 Teaching the Lesson	
Students review the measuring of weight in ounces and in grams and start a classroom Gram & Ounce Museum. They estimate weights and practice conversions between grams and ounces. [Measurement and Reference Frames]	□ *Math Journal 2,* pp. 306 and 307 □ Transparency (*Math Masters,* p. 168; optional) □ balance or scale; standard masses □ nickel (optional) □ index cards ***See*** **Advance Preparation**
2 Ongoing Learning & Practice	
Students continue the World Tour, traveling to Region 5. [multiple strands] Students practice and maintain skills through Math Boxes and Study Link activities.	□ *Math Journal 2,* pp. 308, 345–347, and 354–355 □ *Student Reference Book* □ Teaching Masters (*Math Masters,* pp. 36–38; optional) □ Study Link Master (*Math Masters,* p. 366)
3 Options for Individualizing	
Extra Practice Students play "What's My Weight?," in which they estimate weights of objects. [Measurement and Reference Frames] **Enrichment** Students compare students' weights with those of other mammals. [Measurement and Reference Frames]	□ Teaching Master (*Math Masters,* p. 169) □ different objects for weighing □ index cards □ *Is a Blue Whale the Biggest Thing There Is?* □ *What's Smaller than a Pygmy Shrew?* ***See*** **Advance Preparation**

Additional Information

Advance Preparation In preparation for the Gram & Ounce Museum in Part 1, gather as many different kinds of scales, balances, and standard mass sets as possible (a bathroom scale, a diet scale, a spring scale, and so on) so that students can measure a range of weights. The minimum equipment required is a rocker balance or pan balance and a set of standard masses. If you do not have commercial standard masses, you can use nickels (about 5 grams each) and pennies dated 1983 or later (about 2.5 grams each) for metric standard masses, and quarters (about 0.2 ounce each) for customary standard masses. Coins or other objects, such as washers, can be taped together or placed in resealable plastic bags to make larger standard masses for weighing heavier objects. The index cards will be used to label the objects in the museum.

If possible, give each student a nickel to use in the Math Message.

For the optional Extra Practice activity in Part 3, gather and weigh a collection of objects. For each object, prepare a card with the name of the object, its correct weight, and two incorrect weights. (Use your judgment in choosing the incorrect weights, since the closer they are to the correct weight, the harder it will be to choose a good estimate of the weight.) Make a separate list for yourself of the objects and their correct weights. Each object will be used only once in the game, so the more objects students have, the longer they can play the game. At least 10–15 objects are required to do the activity once. For the optional Enrichment activity in Part 3, obtain copies of the following books: *Is a Blue Whale the Biggest Thing There Is?* by Robert E. Wells (Albert Whitman, 1993) and *What's Smaller than a Pygmy Shrew?* by Robert E. Wells (Albert Whitman, 1995).

Vocabulary • **gram**

Getting Started

Mental Math and Reflexes

Pose addition problems with positive and negative multiples of 10. *Suggestions:*

- 40 + 30 = 70
- −80 + (−30) = −110
- −60 + 10 = −50
- 90 + (−40) = 50

Math Message

A nickel weighs about 5 grams. Find objects you think weigh about

1 gram *10 grams* *25 grams* *100 grams*

Teaching the Lesson

✦ Math Message Follow-Up

WHOLE-CLASS ACTIVITY

Demonstrate or have students demonstrate how to use a scale or balance to weigh some of the objects identified by students for the weights given. For greater accuracy in weighing small objects, weigh several at once and divide to find the weight of a single object. *For example:*

1 gram	cm cube
10 grams	hexagon pattern block
25 grams	compass
100 grams	calculator

NOTE: In this unit, no distinction is made between mass and weight, and the terms are used interchangeably. See the *Teacher's Reference Manual* for a discussion of the difference between mass and weight.

Briefly review the relationship between **grams** and kilograms (1,000 grams = 1 kilogram) and other metric units of mass, including the milligram ($\frac{1}{1,000}$ gram) and the metric ton (1,000 kilograms). Ask what might be measured in milligrams (for example, medicine), grams (food), kilograms (body weight), and metric tons (ships).

Review ounces by asking students to name objects that weigh about 1 ounce. Again, use the scale or balance to weigh some of the objects students suggest. Continue by asking for names of objects that weigh different numbers of ounces (4 ounces, 8 ounces, and so on).

Adjusting the Activity Display a poster in the classroom to remind students of weight equivalencies. *For example:*

Metric Units

1 gram (g) = 1,000 milligrams (mg)
1 kilogram (kg) = 1,000 grams
1 metric ton (t) = 1,000 kilograms

U.S. Customary Units

1 pound (lb) = 16 ounces (oz)
1 ton (T) = 2,000 pounds

✦Setting up a Gram & Ounce Museum

WHOLE-CLASS DISCUSSION

Introduce a project to create a museum of objects of different weights measured in grams and in ounces. Use index cards to label objects in the museum and record their weights. The measuring tools you have available will determine the range of weights you can display in the museum. For example, if you are limited to one balance and coins as standard masses, then you should aim for a modest weight range (possibly up to 500 grams or 16 ounces). If you also have a bathroom scale or a balance that can accommodate larger weights, then you can expand the range of weights.

Discuss with students the goals for the collection, the kinds of objects they should collect, and the procedures for adding objects to the museum. Note that these issues are all related. For example, if you have a balance or scale precise enough to weigh objects to the nearest gram, you may decide to try to find an object for every number of grams from 1 to 100. Since such a collection will have a very large number of objects, you might decide to focus on common items like pebbles or rocks. If the museum is going to have such a large collection, the procedure for adding items should probably be managed by students. Ask students to bring in objects to add to the museum over the next week or two.

ONGOING ASSESSMENT

To ensure accuracy and to assess students' skill in weighing different objects, require that every item added to the museum be weighed by two or three students working independently.

✦ Estimating Weights (*Math Journal 2,* p. 306)

PARTNER ACTIVITY 

Students estimate the weights of different objects. Partners should discuss the possibilities and come to an agreement about which measure is the most reasonable.

✦ Converting between Metric and Customary Weights (*Math Journal 2,* p. 307; *Math Masters,* p. 168)

PARTNER ACTIVITY 

Students use a double-scaled number line to convert between grams and ounces.

Adjusting the Activity If necessary, use a transparency of *Math Masters,* page 168 to demonstrate how to use the number line to convert measures between ounces and grams.

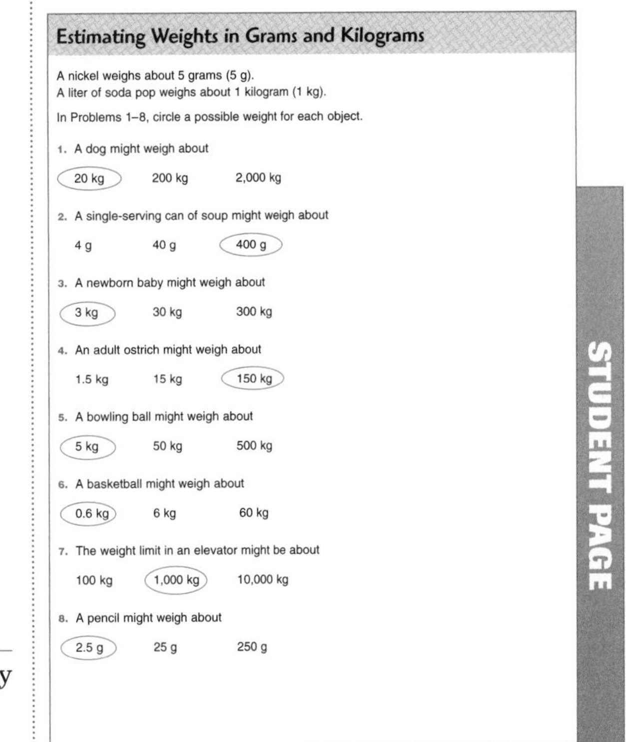

Estimating Weights in Grams and Kilograms

A nickel weighs about 5 grams (5 g).
A liter of soda pop weighs about 1 kilogram (1 kg).

In Problems 1–8, circle a possible weight for each object.

1. A dog might weigh about
   (20 kg) 200 kg 2,000 kg
2. A single-serving can of soup might weigh about
   4 g 40 g (400 g)
3. A newborn baby might weigh about
   (3 kg) 30 kg 300 kg
4. An adult ostrich might weigh about
   1.5 kg 15 kg (150 kg)
5. A bowling ball might weigh about
   (5 kg) 50 kg 500 kg
6. A basketball might weigh about
   (0.6 kg) 6 kg 60 kg
7. The weight limit in an elevator might be about
   100 kg (1,000 kg) 10,000 kg
8. A pencil might weigh about
   (2.5 g) 25 g 250 g

STUDENT PAGE

✧ *Math Journal 2,* p. 306

2 Ongoing Learning & Practice

✦ Updating the World Tour

(*Math Journal 2,* pp. 345–347 and 354–355; *Student Reference Book; Math Masters,* pp. 36–38)

INDEPENDENT ACTIVITY 

Social Studies Link Students follow the established World Tour routine:

- ▷ They update the Route Map by drawing a line segment to connect Beijing, China, and Mexico City, Mexico.
- ▷ They use the World Tour section of the *Student Reference Book* to locate facts about Mexico and Mexico City and fill in the Country Notes pages for this country and capital.
- ▷ Students who are also keeping a Route Log update it.

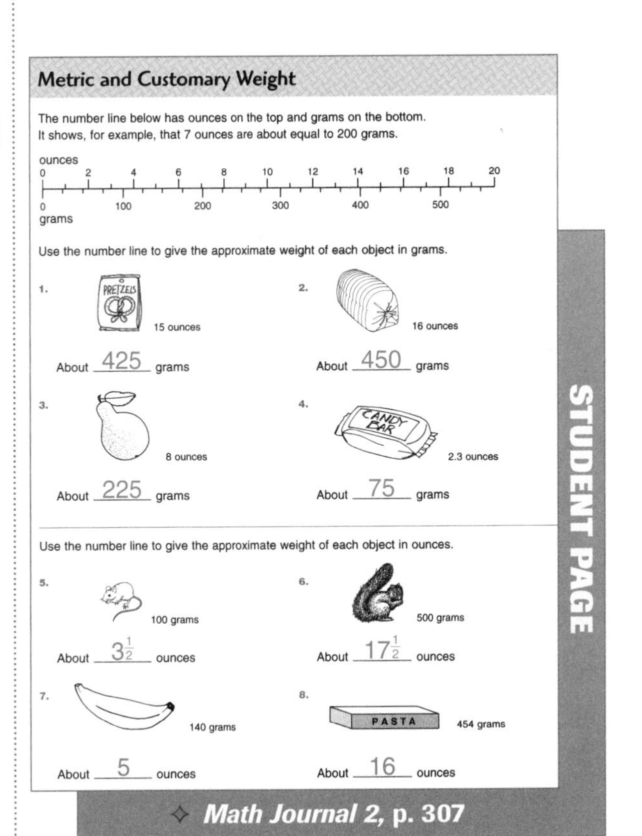

Metric and Customary Weight

The number line below has ounces on the top and grams on the bottom.
It shows, for example, that 7 ounces are about equal to 200 grams.

Use the number line to give the approximate weight of each object in grams.

1. 15 ounces — About 425 grams
2. 16 ounces — About 450 grams
3. 8 ounces — About 225 grams
4. 2.3 ounces — About 75 grams

Use the number line to give the approximate weight of each object in ounces.

5. 100 grams — About $3\frac{1}{2}$ ounces
6. 500 grams — About $17\frac{1}{2}$ ounces
7. 140 grams — About 5 ounces
8. 454 grams — About 16 ounces

STUDENT PAGE

✧ *Math Journal 2,* p. 307

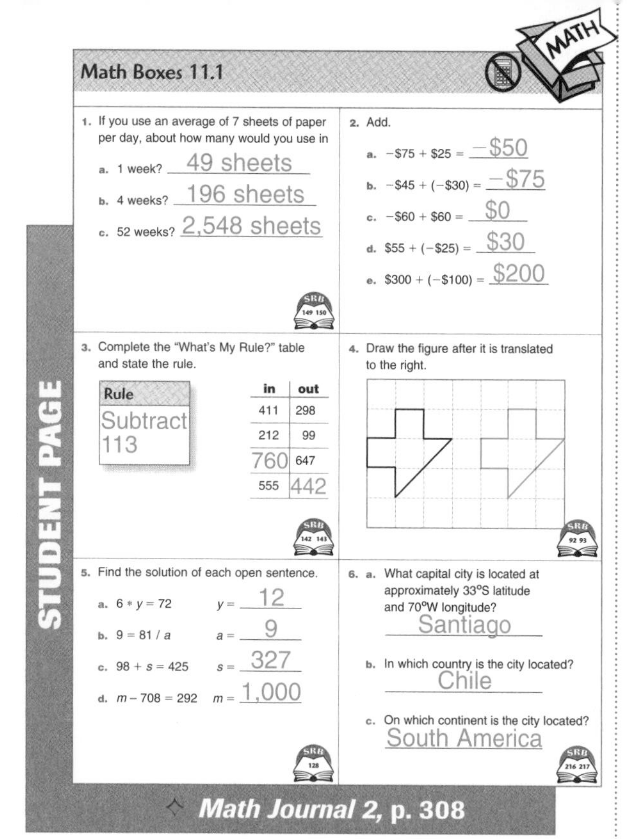

STUDENT PAGE

Math Boxes 11.1

1. If you use an average of 7 sheets of paper per day, about how many would you use in
   a. 1 week? 49 sheets
   b. 4 weeks? 196 sheets
   c. 52 weeks? 2,548 sheets

2. Add.
   a. $-\$75 + \$25 =$ $-\$50$
   b. $-\$45 + (-\$30) =$ $-\$75$
   c. $-\$60 + \$60 =$ \$0
   d. $\$55 + (-\$25) =$ \$30
   e. $\$300 + (-\$100) =$ \$200

3. Complete the "What's My Rule?" table and state the rule.

   Rule: Subtract 113

in	out
411	298
212	99
760	647
555	442

4. Draw the figure after it is translated to the right.

5. Find the solution of each open sentence.
   a. $6 * y = 72$ $y =$ 12
   b. $9 = 81 / a$ $a =$ 9
   c. $98 + s = 425$ $s =$ 327
   d. $m - 708 = 292$ $m =$ 1,000

6. a. What capital city is located at approximately 33°S latitude and 70°W longitude? Santiago
   b. In which country is the city located? Chile
   c. On which continent is the city located? South America

Math Journal 2, p. 308

Allow students a week or more to complete the Country Notes pages. The second page of Country Notes provides space for students to record interesting facts about the countries they are visiting. Discourage rote copying of facts. Encourage students to use classroom and library resources to find facts about the country that are interesting to them and worth sharing with the rest of the class.

✦ Math Boxes 11.1 (*Math Journal 2,* p. 308)

INDEPENDENT ACTIVITY 

Mixed Review Math Boxes in this lesson are paired with Math Boxes in Lesson 11.3. The skill in Problem 1 is a prerequisite for Unit 12.

✦ Study Link 11.1 (*Math Masters,* p. 366)

Home Connection Students estimate and measure the weight of objects. Students who do not have a scale or balance in their home should borrow one from a neighbor.

STUDY LINK MASTER

Weighing Objects — Study Link 11.1

Find a scale or balance around your house or borrow one from a neighbor.

Estimate the weight of 10 objects. Then use the scale or balance to weigh each object. This activity will help you improve your estimation skills.

Be sure to include units in all your estimates and measures. Answers vary.

Object	Estimated Weight	Measured Weight

Math Masters, p. 366

3 Options for Individualizing

✦ EXTRA PRACTICE Playing "What's My Weight?"

WHOLE-CLASS ACTIVITY **15–30 min** 

Divide the class into two teams. Divide each team further into groups of two or three students.

Give each group one object and the weight card for that object. (See Advance Preparation.) Each group should examine its object and decide which of the three weights on the card is correct.

Alternate between teams. Ask the members of each team to identify the weight of their object. If they are correct on the first guess, their team gets 2 points. If they are correct on the second guess, their team gets 1 point. The team with more points at the end wins.

✦ ENRICHMENT Comparing Mammals' Weights (*Math Masters,* p. 169)

PARTNER ACTIVITY  **15–30 min** 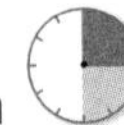

Science Link Students use "times as many" phrasing to compare students' weights with those of other mammals. Point out that students will be seeking *approximate* answers. Have them estimate to the nearest whole number or, if appropriate, to the nearest mixed number. Have students share strategies for their estimates.

Portfolio Ideas

NOTE: Fractions in mixed numbers should be simple—$\frac{1}{2}$, $\frac{3}{4}$, $\frac{2}{3}$, and so on. If mixed numbers prove too difficult, estimates to the nearest whole number are fine.

Literature Link Read the following books or have students read them on their own:

Is a Blue Whale the Biggest Thing There Is?

Summary: The concepts of big, bigger, and biggest are illustrated by comparing the physical measurements of things such as a blue whale, a mountain, and the universe.

What's Smaller than a Pygmy Shrew?

Summary: The concepts of small, smaller, and smallest are illustrated by comparing the physical measurements of things such as a pygmy shrew, an amoeba, and an atom.

Mammal Weights

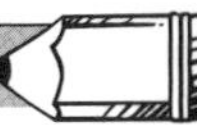

The table below shows typical weights, in pounds and kilograms, of different mammals. The weight of a typical fourth grader is also included.

Mammal	Pounds	Kilograms	Mammal	Pounds	Kilograms
Blue whale	300,000	140,000	Human adult	150	70
African elephant	12,000	5,400	**Fourth grader**	**65**	**30**
Giraffe	2,400	1,100	Raccoon	25	10
Bison	1,800	810	House cat	10	5
Arabian camel	1,200	540	Domestic rabbit	3	1.5
Zebra	650	290	Squirrel	1	0.5
Tiger	500	230	Mouse	0.25	0.1
Mountain gorilla	450	200	Pygmy shrew	0.01	0.005
White-tailed deer	400	180			

Source (for nonhumans): Simon and Schuster's Guide to Mammals

1. For each of the following mammals, tell about how many fourth graders it would take to equal the weight of each mammal.

Mammal	Typical Weight (in kilograms)	Approximate Number of Fourth Graders
Zebra	290	About 10
Mountain gorilla	200	About 7
Tiger	230	About 8
Human adult	70	About 2
Bison	810	About 27
Blue whale	140,000	About 5,000

2. On the back of this page, write additional mammal comparisons. For example, about how many pygmy shrews would it take to equal the weight of a typical fourth grader? Answers vary.

TEACHING MASTER

✦ *Math Masters,* p. 169

11.2 Geometric Solids

OBJECTIVE **To review properties of common geometric solids.**

summaries	materials
1 Teaching the Lesson	
Students review common geometric solids, including prisms, pyramids, cylinders, cones, and spheres, and investigate their properties. [Geometry] Students construct rectangular prisms using straws and twist-ties. [Geometry]	□ *Math Journal 2,* pp. 309 and 310 □ *Student Reference Book,* p. 87 □ Study Link 11.1 □ Teaching Masters (*Math Masters,* pp. 170–172; optional) □ models of geometric solids □ straws and twist-ties □ boxes □ resealable bags (optional) ***See*** **Advance Preparation**
2 Ongoing Learning & Practice	
Students determine how many of each U.S. coin are needed to make a 1-ounce weight. [Measurement and Reference Frames] Students practice and maintain skills through Math Boxes and Study Link activities.	□ *Math Journal 2,* p. 311 □ Study Link Master (*Math Masters,* p. 367) □ balance or scale □ coins ***See*** **Advance Preparation**
3 Options for Individualizing	
Reteaching Students review vocabulary for 2-dimensional shapes. [Geometry] **Extra Practice** Students describe how a given geometric solid is different from two other solids. [Geometry] **Language Diversity** Students create a Word Wall of geometry vocabulary. [Geometry]	□ Teaching Masters (*Math Masters,* pp. 173 and 174) ***See*** **Advance Preparation**

Additional Information

Advance Preparation For Part 1, construct a cube with 12 straws, all the same length. You will need 16 twist-ties, 2 for each vertex. Use this cube to demonstrate how to construct geometric solids.

Place twist-ties and equal numbers of full-size, $\frac{1}{2}$-size, and $\frac{3}{4}$-size straws in four separate boxes. Each pair of students will need 16 twist-ties and 8 straws of each length. If possible, place these materials in a resealable plastic bag for each partnership.

Have models of the following geometric solids available: **rectangular prism, triangular prism, square pyramid, cylinder, cone,** and **sphere.** Gather examples from everyday objects or make them from *Math Masters,* pages 170–172.

For Part 2, students need a balance or scale capable of measuring 1 ounce, as well as pennies, nickels, dimes, and quarters.

For the optional Extra Practice activity in Part 3, prepare copies of *Math Masters,* page 174, which can be cut in half and distributed to students.

Vocabulary • **rectangular prism** • **triangular prism** • **square pyramid** • **cylinder** • **cone** • **sphere** • **geometric solid** • **curved surface** • **cube** • **edge** • **face** • **flat surface** • **vertex (vertices)** • **3-dimensional**

Getting Started

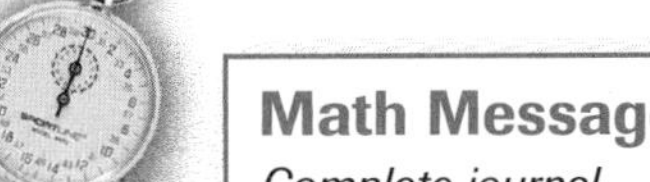

Mental Math and Reflexes

Ask students to stand, space themselves apart, and do the following:

- Rotate clockwise $\frac{1}{4}$ turn.
- Rotate counterclockwise $\frac{1}{2}$ turn.
- Rotate clockwise $\frac{3}{4}$ turn; then counterclockwise $\frac{1}{4}$ turn; and finally counterclockwise $\frac{1}{2}$ turn.
- Rotate 60 degrees clockwise. Ask: *How many more degrees would you have to rotate clockwise to return to your starting position?* 300 degrees
- Rotate counterclockwise 45 degrees; then clockwise 270 degrees; and finally counterclockwise 90 degrees.
- Hold your arm so that it shows a right angle; a 45-degree angle; a 180-degree angle; a 60-degree angle; an acute angle; an obtuse angle.

45°, 90°, and 180° angles

- Hold your arms so that they are parallel to each other; parallel to the floor.

Math Message

Complete journal page 309.

Study Link 11.1 Follow-Up

Students describe some of the objects they weighed and tell how close their estimates were to the actual weights.

Teaching the Lesson

✦ Math Message Follow-Up
(*Math Journal 2,* p. 309)

WHOLE-CLASS ACTIVITY

Display models of the six **geometric solids** shown on journal page 309. Begin with the rectangular prism. Hold it up and ask students to find examples of rectangular prisms in the classroom. You may wish to keep a list on the board or class data pad. Continue this procedure for the remaining solids.

Use the discussion questions on the next page to summarize the activity.

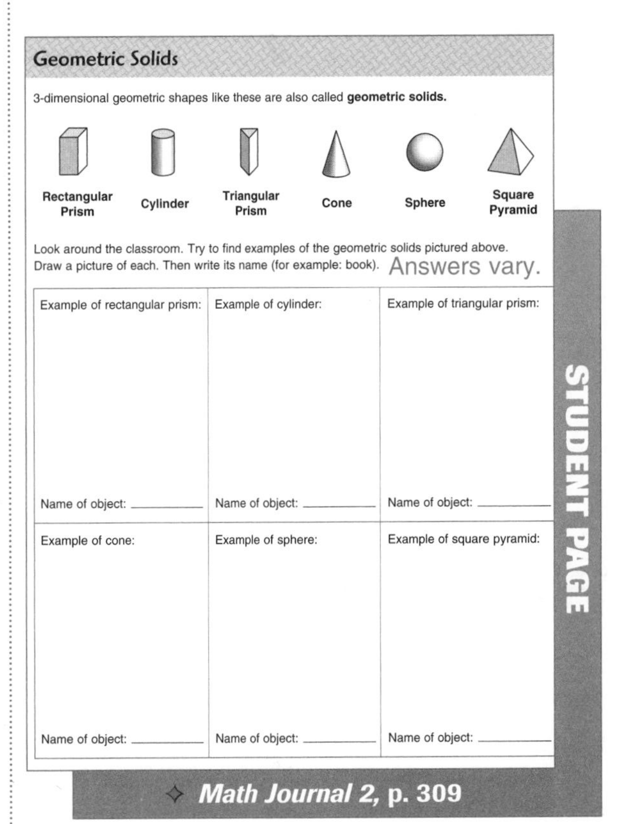

Geometric Solids

3-dimensional geometric shapes like these are also called **geometric solids.**

Rectangular Prism | Cylinder | Triangular Prism | Cone | Sphere | Square Pyramid

Look around the classroom. Try to find examples of the geometric solids pictured above. Draw a picture of each. Then write its name (for example: book). Answers vary.

Example of rectangular prism:	Example of cylinder:	Example of triangular prism:
Name of object: ______	Name of object: ______	Name of object: ______
Example of cone:	Example of sphere:	Example of square pyramid:
Name of object: ______	Name of object: ______	Name of object: ______

STUDENT PAGE

✧ *Math Journal 2,* p. 309

When all of the solids have been discussed, ask students the following:

- Which solids were easy to find? Probably the rectangular prism, cylinder, and sphere
- Which were hard to find? Probably the pyramid, triangular prism, and cone
- Why do you think some solids are more common than others? Probably because they are easier to make or are more useful for storing things

Adjusting the Activity Challenge students to look in their homes or throughout the school for examples of the geometric solids found on journal page 309. They can report their findings to the class.

✦Reviewing Vocabulary for Geometric Solids (*Math Journal 2*, p. 309; *Student Reference Book*, p. 87)

WHOLE-CLASS DISCUSSION 

Use the display models of the six geometric solids and *Student Reference Book,* page 87, to review vocabulary associated with geometric solids. Pose questions like the following:

- Which of these geometric solids has 6 faces? Rectangular prism
- Which solids have a **curved surface**? Sphere, cone, and cylinder
- Which has the most edges? Rectangular prism
- Which has two faces and one curved surface? cylinder

ONGOING ASSESSMENT

Encourage students to use the geometry vocabulary, but do not expect them to be precise at this time.

STUDENT PAGE

Geometry and Constructions

Geometric Solids

Polygons and circles are flat, **2-dimensional** figures. The surfaces they enclose take up a certain amount of area, but they do not have any thickness and do not take up any volume. **Three-dimensional** shapes have length, width, *and* thickness. They take up volume. Boxes, pails, books, and balls are all examples of 3-dimensional shapes.

A **geometric solid** is the surface or surfaces that surround a 3-dimensional shape. The surfaces of a geometric solid may be flat or curved or both. A **flat surface** of a solid is called a **face.** A **curved surface** of a solid does not have any special name.

A **cube** has 6 square faces that are the same size. Three of the cube's faces cannot be seen in the figure at the right.

A **cylinder** has 3 surfaces. The flat top and flat bottom are faces and are formed by circles. A curved surface connects the top and bottom faces. A food can is a good model of a cylinder.

A **cone** has 2 surfaces. The flat bottom is a face that is formed by a circle. A curved surface is connected to the bottom face and comes to a point. An ice cream cone is a good model of a cone. However, keep in mind that a cone is closed; it has a "lid."

The **edges** of a geometric solid are the line segments or curves where surfaces meet. A corner of a geometric solid is called a **vertex** (plural *vertices*). A vertex is usually a point at which edges meet, but the vertex of a cone is an isolated corner. It is completely separated from the edge of the cone.

A **sphere** has one curved surface but no edges and no vertices. A basketball or globe is a good model of a sphere.

no edges, no vertices

CHECK YOUR UNDERSTANDING

1. **a.** How are cylinders and cones alike? **b.** How do they differ?
2. **a.** How are spheres and cones alike? **b.** How do they differ?

Check your answers on page 281.

eighty-seven 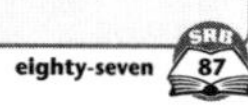

Student Reference Book, p. 87

✦ Modeling Geometric Solids
(*Math Journal 2,* p. 310)

PARTNER ACTIVITY 

Show the class the **cube** you constructed out of straws. (See Advance Preparation.) Point out that it shows only the **edges** of the **faces.** It is a "frame" for the geometric solid; the **flat surfaces** of the cube must be imagined.

Ask students what geometric solid this construction represents. Cube, or rectangular prism Demonstrate how the **vertices** (corners) are put together.

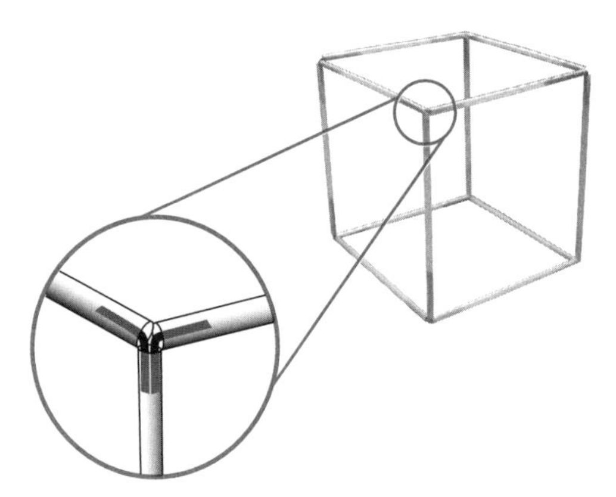

Distribute straws and twist-ties. (See Advance Preparation.) Have partners work together to make a rectangular prism. One way is to start with a rectangle and build up. Have the straw cube, as well as other models of rectangular prisms, available for inspection. Circulate as students work and assist as necessary. When their rectangular prism is finished, partners should complete journal page 310.

NOTE: Problem 3 on journal page 310 asks students to identify the number of square faces in the rectangular prisms they have made. Depending upon the straw sizes used, the prisms will have either 0 or 2 square faces. Students cannot construct cubes (which have 6 square faces) because they have only 8 straws of each length.

 **Adjusting the Activity** Challenge students to make other shapes with the straws and twist-ties.

Modeling a Rectangular Prism

After you make a rectangular prism, answer the questions below.

(edges, vertices, faces)

1. How many faces does your rectangular prism have? 6 faces
2. How many of these faces are formed by rectangles? 6 faces
3. How many of these faces are formed by squares? 0, or 2 faces
4. Pick one of the faces. How many other faces are parallel to it? 1 face(s)
5. How many edges does your rectangular prism have? 12 edges
6. Pick an edge. How many other edges are parallel to it? 3 edges
7. How many vertices does your rectangular prism have? 8 vertices
8. Write T (true) or F (false) for each of the following statements about the rectangular prism you made.
   a. T It has no curved surfaces.
   b. F It is a cylinder.
   c. T All of the faces are polygons.
   d. F It has exactly four faces.
   e. F All of the edges are parallel.
   f. T It has more vertices than faces.

Challenge

9. Draw a picture of your rectangular prism. You can show hidden edges with dashed lines (- - - -).

STUDENT PAGE

✧ *Math Journal 2,* p. 310

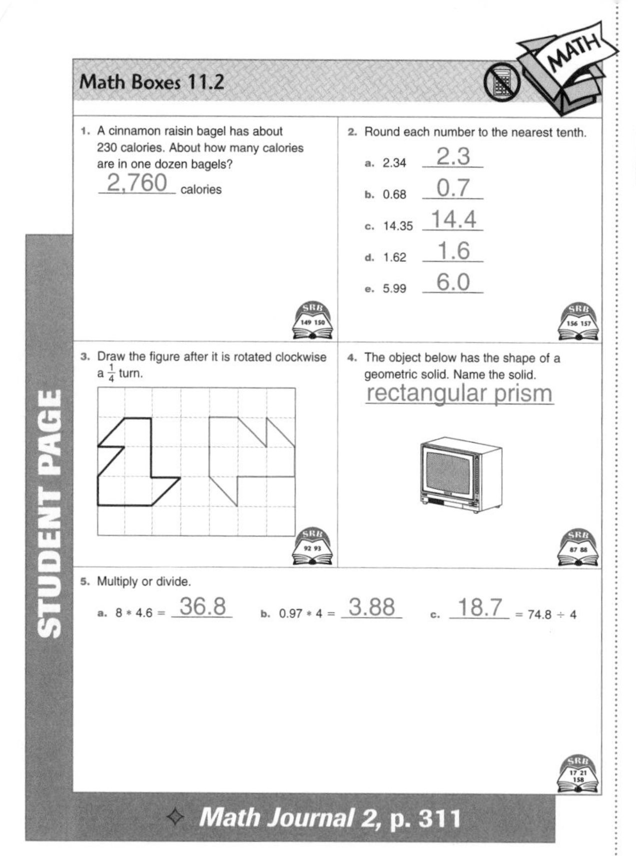
Math Boxes 11.2

1. A cinnamon raisin bagel has about 230 calories. About how many calories are in one dozen bagels?
2,760 calories

2. Round each number to the nearest tenth.
a. 2.34 2.3
b. 0.68 0.7
c. 14.35 14.4
d. 1.62 1.6
e. 5.99 6.0

3. Draw the figure after it is rotated clockwise a $\frac{1}{4}$ turn.

4. The object below has the shape of a geometric solid. Name the solid.
rectangular prism

5. Multiply or divide.
a. 8 ∗ 4.6 = 36.8
b. 0.97 ∗ 4 = 3.88
c. 18.7 = 74.8 ÷ 4

STUDENT PAGE

Math Journal 2, p. 311

2 Ongoing Learning & Practice

Making a 1-Ounce Weight

SMALL-GROUP ACTIVITY 

Students use a balance or scale to determine how many of each available type of U.S. coin are needed to make a 1-ounce weight. Students can display the results of their experiments in the Gram & Ounce Museum.

Math Boxes 11.2 (*Math Journal 2,* p. 311)

INDEPENDENT ACTIVITY 

Mixed Review Math Boxes in this lesson are paired with Math Boxes in Lessons 11.4 and 11.6. The skills in Problems 1 and 2 are prerequisites for Unit 12.

Study Link 11.2 (*Math Masters,* p. 367)

Home Connection Students identify geometric solids represented by various objects. They also identify the vertices and the number of edges in two geometric solids.

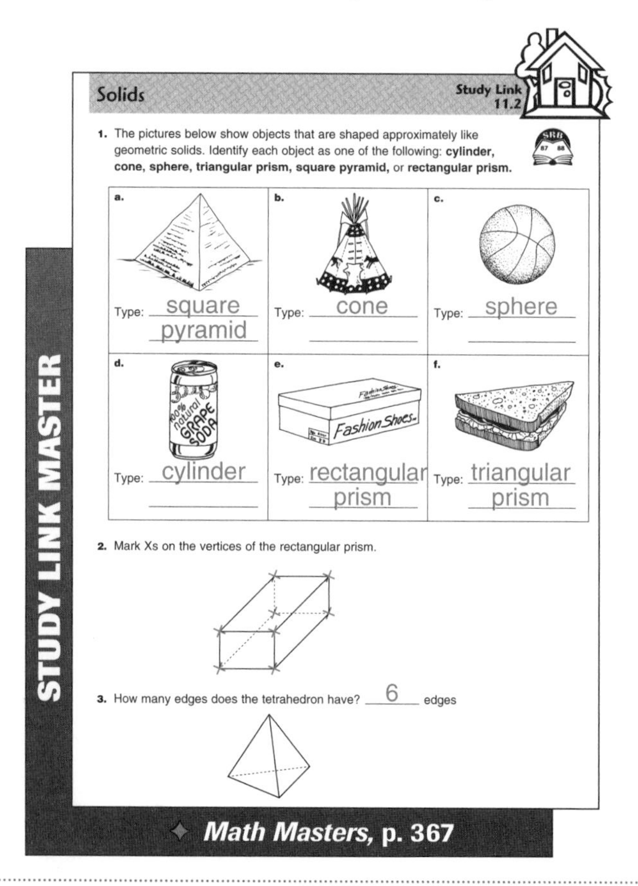
Solids — Study Link 11.2

1. The pictures below show objects that are shaped approximately like geometric solids. Identify each object as one of the following: **cylinder, cone, sphere, triangular prism, square pyramid,** or **rectangular prism.**

a. Type: square pyramid
b. Type: cone
c. Type: sphere
d. Type: cylinder
e. Type: rectangular prism
f. Type: triangular prism

2. Mark Xs on the vertices of the rectangular prism.

3. How many edges does the tetrahedron have? 6 edges

STUDY LINK MASTER

Math Masters, p. 367

Options for Individualizing

✦ RETEACHING Reviewing 2-Dimensional Shapes (*Math Masters,* p. 173)

INDEPENDENT ACTIVITY  **5–15 min** 

To understand **3-dimensional** geometry, it helps to review and extend ideas from 2-dimensional geometry. Polygons are 2-dimensional figures formed by line segments. Geometric solids are 3-dimensional shapes formed by surfaces, some of which may be formed by polygons. Some students may benefit from this vocabulary review.

✦ EXTRA PRACTICE Comparing Geometric Solids (*Math Masters,* p. 174)

INDEPENDENT ACTIVITY  **5–15 min** 

Students describe how a given geometric solid is different from two other geometric solids.

✦ LANGUAGE DIVERSITY Creating a Word Wall

SMALL-GROUP ACTIVITY  **30+ min** 

Many students will benefit from a classroom display of geometry vocabulary. Enlist the help of students to create illustrated definitions of key geometric terms and post them. Some students may find it helpful to make individual booklets.

Geometry Review

Match each description of a geometric figure in Column I with its name in Column II. Some of the items in Column II do not have a match.

I	II
a. a polygon with 4 right angles and 4 sides of the same length	f octagon
b. any polygon that has 4 sides	e rhombus
c. a quadrilateral with exactly one pair of opposite sides that are parallel	i right angle
d. lines that never intersect	___ acute angle
e. a parallelogram with all sides the same length and that is not a rectangle	c trapezoid
f. a polygon with 8 sides	___ hexagon
g. two lines that are at right angles to each other	a square
h. a polygon with 5 sides	j equilateral triangle
i. an angle that measures 90°	g perpendicular lines
j. a triangle with all sides the same length	d parallel lines
	h pentagon
	___ isosceles triangle
	b quadrangle (or quadrilateral)

TEACHING MASTER

✦ *Math Masters,* p. 173

Comparing Geometric Solids

In each of the following lists, tell how the underlined geometric solid is different from the other two solids. Try to give more than one difference. Sample answers:

1. rectangular prism, cone, cylinder
   a. Has no curved surfaces
   b. Has no curved edges
2. cylinder, square pyramid, cone
   a. Has 2 circular faces
   b. Has 2 edges
3. square pyramid, cylinder, cone
   a. Has no curved surfaces
   b. Has more than 1 vertex
4. sphere, cone, cylinder
   a. Has no edges
   b. Has no faces

174

Name ______ Date ______ Time ______

Comparing Geometric Solids

In each of the following lists, tell how the underlined geometric solid is different from the other two solids. Try to give more than one difference.

1. rectangular prism, cone, cylinder
   a. ______
   b. ______
2. cylinder, square pyramid, cone
   a. ______
   b. ______
3. square pyramid, cylinder, cone
   a. ______
   b. ______
4. sphere, cone, cylinder
   a. ______
   b. ______

TEACHING MASTER

✦ *Math Masters,* p. 174

11.3 Constructing Geometric Solids

OBJECTIVES **To identify geometric solids, given their properties; and to construct polyhedrons with straws and twist-ties.**

summaries	materials
1 Teaching the Lesson	
Students practice identifying geometric solids by solving riddles about their properties. [Geometry] Students construct polyhedrons with straws and twist-ties. [Geometry]	□ *Math Journal 2,* p. 312 □ *Student Reference Book,* p. 88 □ Study Link 11.2 □ Teaching Masters (*Math Masters,* pp. 175 and 176; optional) □ Transparencies (*Math Masters,* pp. 177–178; optional) □ models of geometric solids (see Lesson 11.2) □ straws and twist-ties (see Lesson 11.2) □ boxes; resealable bags, optional (see Lesson 11.2) ***See* Advance Preparation**
2 Ongoing Learning & Practice	
Students play the *Credits/Debits Game* to practice addition of positive and negative integers. [Operations and Computation] Students practice and maintain skills through Math Boxes and Study Link activities.	□ *Math Journal 2,* p. 313 □ *Student Reference Book,* p. 192 □ Teaching Master (*Math Masters,* p. 166) □ Study Link Master (*Math Masters,* p. 368) □ deck of number cards per partnership (from the Everything Math Deck, if available)
3 Options for Individualizing	
Enrichment Students write and solve "What am I?" riddles about geometric solids. [Geometry] **Enrichment** Students practice drawing cubes. [Geometry] **Enrichment** Students make a model of a tetrahedron. [Geometry]	□ Teaching Masters (*Math Masters,* pp. 179–182) □ books by Ed Emberley □ staples, tape, or glue □ scissors ***See* Advance Preparation**

Additional Information

Advance Preparation For Part 1, in addition to the geometric solids from Lesson 11.2 (rectangular prism, triangular prism, square pyramid, cylinder, cone, and sphere) you will need a triangular pyramid and a cube. Gather examples from everyday objects or make them from *Math Masters,* pages 175 and 176.

For the second optional Enrichment activity in Part 3, obtain as many of the following books by Ed Emberley as possible: *Ed Emberley's Big Green Drawing Book* (Little, Brown, 1979); *Ed Emberley's Big Orange Drawing Book* (Little, Brown, 1980); *Ed Emberley's Big Purple Drawing Book* (Little, Brown, 1981); *Ed Emberley's Big Red Drawing Book* (Little, Brown, 1987). For the third optional Enrichment activity in Part 3, students each need one copy of *Math Masters,* page 181 and two copies of *Math Masters,* page 182 to construct a tetrahedron.

Vocabulary • **polyhedron** • **triangular pyramid (tetrahedron)** • **dodecahedron**

Getting Started

Mental Math and Reflexes

Tell students that a kilogram is a little more than 2 pounds. (It's about 2.2 pounds.) Pose the following questions. For each question, ask students if the actual weight is more or less than their approximation.

- If a tiger weighs 300 kilograms, what is its approximate weight in pounds? 600, more
- If a gorilla weighs 220 kilograms, what is its approximate weight in pounds? 440, more
- If a grizzly bear weighs 1,720 pounds, what is its approximate weight in kilograms? 860, less
- If an African elephant weighs 11,023 pounds, what is its approximate weight in kilograms? 5,500, less

Math Message

Open your Student Reference Book *to page 88.*
Solve the following riddle:
I have the same number of faces as vertices. What am I?

Study Link 11.2 Follow-Up

Review answers.

1 Teaching the Lesson

✦ Math Message Follow-Up
(*Student Reference Book,* p. 88)

WHOLE-CLASS DISCUSSION

All of the pyramids shown at the top of page 88 of the *Student Reference Book* have the same number of faces as vertices. Pose another riddle: *I have 6 faces. All of my faces are rectangles. What am I?* Rectangular prism

Emphasize that a **polyhedron** (plural *polyhedrons* or *polyhedra*) is a geometric solid whose surfaces are all formed by polygons. A polyhedron does not have any curved surfaces.

Display the six geometric solids from Lesson 11.2 and the triangular pyramid and cube. Ask: *Which of these solids is NOT a polyhedron?* Cylinder, sphere, and cone

Geometry and Constructions

Polyhedrons

A **polyhedron** is a geometric solid whose surfaces are all formed by polygons. These surfaces are the faces of the polyhedron. A polyhedron does not have any curved surfaces.

Pyramids and **prisms** are two important kinds of polyhedrons.

All of the following polyhedrons are pyramids.

base — triangular pyramid; square pyramid; pentagonal pyramid; hexagonal pyramid

The shaded face of each of these pyramids is called the **base** of the pyramid. The shape of the base is used to name the pyramid. For example, the base of a triangular pyramid has a triangular shape.

All of the faces of a pyramid that are not a base meet at the same vertex.

All of the following polyhedrons are prisms.

base — triangular prism; rectangular prism; pentagonal prism; hexagonal prism

The two shaded faces of each prism are called the **bases** of the prism. The bases of a prism are the same size and shape. They are parallel.

The shape of the bases of a prism are used to name the prism. For example, the bases of a pentagonal prism have the shape of a pentagon.

Many polyhedrons are not pyramids or prisms. Some are illustrated below.

Polyhedrons that Are NOT Pyramids or Prisms

SRB 88 eighty-eight

STUDENT PAGE

✦ *Student Reference Book,* p. 88

✦ Solving Geometry Riddles
(*Math Masters,* pp. 177 and 178)

WHOLE-CLASS ACTIVITY

On the board, write additional riddles for students to solve, or use overhead transparencies of *Math Masters,* pages 177 and 178. The riddles that appear on these two masters are given below. You might uncover one clue at a time and have students guess each time. When all clues have been given, ask a student to come up and display the correct solid or to show a picture of it in the *Student Reference Book* and name it. Ask the student to explain how he or she knew it was that particular solid.

Riddle 1
I am a geometric solid.
I have six faces.
All of my faces are squares.
What am I? cube

Riddle 2
I am a geometric solid.
I have 2 surfaces.
My base is formed by a circle.
I come to a point at the top.
What am I? cone

Riddle 3
I am a polyhedron.
I have the fewest number of faces of all the polyhedrons.
All of my faces are triangular.
I come to a point at the top.
What am I? **triangular pyramid,** or **tetrahedron**

Riddle 4
I am a polyhedron.
My faces are pentagons.
I am useful for calendars.
My picture is on page 89 of the *Student Reference Book.*
What am I? **dodecahedron**

Riddle 5

I am a polyhedron.
I have two triangular bases.
My other faces are rectangles.
Sometimes I am used for keeping doors open.
What am I? triangular prism

Riddle 6

I am a geometric solid.
I have only one surface.
My one surface is curved.
I have no base.
What am I? sphere

Adjusting the Activity Consider turning the riddle activity into a game. Divide the class into two teams. If a team needs only one clue to solve the riddle, they get 1 point; if they need two clues, 2 points, and so on. The team with fewer points wins.

✦ Using Straws and Twist-Ties to Model Polyhedrons (*Math Journal 2,* p. 312)

PARTNER ACTIVITY 

Remind students how the straws and twist-ties were used to make the frames for cubes and rectangular prisms in Lesson 11.2. Students should work with partners to construct polyhedrons and answer the riddles on journal page 312. After students have had enough time, review answers. Even though students may have constructed solids that differ in size depending on the lengths of the straws they used, the shapes should have the same properties.

Adjusting the Activity Some students may find it helpful to have the geometric solids available as they work in the journal. If possible, put out more than one set.

Construction of Polyhedrons

Polyhedrons are geometric solids with flat surfaces formed by polygons.

For each problem below—

- Decide what the polyhedron should look like.
- Use straws and twist-ties to model the polyhedron.
- Answer the questions about the polyhedron.

Look at page 88 of the *Student Reference Book* if you need help with the name.

1. I am a polyhedron.
   I have 5 faces.
   Four of my faces are formed by triangles.
   One of my faces is a square.
   a. After you make me, draw a picture of me. Sample answer:
   b. What am I? square pyramid
   c. How many corners (vertices) do I have? 5 vertices
   d. What shape is my base? square

2. I am a polyhedron.
   I have 4 faces.
   All of my faces are formed by equilateral triangles.
   All of my faces are the same size.
   a. After you make me, draw a picture of me. Sample answer:
   b. What am I? triangular pyramid
   c. How many corners (vertices) do I have? 4 vertices
   d. What shape is my base? triangle

STUDENT PAGE

✧ *Math Journal 2,* p. 312

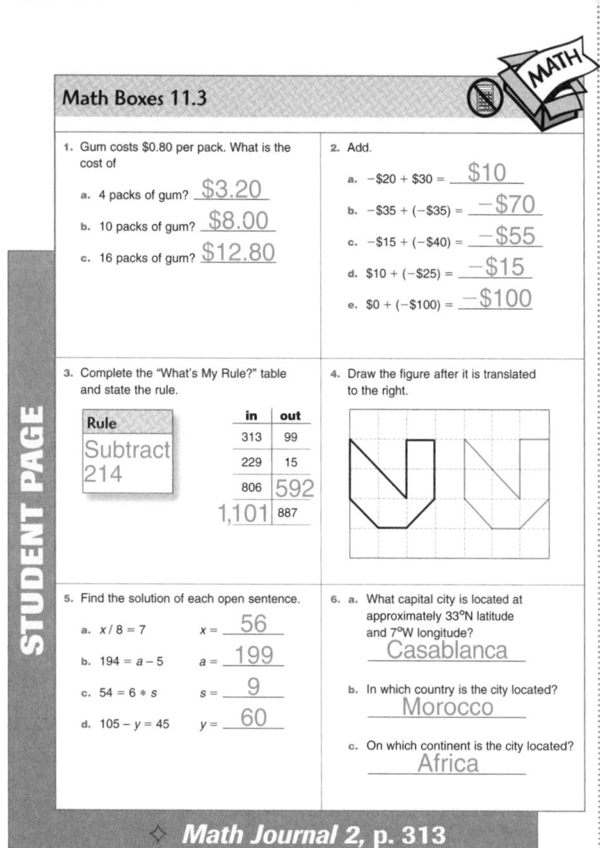

Math Boxes 11.3

1. Gum costs $0.80 per pack. What is the cost of
   a. 4 packs of gum? $3.20
   b. 10 packs of gum? $8.00
   c. 16 packs of gum? $12.80

2. Add.
   a. −$20 + $30 = $10
   b. −$35 + (−$35) = −$70
   c. −$15 + (−$40) = −$55
   d. $10 + (−$25) = −$15
   e. $0 + (−$100) = −$100

3. Complete the "What's My Rule?" table and state the rule.

Rule: Subtract 214

in	out
313	99
229	15
806	592
1,101	887

4. Draw the figure after it is translated to the right.

5. Find the solution of each open sentence.
   a. $x / 8 = 7$ x = 56
   b. $194 = a - 5$ a = 199
   c. $54 = 6 * s$ s = 9
   d. $105 - y = 45$ y = 60

6. a. What capital city is located at approximately 33°N latitude and 7°W longitude? Casablanca
   b. In which country is the city located? Morocco
   c. On which continent is the city located? Africa

STUDENT PAGE

Math Journal 2, p. 313

2 Ongoing Learning & Practice

Playing the *Credits/Debits Game* (*Student Reference Book,* p. 192; *Math Masters,* p. 166)

PARTNER ACTIVITY

Students practice adding positive and negative integers as they keep track of the "bottom line" for a business.

ONGOING ASSESSMENT

In Lesson 11.6, students subtract positive and negative integers. It is important that students are comfortable adding such numbers before they begin that lesson.

Math Boxes 11.3 (*Math Journal 2,* p. 313)

INDEPENDENT ACTIVITY 

Mixed Review Math Boxes in this lesson are paired with Math Boxes in Lesson 11.1. The skill in Problem 1 is a prerequisite for Unit 12.

Study Link 11.3 (*Math Masters,* p. 368)

Home Connection Students solve riddles about geometric solids. They may use the *Student Reference Book* to verify their solutions.

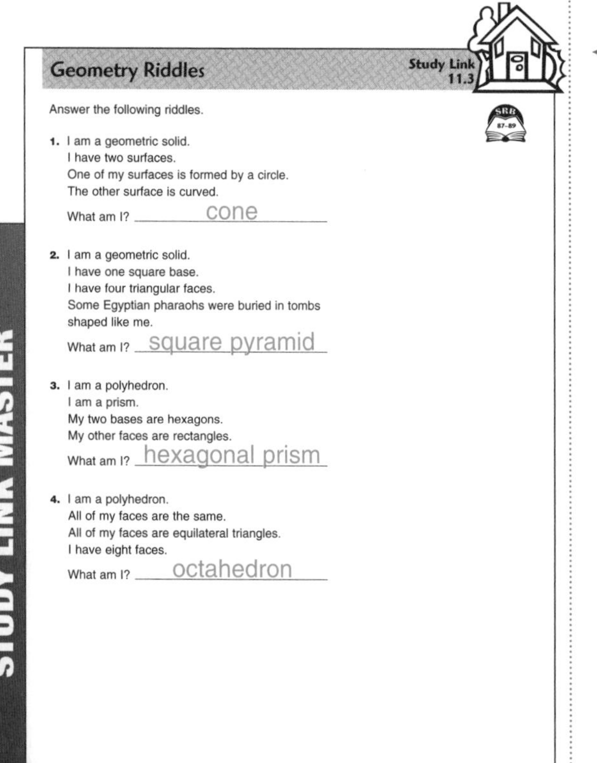

Geometry Riddles — Study Link 11.3

Answer the following riddles.

1. I am a geometric solid.
   I have two surfaces.
   One of my surfaces is formed by a circle.
   The other surface is curved.
   What am I? cone

2. I am a geometric solid.
   I have one square base.
   I have four triangular faces.
   Some Egyptian pharaohs were buried in tombs shaped like me.
   What am I? square pyramid

3. I am a polyhedron.
   I am a prism.
   My two bases are hexagons.
   My other faces are rectangles.
   What am I? hexagonal prism

4. I am a polyhedron.
   All of my faces are the same.
   All of my faces are equilateral triangles.
   I have eight faces.
   What am I? octahedron

STUDY LINK MASTER

Math Masters, p. 368

Options for Individualizing

✦ ENRICHMENT Writing and Solving "What Am I?" Riddles

INDEPENDENT ACTIVITY  **5–15 min** 

Language Arts Link Show students how to make up their own riddles. Here is a simple approach.

1. Think of the answer.
2. Make up several clues. The clues should enable a clever-enough person to guess the riddle. Point out that riddles move from vague statements ("I am a geometric solid") to specific descriptions ("My base is formed by a circle").
3. Check to make sure the riddle is correct. Do all the clues fit? Is there more than one answer?

Challenge students to draw the shape next to each riddle. The drawing should be covered so that other students must use the clues to guess the hidden shape. You can make either a bulletin-board display or a class book of riddles.

✦ ENRICHMENT Drawing a Cube
(*Math Masters,* pp. 179 and 180)

INDEPENDENT ACTIVITY  **30+ min** 

Art Link Students experiment with different ways to draw a cube.

The following books provide step-by-step instructions for using simple sketches to draw a variety of pictures:

Ed Emberley's Big Green Drawing Book

Ed Emberley's Big Orange Drawing Book

Ed Emberley's Big Purple Drawing Book

Ed Emberley's Big Red Drawing Book

Drawing a Cube

Knowing how to draw is a useful skill in mathematics. There are several ways to draw a cube. Here are a few ways. Try them and experiment on your own.

A Basic Cube

Draw a square.

Draw another square that overlaps your first square. The second square should be the same size as the first.

Connect the corners of your two squares as shown. This picture doesn't look much like a real cube. One problem is that the picture shows all 12 edges, even though not all the edges of a real cube can be seen at one time. Another problem is that it's hard to tell which face of the cube is in front.

A Better Cube

Begin with a square.

Next, draw 3 parallel line segments going right and up from three corners of your square. The segments should all be the same length.

Finally, connect the ends of the 3 line segments.

This cube is better than before, but it shows only the edges and corners, not the faces. If you want, try shading your cube to make it look more realistic.

TEACHING MASTER

✦ *Math Masters,* p. 179

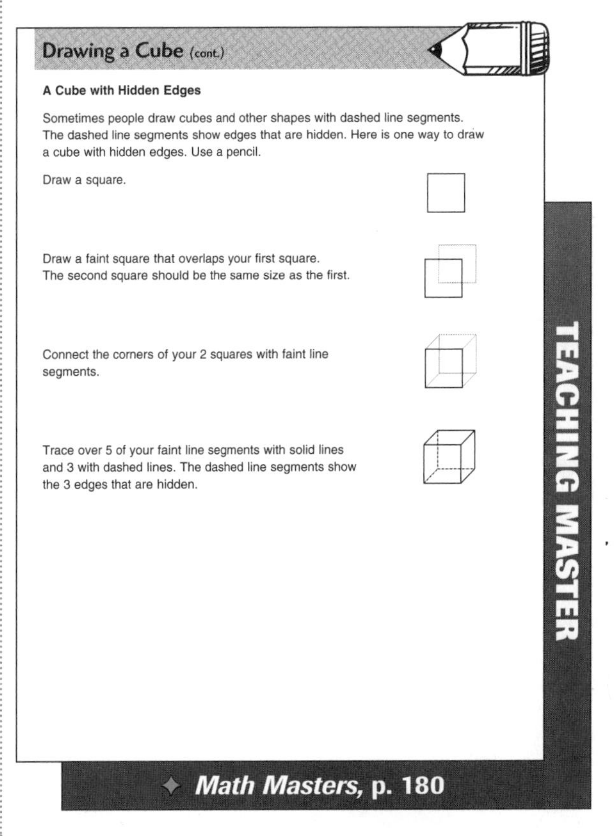
Drawing a Cube (cont.)

A Cube with Hidden Edges

Sometimes people draw cubes and other shapes with dashed line segments. The dashed line segments show edges that are hidden. Here is one way to draw a cube with hidden edges. Use a pencil.

Draw a square.

Draw a faint square that overlaps your first square. The second square should be the same size as the first.

Connect the corners of your 2 squares with faint line segments.

Trace over 5 of your faint line segments with solid lines and 3 with dashed lines. The dashed line segments show the 3 edges that are hidden.

TEACHING MASTER

✦ *Math Masters,* p. 180

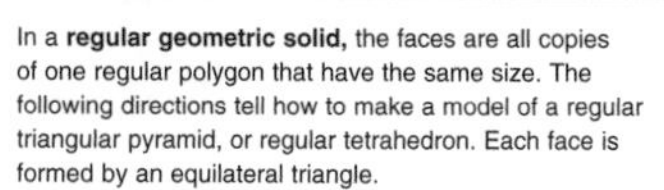

TEACHING MASTER

Making a Model of a Tetrahedron

In a **regular geometric solid,** the faces are all copies of one regular polygon that have the same size. The following directions tell how to make a model of a regular triangular pyramid, or regular tetrahedron. Each face is formed by an equilateral triangle.

Step 1

Cut out 4 circles with equilateral triangles from two copies of *Math Masters,* page 182, "Circle and Equilateral Triangle Patterns."

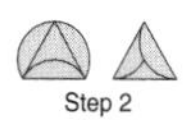

Step 1

Step 2

Fold each circle along all three sides of the triangle.

Step 2

Step 3

Lay down one of your paper circles and unfold it so that the three curved flaps stick up. It will be the base.

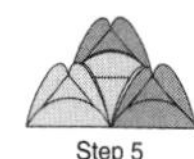

Steps 3 and 4

Step 4

Take another paper circle. Match one side of its triangle with a side of the triangle on the base. Use staples, tape, or glue to fasten the two curved flaps together.

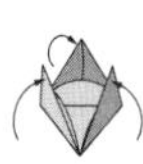

Step 5

Step 5

In the same way, attach the other two paper circles to other sides of the base.

Step 6

Fold up the three paper circles that you attached to the base. The triangles come together to form the tetrahedron. Either push all the flaps inside and tape the edges together, or leave two or three flaps outside and tape or glue them to the tetrahedron.

Finished

✦ *Math Masters,* p. 181

TEACHING MASTER

Circle and Equilateral Triangle Patterns

✦ *Math Masters,* p. 182

✦ ENRICHMENT Making a Model of a Tetrahedron (*Math Masters,* pp. 181 and 182)

INDEPENDENT ACTIVITY  **30+ min** 

Students follow the instructions on *Math Masters,* page 181 to construct a regular tetrahedron. They each need 2 copies of *Math Masters,* page 182.

Some students may find that the tetrahedron can be formed with only three paper circles. The fourth face can be formed with the flaps of the other three paper circles.

Adjusting the Activity If you prefer, ask students to draw their own circles and equilateral triangles rather than giving them copies of *Math Masters,* page 182. They can apply the techniques learned in Unit 1, in which they drew circles and divided them into six equal parts. Connecting alternating points yields an equilateral triangle. Students must be sure that their four circles all have the same radius.

For students who are learning to speak and write in English, you might have them look up the word parts *tetra-, -hedron, poly-, deca-,* and *dodeca-* in the dictionary to give them a better understanding of the origins and meanings of geometric terms.

11.4 A Volume Exploration

OBJECTIVE **To review concepts and units of volume.**

summaries	materials
1 Teaching the Lesson	
Students read and discuss an essay about volume in the *Student Reference Book.* [Measurement and Reference Frames] Students use base-10 blocks and metersticks to visualize the sizes of various metric cubic units. They also make open boxes and fill them with centimeter cubes to determine their volume. [Measurement and Reference Frames]	☐ *Student Reference Book,* p. 117 ☐ Study Link 11.3 ☐ Teaching Master (*Math Masters,* p. 20) ☐ slate ☐ base-10 blocks ☐ cm cubes ☐ tape ☐ metersticks; cones and string (optional) ☐ scissors ***See*** **Advance Preparation**
2 Ongoing Learning & Practice	
Students practice converting between ounces, pounds, and tons as they solve problems involving some of the world's largest foods. [Measurement and Reference Frames] Students practice and maintain skills through Math Boxes and Study Link activities.	☐ *Math Journal 2,* pp. 314 and 315 ☐ Study Link Master (*Math Masters,* p. 369) ☐ scissors
3 Options for Individualizing	
Language Diversity Students look up the word *volume* in a dictionary and record as many different definitions as they can find. [Measurement and Reference Frames] **Extra Practice** Students use rulers, yardsticks, and grocery bags to visualize the sizes of various U.S. customary cubic units. [Measurement and Reference Frames]	☐ Teaching Master (*Math Masters,* p. 183) ☐ dictionary ☐ inch cube for demonstration purposes ☐ at least 3 12-inch rulers or 3 yardsticks per group; or 2 brown paper shopping bags, 12-inch ruler, and scissors per group

Additional Information

Advance Preparation For the cubic meter demonstration in Part 1, you will need 3 metersticks; for the alternative demonstration, you will need 4 metersticks, 4 traffic cones, and string; or 2 metersticks, 2 traffic cones, string, and tape. See the illustrations on page 803.

Vocabulary • **cubic units** • **volume** • **dimensions**

Getting Started

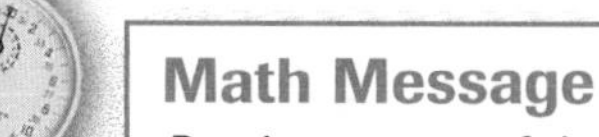

Mental Math and Reflexes

Pose problems about symmetry and have students draw their answers on their slates.
Suggestions

- Draw a picture that has no lines of symmetry.
- Draw a picture that has exactly 1 line of symmetry.
- Draw a picture that has more than 2 lines of symmetry.

Math Message

Read page 117 of the Student Reference Book. *Be prepared to explain why there is a picture of a sandbox on the page.*

Study Link 11.3 Follow-Up

Review answers.

1 Teaching the Lesson

✦ Math Message Follow-Up (*Student Reference Book,* p. 117)

WHOLE-CLASS DISCUSSION

Review the information on *Student Reference Book,* page 117. Once students explain the significance of the picture of the sandbox, ask them to give other examples in which it is useful to know the volume of an object.

Examples

▷ buying a cooler—to decide whether it is big enough to hold all the food taken on a camping trip

▷ renting a car—to decide if the trunk is large enough to hold all the family's luggage

✦ Visualizing Metric Cubic Units

WHOLE-CLASS ACTIVITY

Discuss the following:

▷ Linear measurements are usually given in standard units (such as feet or meters), and area measurements are often given in squares of those units (such as square feet or square meters). Many volume measurements are given in cubes of standard units, or **cubic units.**

STUDENT PAGE

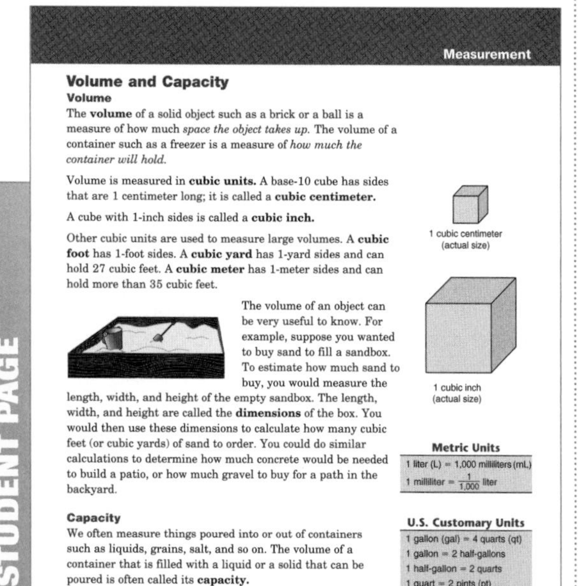

Measurement

Volume and Capacity

Volume

The **volume** of a solid object such as a brick or a ball is a measure of how much *space the object takes up.* The volume of a container such as a freezer is a measure of *how much the container will hold.*

Volume is measured in **cubic units.** A base-10 cube has sides that are 1 centimeter long; it is called a **cubic centimeter.**

A cube with 1-inch sides is called a **cubic inch.**

Other cubic units are used to measure large volumes. A **cubic foot** has 1-foot sides. A **cubic yard** has 1-yard sides and can hold 27 cubic feet. A **cubic meter** has 1-meter sides and can hold more than 35 cubic feet.

1 cubic centimeter (actual size)

1 cubic inch (actual size)

The volume of an object can be very useful to know. For example, suppose you wanted to buy sand to fill a sandbox. To estimate how much sand to buy, you would measure the length, width, and height of the empty sandbox. The length, width, and height are called the **dimensions** of the box. You would then use these dimensions to calculate how many cubic feet (or cubic yards) of sand to order. You could do similar calculations to determine how much concrete would be needed to build a patio, or how much gravel to buy for a path in the backyard.

Capacity

We often measure things poured into or out of containers such as liquids, grains, salt, and so on. The volume of a container that is filled with a liquid or a solid that can be poured is often called its **capacity.**

Capacity is usually measured in units such as **gallons, quarts, pints, cups, fluid ounces, liters,** and **milliliters.** These are standard units, but they are not cubic units.

The tables at the right compare different units of capacity.

Metric Units
1 liter (L) = 1,000 milliliters (mL)
1 milliliter = $\frac{1}{1,000}$ liter

U.S. Customary Units
1 gallon (gal) = 4 quarts (qt)
1 gallon = 2 half-gallons
1 half-gallon = 2 quarts
1 quart = 2 pints (pt)
1 pint = 2 cups (c)
1 cup = 8 fluid ounces (fl oz)
1 pint = 16 fluid ounces
1 quart = 32 fluid ounces
1 half-gallon = 64 fluid ounces
1 gallon = 128 fluid ounces

one hundred seventeen SRB 117

✦ *Student Reference Book,* p. 117

▷ The area of a closed 2-dimensional figure is the number of unit squares and fractions of unit squares needed to fill the interior of the figure. The **volume** of a 3-dimensional object is the number of unit cubes and fractions of unit cubes needed to fill the space taken up by the object.

Use base-10 blocks and metersticks to help students visualize the sizes of various metric cubic units.

▷ Hold up a cm cube. Point out that each edge is 1 centimeter long, and so the volume of a cm cube is 1 cubic centimeter.

▷ Hold up a "big cube." Point out that each edge is 10 centimeters, or 1 decimeter, long, and so the volume of a "big cube" is 1 cubic decimeter.

Ask: *How many cubic centimeters are there in 1 cubic decimeter?* Have students use base-10 blocks to "prove" their answers. There are 10 cubic centimeters in 1 long; there are 10 longs, or 100 cubic centimeters, in 1 flat. You can fill a cubic decimeter container with 10 flats, or 1,000 cubic centimeters. Therefore, 1 cubic decimeter equals 1,000 cubic centimeters.

You will not have enough base-10 blocks to build a 1-meter cube, but you can help students visualize such a cube with the help of three metersticks. Place two metersticks on a flat surface at right angles to each other. Then hold up a third meterstick perpendicular to the other metersticks, so that all three sticks meet in one corner. With the help of this partial frame, students can imagine a cube whose edges are the length of a meterstick. The volume of this cube is 1 cubic meter.

Another way to model a cubic meter is to use hollow traffic cones, which you may be able to borrow from the gym.

Place four cones on the floor at the corners of a square, 1 meter on a side. Put a meterstick through the top of each cone so that each stick stands straight up. Connect the tops of the metersticks with string to form a square. The strings should be as close to the top of the metersticks as possible.

A variation of this model uses two cones and two metersticks. Place the cones 1 meter from a wall and 1 meter apart. Connect the tops of the metersticks with a string. Then run a string from the top of each meterstick to the wall, at a height of 1 meter, and tape the string to the wall.

Adjusting the Activity Challenge students with the following questions: *How many cubic decimeters are in 1 cubic meter?* 1,000 *How many cubic centimeters are in 1 cubic meter?* 1,000 ∗ 1,000 = 1,000,000

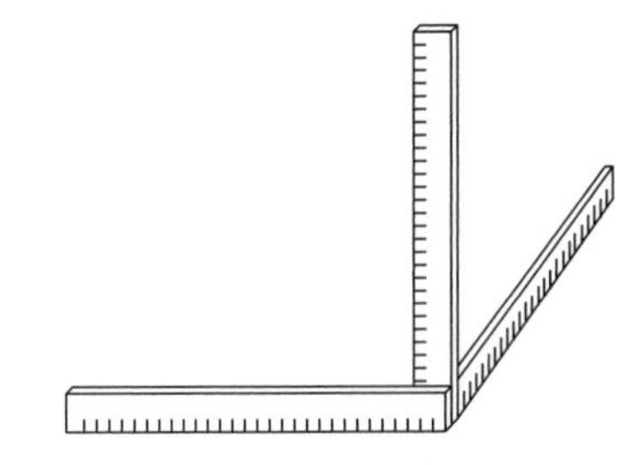

Modeling the dimensions of a meter cube

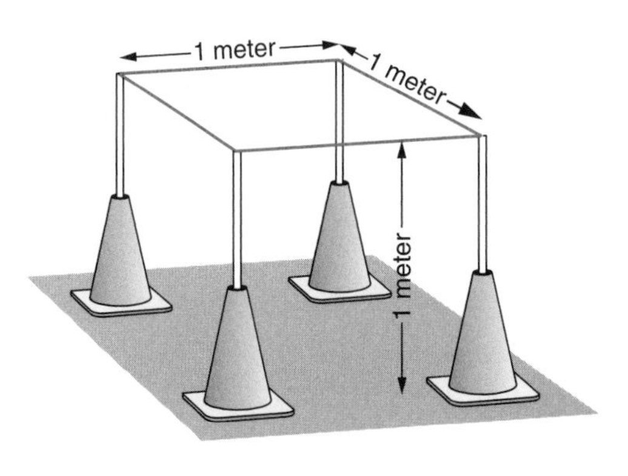

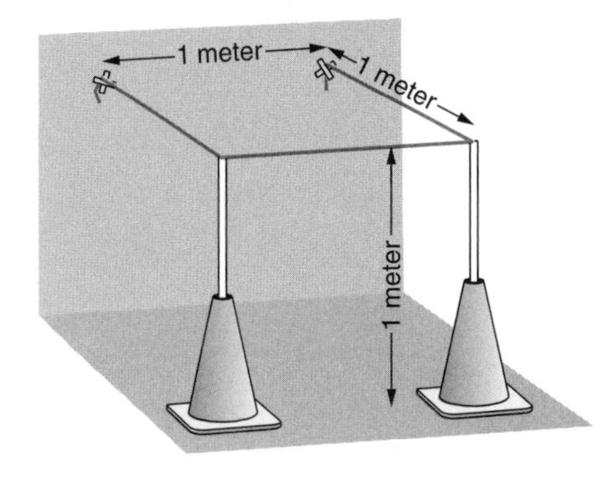

Two methods for modeling a meter cube using metersticks and traffic cones

STUDENT PAGE

The World's Largest Foods

Food	Weight	Date	Location
apple	3 pounds, 11 ounces	not available	Linton, England
broccoli	35 pounds	1993	Palmer, Alaska
bowl of spaghetti	605 pounds	August 16, 1998	London, England
Chinese dumpling	1,058 pounds, 3 ounces	July 5, 1997	Hong Kong
gyro	1.03 tons	July 1998	Zurich, Switzerland
hamburger	2.5 tons	August 5, 1989	Seymour, Wisconsin
ice cream sundae	22.59 tons	July 24, 1988	Alberta, Canada
jelly doughnut	1.5 tons	January 21, 1993	Utica, New York
pineapple	17 pounds, 12 ounces	1994	Ais Village, Papua New Guinea
pumpkin	1,092 pounds	October 3, 1998	Ontario, Canada

Source: Guinness World Records 2000, Millennium Edition

Use the information in the table to solve the following problems.

1. The largest apple weighed 59 ounces.
2. The largest Chinese dumpling weighed 16,931 ounces.
3. How much more did the largest broccoli weigh than the largest pineapple?
   17 pounds, 4 ounces
4. A ton is equal to 2,000 pounds. The largest hamburger weighed about
   5,000 pounds.
5. Which two foods each weighed about $\frac{1}{2}$ ton?
   Chinese dumpling and pumpkin
6. A kilogram is a little more than 2 pounds. Which of the foods weighed about 275 kilograms? bowl of spaghetti

✧ *Math Journal 2*, p. 314

Remind students of alternative ways of writing square units: square m, sq m, or m^2; square cm, sq cm, or cm^2; square in., sq in., or in.^{2}. Similarly, cubic units may be written as m^3, cm^3, in.^{3}, and so on. These are read as "cubic meter," "cubic centimeter," "cubic inch," and so on.

✦ Using Cubes to Find the Volume of a Rectangular Prism (*Math Masters,* p. 20)

PARTNER ACTIVITY

Model the following activity for students before they work in partnerships to do it on their own:

1. On a sheet of centimeter grid paper (*Math Masters,* page 20), draw a pattern for an open box. The bottom of the box should be a rectangle 4 centimeters long and 3 centimeters wide. The box should be 2 centimeters high.

2 cm

3 cm

4 cm

Pattern for open box

2. Cut out the pattern. Fold up the sides and tape them together.
3. Fill the box with centimeter cubes. The number of cubes needed to fill the box is the volume of the box.

Partners may make boxes with any **dimensions** they wish.

Adjusting the Activity If some students are having difficulty drawing an open box, you may want to have open boxes of different sizes already drawn on centimeter grid paper. Discuss the dimensions of the boxes with students. Then have them cut out the boxes and continue the activity.

Ongoing Learning & Practice

✦ Solving Problems about the World's Largest Foods (*Math Journal 2,* p. 314)

INDEPENDENT ACTIVITY 

Students convert between ounces, pounds, and tons as they solve problems involving some of the world's largest foods.

Adjusting the Activity Encourage students to use the data on journal page 314 to write and solve additional problems.

NOTE: Remind students to add items to the Gram & Ounce Museum.

✦ Math Boxes 11.4 (*Math Journal 2,* p. 315)

INDEPENDENT ACTIVITY 

Mixed Review Math Boxes in this lesson are paired with Math Boxes in Lessons 11.2 and 11.6. The skills in Problems 1 and 2 are prerequisites for Unit 12.

✦ Study Link 11.4 (*Math Masters,* p. 369)

Home Connection Students cut out and assemble an open box. They search for items at home that have volumes equal to about $\frac{1}{2}$ of, the same as, and 2 times the volume of the open box.

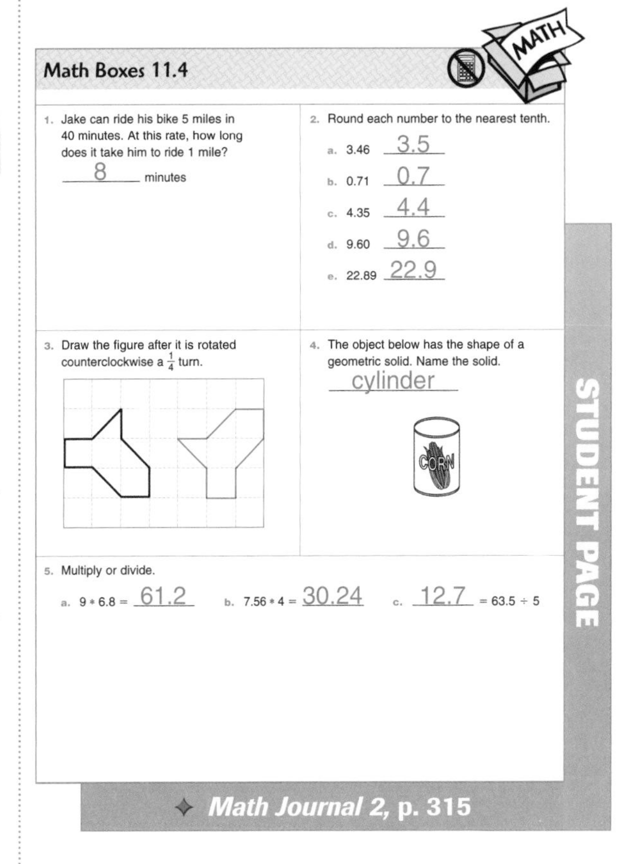

Math Boxes 11.4

1. Jake can ride his bike 5 miles in 40 minutes. At this rate, how long does it take him to ride 1 mile?
   8 minutes

2. Round each number to the nearest tenth.
   a. 3.46 3.5
   b. 0.71 0.7
   c. 4.35 4.4
   d. 9.60 9.6
   e. 22.89 22.9

3. Draw the figure after it is rotated counterclockwise a $\frac{1}{4}$ turn.

4. The object below has the shape of a geometric solid. Name the solid.
   cylinder

5. Multiply or divide.
   a. $9 * 6.8 =$ 61.2
   b. $7.56 * 4 =$ 30.24
   c. 12.7 $= 63.5 \div 5$

✦ *Math Journal 2,* p. 315

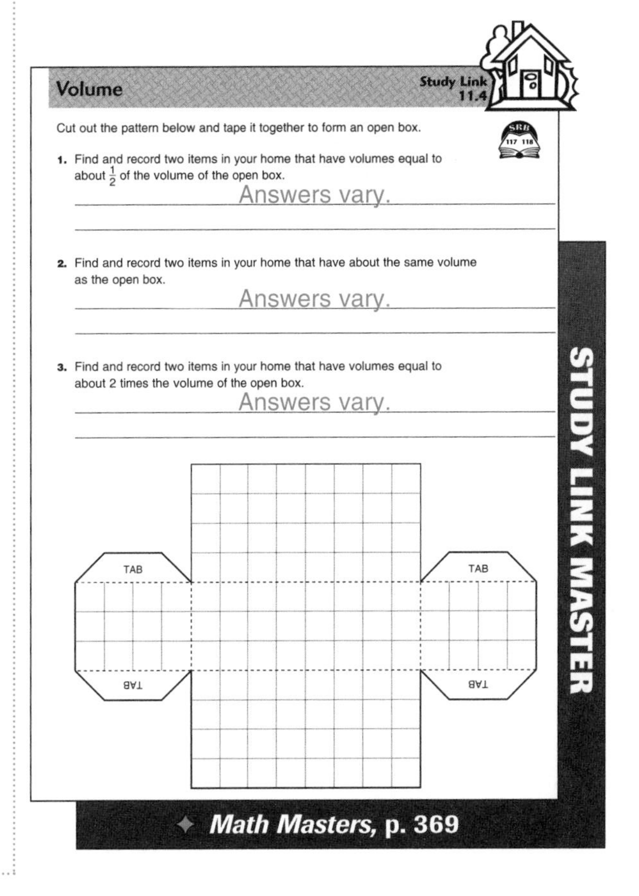

Volume — Study Link 11.4

Cut out the pattern below and tape it together to form an open box.

1. Find and record two items in your home that have volumes equal to about $\frac{1}{2}$ of the volume of the open box.
   Answers vary.

2. Find and record two items in your home that have about the same volume as the open box.
   Answers vary.

3. Find and record two items in your home that have volumes equal to about 2 times the volume of the open box.
   Answers vary.

✦ *Math Masters,* p. 369

What Is Volume?

Use your dictionary to find as many different meanings of the word *volume* as you can.

Write each definition below. For each definition, write a sentence containing the word *volume*. Answers vary.

	Meaning of *volume*	Sentence that uses the word *volume*
1.		
2.		
3.		
4.		

TEACHING MASTER

✦ *Math Masters,* p. 183

Grocery bags cut so that together they have a volume of about 1 cubic foot

3 Options for Individualizing

✦ LANGUAGE DIVERSITY Building Background for Mathematics Words (*Math Masters,* p. 183)

PARTNER ACTIVITY  **5–15 min** 

Students look up the word *volume* in a dictionary and record as many different definitions as they can find. The following meanings should be included:

▷ A book is often called a *volume.* The books in a set of related books, such as an encyclopedia, are frequently numbered as *Volume 1, Volume 2,* and so on.

▷ *Volume* can mean *loudness.* Someone might say, "Adjust the volume," or "Turn down the volume."

▷ *Volume* is often used to refer to a quantity, as in "Yesterday, a large volume of orders was received for tickets to the school play."

▷ The *volume* of a container is a measure of how much the container can hold. This measure is also called *capacity.*

▷ The *volume* of a 3-dimensional object is a measure of how much space the object takes up.

✦ EXTRA PRACTICE Visualizing U.S. Customary Cubic Units

SMALL-GROUP ACTIVITY  **5–15 min** 

Hold up an inch cube. The volume of a cube whose edges are 1 inch long is 1 cubic inch. Similarly, the volume of a cube whose edges are 1 foot long is 1 cubic foot; and one whose edges are 1 yard long, 1 cubic yard. Have students use 12-inch rulers or yardsticks to visualize the size of 1 cubic foot or 1 cubic yard (*see margin, page 803*).

A cubic foot can also be constructed with two large, brown paper grocery bags. Direct students to cut each bag to a height of 12 inches. The bottom of each bag is about 1 foot long and $\frac{1}{2}$ foot wide. If students open the bags and place them side by side, together they have a volume of about 1 cubic foot.

11.5 A Formula for the Volume of Rectangular Prisms

OBJECTIVE **To derive and use a formula for the volume of a rectangular prism.**

summaries	materials
1 Teaching the Lesson	
Students solve cube-stacking problems and use the results to derive a formula for the volume of a rectangular prism. [Measurement and Reference Frames]	□ *Math Journal 2,* pp. 316–318 □ *Student Reference Book,* p. 88 □ Study Link 11.4 □ Teaching Master (*Math Masters,* p. 184) □ centimeter cubes □ centimeter ruler ***See*** **Advance Preparation**
2 Ongoing Learning & Practice	
Students play the *Credits/Debits Game* to practice addition of positive and negative integers. [Operations and Computation] Students practice and maintain skills through Math Boxes and Study Link activities.	□ *Math Journal 2,* p. 319 □ *Student Reference Book,* p. 192 □ Teaching Master (*Math Masters,* p. 166) □ Study Link Master (*Math Masters,* p. 370) □ deck of number cards per partnership (from the *Everything Math Deck,* if available)
3 Options for Individualizing	
Reteaching Students build rectangular prisms and use the results to derive an alternative formula for the volume of a rectangular prism. [Measurement and Reference Frames] **Enrichment** Students estimate the volume of a sheet of notebook paper. [Measurement and Reference Frames]	□ Teaching Masters (*Math Masters,* pp. 185 and 186) □ 36 cm cubes per partnership □ sheet of notebook paper □ scissors

Additional Information

Advance Preparation For Part 1, make one copy of *Math Masters,* page 184 for every 2 students. Cut the masters apart and place the slips next to the Math Message.

Vocabulary • **rectangular prism** • **formula**

Getting Started

Mental Math and Reflexes

Have students open the *Student Reference Book* to page 88. Pose questions like the following:

- How many faces does a hexagonal prism have? 8
- How many of these faces have a rectangular shape? 6
- How many edges does a hexagonal prism have? 18
- How many vertices? 12
- What is the shape of the base of a hexagonal prism? hexagon

Math Message

Take a slip of paper. Solve the problems.

Study Link 11.4 Follow-Up

Students describe the items in their home that had volumes equal to about $\frac{1}{2}$ of, the same as, and 2 times the volume of the open box. Ask students to use centimeter cubes to determine the volume of the box. 96 cm^3

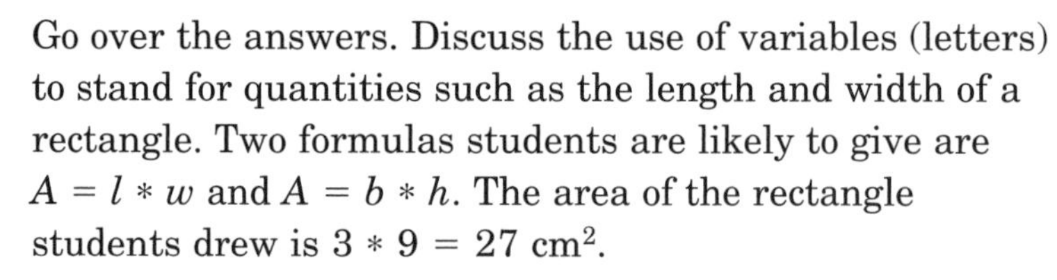

1 Teaching the Lesson

✦ Math Message Follow-Up
(*Math Masters,* p. 184)

WHOLE-CLASS DISCUSSION

Go over the answers. Discuss the use of variables (letters) to stand for quantities such as the length and width of a rectangle. Two formulas students are likely to give are $A = l * w$ and $A = b * h$. The area of the rectangle students drew is $3 * 9 = 27$ cm^2.

NOTE: If students need a refresher on finding the area of a rectangle, refer them to page 114 of the *Student Reference Book*.

✦ Solving Cube-Stacking Problems
(*Math Journal 2,* pp. 316 and 317)

PARTNER ACTIVITY

Each problem on journal pages 316 and 317 shows a picture of a box that is partially filled with cubes. Students find the number of cubes needed to completely fill each box and record the results in the table on journal page 316.

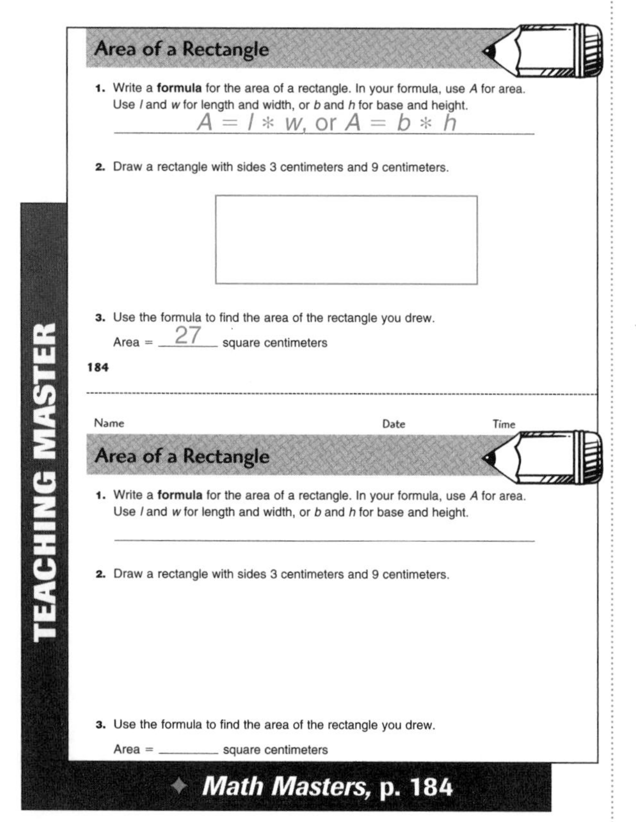

TEACHING MASTER

Area of a Rectangle

1. Write a **formula** for the area of a rectangle. In your formula, use *A* for area. Use *l* and *w* for length and width, or *b* and *h* for base and height.
$A = l * w$, or $A = b * h$
2. Draw a rectangle with sides 3 centimeters and 9 centimeters.
3. Use the formula to find the area of the rectangle you drew.
Area = 27 square centimeters

184

Name Date Time

Area of a Rectangle

1. Write a **formula** for the area of a rectangle. In your formula, use *A* for area. Use *l* and *w* for length and width, or *b* and *h* for base and height.
______
2. Draw a rectangle with sides 3 centimeters and 9 centimeters.
3. Use the formula to find the area of the rectangle you drew.
Area = ______ square centimeters

✦ *Math Masters,* **p. 184**

Fill in the column for Box 1 with the class. You may wish to use the following prompts:

- How many cubes can be placed along the longer side of the box? 8 Along the shorter side? 4
- How many cubes are needed to cover the bottom of the box? 32
- How many layers of cubes are needed to fill the box? 5 How can you tell? There are 5 cubes in the stack.
- How many cubes are needed to fill the box? Since there are 5 layers with 32 cubes in each layer, 5 * 32, or 160 cubes are needed to fill the box.

Have students complete the rest of the problems with their partners.

ONGOING ASSESSMENT
Watch for students who try to find the volume by counting only the cubes shown in the picture.

✦ Deriving a Formula for the Volume of a Rectangular Prism (*Math Journal 2*, pp. 316 and 317)

PARTNER ACTIVITY 

Remind students that geometric solids, such as those pictured on journal pages 316 and 317, are called **rectangular prisms.** Quickly review the properties of rectangular prisms:

▷ A rectangular prism has 6 rectangular faces, 12 edges, and 8 corners.

▷ Pairs of opposite faces are the same size.

▷ *Any face* of a rectangular prism can be designated as a base of the prism. The height of the prism is the distance between the base and the face opposite the base.

Allow students 10 to 15 minutes to complete the journal pages. Then bring the class together to discuss students' results.

Draw a rectangular prism on the board and label a base and the height, as shown below.

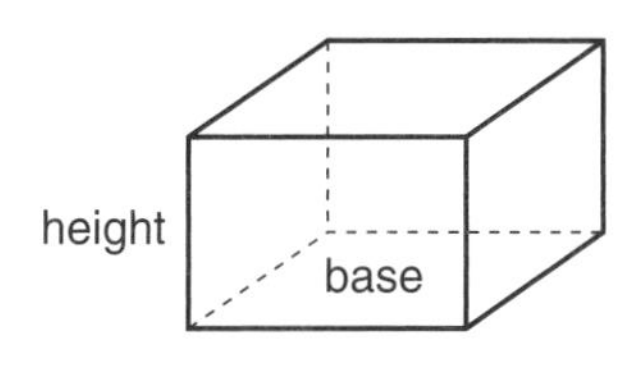

Rectangular prism

Cube-Stacking Problems

Imagine that each picture at the bottom of this page and on the next page shows a box, partially filled with cubes. The cubes in each box are the same size. Each box has at least one stack of cubes that goes all the way up to the top.

Your task is to find the number of cubes needed to completely fill each box.

Record your answers in the table below.

Table of Volumes

Placement of Cubes	Box 1	Box 2	Box 3	Box 4	Box 5	Box 6
Number of cubes needed to cover the bottom	32	40	24	16	35	25
Number of cubes in the tallest stack (Be sure to count the bottom cube.)	5	7	4	5	6	5
Number of cubes needed to fill the box	160	280	96	80	210	125

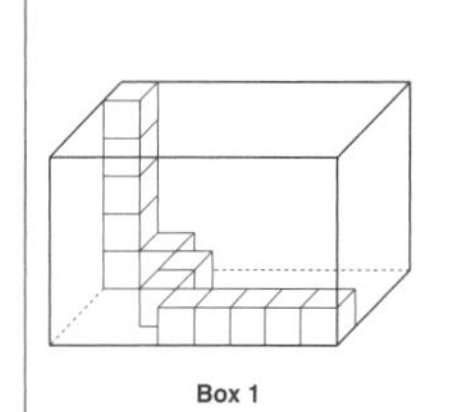

Box 1

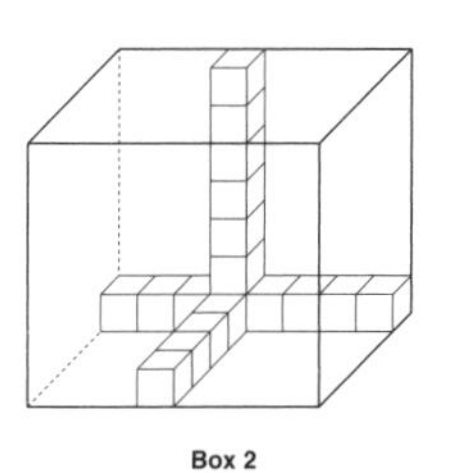

Box 2

STUDENT PAGE

✧ *Math Journal 2*, p. 316

NOTE: These properties are true of *right* rectangular prisms. The *oblique* rectangular prism shown below has only two rectangular faces. Oblique rectangular prisms will not be used, and the term *rectangular prism* will refer only to a right rectangular prism.

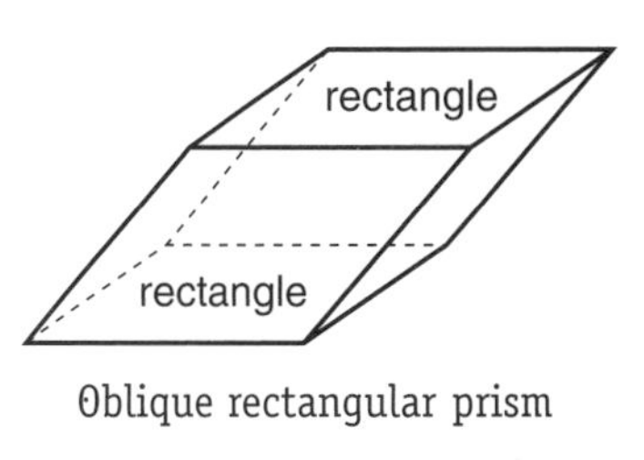

Oblique rectangular prism

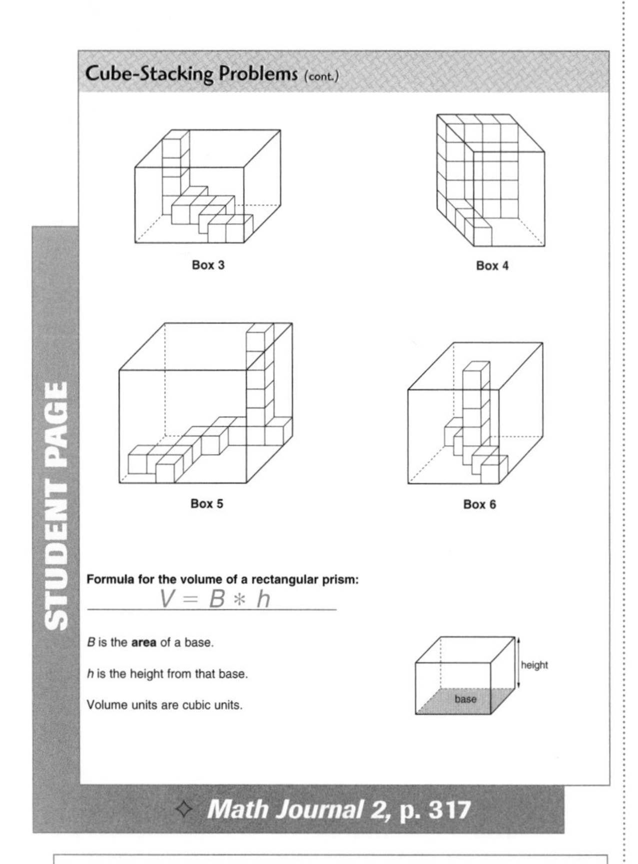
STUDENT PAGE

Cube-Stacking Problems *(cont.)*

Box 3 Box 4

Box 5 Box 6

Formula for the volume of a rectangular prism:

$V = B * h$

B is the **area** of a base.

h is the height from that base.

Volume units are cubic units.

✧ ***Math Journal 2*, p. 317**

NOTE: Traditionally, lowercase letters are used in formulas to represent length, and uppercase letters are used to represent area or volume. For example, b stands for the length of the base of a polygon, and B for the area of the base of a geometric solid.

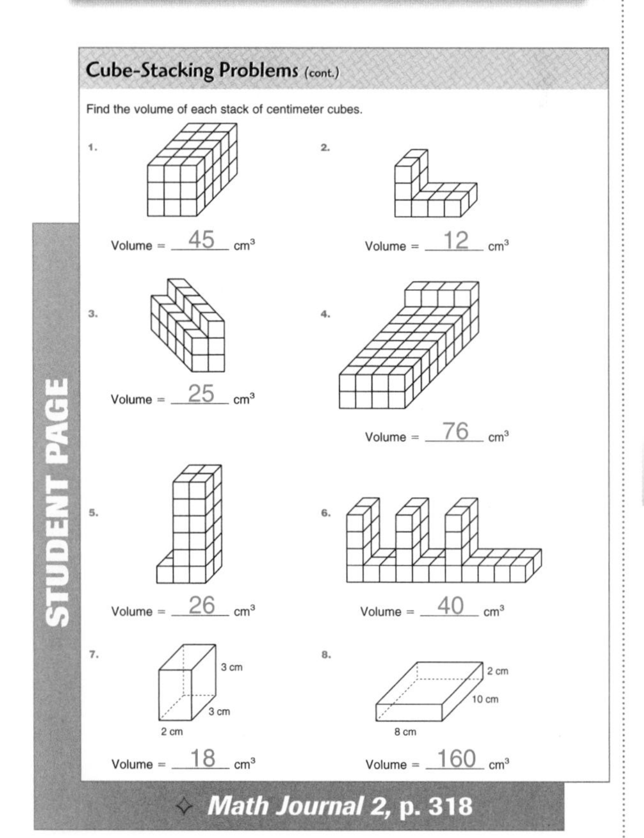
STUDENT PAGE

Cube-Stacking Problems *(cont.)*

Find the volume of each stack of centimeter cubes.

1. Volume = 45 cm³
2. Volume = 12 cm³
3. Volume = 25 cm³
4. Volume = 76 cm³
5. Volume = 26 cm³
6. Volume = 40 cm³
7. 3 cm, 3 cm, 2 cm — Volume = 18 cm³
8. 2 cm, 10 cm, 8 cm — Volume = 160 cm³

✧ ***Math Journal 2*, p. 318**

Ask students to look for a pattern in the table on journal page 316. To find the total number of cubes needed to fill each box, multiply the number of cubes needed to cover the bottom of the box by the number of cubes in the tallest stack.

Then call students' attention to the following relationships:

▷ The number of cubes needed to cover the bottom of the box is the same as the number of squares needed to cover the base—that is, the area of the base of the box.

▷ The number of cubes in the tallest stack is the same as the height of the box.

▷ Therefore, you can find the volume of a rectangular prism by multiplying the area of a base by the height of the prism.

Volume of rectangular prism = area of base * height

Written with variables, this becomes

$$V = B * h$$

where V is the volume of the rectangular prism, B is the area of the base, and h is the height of the prism.

Have students record the **formula** at the bottom of journal page 317.

✦ Finding Volume (*Math Journal 2,* p. 318)

PARTNER ACTIVITY 

Students find the volume of stacks of cm cubes and calculate the volume of rectangular prisms.

Adjusting the Activity Some students may benefit from actually using cubes to build the stacks pictured on the journal page.

2 Ongoing Learning & Practice

✦ Playing the *Credits/Debits Game* (*Student Reference Book,* p. 192; *Math Masters,* p. 166)

PARTNER ACTIVITY

Students practice adding positive and negative integers as they keep track of the "bottom line" for a business.

ONGOING ASSESSMENT

In Lesson 11.6, students will subtract positive and negative integers. It is important that students are comfortable adding such numbers before they begin that lesson.

✦ Math Boxes 11.5 (*Math Journal 2,* p. 319)

INDEPENDENT ACTIVITY 

Mixed Review Math Boxes in this lesson are paired with Math Boxes in Lesson 11.7. The skill in Problem 1 is a prerequisite for Unit 12.

✦ Study Link 11.5 (*Math Masters,* p. 370)

Home Connection Students find the volume of stacks of centimeter cubes, calculate the volume of rectangular prisms, and determine the number of cubes that are needed to fill boxes.

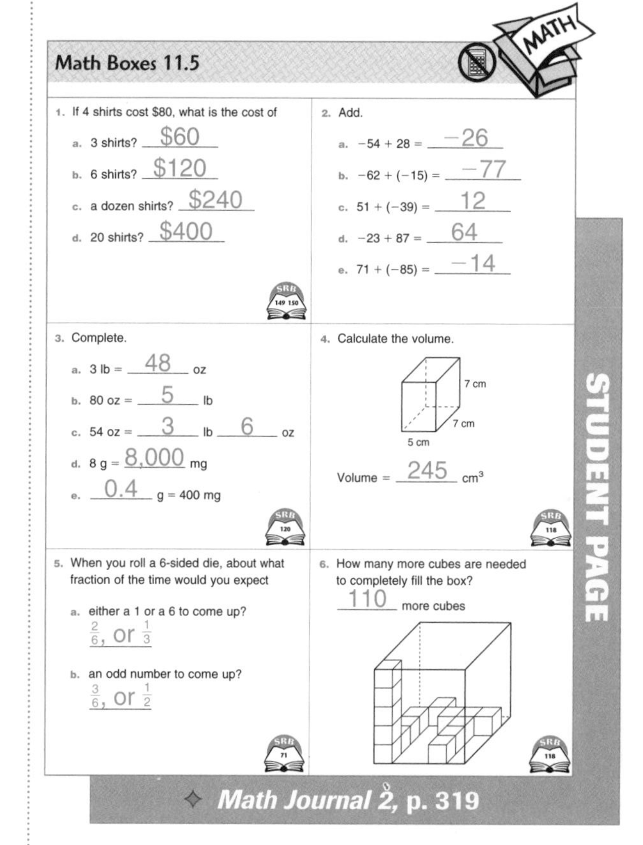

Math Boxes 11.5

1. If 4 shirts cost \$80, what is the cost of
   a. 3 shirts? \$60
   b. 6 shirts? \$120
   c. a dozen shirts? \$240
   d. 20 shirts? \$400

2. Add.
   a. $-54 + 28 =$ -26
   b. $-62 + (-15) =$ -77
   c. $51 + (-39) =$ 12
   d. $-23 + 87 =$ 64
   e. $71 + (-85) =$ -14

3. Complete.
   a. 3 lb = 48 oz
   b. 80 oz = 5 lb
   c. 54 oz = 3 lb 6 oz
   d. 8 g = 8,000 mg
   e. 0.4 g = 400 mg

4. Calculate the volume.
   7 cm, 7 cm, 5 cm
   Volume = 245 cm³

5. When you roll a 6-sided die, about what fraction of the time would you expect
   a. either a 1 or a 6 to come up? $\frac{2}{6}$, or $\frac{1}{3}$
   b. an odd number to come up? $\frac{3}{6}$, or $\frac{1}{2}$

6. How many more cubes are needed to completely fill the box?
   110 more cubes

✦ *Math Journal 2,* p. 319

STUDENT PAGE

3 Options for Individualizing

✦ RETEACHING Exploring Volume by Building Prisms (*Math Masters,* pp. 185 and 186)

PARTNER ACTIVITY  **30+ min**

The authors prefer the formula $V = B * h$ for the volume of a rectangular prism, because it is more general: It can be used, along with variations, to find the volume of solids that are not rectangular prisms, including other prisms and all cylinders. However, some students may feel more comfortable with the alternative version $V = l * w * h$. If so, try the activity that follows on page 812.

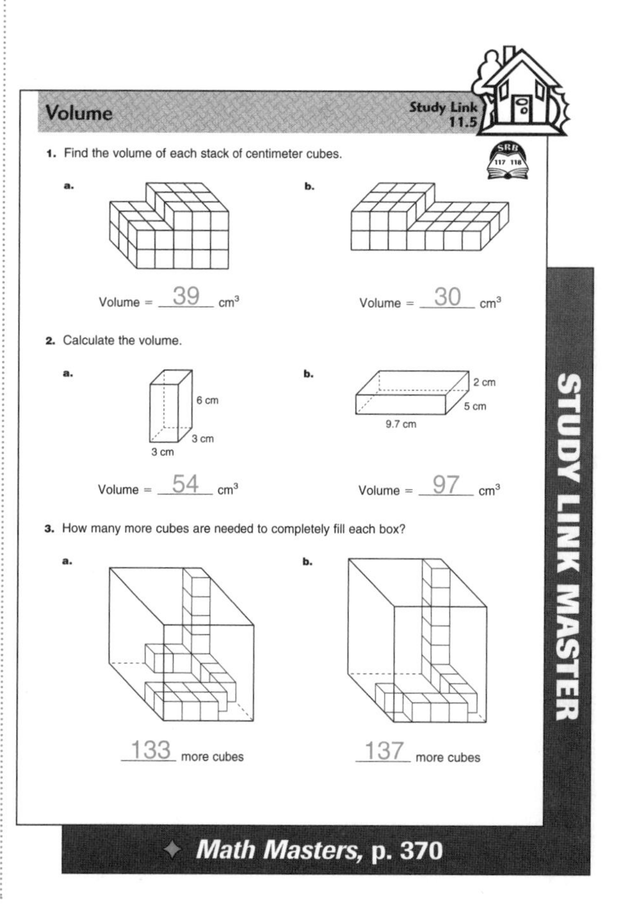

Volume — Study Link 11.5

1. Find the volume of each stack of centimeter cubes.
   a. Volume = 39 cm³
   b. Volume = 30 cm³

2. Calculate the volume.
   a. 6 cm, 3 cm, 3 cm — Volume = 54 cm³
   b. 2 cm, 5 cm, 9.7 cm — Volume = 97 cm³

3. How many more cubes are needed to completely fill each box?
   a. 133 more cubes
   b. 137 more cubes

✦ *Math Masters,* p. 370

STUDY LINK MASTER

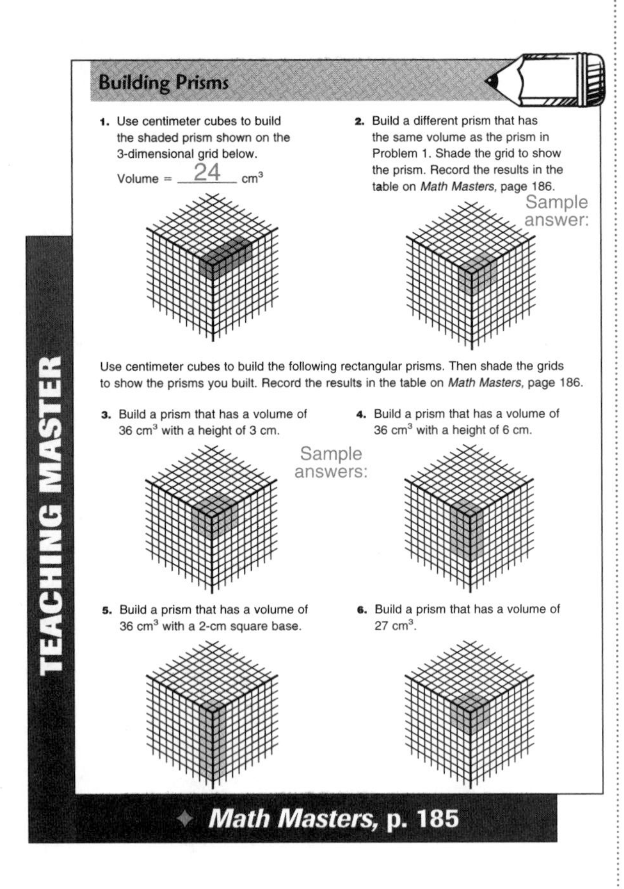
TEACHING MASTER

Building Prisms

1. Use centimeter cubes to build the shaded prism shown on the 3-dimensional grid below.
   Volume = 24 cm³

2. Build a different prism that has the same volume as the prism in Problem 1. Shade the grid to show the prism. Record the results in the table on *Math Masters*, page 186.
   Sample answer:

Use centimeter cubes to build the following rectangular prisms. Then shade the grids to show the prisms you built. Record the results in the table on *Math Masters*, page 186.

3. Build a prism that has a volume of 36 cm³ with a height of 3 cm.

4. Build a prism that has a volume of 36 cm³ with a height of 6 cm.

Sample answers:

5. Build a prism that has a volume of 36 cm³ with a 2-cm square base.

6. Build a prism that has a volume of 27 cm³.

✦ *Math Masters*, p. 185

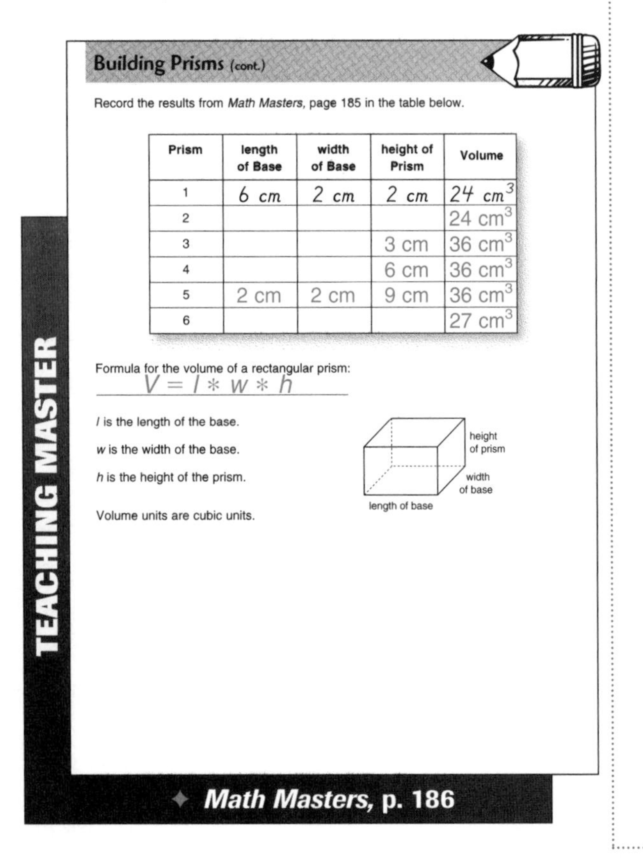
TEACHING MASTER

Building Prisms (cont.)

Record the results from *Math Masters*, page 185 in the table below.

Prism	length of Base	width of Base	height of Prism	Volume
1	6 cm	2 cm	2 cm	24 cm³
2				24 cm³
3			3 cm	36 cm³
4			6 cm	36 cm³
5	2 cm	2 cm	9 cm	36 cm³
6				27 cm³

Formula for the volume of a rectangular prism:
$V = l * w * h$

l is the length of the base.

w is the width of the base.

h is the height of the prism.

Volume units are cubic units.

✦ *Math Masters*, p. 186

Distribute at least 36 cm cubes to each partnership. Work with students to complete the first problem on *Math Masters,* page 185. Point out that the shaded part of the grid represents a rectangular prism. Ask students to do the following:

▷ Build the prism out of cm cubes.

▷ Find the volume of the prism and record it on the master. 24 cm³

Then ask students to build a different prism having the same volume and to show the prism by shading the grid in Problem 2. Have students record the results in the table on *Math Masters,* page 186.

Students can work on the rest of the page on their own. Circulate and assist as needed.

Bring students together to share the results in the table. The results lead to the alternative version of the volume formula:

$$V = l * w * h$$

where l is the length of a base, w is the width of that base, and h is the height of the prism from that base.

✦ ENRICHMENT Estimating the Volume of a Sheet of Paper

INDEPENDENT ACTIVITY  **15–30 min**

Challenge students to estimate the volume of a sheet of notebook paper. Have them write a brief report describing their strategy. One possible strategy is given below.

1. Cut the sheet of paper into 1-inch squares.
2. Stack the squares into a neat pile. Measure the height of the pile of squares. About $\frac{1}{4}$ inch high The area of the base of the pile is 1 square inch.
3. Use the formula $V = B * h$.
   $V = 1 * \frac{1}{4}$
   $V = \frac{1}{4}$
4. The volume of a sheet of notebook paper is about 0.25 cubic inch.

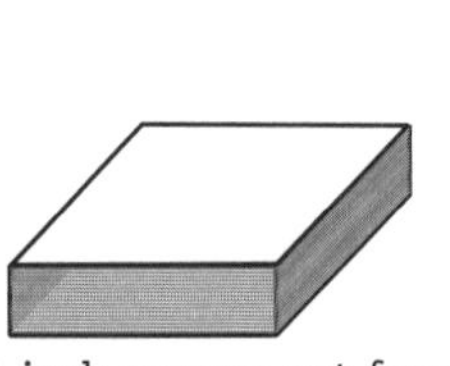
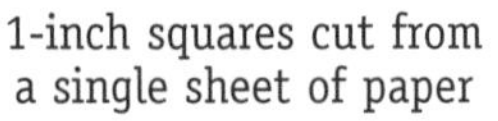
1-inch squares cut from a single sheet of paper

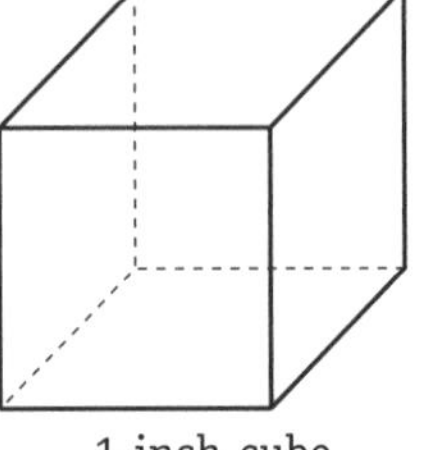
1-inch cube

11.6 Subtraction of Positive and Negative Numbers

OBJECTIVE **To add and subtract positive and negative integers.**

summaries	materials
1 Teaching the Lesson	
Students discuss and practice subtraction of positive and negative integers, as well as addition of such numbers, in the context of an accounting problem. [Operations and Computation] Students play the *Credits/Debits Game* (Advanced Version). [Operations and Computation]	□ *Math Journal 2,* p. 320 □ *Student Reference Book,* p. 193 □ Study Link 11.5 □ Teaching Master (*Math Masters,* p. 187; optional) □ Transparency (*Math Masters,* p. 165; optional) □ 1 penny per partnership □ deck of number cards per partnership (from the Everything Math Deck, if available) □ semipermanent chalk (optional) ***See* Advance Preparation**
2 Ongoing Learning & Practice	
Students summarize the Gram & Ounce Museum. [Measurement and Reference Frames] Students practice and maintain skills through Math Boxes and Study Link activities.	□ *Math Journal 2,* p. 321 □ Study Link Master (*Math Masters,* p. 371) □ Assessment Master (*Math Masters,* p. 471 or 475; optional)
3 Options for Individualizing	
Reteaching Students use a number line to add and subtract positive and negative numbers. [Operations and Computation]	□ Teaching Master (*Math Masters,* p. 188) □ number line (optional)

Additional Information

Background Information For additional information on semipermanent chalk, see the *Teacher's Reference Manual.*

Advance Preparation For Part 1, make an overhead transparency of the ledger page on *Math Masters,* page 165 to display and record results for the credits-and-debits activity. Alternatively, draw the ledger on the board, preferably in semipermanent chalk and in a place where it can be kept for a few days.

Getting Started

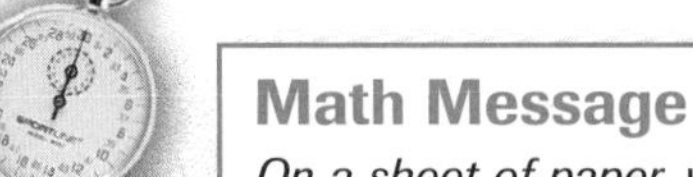

Mental Math and Reflexes

Sketch rectangular prisms with their dimensions on the board, or simply give the dimensions. Students write the volume of each prism, including the appropriate unit. *Suggestions:*

- 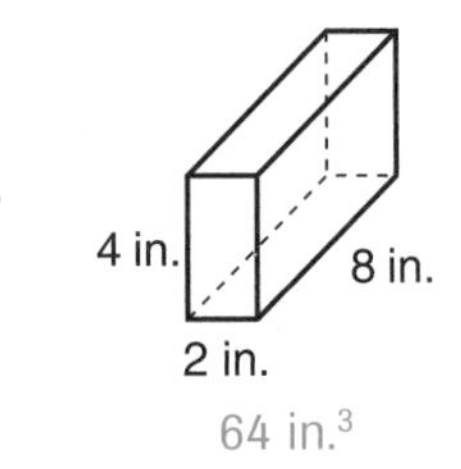

64 $in.^3$

- 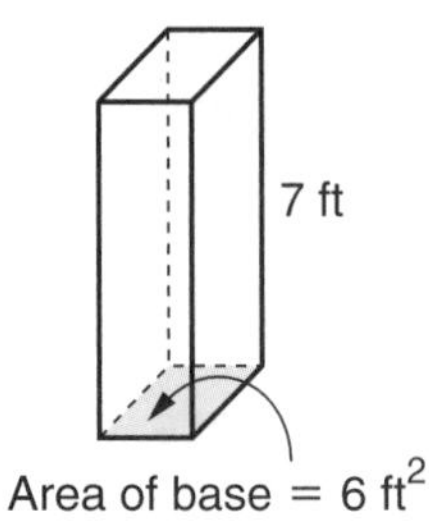

42 ft^3

- Area of base = 9 square meters, height of prism = 6 meters 54 m^3
- length of base = 6 cm, width of base = 4 cm, height of prism = 2 cm 48 cm^3

Math Message

On a sheet of paper, write down any shortcuts that you use when you add credits and debits (positive and negative numbers).

Study Link 11.5 Follow-Up

Review answers.

1 Teaching the Lesson

✦Math Message Follow-Up

WHOLE-CLASS DISCUSSION

Ask students to share any shortcuts they devised the last time they used credits and debits. *For example:*

▷ When two positive numbers are added, the result is "more positive."

▷ When two negative numbers are added, the result is "more negative."

▷ When a positive and a negative number are added, the result is the difference of the two addends (ignoring the signs); the sign in the answer is that of whichever addend is "bigger," again ignoring the signs.

✦Using Credits and Debits to Practice Subtraction of Positive and Negative Numbers (*Math Masters,* p. 165)

WHOLE-CLASS ACTIVITY

Students are asked to pretend that they are accountants, as in Lesson 10.6. They record what happens as they help start a business and keep track of the "bottom line" by posting credits and debits.

Mention that this is a new business. Students should pretend that there are still kinks in the accounting system; that is, the credits or debits are sometimes reported incorrectly. The subtraction of positive and negative numbers can be understood as the taking away or subtracting from the bottom line what were considered to be credits or debits.

When a debit (negative number) is taken away or subtracted, the result is an increase in the bottom line. When a credit (positive number) is taken away or subtracted, the result is a decrease in the bottom line.

Remind students that you are labeling credits with "+" and debits with "−" to help keep track of them as positive or negative numbers. As credits and debits come in, the class will figure out the bottom line as you post transactions on an overhead transparency of *Math Masters,* page 165 or on the ledger you drew on the board earlier.

Following is a suggested series of transactions. Entries in black would be reported to the class; entries in color are appropriate student responses.

NOTE: Try to consistently use the terms "positive" and "negative" for numbers and amounts and "add" or "subtract" for operations. It is important to be consistent in "subtracting" the credits and debits as positive and negative numbers when there is an error.

Event	Start	Change	End, and next start
New business. Start at $0.	$0	$0	$0
Credit (payment) of $8 comes in	$0	add +$8	+$8
Credit of $3	+$8	add +$3	+$11
Debit of $4	+$11	add −$4	+$7
Credit of $3 was an error. Adjust account.	+$7	subtract +$3	+$4
Debit of $6	+$4	add −$6	−$2
Credit of $5	−$2	add +$5	+$3
Debit of $4 was an error. Adjust account.	+$3	subtract −$4	+$7
Debit of $6 was an error. Adjust account.	+$7	subtract −$6	+$13

Continue, or start a new problem, until most students respond comfortably.

STUDENT PAGE

Credits/Debits Game (Advanced Version) Recording Sheets

Game 1

	Start	Change: Addition or Subtraction	Change: Credit or Debit	End, and next start
1	+ $10			
2				
3				
4				
5				
6				
7				
8				
9				
10				

Game 2

	Start	Change: Addition or Subtraction	Change: Credit or Debit	End, and next start
1	+ $10			
2				
3				
4				
5				
6				
7				
8				
9				
10				

✧ *Math Journal 2,* p. 320

✦Playing the *Credits/Debits Game* (Advanced Version) (*Math Journal 2,* p. 320; *Student Reference Book,* p. 193; *Math Masters,* p. 187)

PARTNER ACTIVITY

Have students read the rules for the *Credits/Debits Game* (Advanced Version) on page 193 of the *Student Reference Book.* Play one round as a class to be sure that students understand how the game is played. Have students record their steps on journal page 320. (Additional record forms are available on *Math Masters,* page 187.)

Adjusting the Activity Simplify the game for struggling students by having them use only the number cards 1–10.

ONGOING ASSESSMENT

As students play, circulate and assess the strategies they are using. Observe whether some are beginning to devise shortcuts for finding answers. For example, some students may notice that subtracting a negative number is the same as adding a positive number. Don't try too hard to elicit explanations of these strategies; they will evolve over time as students acquire experiences manipulating positive and negative numbers.

STUDENT PAGE

Games

Credits/Debits Game (Advanced Version)

Materials ☐ 1 complete deck of number cards
☐ 1 penny
☐ recording sheet for each player (*Math Masters,* p. 187)

Players 2

Directions

Pretend that you are an accountant for a business. Your job is to keep track of the company's current balance, also called the "bottom line."

Recording Sheet

	Start	Change: Addition or Subtraction	Change: Credit or Debit	End, and next start
1	+$10			
2				
3				
4				
5				
6				
7				
8				
9				
10				

1. Shuffle the deck and lay it facedown between the players.
2. The black-numbered cards are the "credits," and the blue- or red-numbered cards are the "debits."
3. The heads side of the coin tells you to **add** a credit or debit to the bottom line. The tails side of the coin tells you to **subtract** a credit or debit from the bottom line.
4. Each player begins with a bottom line of +$10.
5. Players take turns. On your turn, do the following:
   - Flip the coin. This tells you whether to add or subtract.
   - Draw a card. The card tells you what amount in dollars (positive or negative) to add or subtract from the bottom line. Red or blue numbers are negative numbers.
   - Record the result in the table.

EXAMPLE Max has a "Start" balance of \$5. He draws a red 8 and records −\$8 in the "Credit or Debit" column. His coin lands heads-side up and he records + in the "Addition or Subtraction" column. Max adds: \$5 + (−\$8) = −\$3. He records −\$3 in the "End" balance column and in the "Start" column on the next line.

Beth has a "Start" balance of −\$20. Her coin lands tails-side up, which means subtract. She draws a black 11 (+\$11). She subtracts: −\$20 − (+\$11) = −\$31. Her "End" balance is −\$31.

Scoring: After 10 turns each, the player with more money is the winner of the round. If both players have negative dollar amounts, the player whose amount is closer to 0 wins.

one hundred ninety-three SRB 193

✧ *Student Reference Book,* p. 193

2 Ongoing Learning & Practice

✦ Summarizing the Gram & Ounce Museum

WHOLE-CLASS DISCUSSION 

Take a few minutes to discuss the Gram & Ounce Museum. Encourage students to continue to work to develop their "weight measure sense"—their ability to estimate weight and judge whether given weights are reasonable.

ONGOING ASSESSMENT

Consider asking students to respond to one of the following questions in a Math Log (*Math Masters,* page 471) or on an Exit Slip (*Math Masters,* page 475):

- What did you learn from the Gram & Ounce Museum?
- What surprised you as you were collecting items for the museum?

✦ Math Boxes 11.6 (*Math Journal 2,* p. 321)

INDEPENDENT ACTIVITY 

Mixed Review Math Boxes in this lesson are paired with Math Boxes in Lessons 11.2 and 11.4. The skills in Problems 1 and 2 are prerequisites for Unit 12.

✦ Study Link 11.6 (*Math Masters,* p. 371)

Home Connection Students compare and order positive and negative numbers and add and subtract positive and negative integers.

Math Boxes 11.6

1. Two cups of flour are needed to make about 20 medium-size peanut butter cookies. How many cups of flour will you need to make about
   a. 40 cookies? 4 cups
   b. 60 cookies? 6 cups
   c. 50 cookies? 5 cups

2. Round each number to the nearest tenth.
   a. 8.99 9.0
   b. 0.06 0.1
   c. 21.76 21.8
   d. 1.53 1.5
   e. 0.92 0.9

3. Draw the figure after it is rotated clockwise a $\frac{1}{2}$ turn.

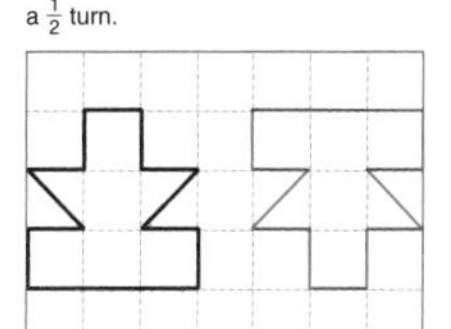

4. The object below has the shape of a geometric solid. Name the solid. cone

5. Multiply or divide.
   a. $6 * 32.9 =$ 197.4
   b. $98.7 \div 3 =$ 32.9
   c. 4.6 $= 55.2 \div 12$

STUDENT PAGE

✧ *Math Journal 2,* p. 321

Positive and Negative Numbers Study Link 11.6

Write < or > to make a true number sentence.

1. $0 - 7$ < -6
2. -11 < $-13 - (-5)$
3. $7 + (-2)$ > -8
4. $18 + (-8)$ > -18
5. $26 - (-14)$ > $27 + (-16)$
6. $9 - (-11)$ > $0 + (-20)$

List the numbers in order from least to greatest.

7. $\frac{30}{6}$, 8, −14, −0.7, 5.6, −2.5
   −14 (least), −2.5, −0.7, $\frac{30}{6}$, 5.6, 8 (greatest)
8. 0.02, $-\frac{3}{5}$, −7, 4, 0.46, $-\frac{24}{6}$
   −7 (least), $-\frac{24}{6}$, $-\frac{3}{5}$, 0.02, 0.46, 4 (greatest)
9. Write two subtraction problems with an answer of −8. Sample answers:
   $4 - 12 = -8$ $-20 - (-12) = -8$
10. Write two addition problems with an answer of −30. Sample answers:
   $-50 + 20 = -30$ $-15 + (-15) = -30$

Add or subtract.

11. $-40 + (-70) =$ −110
12. $12 - 20 =$ −8
13. −8 $= -14 - (-6)$
14. 15 $= 10 - (-5)$
15. $15 + (-1) =$ 14
16. $-12 - 7 =$ −19
17. −70 $= 60 + (-130)$
18. 18 $= -2 - (-20)$

STUDY LINK MASTER

✦ *Math Masters,* p. 371

Options for Individualizing

✦ RETEACHING Using a Number Line to Add and Subtract Positive and Negative Numbers
(*Math Masters,* p. 188)

INDEPENDENT ACTIVITY  **15–30 min** 

Some students may find it easier to think about addition and subtraction of positive and negative numbers in terms of a number line rather than credits and debits. Have them read and discuss *Math Masters,* page 188. Pose additional problems as necessary. *Suggestions:*

▷ $-7 - (-6) = -1$; $-7 + (+6) = -1$

▷ $8 - (+2) = 6$; $8 + (-2) = 6$

▷ $10 - 14 = -4$; $10 + (-14) = -4$

▷ $-3 - (-7) = 4$; $-3 + (+7) = 4$

TEACHING MASTER

Positive and Negative Numbers

One way to add and subtract positive and negative numbers is to imagine you are walking on a number line.

- The first number tells you where to start.
- The operation sign (+ or −) tells you which way to face:
  - + means face toward the positive end of the number line.
  - − means face toward the negative end of the number line.
- If the second number is negative (has a − sign), then you walk backward. Otherwise, you walk forward.
- The second number tells you how many steps to walk.
- The number where you stop is the answer.

Example $-4 + 3$

- Start at −4.
- Face toward the positive end of the number line.
- Walk forward 3 steps.
- You are now at −1. So $-4 + 3 = -1$.

$-4 + 3$ — Start at −4. / Face positive. / Walk forward 3 steps.

−5 −4 −3 −2 −1 0 1 2 3

Example $5 - (-2)$

- Start at 5.
- Face toward the negative end of the number line.
- Walk backward 2 steps.
- You are now at 7. So $5 - (-2) = 7$.

$5 - (-2)$ — Start at 5. / Face negative. / Walk backward 2 steps.

−1 0 1 2 3 4 5 6 7

Solve.

1. $-4 + (-3) =$ <u>−7</u> **2.** $6 - 9 =$ <u>−3</u> **3.** $-4 - (-6) =$ <u>+2</u>

✦ *Math Masters,* **p. 188**

11.7 Capacity and Weight

OBJECTIVE **To review customary units of capacity.**

summaries	materials
1 Teaching the Lesson	
Students review equivalencies between units of capacity. They find the weight of one cup of uncooked rice and use this information to estimate the weight of an average Thai family's annual rice consumption. [Measurement and Reference Frames]	☐ *Math Journal 2,* p. 322 ☐ Study Link 11.6 ☐ measuring cup, empty milk cartons, rice, pourable substance, and scale ***See* Advance Preparation**
2 Ongoing Learning & Practice	
Students practice and maintain skills through Math Boxes and Study Link activities.	☐ *Math Journal 2,* p. 323 ☐ Study Link Master (*Math Masters,* p. 372)
3 Options for Individualizing	
Enrichment Students try to visualize the amount of rice a typical Thai family of four eats in a year by estimating how many empty cartons of copy paper would be needed to hold that amount of rice. [Measurement and Reference Frames] **Enrichment** Students explore the power of doubling by reading versions of a classic folktale about grains of rice that are doubled each day. [Operations and Computation]	☐ *Math Journal 2,* p. 322 ☐ Per group: empty copy-paper carton, measuring cup, and pourable substance, such as sand ☐ *The King's Chessboard* ☐ *One Grain of Rice: A Mathematical Folktale* ☐ *The Token Gift* ☐ *A Grain of Rice* ☐ calculator ***See* Advance Preparation**

Additional Information

Advance Preparation For Part 1, you will need the following: measuring cup; empty pint, quart, half-gallon, and gallon milk cartons; a little more than 1 cup of uncooked rice; at least 1 gallon of a liquid or other pourable substance, such as sand, popcorn, or packing pellets; and a scale (accurate to the nearest ounce).

For the second optional Enrichment activity in Part 3, obtain as many of the following books as possible: *The King's Chessboard* by David Birch (Dial, 1988); *One Grain of Rice: A Mathematical Folktale* by Demi (Scholastic, 1997); *The Token Gift* by Hugh William McKibbon (Annick, 1996); and *A Grain of Rice* by Helena Clare Pittman (Bantam, 1996).

Vocabulary • **capacity**

Getting Started

Mental Math and Reflexes

Pose addition and subtraction problems with positive and negative integers. *Suggestions:*

- $5 + (-9) = -4$
- $-23 + (-7) = -30$
- $-3 - (+7) = -10$
- $-12 + 18 = 6$
- $8 - (-6) = 14$
- $-4 - (-1) = -3$

Math Message

Fill in the missing numbers in the Math Message problems at the top of journal page 322.

Study Link 11.6 Follow-Up

Review answers. Use a number line as necessary.

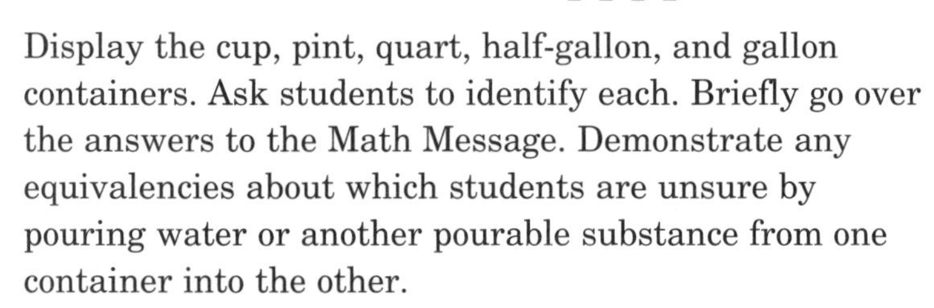

1 Teaching the Lesson

✦ Math Message Follow-Up
(*Math Journal 2,* p. 322)

WHOLE-CLASS DISCUSSION

Display the cup, pint, quart, half-gallon, and gallon containers. Ask students to identify each. Briefly go over the answers to the Math Message. Demonstrate any equivalencies about which students are unsure by pouring water or another pourable substance from one container into the other.

Ask: *Did anyone figure out the meaning of the picture next to the Math Message problems?* The "frame" is in the shape of the letter G. It represents the word *gallon*. Inside the G, there are four Qs. Each Q represents the word *quart*. Inside each Q, there are two Ps. Each P represents the word *pint*. Inside each P, there are two Cs. Each C represents the word *cup*.

Explain that a pint, quart, and gallon are units of **capacity** in the U.S. customary system. Capacity is a measure of the amount of liquid or other pourable substance a container can hold. Capacity is a type of volume measure.

STUDENT PAGE

Converting Measurements

Math Message

1 pint = 2 cups
1 quart = 2 pints
1 half-gallon = 2 quarts
1 gallon = 4 quarts

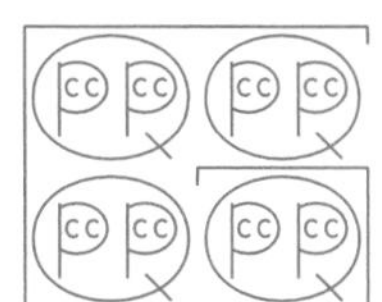

How can the picture above help you remember how many cups are in a pint, how many pints are in a quart, and how many quarts are in a gallon?

Rice Consumption

Answers may vary for Problem 1. Answers for Problems 2–5 assume that the answer for Problem 1 is 8 ounces.

1. Round your answer to the nearest ounce.
   One cup of dry (uncooked) rice weighs about 8 ounces.
2. Use the answer in Problem 1 to complete the following:
   a. 1 pint of rice weighs about 16 ounces.
   b. 1 quart of rice weighs about 32 ounces.
   c. 1 gallon of rice weighs about 128 ounces.
   d. 1 gallon of rice weighs about 8 pounds. (1 pound = 16 ounces)
3. On average, a family of 4 in Japan eats about 40 pounds of rice a month.
   a. That's about how many **pounds** a year? 480 pounds
   b. How many **gallons**? 60 gallons
4. On average, a family of 4 in the United States eats about 88 pounds of rice a year. That's about how many gallons a year? 11 gallons
5. On average, a family of 4 in Thailand eats about 3 gallons of rice a week.
   a. That's about how many gallons a year? 156 gallons
   b. How many pounds? 1,248 pounds

✧ *Math Journal 2,* p. 322

✦ Finding the Weight of a Cup of Rice
(*Math Journal 2,* p. 322)

WHOLE-CLASS ACTIVITY

Ask students the following questions:

- How would you measure rice if you needed a certain amount for a recipe? Probably with a measuring cup
- How would you find the weight of one cup of uncooked rice? One method: Weigh an empty measuring cup. Fill it with rice to the 1-cup level. Weigh the cup. Subtract the weight of the empty cup from the weight of the cup containing rice.
- About how many ounces do you think a cup of uncooked rice weighs? (Record a few estimates on the board.)

Ask two students to weigh 1 cup of rice as accurately as they can. Expect a range of $7\frac{1}{2}$ to $8\frac{1}{2}$ ounces for 1 cup. Have the class round the result to the nearest ounce and record it in Problem 1 on journal page 322.

Adjusting the Activity Ask students if they think cooked rice weighs more than uncooked rice. Some students might want to check this at home and report their findings to the class. Cooked rice weighs only a little more than uncooked rice.

✦ Solving Problems Involving Units of Weight and Capacity (*Math Journal 2,* p. 322)

PARTNER ACTIVITY

Students use the weight of 1 cup of rice to solve Problems 2–5 on journal page 322. These problems involve conversions between gallons and pounds. Circulate and assist as needed. After a few minutes, bring the class together to go over the answers.

Problem 2: Assuming that 1 cup of uncooked rice weighs about 8 ounces, then 1 pint weighs about 16 ounces, 1 quart about 32 ounces, and 1 gallon about 128 ounces. Since there are 16 ounces in 1 pound, 128 ounces is equivalent to 8 pounds ($128 \div 16 = 8$). You can use the same procedure if 1 cup of rice is found to weigh about 7 ounces. Then 1 gallon would weigh about 7 pounds.

Problem 3: To find the number of gallons, divide the total weight by 8. $480 \div 8 = 60$ gallons

Problem 4: $88 \div 8 = 11$ gallons

Problem 5: A family of 4 in Thailand eats about 3 gallons of rice a week. That is equivalent to 156 gallons per year. To find the weight of the rice consumed, multiply 156 by 8. 1,248 pounds

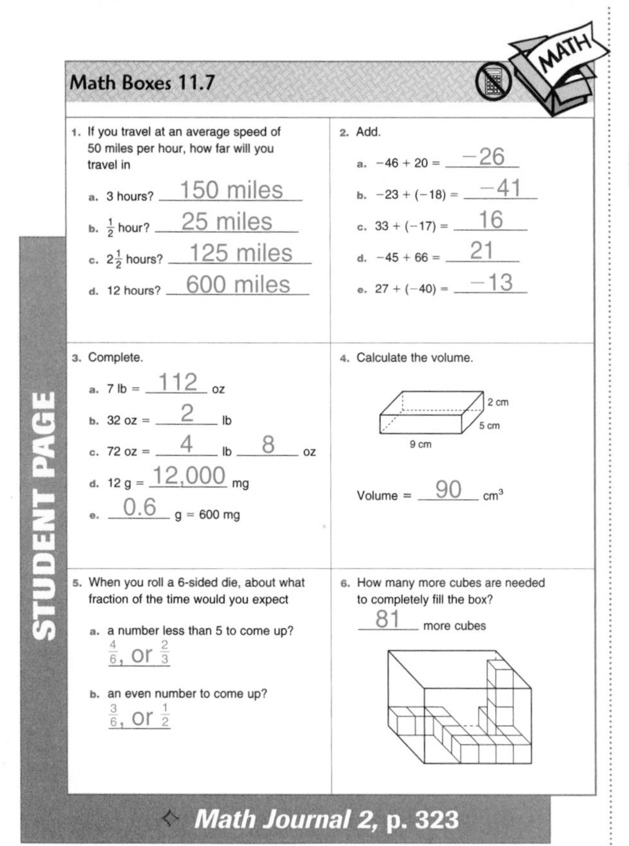

Math Boxes 11.7

1. If you travel at an average speed of 50 miles per hour, how far will you travel in
   a. 3 hours? 150 miles
   b. $\frac{1}{2}$ hour? 25 miles
   c. $2\frac{1}{2}$ hours? 125 miles
   d. 12 hours? 600 miles

2. Add.
   a. $-46 + 20 =$ −26
   b. $-23 + (-18) =$ −41
   c. $33 + (-17) =$ 16
   d. $-45 + 66 =$ 21
   e. $27 + (-40) =$ −13

3. Complete.
   a. 7 lb = 112 oz
   b. 32 oz = 2 lb
   c. 72 oz = 4 lb 8 oz
   d. 12 g = 12,000 mg
   e. 0.6 g = 600 mg

4. Calculate the volume.
   2 cm
   5 cm
   9 cm
   Volume = 90 cm^3

5. When you roll a 6-sided die, about what fraction of the time would you expect
   a. a number less than 5 to come up? $\frac{4}{6}$, or $\frac{2}{3}$
   b. an even number to come up? $\frac{3}{6}$, or $\frac{1}{2}$

6. How many more cubes are needed to completely fill the box?
   81 more cubes

STUDENT PAGE

Math Journal 2, p. 323

2 Ongoing Learning & Practice

Math Boxes 11.7 (*Math Journal 2,* p. 323)

INDEPENDENT ACTIVITY 

Mixed Review Math Boxes in this lesson are paired with Math Boxes in Lesson 11.5. The skill in Problem 1 is a prerequisite for Unit 12.

Study Link 11.7 (*Math Masters,* p. 372)

Home Connection Students find containers that hold less than 1 pint, 1 pint, 1 quart, and more than 1 quart. They solve problems about equivalent capacities.

Capacity — Study Link 11.7

Find at least one container that holds each of the amounts listed below. Describe each container and record all the **capacity** measurements on the label. SRB 117

Answers vary.

1. Less than 1 Pint

Container	Capacity Measurements on Label
bottle of hot chili sesame oil	5 fl oz, 148 mL

2. 1 Pint

Container	Capacity Measurements on Label
bottle of cooking oil	16 fl oz, 473 mL

3. 1 Quart

Container	Capacity Measurements on Label

4. More than 1 Quart

Container	Capacity Measurements on Label

Solve.

5. 2 quarts = 4 pints
6. 3 gallons = 48 cups
7. 2 pints = 4 cups
8. 3 quarts = 12 cups
9. 6 pints = 3 quarts
10. 10 quarts = $2\frac{1}{2}$ gallons

STUDY LINK MASTER

Math Masters, p. 372

Options for Individualizing

✦ ENRICHMENT Modeling the Capacity of Annual Rice Consumption

(*Math Journal 2,* p. 322)

SMALL-GROUP ACTIVITY **30+ min**

Display an empty copy-paper carton and ask students to estimate about how many of these size cartons would be needed to store all of the rice a Thai family of four eats in a year. A family of four eats about 156 gallons, or 1,248 pounds of uncooked rice a year, assuming that 1 gallon of rice weighs about 8 pounds.

Write students' estimates on the board. Then ask students to propose a method for checking their estimates.

▷ The most obvious approach is to find about how many pounds a copy-paper carton of rice weighs and divide the number of *pounds* of rice consumed in a year by the weight of a carton of rice. But this is not practical, since you would need a large quantity of rice to find the weight of a filled carton.

▷ Another way is to use a measuring cup to find about how many *gallons* a copy-paper carton holds. Then divide the number of gallons of rice consumed in a year by the number of gallons a carton holds. If students follow this approach, they can use any pourable substance, such as sand. Popcorn or light packing material is recommended, but large amounts may be hard to obtain. One possible solution would be to fill the carton to about $\frac{1}{6}$ of its height and multiply the result by 6.

Once the capacity of a carton has been determined, encourage students to estimate the number of cartons needed to hold the total yearly consumption of rice. A possible strategy: The capacity of a carton of copy paper is about $7\frac{1}{2}$ gallons. This means that 2 cartons would hold about 15 gallons, and 20 cartons about 150 gallons. Students can check their estimates on their calculators.

Have students present their strategies and solutions in a brief report.

✦ ENRICHMENT Doubling Grains of Rice

SMALL-GROUP ACTIVITY  **30+ min** 

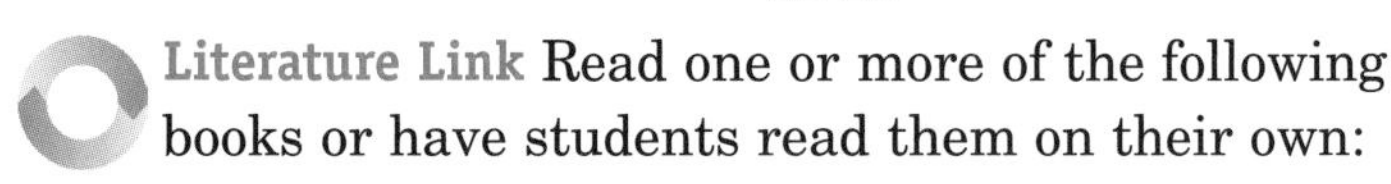

Literature Link Read one or more of the following books or have students read them on their own:

The King's Chessboard

One Grain of Rice: A Mathematical Folktale

The Token Gift

A Grain of Rice

Summary: Each of these books presents a version of a classic folktale about the power of doubling. The common theme is doubling the number of grains of rice each day. For example, on the first day, there is 1 grain of rice, on the second day 2 grains of rice, on the third day 4 grains, and so on.

Language Arts Link After students have read different versions of the folktale, ask them to describe the similarities and differences among these versions.

11.8 Unit 11 Review and Assessment

OBJECTIVE **To review and assess students' progress on the material covered in Unit 11.**

1 Assess Progress

learning goals	activities
11a **Beginning Goal** Use a formula to calculate volumes of rectangular prisms. **(Lesson 11.5)**	❑ Written Assessment, Problem 7 ❑ Alternative Assessment Option
11b **Beginning Goal** Subtract positive and negative integers. **(Lesson 11.6)**	❑ Slate Assessment, Problem 1 ❑ Written Assessment, Problem 9
11c **Developing Goal** Add positive and negative integers. **(Lessons 11.5 and 11.6)**	❑ Slate Assessment, Problem 1 ❑ Written Assessment, Problem 8
11d **Developing Goal** Estimate the weight of objects in ounces or grams; weigh objects in ounces or grams. **(Lessons 11.1 and 11.7)**	❑ Oral Assessment, Problem 1 ❑ Written Assessment, Problem 10
11e **Developing Goal** Solve cube-stacking volume problems. **(Lessons 11.4 and 11.5)**	❑ Oral Assessment, Problem 2 ❑ Written Assessment, Problem 6
11f **Developing Goal** Describe properties of geometric solids. **(Lessons 11.2 and 11.3)**	❑ Written Assessment, Problems 1–5

materials

- ☐ *Math Journal 2,* p. 324
- ☐ Study Link 11.7
- ☐ Teaching Master (*Math Masters,* p. 189)
- ☐ Assessment Masters (*Math Masters,* pp. 411 and 412)
- ☐ slate
- ☐ cm cubes

2 Build Background for Unit 12

summaries	materials
Students practice and maintain skills through Math Boxes and Study Link activities.	☐ *Math Journal 2,* p. 325 ☐ Study Link Masters (*Math Masters,* pp. 373–376)

Each **learning goal** listed above indicates a level of performance that might be expected at this point in the *Everyday Mathematics* K–6 curriculum. For a variety of reasons, the levels indicated may not accurately portray your class's performance.

Additional Information

Advance Preparation For additional information on assessment for Unit 11, see the *Assessment Handbook,* pages 69–71. For assessment checklists, see *Math Masters,* pages 446, 447, and 465–467.

Getting Started

Math Message

Complete the Time to Reflect *questions on journal page 324.*

Study Link 11.7 Follow-Up

Review answers.

1 Assess Progress

✦ Math Message Follow-Up
(*Math Journal 2,* p. 324)

WHOLE-CLASS DISCUSSION

Students share their answers. Problem 1 provides students with an opportunity to describe some of the properties of 2- and 3-dimensional figures. Problem 2 allows students to evaluate their own skill at adding and subtracting positive and negative numbers. Problems 3 and 4 give students a chance to evaluate the activities in Unit 11.

STUDENT PAGE

Time to Reflect

1. In your own words, describe the difference between a 2-dimensional figure and a 3-dimensional shape.
   Sample answer: A 2-dimensional figure has length and width; it is a flat figure and has no thickness. A 3-dimensional shape has length, width, and thickness.
2. You played the *Credits/Debits Game* again in this unit. You also played the *Credits/Debits Game* (Advanced Version). What do you think is the most difficult part of these games? What is the easiest part? Explain your answers.
   Answers vary.
3. What were some of your least favorite activities in this unit? Explain why you disliked them.
   Answers vary.
4. What were some of your favorite activities in this unit? Explain why you liked them.
   Answers vary.

✧ *Math Journal 2,* p. 324

✦ Oral and Slate Assessments

WHOLE-CLASS ACTIVITY

If the suggested problems are not appropriate for your class's level of performance, adjust the numbers or the problems themselves to better assess your students' abilities.

Oral Assessment Suggestions

1. Display a collection of small objects. Ask students to first estimate the weight of each object and then use a scale to weigh it. **Goal 11d**

2. Provide a supply of cm cubes. Ask students to build rectangular prisms with given volumes or with given dimensions. **Goal 11e**

- volume = 24 cm^3
- volume = 30 cm^3
- length of base = 5 cm, width of base = 4 cm, height of prism = 2 cm
- length of base = 3 cm, width of base = 2 cm, height of prism = 3 cm

Slate Assessment Suggestions

1. Pose addition and subtraction problems involving positive and negative integers. **Goals 11b and 11c**

- $19 + (-6) = 13$
- $(-30) + 14 = -16$
- $-4 - (-7) = 3$
- $-5 - (+6) = -11$
- $-9 + (-7) = -16$
- $8 - (-6) = 14$
- $-16 - (-11) = -5$

2. Pose problems about equivalent capacities.

- 1 gallon = 4 quarts
- 2 gallons = 8 quarts
- $4\frac{1}{2}$ gallons = 18 quarts
- 1 quart = 2 pints
- 3 quarts = 6 pints
- $5\frac{1}{2}$ quarts = 11 pints

✦Written Assessment
(*Math Masters,* pp. 411 and 412)

INDEPENDENT ACTIVITY 

Depending on the needs of students, you may want to work through an example together, reading a problem aloud, discussing it, and providing additional examples as necessary before students work the problem independently.

Each of the problems is listed on the next page and paired with one of this unit's learning goals. Circulate and assist as students work.

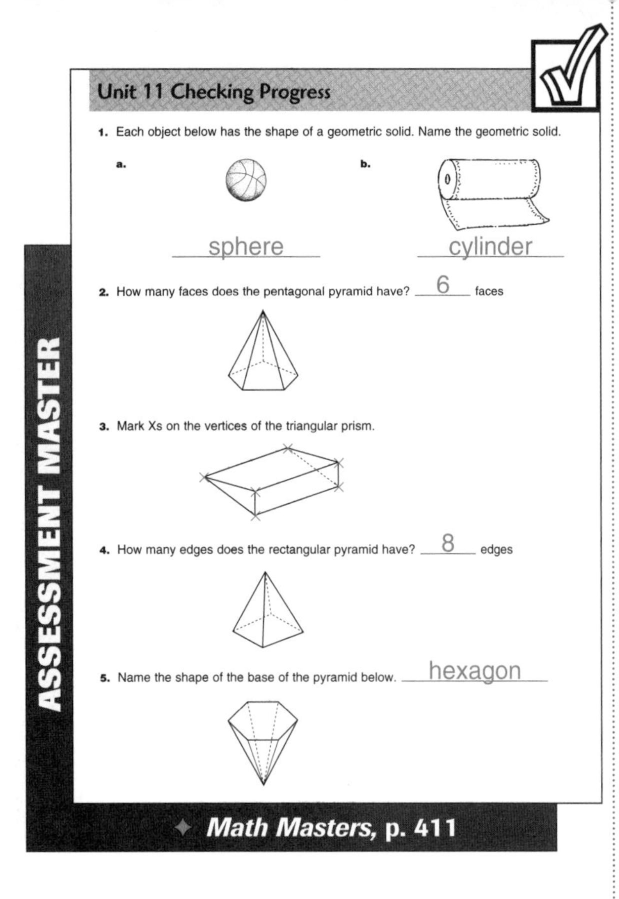
Unit 11 Checking Progress

ASSESSMENT MASTER

1. Each object below has the shape of a geometric solid. Name the geometric solid.

a. sphere

b. cylinder

2. How many faces does the pentagonal pyramid have? 6 faces

3. Mark Xs on the vertices of the triangular prism.

4. How many edges does the rectangular pyramid have? 8 edges

5. Name the shape of the base of the pyramid below. hexagon

✦ *Math Masters,* p. 411

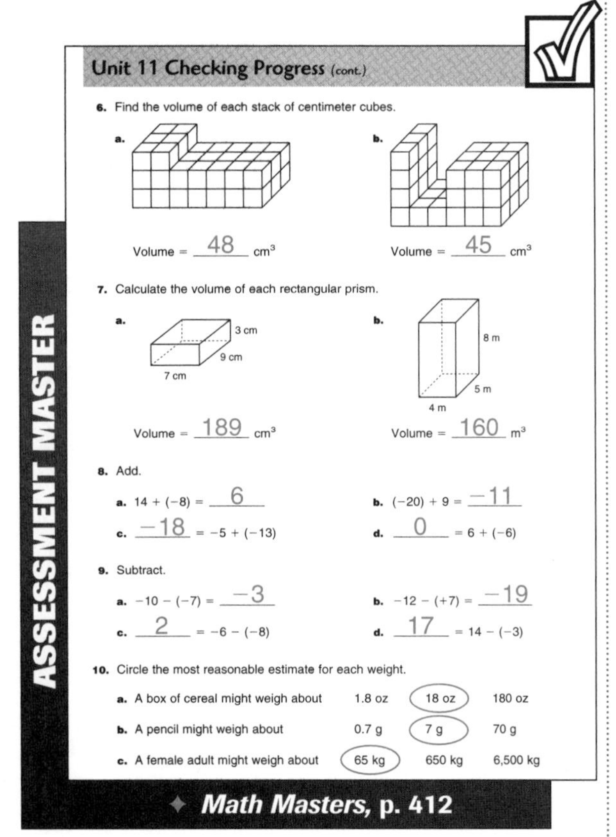
Unit 11 Checking Progress (cont.)

ASSESSMENT MASTER

6. Find the volume of each stack of centimeter cubes.

a. Volume = 48 cm³

b. Volume = 45 cm³

7. Calculate the volume of each rectangular prism.

a. 3 cm, 9 cm, 7 cm — Volume = 189 cm³

b. 8 m, 5 m, 4 m — Volume = 160 m³

8. Add.

a. 14 + (−8) = 6

b. (−20) + 9 = −11

c. −18 = −5 + (−13)

d. 0 = 6 + (−6)

9. Subtract.

a. −10 − (−7) = −3

b. −12 − (+7) = −19

c. 2 = −6 − (−8)

d. 17 = 14 − (−3)

10. Circle the most reasonable estimate for each weight.

a. A box of cereal might weigh about	1.8 oz	(18 oz)	180 oz
b. A pencil might weigh about	0.7 g	(7 g)	70 g
c. A female adult might weigh about	(65 kg)	650 kg	6,500 kg

✦ *Math Masters,* p. 412

- Tell what geometric solid an object resembles. (Problem 1) **Goal 11f**
- Tell how many faces a pentagonal pyramid has. (Problem 2) **Goal 11f**
- Mark Xs on the vertices of a triangular prism. (Problem 3) **Goal 11f**
- Tell how many edges a rectangular pyramid has. (Problem 4) **Goal 11f**
- Name the figure that forms the base of a pyramid. (Problem 5) **Goal 11f**
- Find the volume of a stack of cm cubes. (Problem 6) **Goal 11e**
- Use a formula to calculate the volume of two rectangular prisms. (Problem 7) **Goal 11a**
- Add signed numbers. (Problem 8) **Goal 11c**
- Subtract signed numbers. (Problem 9) **Goal 11b**
- Circle the most reasonable estimate for the weight of given objects. (Problem 10) **Goal 11d**

✦ ALTERNATIVE ASSESSMENT OPTION

Solve a Record Rainfall Problem
(*Math Masters,* p. 189)

SMALL-GROUP ACTIVITY 

Students solve a challenging problem involving an understanding of volume and equivalencies between volume and weight. The problem does not contain all the information that students need, so they must determine what information is missing.

If students are having difficulty, you might suggest the following strategy:

1. Find the area of the classroom floor in square feet. If the floor is rectangular, measure its length and width to the nearest $\frac{1}{2}$ foot and multiply.
2. Convert the height of the rainwater from inches to feet. 42 inches = $3\frac{1}{2}$, or 3.5 feet
3. Multiply the area of the classroom floor by 3.5 feet to find the volume of rainwater in cubic feet.
4. 1 cubic foot of water weighs about 62.5 pounds. Multiply the volume of the rainwater in cubic feet by 62.5 to find the weight of the water in the classroom.

Build Background for Unit 12

✦ Math Boxes 11.8 (*Math Journal 2,* p. 325)

INDEPENDENT ACTIVITY 

Mixed Review The skills in Problems 1–6 are prerequisites for Unit 12.

✦ Study Link 11.8: Unit 12 Family Letter (*Math Masters,* pp. 373–376)

Home Connection This Study Link is a four-page newsletter that introduces parents and guardians to Unit 12's topics and terms. The letter also offers ideas for mathematics activities that are supportive of classroom work and can be done at home.

A Record Rainfall

According to the National Weather Service, the most rain that fell in the United States in a 24-hour period was 42 inches. This happened in Alvin, Texas, on July 25 and 26, 1979.

Imagine that it rained 42 inches in your classroom. About how many pounds would the water weigh?

Work with your group to solve the problem.

> *Hints:* 1 cubic foot of water weighs about 62.5 pounds.
> 1 ton equals 2,000 pounds.

1. About how many pounds would 42 inches of rainwater in your classroom weigh? Answers vary for Problems 1–4.
   About ______ pounds
2. About how many tons is that?
   About ______ tons
3. What information did you use to solve the problem? How did you find this information?
   ______
4. Explain what you did to solve the problem.
   ______

TEACHING MASTER

✦ *Math Masters,* p. 189

Family Letter

Study Link 11.8

Unit 12: Rates

For the next two or three weeks, your child will be studying rates. Rates are among the most common applications of mathematics in daily life.

A rate is a comparison involving two different units. Familiar examples come from working (dollars per hour), driving (miles per hour), eating (calories per serving), reading (pages per day), and so on.

Our exploration of rates will begin with students collecting data on the rate at which their classmates blink their eyes. The class will try to answer the question, "Does a person's eye-blinking rate depend on what the person is doing?"

During this unit, students will collect many examples of rates to display in a Rates Museum. Then they will use these examples to make up rate problems, such as the following:

1. If cereal costs $2.98 per box, what will 4 boxes cost?
2. If a car's gas mileage is about 20 miles per gallon, how far can the car travel on a full tank of gas (16 gallons)?
3. If I make $6.25 per hour, how long must I work to earn enough to buy shoes that cost $35?

Then the class will work together to develop strategies for solving rate problems.

The unit emphasizes the importance of mathematics to smart consumers. Your child will learn about unit-pricing labels on supermarket shelves and how to use these labels to decide which of two items is the better buy. Your child will see that comparing prices is only *part* of being a smart consumer. Other factors to consider include quality, the need for the product, and, perhaps, the product's effect on the environment.

This unit provides a great opportunity for your child to help with the family shopping. Have your child help you decide whether the largest size is necessarily the best buy. Is an item on sale necessarily a better buy than a similar product that is not on sale?

Finally, students will look back on their experiences in the yearlong World Tour and share them with one another.

Nutrition Facts
Serving Size 1 link (45 g)
Servings per Container 10

Amount per Serving	
Calories 150	Calories from Fat 120
	% Daily Value
Total Fat 13 g	20%
Total Carbohydrate 1 g	<1%
Protein 7 g	

STUDY LINK MASTERS

✦ *Math Masters,* pp. 373–376

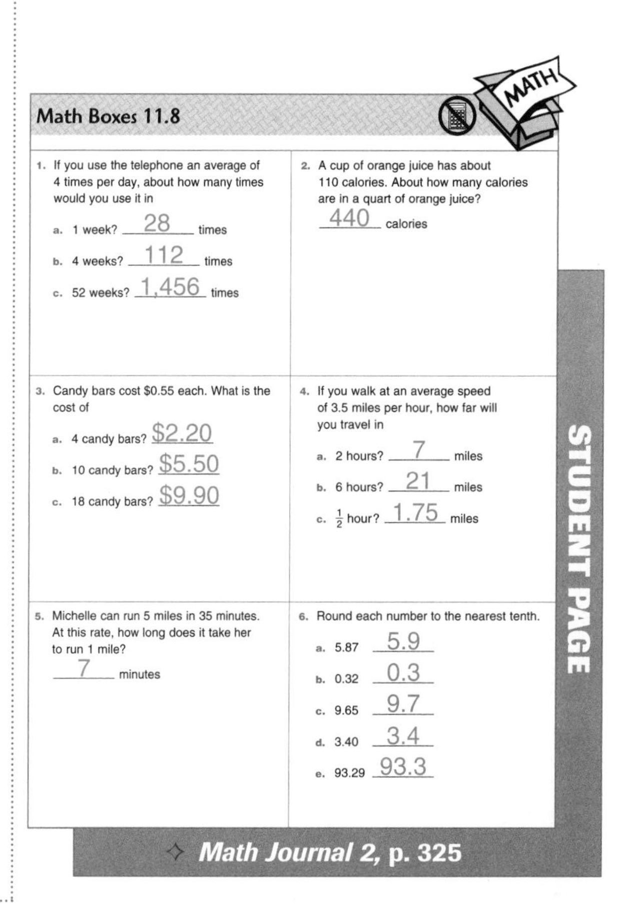

Math Boxes 11.8

1. If you use the telephone an average of 4 times per day, about how many times would you use it in
   a. 1 week? 28 times
   b. 4 weeks? 112 times
   c. 52 weeks? 1,456 times
2. A cup of orange juice has about 110 calories. About how many calories are in a quart of orange juice?
   440 calories
3. Candy bars cost $0.55 each. What is the cost of
   a. 4 candy bars? $2.20
   b. 10 candy bars? $5.50
   c. 18 candy bars? $9.90
4. If you walk at an average speed of 3.5 miles per hour, how far will you travel in
   a. 2 hours? 7 miles
   b. 6 hours? 21 miles
   c. $\frac{1}{2}$ hour? 1.75 miles
5. Michelle can run 5 miles in 35 minutes. At this rate, how long does it take her to run 1 mile?
   7 minutes
6. Round each number to the nearest tenth.
   a. 5.87 5.9
   b. 0.32 0.3
   c. 9.65 9.7
   d. 3.40 3.4
   e. 93.29 93.3

STUDENT PAGE

✧ *Math Journal 2,* p. 325

Unit 12
Rates

overview

Rates, ratios, and proportional thinking are very common in the everyday world, and there is probably no better indication of good "number sense" and "measure sense" than the ability to handle such problems with ease. Unfortunately for many people, everyday uses of rates seem to be among the most difficult aspects of mathematics. Many of the reports of poor achievement in mathematics are based on failures with rate or ratio problems on inventory tests, or with proportional thinking in the workplace.

The key to understanding rates is repeated exposure to the many uses of rates in everyday life. From the outset, in Lesson 12.1, students start a Rates Museum—a class list of examples of rates, which they will augment throughout the unit. Be sure to give students plenty of time to share the examples they collect.

contents

Lesson	Objective	Page
12.1	**Introducing Rates** *To introduce rates; and to collect and compare rate data.*	842
12.2	**Solving Rate Problems** *To use a rate table to record rate information; and to solve rate problems.*	848
12.3	**Converting between Rates** *To check the validity of data by converting them to more accessible rates.*	854
12.4	**Comparison Shopping: Part 1** *To calculate the unit price for a product; to compare unit prices; and to identify information needed for comparison shopping.*	860
12.5	**Comparison Shopping: Part 2** *To calculate and compare unit prices that involve fractions of cents.*	865
12.6	**World Tour Wrap-Up** *To reflect on this year's World Tour experiences.*	870
12.7	**Unit 12 Review and Assessment** *To review and assess students' progress on the material covered in Unit 12.*	874

UNIT 12

learning goals in perspective

learning goals	links to the past	links to the future
12a **Developing Goal** Find unit rates. **(Lessons 12.2–12.5)**	Grade 2: Solve comparison number stories; use comparison diagrams and write number models. Grade 3: Practice rate multiplication in number stories. Grade 4: Compare numbers (Unit 4).	Grade 5: Review the meaning and uses of rates; represent rates with formulas, tables of values, and graphs. Solve rate and ratio number stories. Measure heart rates. Grade 6: Model rate and ratio problems with proportions; solve proportions by cross multiplication and other methods.
12b **Developing Goal** Calculate unit prices to determine which product is the "better buy." **(Lessons 12.4 and 12.5)**	Grade 3: Compare estimated costs to exact costs. Make up and solve problems about costs of multiple items.	Grades 5 and 6: Applications and maintenance.
12c **Developing Goal** Evaluate reasonableness of rate data. **(Lesson 12.3)**	Grades 2 and 3: Make ballpark estimates as a check for reasonableness of answers.	Grade 5: Make magnitude estimates for quotients. Grade 6: Use benchmarks to decide reasonableness of number-and-word statements. Explore how displays of data can be manipulated to be persuasive.
12d **Developing Goal** Collect and compare rate data. **(Lessons 12.1 and 12.3–12.5)**	Grades 2 and 3: Collect, organize, interpret, and display data.	Grades 5 and 6: Collect, organize, interpret, and display data.
12e **Secure Goal** Use rate tables, if necessary, to solve rate problems. **(Lessons 12.2–12.4 and 12.6)**	Grades 2 and 3: Organize data in tables. Solve "What's My Rule?" problems.	Grade 5: Represent rates with formulas, tables of values, and graphs. Solve rate and ratio number stories. Grade 6: Estimate travel time based on rate information. Model rate and ratio problems with proportions; solve proportions by cross multiplication and other methods.

assessment

ongoing • product • periodic

Informal Assessment

Math Boxes These *Math Journal* pages provide opportunities for cumulative review or assessment of concepts and skills.

Ongoing Assessment: Kid Watching Use the Ongoing Assessment suggestions in the following lessons to make quick, on-the-spot observations about students' understanding of:
- Data and Chance **(Lesson 12.1, Part 1)**
- Patterns, Functions, and Algebra **(Lesson 12.2, Part 1; Lesson 12.6, Part 2)**
- Operations and Computation **(Lesson 12.5, Part 2)**
- Numeration **(Lesson 12.5, Part 1)**

Portfolio Ideas Samples of students' work may be obtained from the following assignments:
- Collecting Follow-Up Data on Eye-Blinking Rates **(Lesson 12.1)**
- Solving More Rate Problems **(Lesson 12.2)**
- Solving Mammal Speeds Problems **(Lesson 12.2)**
- Solving Mammal Heart Rates Problems; Analyzing Data **(Lesson 12.3)**
- Calculating Unit Prices; Comparing Prices **(Lesson 12.5)**
- Solve Multi-Step Problems Involving Rates **(Lesson 12.7)**

Unit 12 Review and Assessment

Math Message Use the Time to Reflect questions in Lesson 12.7 to assess students' progress toward the following learning goals: **Goals 12a–12e**

Oral and Slate Assessments Use oral or slate assessments during Lesson 12.7 to assess students' progress toward the following learning goals: **Goals 12a, 12c, and 12e**

Written Assessment Use a written review during Lesson 12.7 to assess students' progress toward the following learning goals: **Goals 12a–12e**

Alternative Assessment Option Use the small-group alternative assessment option in Lesson 12.7 to assess students' progress toward the following learning goals: **Goals 12a and 12b**

assessment handbook

For more information on how to use different types of assessment in Unit 12, see the Assessment Overview on pages 72–74 in the *Assessment Handbook*. The following Assessment Masters can be found in the *Math Masters* book:
- Unit 12 Checking Progress, pp. 413 and 414
- Unit 12 Class Checklist, p. 448
- Unit 12 Individual Profile of Progress, p. 449
- Class Progress Indicator, p. 467
- Interest Inventories, pp. 468 and 469
- Math Logs, pp. 470–472
- Self-Assessment Forms, pp. 473 and 474

problemsolving

A process of modeling everyday situations using tools from mathematics

Encourage students to use a variety of strategies when attacking a given problem—and to explain those strategies. *Strategies students might use in this unit:*

- Acting out the problem
- Making a table
- Using computation
- Using estimation

Four Problem-Solving REPRESENTATIONS

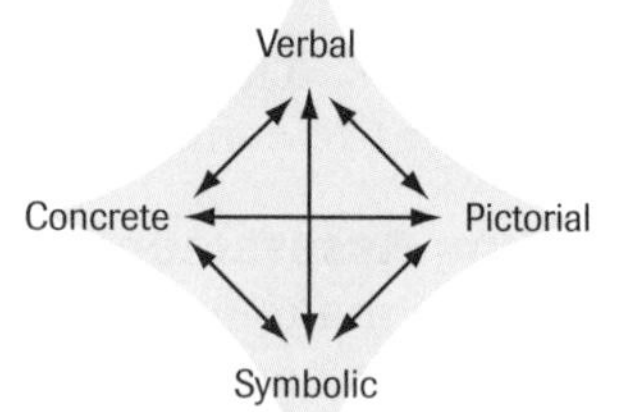

Lessons that teach *through* problem solving, not just *about* problem solving

Lesson	Activity	Lesson	Activity
12.1	Collecting data and comparing eye-blinking rates for when a person is reading and at rest	**12.4**	Calculating and comparing unit prices
12.2, 12.4, 12.6	Solving rate problems involving a variety of situations	**12.5**	Solving problems involving unit pricing
12.3	Using rates to check whether "in an average lifetime" data makes sense	**12.6**	Solving a variety of problems involving data from different countries

For more information about problem solving in *Everyday Mathematics,* see the *Teacher's Reference Manual.*

cross-curricularlinks

literature

- Students learning English read *Each Orange Had Eight Slices: A Counting Book* by Paul Giganti, Jr. to practice using rate language. **(Lesson 12.1)**
- Students examine statistics given in the book *In the Next Three Seconds* by Rowland Morgan. **(Lesson 12.3)**
- Students read about various countries in the *Count Your Way through* ... series by Jim Haskins and Kathleen Benson. **(Lesson 12.6)**

social studies

- Students record examples of rates found in the World Tour section of the *Student Reference Book.* **(Lesson 12.1)**
- Students reflect on their World Tour experiences. **(Lesson 12.6)**

consumer

- Students "comparison shop" by calculating and comparing unit prices for various products. **(Lessons 12.4 and 12.5)**

science

- Students predict the outcome of a race between different types of mammals. **(Lesson 12.2)**
- Students compare their own heart rates with those of other mammals. **(Lesson 12.3)**
- Students solve rate problems involving the activities of mammals. **(Lesson 12.4)**

meeting INDIVIDUAL needs

UNIVERSAL ACCESS

✦ RETEACHING

The following features provide additional instructional support:

Adjusting the Activity

- **Lesson 12.4, Part 1**
- **Lesson 12.4, Part 2**
- **Lesson 12.5, Part 1**

Options for Individualizing

- **Lesson 12.1** Using Multiplication/Division Diagrams to Solve Rate Problems

✦ ENRICHMENT

The following features suggest some enrichment and extension activities found in this unit:

Adjusting the Activity

- **Lesson 12.1, Part 1**
- **Lesson 12.3, Part 1**
- **Lesson 12.5, Part 1**
- **Lesson 12.6, Part 1**

Options for Individualizing

- **Lesson 12.1** Collecting Follow-Up Data on Eye-Blinking Rates
- **Lesson 12.2** Solving Mammal Speeds Problems
- **Lesson 12.3** Solving Mammal Heart Rates Problems
- **Lesson 12.3** Analyzing Data
- **Lesson 12.4** Testing Products with *Zillions* Magazine
- **Lesson 12.5** Comparing Prices
- **Lesson 12.6** Exploring the Culture, Geography, and History of Countries through Numbers

✦ LANGUAGE DIVERSITY

The following features suggest some ways to support students who are acquiring proficiency in English:

Adjusting the Activity

- **Lesson 12.6, Part 1**

Options for Individualizing

- **Lesson 12.1** Using the Language of Rates

✦ MULTIAGE CLASSROOM

The following chart lists related lessons from Grades 3 and 5 that can help you meet your instructional needs:

Grade 3	2.6		2.6	7.7 9.5	7.7 9.5	
Grade 4	12.1	12.2	12.3	12.4	12.5	12.6
Grade 5		12.5	12.6 12.8		8.9 12.4	

materials

lesson	math masters pages	manipulative kit items	other items
12.1	Study Link Master, p. 377		slate timer or clock with a second hand calculator (optional) large sheet of paper *Each Orange Had Eight Slices: A Counting Book* ***See* Advance Preparation, p. 842**
12.2	Study Link Master, p. 378 Teaching Masters, pp. 187 and 190–193 transparency of Teaching Master, p. 190 (optional) Assessment Master, p. 471 or 475 (optional) ***See* Advance Preparation, p. 848**		
12.3	Study Link Master, p. 379 Teaching Masters, pp. 194–197		calculator *In the Next Three Seconds* ***See* Advance Preparation, p. 854**
12.4	Study Link Master, p. 380 Teaching Master, p. 190 (optional)		calculator computer with Internet access *Zillions* Magazine (optional) ***See* Advance Preparation, p. 860**
12.5	Study Link Master, p. 381 Teaching Masters, pp. 190, 194, and 198 ***See* Advance Preparation, p. 865**		calculator supermarket ads
12.6	Study Link Master, p. 382 Assessment Master, p. 471 or 475 (optional)		*Count Your Way through ...* books ***See* Advance Preparation, p. 870**
12.7	Study Link Masters, pp. 383–386 Teaching Masters, pp. 199 and 200 Assessment Masters, pp. 413, 414, and 419–425		slate calculator

planningtips

Pacing

Pacing depends on a number of factors, such as students' individual needs and how long your school has been using *Everyday Mathematics.* At the beginning of Unit 12, review your Content by Strand Poster to help you set a monthly pace.

APRIL	MAY	JUNE

←MOST CLASSROOMS→ (late May to early June)

Using the Projects

Use Project 5, Which Soft Drink Is the Best Buy?, to calculate the unit price of various soft drinks and to decide which is the best buy. The Projects can be found at the back of this book.

Home Communication

Share Study Links 12.1–12.6 with families to help them understand the content and procedures in this unit. At the end of the unit, use Study Link 12.7 to suggest review activities that can be used during summer vacation. Supplemental information can be found in the *Home Connection Handbook*.

NCTM Standards

Standard	1	2	3	4	5	6	7	8	9	10
Unit 12 Lessons	2, 3, 5, 6	1–6		6	1, 3, 6	1–7	1–7	1–7	1–7	1–7

Content Standards
1 Number and Operations
2 Algebra
3 Geometry
4 Measurement
5 Data Analysis and Probability

Process Standards
6 Problem Solving
7 Reasoning and Proof
8 Communication
9 Connections
10 Representation

PRACTICE *through* Games

Everyday Mathematics uses games to help students develop good fact power and other math skills.

- *Credits/Debits Game* (Advanced Version) to practice the addition and subtraction of positive and negative integers **(Lesson 12.2)**

unit 12 content highlights

The discussion below highlights the major content ideas presented in Unit 12 and may help you establish instructional priorities.

NOTE: As students explore rates and ratios, calculator use should be encouraged. The no-calculator icon appears only on selected Math Boxes pages.

Solving Rate Problems (Lesson 12.2)

After students have discussed examples of rates in Lesson 12.1, they begin to solve rate problems in Lesson 12.2. Rate tables, which some students may recognize as a special kind of "What's My Rule?" table, are also introduced as an aid to problem solving. By completing such tables, students develop a sense that rate problems usually involve a search for equivalent rates, leading to the solution of problems. As you and your students make up and solve problems, three basic types of rate problems should emerge. These types are illustrated by the following examples:

1. Bill's new car can travel 35 miles on 1 gallon of gasoline. At this rate, how far can the car travel on 7 gallons of gasoline?

   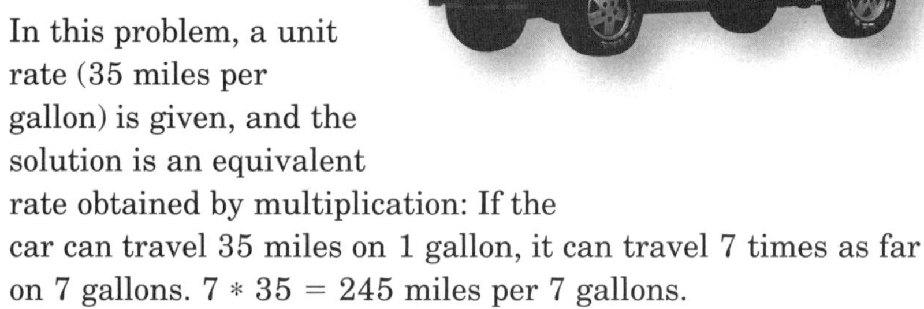

   In this problem, a unit rate (35 miles per gallon) is given, and the solution is an equivalent rate obtained by multiplication: If the car can travel 35 miles on 1 gallon, it can travel 7 times as far on 7 gallons. $7 * 35 = 245$ miles per 7 gallons.

2. Jennifer received an allowance of $8 in 4 weeks. At this rate, how much allowance did she receive per week?

   In this problem, a rate that is not a unit rate ($8 in 4 weeks) is given, and the solution is an equivalent unit rate obtained by division: If Jennifer received $8 in 4 weeks, she received $\frac{1}{4}$ of $8 in 1 week. 8 / 4 = $2 per week.

3. A gray whale's heart beats 24 times in 3 minutes. At this rate, how many times does a gray whale's heart beat in 2 minutes?

   In this problem, a rate that is not a unit rate (24 beats in 3 minutes) is given, and the solution is an equivalent rate that is not a unit rate. The solution can be obtained by first finding the equivalent unit rate by division and then using the unit rate to find the solution by multiplication: If the gray whale's heart beats 24 times in 3 minutes, it beats $\frac{1}{3}$ of 24 times in 1 minute ($24 / 3 = 8$) and twice as many times in 2 minutes ($2 * 8 = 16$ beats per 2 minutes).

The Unit-Rate Strategy (Lessons 12.2 and 12.3)

The strategy illustrated in the last example—in which rate information given for a *number* of things is converted to the equivalent *unit* rate, from which other equivalent rates are calculated—is a powerful one. This strategy is practiced throughout the unit in various pricing and purchasing exercises, where students explore the "reasonableness" of rate estimates involving very large numbers. While there are other, more advanced strategies for dealing with rates, this basic strategy is perhaps the most universally useful one and the one advocated by many science and mathematics educators. (See *Sci-Math,* by Madeline P. Goodstein, Addison-Wesley, 1983.)

The authors recommend frequent, brief practice sessions for solving such problems. Use them as Mental Math and Reflexes routines. Even a single problem, followed by a brief sharing of solutions, should help your students improve their problem-solving skills.

Units Analysis in Rate Problems (Lessons 12.3 and following)

Scientists and science educators often complain that mathematics teaching does not prepare students for the study of science. One of their main criticisms is that too much teaching of arithmetic deals strictly with numbers and ignores the role of units of measure that are nearly always attached to those numbers. With this problem in mind, the authors of *Everyday Mathematics* have insisted, starting in Kindergarten, that nearly every number must come with a count or measure unit. You might want to extend the work with units to a basic strategy used throughout the natural sciences, called units analysis. This strategy involves combining and canceling units in calculations involving measures.

Examples

- There are 6 rows of chairs with 4 chairs per row. How many chairs are there in all?

  $6 \text{ r}\cancel{\text{ow}}\text{s} * \frac{4 \text{ chairs}}{1 \cancel{\text{row}}} = 24 \text{ chairs}$

  The "row" units cancel in much the same way as do numbers in the numerators and denominators in the multiplication of fractions.

- Marsha earned \$56 for 8 hours of work. How much did she earn per hour?

  $\frac{56 \text{ dollars}}{8 \text{ hours}} = 7 \text{ dollars per hour}$

  Dollars divided by hours = dollars per hour

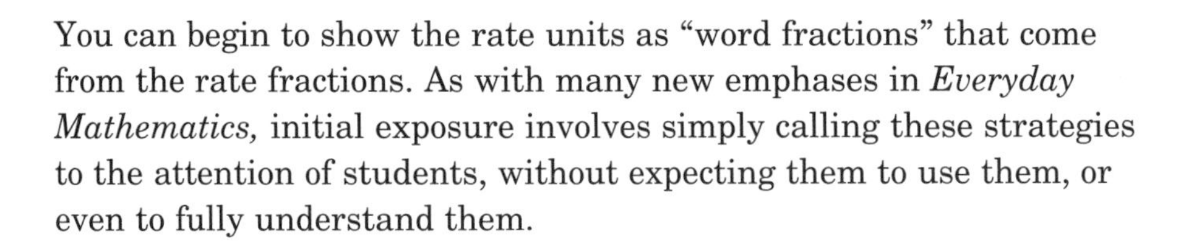

Nutrition Facts
Serving Size 2 Tbsp (32g)
Servings Per Container about 24

Amount Per Serving	
Calories 190 Calories from Fat 130	
	% Daily Value*
Total Fat 16g	25%
Saturated Fat 3g	15%
Cholesterol 0mg	0%
Sodium 140mg	6%
Total Carbohydrate 7g	2%
Dietary Fiber 2g	8%
Sugars 3g	
Protein 7g	

Nutrition labels include rate information.

You can begin to show the rate units as "word fractions" that come from the rate fractions. As with many new emphases in *Everyday Mathematics,* initial exposure involves simply calling these strategies to the attention of students, without expecting them to use them, or even to fully understand them.

Comparison Shopping (Lessons 12.4 and 12.5)

Lessons 12.4 and 12.5 deal with a specific application of the unit-rate strategy—calculating unit prices in order to compare the costs of similar items. This application has become so commonplace that most supermarkets display unit-price labels along with the price of the items on their shelves. Students collect real data from newspaper ads, visits to grocery stores, and other places of business; represent them symbolically, usually in fraction form; and convert them to decimal form by doing the indicated division. Performing these operations with a calculator will usually result in an answer with more decimal places than are needed. Hence, these activities also provide practice with simplifying complicated results by rounding.

You may need to review problems involving dollars and cents. For example, if a 3-pound bag of apples costs \$1.49, the unit price is obtained by dividing \$1.49 by 3. On a calculator, this result may be displayed as 0.4966666667. The digit in the first place to the right of the decimal point represents dimes, the second digit represents pennies, and the third digit represents tenths of cents. In this problem then, the calculator display is interpreted as 4 dimes, 9 pennies, 6 tenths of a cent, and so on. This is equivalent to 49.7 cents when rounded to the nearest tenth of a cent.

World Tour Wrap-Up (Lesson 12.6)

Students have participated in the World Tour Project for most of the school year. Be sure to reserve time for at least one sharing session, in which students describe and compare their experiences.

Review and Assessment (Lesson 12.7)

The Unit 12 assessment in Lesson 12.7 includes oral, slate, and written assessments of the following concepts and skills:

- finding unit rates
- calculating unit prices to determine which product is the "better buy"
- evaluating the reasonableness of rate data
- collecting and comparing rate data
- solving rate problems and using rate tables

If you are planning a quarterly assessment for Units 10–12, you may want to refer to the *Assessment Handbook.* The quarterly learning goals Class Checklist and Individual Profile of Progress checklist (*Math Masters,* pages 461–463) are useful tools for keeping track of students' progress.

NOTE: The End-of-Year Assessment (*Math Masters,* pages 419–425) provides an additional assessment opportunity that you may want to use as part of your balanced assessment plan. This test covers many of the important concepts and skills presented in *Fourth Grade Everyday Mathematics.* It should be used along with ongoing, product, and periodic assessments. Please see the *Assessment Handbook* for further information.

For additional information on the following topics, see the *Teacher's Reference Manual:*

- comparison shopping
- consumer
- proportions
- rate
- rate table
- ratio
- unit rate
- unit price and unit-price label

12.1 Introducing Rates

OBJECTIVES **To introduce rates; and to collect and compare rate data.**

summaries	materials
1 Teaching the Lesson	
Students collect data on how many times classmates blink in one minute. They compare median blinking rates for students at rest and for students who are reading. Students start making lists of other examples of rates; these lists are combined to create a classroom Rates Museum. [Data and Chance; Patterns, Functions, and Algebra]	□ *Math Journal 2,* p. 326 □ *Student Reference Book,* pp. 214 and 243 □ slate □ timer or clock with a second hand □ calculator (optional) □ large sheet of paper ***See* Advance Preparation**
2 Ongoing Learning & Practice	
Students practice and maintain skills through Math Boxes and Study Link activities.	□ *Math Journal 2,* p. 327 □ Study Link Master (*Math Masters,* p. 377)
3 Options for Individualizing	
Enrichment Students collect and compare follow-up data on eye-blinking rates. [Data and Chance] **Language Diversity** Students who are learning English work with proficient English speakers to give examples of rates from a story. [Patterns, Functions, and Algebra] **Reteaching** Students use multiplication/division diagrams to solve rate problems. [Patterns, Functions, and Algebra]	□ timer or clock with a second hand □ *Each Orange Had Eight Slices: A Counting Book* ***See* Advance Preparation**

Additional Information

Advance Preparation For Part 1, read the description of the eye-blinking experiment before class and decide how best to conduct it. Post a large sheet of paper on which to list examples of rates for a Rates Museum.

For the optional Language Diversity activity in Part 3, you will need a copy of *Each Orange Had Eight Slices: A Counting Book* by Paul Giganti, Jr. (Greenwillow Books, 1992).

Vocabulary • **rate** • **per**

Getting Started

Mental Math and Reflexes

Pose addition and subtraction problems with positive and negative integers. *Suggestions:*

- 40 + (−60) −20
- −130 + 210 80
- −410 + (−360) −770
- 80 − (−70) 150
- −4,000 − 3,000 −7,000
- −120 − (−30) −90

Math Message

Find the median (middle value) for each set of numbers. Write your answers on your slate.

a. 4, 9, 3, 12, 15, 9, 7 **b.** 2, 10, 6, 9

1 Teaching the Lesson

✦Math Message Follow-Up

WHOLE-CLASS DISCUSSION 

The median of a set of numbers is the middle number, when the numbers are listed in order from smallest to largest or from largest to smallest. Nine is the median of the first set of numbers because in the ordered list 3, 4, 7, 9, 9, 12, 15, the number 9 is the middle number.

If there is an even number of numbers in the set, the median is the mean (average) of the two middle numbers. In the ordered list 2, 6, 9, 10, there are two middle numbers. The median is (6 + 9) / 2, or $7\frac{1}{2}$.

ONGOING ASSESSMENT

Most students should be able to find the median of a set of data. This skill is a prerequisite for comparing eye-blinking rates in the activity that follows.

✦Collecting Eye-Blinking Data

WHOLE-CLASS ACTIVITY

Take half the class aside, outside the hearing range of the other half. Tell these students that they are going to collect data on their classmates' eye-blinking rates but that they must do so secretly. Explain the procedure they are to follow:

▷ Each student in the data-collecting group—Group A—will be paired with a student in the other group—Group B. Partners will sit across from each other and, at your signal, will be instructed to look at each other.

Rates

1. While at rest, a typical student in my class blinks Answers times in one minute.

2. While reading, a typical student in my class blinks vary. times in one minute.

3. List as many examples of rates as you can.

Sample answers: Miles per hour; dollars per pound; beats per minute; students per classroom

4. Find at least two examples of rates in your *Student Reference Book.* (*Hint:* Look at pages 214 and 243.)

Sample answers: The world's population is now increasing by about 77 million people per year. About 62 of every 100 people in Algeria are literate (can read and write). There are about 71 televisions in Algeria for every 1,000 people.

STUDENT PAGE

✧ *Math Journal 2,* p. 326

Number of Blinks in 1 Minute	
At rest	Reading
14	10
18	1
2	2

Table for recording blinking rates (sample data provided)

▷ While looking at each other, students in Group A will count the number of times their partners in Group B blink in one minute. At the end of one minute, you will give the signal to stop. Students in Group A will make a mental (or written) note of the number of times their partners blinked in one minute.

▷ Next, you will instruct the students in Group B to open a book. At your signal, the students in Group B will start reading, while the students in Group A again count their partners' number of blinks. Again, you will give the signal to stop at the end of one minute.

▷ The students in Group A will then make a note of the number of times their partners blinked in one minute, both while at rest and while reading.

Tell students in Group A that they will follow this procedure because it is important that the person whose blinks are being counted remains unaware of what is taking place. Otherwise, that person might become self-conscious and not blink in a natural way.

Bring the class together and conduct the experiment.

✦Comparing Eye-Blinking Rates
(*Math Journal 2,* p. 326)

WHOLE-CLASS ACTIVITY

Ask one of the students in Group A to describe the experiment. Then ask the students in Group B to speculate about whether a person blinks more often while reading or while doing nothing in particular; or, do they think the number of blinks remains about the same?

Take a vote and ask students to discuss why they voted the way they did. Then make a table on the board (*see margin*) and record each student's blinking rates on a separate line.

Ask partners to find the median for each set of data ("at rest" and "reading") and to record the medians in Problems 1 and 2 in their journals.

Bring the class together to discuss the results. Ask:

- Why might a person's blinking rate vary, depending on the activity? Possible response: A person may concentrate more and blink less when reading.
- What might be some other factors that can affect the number of times a person blinks? Possible responses: The brightness of the light; how relaxed or tired a person feels; whether a person wears glasses or contact lenses; whether a person is interested or bored

Adjusting the Activity Challenge students to use calculators to find the mean (average) for each set of data. For example, to find the mean number of blinks at rest, add the numbers in column 1 of the table and divide by the number of data items. The median and the mean for a set of data are usually not equal, but the mean is very often close to the median (middle value). For example, for Math Message Problem a, the mean is 8.4 and the median is 9; for Problem b, the mean is 6.75 and the median is 7.5.

✦ Listing Examples of Rates

(*Math Journal 2,* p. 326; *Student Reference Book,* pp. 214 and 243)

PARTNER ACTIVITY 

Remind the class that the number of times a person blinks in one minute is an example of a rate. A **rate** tells how many there are of one thing for a certain number of another thing. Rates often contain the word **per,** which means *for each,* such as in *15 blinks per minute* or *55 miles per hour.* A rate can be written with a slash to represent the word *per,* as in *$2.25/lb.*

Ask students to list other examples of rates in Problem 3 in their journals. To help them get started, you might suggest a few categories:

▷ Food: calories per serving

▷ Packaging: paper clips per box

▷ Price: dollars per pound

▷ Transportation: miles per gallon

▷ Sports: minutes per half in football

▷ Animals: number of legs per ostrich

Social Studies Link In Problem 4, have students record at least two examples of rates from pages 214 and 243 of the World Tour section in the *Student Reference Book.*

After a few minutes, bring students together to share their examples of rates. Record the examples on the class data pad or on a large sheet of paper to start a Rates Museum. Ask the class to add other examples of rates to the list during the next few days.

World Tour

Facts about the World

Continents are large land masses. There are seven continents on the Earth, although Europe and Asia are sometimes thought of as one continent. Most continents contain many countries, but there are no countries at all in Antarctica.

A **country** is a territory and the people who live there under one government. The number of countries in the world often changes as countries split apart or join with other countries. At this time, there are about 200 countries in the world.

Population is the number of people who live in a certain region. Population growth is the change in the population every year after all births and deaths are accounted for. The **population growth rate** is the percent of change in the population.

The world's population is now increasing by about 210,000 people per day, or about 77 million people per year. Over the last 40 years, the world's population has about doubled. It reached the 6 billion mark in 1999. World population is expected to reach about 9 billion people by the year 2050.

Dimensions of the Earth

Equatorial circumference*: about 24,900 miles (40,000 kilometers)

Equatorial diameter:** about 7,930 miles (12,760 kilometers)

Volume: 2.6×10^{11} cubic miles (1.1×10^{12} cubic kilometers)

Weight (mass): 6.6×10^{21} tons (6.0×10^{21} metric tons)

Total world water area: about 139,433,000 square miles (361,129,000 square kilometers)

*Circumference is the distance around a circle or sphere.

**Diameter is the distance measured by a straight line passing from one side of a circle or sphere, through the center, to the other side.

The Continents

Continent	Population*	Percent of World Population	Area (sq miles)	Percent of Land Area
North America	482,000,000	7.9%	9,400,000	16.2%
South America	347,000,000	5.7	6,900,000	11.9
Europe	736,000,000	12.1	3,800,000	6.6
Asia	3,688,000,000	60.7	17,400,000	30.1
Africa	788,000,000	13.0	11,700,000	20.2
Australia	30,000,000	0.5	3,300,000	5.7
Antarctica	0	0.0	5,400,000	9.3
World Totals	**6,071,000,000 (about 6.1 billion)**	**100.0%**	**57,900,000**	**100.0%**

*Data are for the year 2000.
World population growth rate for the year 2000: about 1.3% per year

two hundred fourteen

STUDENT PAGE

✧ *Student Reference Book,* p. 214

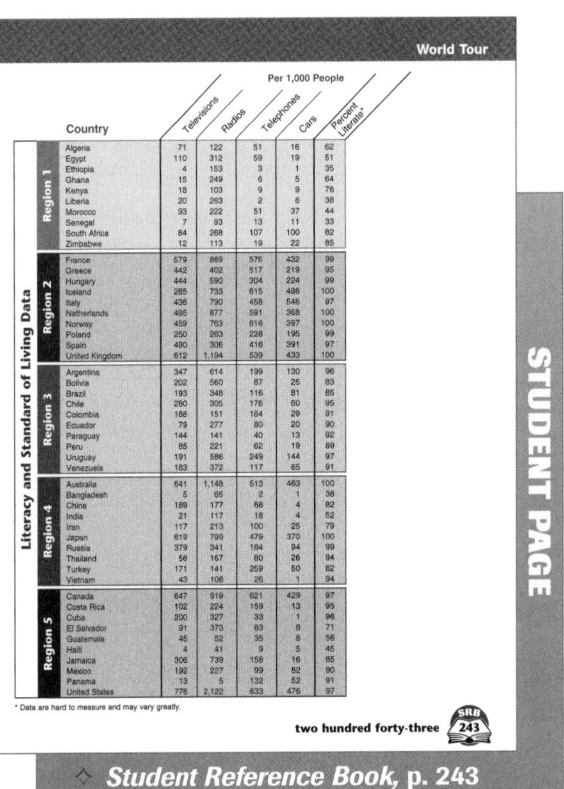

World Tour

Literacy and Standard of Living Data

Region	Country	Televisions (per 1,000 people)	Radios (per 1,000 people)	Telephones (per 1,000 people)	Cars (per 1,000 people)	Percent Literate*
Region 1	Algeria	71	122	51	16	62
	Egypt	110	312	59	19	51
	Ethiopia	4	153	3	1	35
	Ghana	15	249	6	5	64
	Kenya	18	103	9	9	78
	Liberia	20	263	2	6	38
	Morocco	93	222	51	37	44
	Senegal	7	93	13	11	33
	South Africa	84	268	107	100	82
	Zimbabwe	12	113	19	22	85
Region 2	France	579	869	576	432	99
	Greece	442	402	517	219	95
	Hungary	444	590	304	224	99
	Iceland	285	733	615	486	100
	Italy	436	790	458	546	97
	Netherlands	495	877	591	368	100
	Norway	459	763	616	397	100
	Poland	250	263	228	195	99
	Spain	490	306	416	391	97
	United Kingdom	612	1,194	539	433	100
Region 3	Argentina	347	614	199	130	96
	Bolivia	202	560	67	25	83
	Brazil	193	348	116	81	85
	Chile	280	305	176	60	95
	Colombia	188	151	164	29	91
	Ecuador	79	277	80	20	90
	Paraguay	144	141	40	13	92
	Peru	85	221	62	19	89
	Uruguay	191	586	249	144	97
	Venezuela	183	372	117	65	91
Region 4	Australia	641	1,148	513	463	100
	Bangladesh	5	65	2	1	38
	China	189	177	68	4	82
	India	21	117	18	4	52
	Iran	117	213	100	25	79
	Japan	619	799	479	370	100
	Russia	379	341	184	94	99
	Thailand	56	167	80	26	94
	Turkey	171	141	259	50	82
	Vietnam	43	106	26	1	94
Region 5	Canada	647	919	621	429	97
	Costa Rica	102	224	159	13	95
	Cuba	200	327	33	1	96
	El Salvador	91	373	83	6	71
	Guatemala	45	52	35	8	56
	Haiti	4	41	9	5	45
	Jamaica	306	739	158	16	85
	Mexico	192	227	99	82	90
	Panama	13	5	132	52	91
	United States	776	2,122	633	476	97

* Data are hard to measure and may vary greatly.

two hundred forty-three SRB 243

STUDENT PAGE

✧ *Student Reference Book,* p. 243

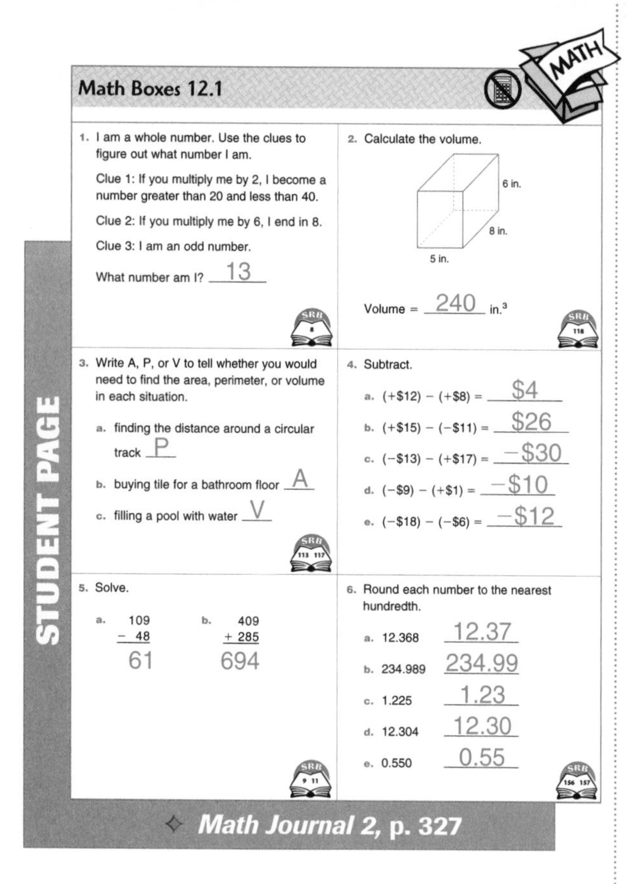
Math Boxes 12.1

1. I am a whole number. Use the clues to figure out what number I am.

Clue 1: If you multiply me by 2, I become a number greater than 20 and less than 40.

Clue 2: If you multiply me by 6, I end in 8.

Clue 3: I am an odd number.

What number am I? 13

2. Calculate the volume.

6 in.
8 in.
5 in.

Volume = 240 in.^{3}

3. Write A, P, or V to tell whether you would need to find the area, perimeter, or volume in each situation.

a. finding the distance around a circular track P

b. buying tile for a bathroom floor A

c. filling a pool with water V

4. Subtract.

a. (+\$12) − (+\$8) = \$4

b. (+\$15) − (−\$11) = \$26

c. (−\$13) − (+\$17) = −\$30

d. (−\$9) − (+\$1) = −\$10

e. (−\$18) − (−\$6) = −\$12

5. Solve.

a. 109 − 48 = 61

b. 409 + 285 = 694

6. Round each number to the nearest hundredth.

a. 12.368 12.37

b. 234.989 234.99

c. 1.225 1.23

d. 12.304 12.30

e. 0.550 0.55

STUDENT PAGE

Math Journal 2, p. 327

2 Ongoing Learning & Practice

✦ Math Boxes 12.1 (*Math Journal 2,* p. 327)

INDEPENDENT ACTIVITY 

Mixed Review Math Boxes in this lesson are paired with Math Boxes in Lesson 12.3.

✦ Study Link 12.1 (*Math Masters,* p. 377)

Home Connection Students look for examples of rates in newspapers, in magazines, and on labels and bring them to class.

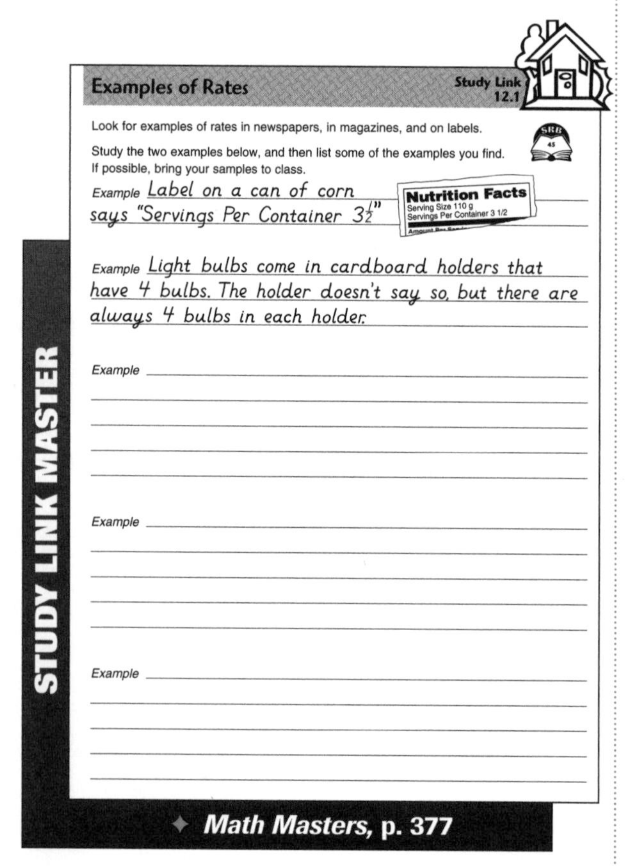
Examples of Rates — Study Link 12.1

Look for examples of rates in newspapers, in magazines, and on labels.

Study the two examples below, and then list some of the examples you find. If possible, bring your samples to class.

Example Label on a can of corn says "Servings Per Container $3\frac{1}{2}$"

Nutrition Facts
Serving Size 110 g
Servings Per Container 3 1/2

Example Light bulbs come in cardboard holders that have 4 bulbs. The holder doesn't say so, but there are always 4 bulbs in each holder.

Example ______

Example ______

Example ______

STUDY LINK MASTER

Math Masters, p. 377

3 Options for Individualizing

✦ ENRICHMENT Collecting Follow-Up Data on Eye-Blinking Rates

PARTNER ACTIVITY  **15–30 min**

Some students might be interested in additional investigations. *Suggestions:*

▷ How long can a person keep from blinking?

▷ How many times will a person blink in 5 minutes when trying not to blink?

As before, students work with a partner. One student times his or her partner and records the results. (For the two questions suggested above, it is *not* necessary that the student being observed remains unaware of what is taking place.) All students who collect this additional data can combine their results and calculate a median and/or mean value. Students should summarize their results in a brief written report.

✦ LANGUAGE DIVERSITY Using the Language of Rates

PARTNER ACTIVITY **15–30 min** 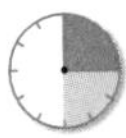

Literature Link Pair a student learning English with a proficient English speaker. Have them read *Each Orange Had Eight Slices: A Counting Book* together. Students practice using rate language to describe each situation. For example: "Two juicy oranges. Eight slices *per* orange. Two seeds *per* slice."

NOTE: *Each Orange Had Eight Slices: A Counting Book* was recommended in Lesson 3.1 to review multiplication concepts.

✦ RETEACHING Using Multiplication/Division Diagrams to Solve Rate Problems

SMALL-GROUP ACTIVITY  **5–15 min** 

In Lesson 6.3, students used a multiplication/division diagram to help them organize information in number stories and decide what to do.

Some students may find it helpful to review how this diagram can be used to organize the information in simple rate multiplication problems.

Example

There are 6 rows of chairs, with 4 chairs in each row. How many chairs are there in all?

Rows	Chairs per Row	Chairs
6	4	?

In this problem, the number of groups and the number of objects per group are known. The total number of objects is sought.

Pose similar problems to students and have them fill in multiplication/division diagrams before solving the problems. Once students are comfortable with the activity, have them work in partnerships and pose problems for each other to solve.

12.2 Solving Rate Problems

OBJECTIVES **To use a rate table to record rate information; and to solve rate problems.**

summaries	materials
1 Teaching the Lesson	
Students use a version of the "What's My Rule?" table, called a rate table, to solve rate problems. They record given rate information in the rate table and generate equivalent rates that lead to a solution of the problem. [Patterns, Functions, and Algebra]	☐ *Math Journal 2,* p. 328 ☐ Study Link 12.1 ☐ Transparency (*Math Masters,* p. 190; optional) ☐ Assessment Master (*Math Masters,* p. 471 or 475; optional) ***See* Advance Preparation**
2 Ongoing Learning & Practice	
Students play the *Credits/Debits Game* (Advanced Version). [Operations and Computation] Students practice and maintain skills through Math Boxes and Study Link activities.	☐ *Math Journal 2,* p. 329 ☐ *Student Reference Book,* p. 193 ☐ Teaching Master (*Math Masters,* p. 187) ☐ Study Link Master (*Math Masters,* p. 378)
3 Options for Individualizing	
Extra Practice Students use rate tables to solve rate problems. [Patterns, Functions, and Algebra] **Enrichment** Students solve problems involving the speed of travel for mammals. [Patterns, Functions, and Algebra]	☐ Teaching Masters (*Math Masters,* pp. 190 and 191–193) ***See* Advance Preparation**

Additional Information

Advance Preparation For Part 1, make an overhead transparency of *Math Masters,* page 190 or draw several blank rate tables on the board, like those shown on the master.

For the optional Extra Practice activity in Part 3, make a copy of *Math Masters,* page 190. On the copy, write rate problems (see Part 3, page 853 for suggestions). Then make sufficient copies of the completed master.

Vocabulary • **rate table** • **unit rate**

Getting Started

Mental Math and Reflexes

Sketch rectangular prisms on the board and label them with their dimensions, or simply give the dimensions. Students calculate the volume and write the appropriate unit.

- 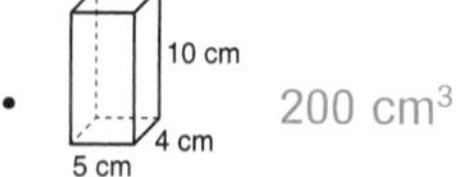

$200\ cm^3$
- 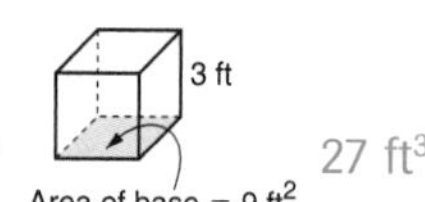

$27\ ft^3$
- Area of base = 4 in.^{2}, height of prism = 9 in. Find the volume. $36\ in.^3$
- length of base = 6 m, width of base = 2 m, height of prism = 5 m. Find the volume. $60\ m^3$

Math Message

Flashlight batteries are on sale at 2 packages for $3.00. What is the cost of 6 packages of batteries?

Study Link 12.1 Follow-Up

Ask students to share the examples of rates they have brought from home and to add them to the Rates Museum. Encourage students to continue to look for examples of rates for the museum.

Teaching the Lesson

✦ Math Message Follow-Up

WHOLE-CLASS DISCUSSION

Ask students to share solution strategies. If necessary, draw pictures on the board to illustrate their strategies.

Some possible strategies might include the following:

▷ 6 packages is 3 times as much as 2 packages.

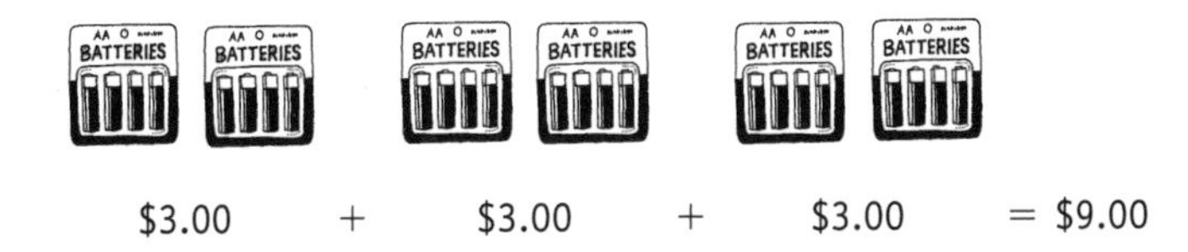

$3.00 + $3.00 + $3.00 = $9.00

▷ If 2 packages cost $3.00, then 1 package costs half as much: $\frac{1}{2}$ of $3.00 = $1.50. Six packages cost 6 times as much as 1 package: 6 * $1.50 = $9.00.

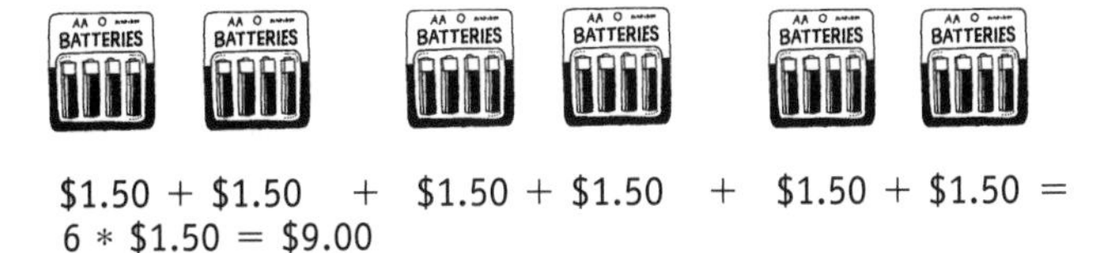

$1.50 + $1.50 + $1.50 + $1.50 + $1.50 + $1.50 =
6 * $1.50 = $9.00

After several strategies have been shared, move on to the next activity.

✦ Introducing Rate Tables

WHOLE-CLASS ACTIVITY

The information provided by a rate can be extended to show other equivalent rates. Make a **rate table** and fill in the cost of 2 packages and 6 packages of batteries (*see margin*). Students should recognize this as a "What's My Rule?" table: the "In" numbers (packages) are known; most of the "Out" numbers (cost) are to be found.

Batteries: 2 packages/$3.00

Packages	Cost
1	$1.50
2	$3.00
3	$4.50
4	$6.00
5	$7.50
6	$9.00
7	$10.50
8	$12.00
9	$13.50

Rate Table

TEACHING MASTER

Rate Tables

For each problem, fill in the rate table. Then answer the question below the table.

1. ______ ? ______ (unit)

2. ______ ? ______ (unit)

3. ______ ? ______ (unit)

4. ______ ? ______ (unit)

✦ *Math Masters,* **p. 190**

NOTE: The *unit rate* is a version of the rate that tells how many of some thing for each 1 of a second thing. 27 minutes for 9 buttons is not a unit rate; but 3 minutes for 1 button is a unit rate. $3.00 for 2 packages is not a unit rate; but $1.50 for 1 package is a unit rate. It is usually easier to fill in the other cells of a rate table if the unit rate is filled in first.

Then fill in the rest of the table with the help of the class. As you do so, ask questions such as the following:

- If 2 packages cost $3.00, how can you find the cost of 1 package? Divide $3.00 by 2.
- How can you find the cost of 3 packages? Multiply the cost of 1 package by 3: 3 * $1.50 = $4.50. Or add the cost of 1 package to the cost of 2 packages: $3.00 + $1.50 = $4.50.
- How can you find the cost of 8 packages? Multiply the cost of 2 packages by 4: 4 * $3.00 = $12.00.

✦ Solving Rate Problems (*Math Masters,* p. 190)

WHOLE-CLASS ACTIVITY

There are a number of different ways of solving rate problems. At first, the authors recommend that you use the following routine. Use your overhead transparency of *Math Masters,* page 190, or the blank rate tables you have drawn on the board.

1. Enter the given rate in a rate table.

2. Fill in the rest of the cells in the rate table.

3. Answer the question posed in the problem.

Example: Mr. Rankin sews buttons on shirts. He sewed 9 buttons in 27 minutes. At that rate, how many buttons had he sewn after 15 minutes?

1. Make a rate table and enter the given rate.

9 buttons in 27 minutes

Buttons	1	2	3	4	5	6	7	8	9
Minutes									27

2. Fill in the rest of the cells in the rate table.

a. Fill in the cell for 1 button first; this is called a **unit rate.**

9 buttons in 27 minutes

Buttons	1	2	3	4	5	6	7	8	9
Minutes	3								27

b. Then fill in the other cells.

9 buttons in 27 minutes

Buttons	1	2	3	4	5	6	7	8	9
Minutes	3	6	9	12	15	18	21	24	27

3. Answer the question posed in the problem: At that rate, Mr. Rankin had sewn 5 buttons after 15 minutes.

Once you feel that students have grasped this method, encourage them to invent their own methods and to look for strategies that particularly fit given problems.

Work with the whole class to solve these suggested problems:

- A building has a height of 60 feet. If each story is 12 feet high, how many stories does the building have? 5 stories. In this problem, the unit rate 12ft/1 story is given.
- Billy receives $4 per week as an allowance. If he saves all his money, how much will he have after one year? $208. In this problem, the unit rate $4/1 week is given.
- In one week, Jill mowed 12 lawns and made $72. If she charged each customer the same amount, how much did she charge per lawn? $6. In this problem, the given rate $72 per 12 lawns is not a unit rate. Division is used to find the unit rate: 72 ÷ 12 = $6 per 1 lawn. How much had she earned after she mowed 4 lawns? $24. Now that we have found the unit rate of $6 per lawn, multiplication is used to find an equivalent rate: 4 * 6 = $24 per 4 lawns.

If more practice is needed, you might make up problems based on examples in the Rates Museum.

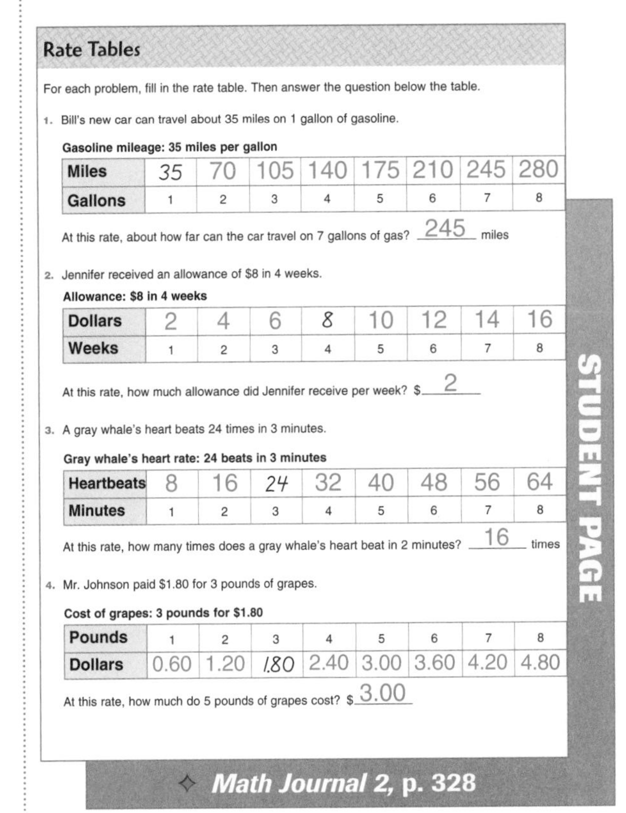

Rate Tables

For each problem, fill in the rate table. Then answer the question below the table.

1. Bill's new car can travel about 35 miles on 1 gallon of gasoline.

Gasoline mileage: 35 miles per gallon

Miles	35	70	105	140	175	210	245	280
Gallons	1	2	3	4	5	6	7	8

At this rate, about how far can the car travel on 7 gallons of gas? 245 miles

2. Jennifer received an allowance of $8 in 4 weeks.

Allowance: $8 in 4 weeks

Dollars	2	4	6	8	10	12	14	16
Weeks	1	2	3	4	5	6	7	8

At this rate, how much allowance did Jennifer receive per week? $2

3. A gray whale's heart beats 24 times in 3 minutes.

Gray whale's heart rate: 24 beats in 3 minutes

Heartbeats	8	16	24	32	40	48	56	64
Minutes	1	2	3	4	5	6	7	8

At this rate, how many times does a gray whale's heart beat in 2 minutes? 16 times

4. Mr. Johnson paid $1.80 for 3 pounds of grapes.

Cost of grapes: 3 pounds for $1.80

Pounds	1	2	3	4	5	6	7	8
Dollars	0.60	1.20	1.80	2.40	3.00	3.60	4.20	4.80

At this rate, how much do 5 pounds of grapes cost? $3.00

STUDENT PAGE

Math Journal 2, p. 328

Practicing with Rate Problems
(*Math Journal 2,* p. 328)

PARTNER ACTIVITY 

Assign journal page 328. The unit rate is given for Problem 1. For the remaining problems, students should find the unit rate first and then fill in the remainder of the rate table. Circulate and assist as needed.

ONGOING ASSESSMENT

Ask students to respond to the following problem in a Math Log or on an Exit Slip (*Math Masters,* page 471 or 475).

The Jefferson family plans to sit down to Thanksgiving dinner at 6:00 P.M. They have bought an 18-pound turkey. The turkey needs to cook about 20 minutes for every pound. At what time should the turkey go in the oven? 12:00 noon **Explain what you did to solve the problem.** Possible response: The turkey will take 18 * 20 minutes, or 360 minutes to cook. 360 minutes equals 6 hours. 6 hours before 6:00 P.M. is 12:00 noon.

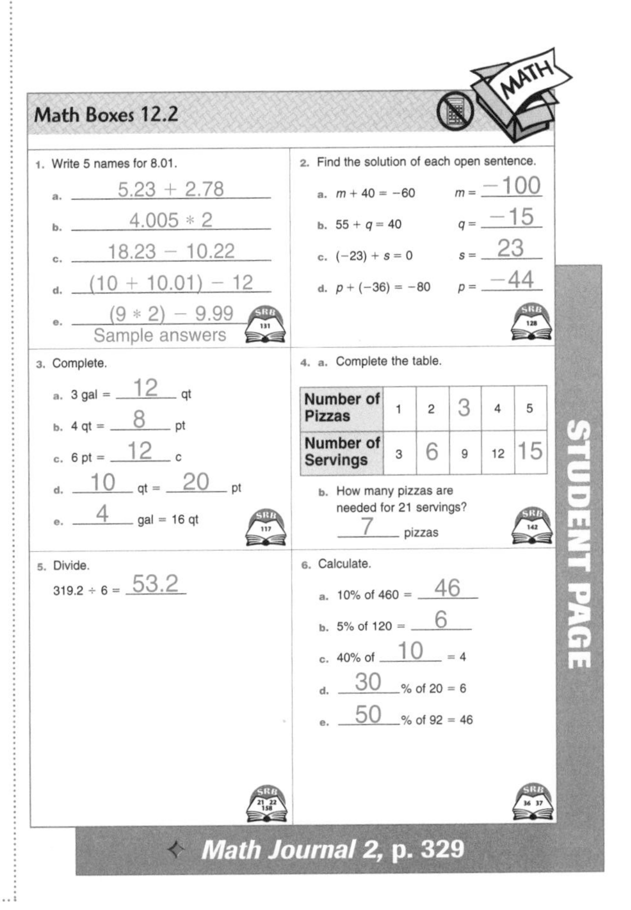

Math Boxes 12.2

1. Write 5 names for 8.01.
   a. 5.23 + 2.78
   b. 4.005 * 2
   c. 18.23 − 10.22
   d. (10 + 10.01) − 12
   e. (9 * 2) − 9.99
   Sample answers

2. Find the solution of each open sentence.
   a. $m + 40 = -60$ $m =$ −100
   b. $55 + q = 40$ $q =$ −15
   c. $(-23) + s = 0$ $s =$ 23
   d. $p + (-36) = -80$ $p =$ −44

3. Complete.
   a. 3 gal = 12 qt
   b. 4 qt = 8 pt
   c. 6 pt = 12 c
   d. 10 qt = 20 pt
   e. 4 gal = 16 qt

4. a. Complete the table.

Number of Pizzas	1	2	3	4	5
Number of Servings	3	6	9	12	15

   b. How many pizzas are needed for 21 servings? 7 pizzas

5. Divide.
   319.2 ÷ 6 = 53.2

6. Calculate.
   a. 10% of 460 = 46
   b. 5% of 120 = 6
   c. 40% of 10 = 4
   d. 30 % of 20 = 6
   e. 50 % of 92 = 46

STUDENT PAGE

Math Journal 2, p. 329

STUDY LINK MASTER

Rates

Study Link 12.2

SRB 149 150

Solve the problems.

1. Hotels R Us charges $45 a night for a single room. At that rate, how much does a single room cost *per week*? $ 315

2. The Harrison family spends about $84 a week for food. On average, how much do they spend *per day*? $ 12

3. Sharon practices playing the piano the same amount of time each day. She practiced a total of 4 hours on Monday and Tuesday. At that rate, how many hours would she practice *in a week*? 14 hours

Hours	2	4	6	8	10	12	14
Days	1	2	3	4	5	6	7

Challenge

4. People in the United States spend an average of 6 hours and 4 minutes each week reading newspapers.
   a. That's how many minutes *per week*? 364 minutes per week
   b. At that rate, how much time does an average person spend reading newspapers in a *3-day period*? 156 minutes

Minutes	52	104	156	208	260	312	364
Days	1	2	3	4	5	6	7

✦ *Math Masters,* p. 378

TEACHING MASTER

Mammal Speeds

Introduction

The speed at which mammals walk or run is important for many of them. It helps them avoid or run from danger. Speed also helps a predator when it hunts other animals for food. Speed is useful when mammals search for food, water, or shelter.

The speed of mammals varies widely. The fastest mammals, including some antelopes and gazelles, can run two to three times as fast as the fastest human. On the other hand, some mammals move very slowly. Can you think of any? (Remember that a turtle is not a mammal.) A three-toed sloth might take 43 minutes to travel the length of a football field.

Some mammals can maintain fast speeds for long distances. Antelopes, zebras, and horses, as well as dolphins and whales, can travel for hours at average speeds of 20 miles per hour or more. Most mammals, however, are not marathon runners. They sprint, or move quickly, over short distances.

How does your speed compare to the speed of other mammals?

It couldn't happen, of course, but suppose that you, an elephant, and a cheetah were to race a distance of 100 yards, or 300 feet. Which of you would win? Which would come in second? Third? Answers vary.

My Prediction: First ________ Second ________ Third ________

On the line below, show the winner crossing the finish line. (Use "C" for the cheetah, "E" for the elephant, and "Me" for yourself.) Show where you think the second-place and third-place mammals will be when the fastest mammal crosses the finish line.

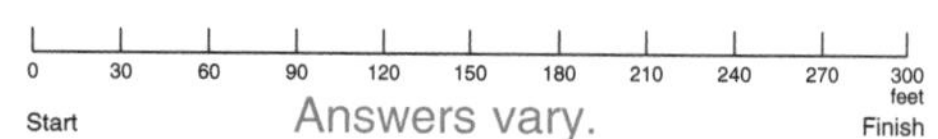

Answers vary.

What information would help you predict the winner?
Sample answer: Each animal's sprint speed in feet per second

✦ *Math Masters,* p. 191

2 Ongoing Learning & Practice

✦ Playing the *Credits/Debits Game* (Advanced Version) (*Student Reference Book,* p. 193; *Math Masters,* p. 187)

PARTNER ACTIVITY 

Students practice adding and subtracting positive and negative integers by playing the *Credits/Debits Game* (Advanced Version). For detailed instructions, see page 193 in the *Student Reference Book.*

✦ Math Boxes 12.2 (*Math Journal 2,* p. 329)

INDEPENDENT ACTIVITY 

Mixed Review Math Boxes in this lesson are paired with Math Boxes in Lessons 12.4 and 12.6.

✦ Study Link 12.2 (*Math Masters,* p. 378)

Home Connection Students solve problems involving rates. In some problems, students need to calculate the unit rate when it is not given.

3 Options for Individualizing

✦ EXTRA PRACTICE Solving More Rate Problems (*Math Masters,* p. 190)

INDEPENDENT ACTIVITY  **5–15 min**

Math Masters, page 190 is a blank template designed for rate problems. This template allows you to customize problems to the needs of students with a wide range of ability levels. Write the rate information above the rate table and the question under the table. See the next page for problem suggestions.

Use some of the following rate-problem suggestions, or you may want to use the Rates Museum as a source for problem ideas.

▷ Store rates: dollars per dozen; dollars per 6-pack

▷ Allowance: dollars per week; dollars per month

▷ Rent payments: dollars per month

▷ Heart rates: heartbeats per minute

▷ Speed: miles per hour

▷ Mileage: miles per gallon

▷ Currency exchange rates: pesos per dollar

▷ Hotel rates: cost per night

▷ Rental car rates: cost per mile; cost per day

Students solve the rate problems. They record given rate information in the rate table and generate equivalent rates that lead to a solution of the problem.

✦ ENRICHMENT Solving Mammal Speeds Problems (*Math Masters,* pp. 191–193)

PARTNER ACTIVITY  **15–30 min**

Science Link Students predict and diagram the outcome of a 100-yard race between a fourth grader, an elephant, and a cheetah. Then students use data on *Math Masters,* page 192 to develop a Mammal Speeds Table and discover how the race might actually turn out. They compare their predictions to their findings and explore some additional implications.

NOTE: Students should not be overly concerned about the feasibility of such a race.

Mammal Speeds (cont.)

Check whether your prediction is correct.

The table below will help you figure out who would win the race and by how much.

Top Sprint Speeds (approximate) **in Feet per Second**	
Fourth grader . . . 20 ft/sec	Polar bear . . . . . . 58 ft/sec
Squirrel . . . . 18 ft/sec	Elephant . . . . 36 ft/sec
House cat. . . . . . 45 ft/sec	Quarter horse . . . 70 ft/sec
Cheetah . . . . . . 102 ft/sec	Fast human . . . . 30 ft/sec

Source (for nonhumans): International Wildlife

Rewrite the data above in the Mammal Speeds Table below.
Put the fastest mammal first, the second-fastest second, and so on.

Mammal Speeds Table

Mammal	Top Sprint Speed (approximate)
1. Cheetah	102 ft/sec
2. Quarter horse	70 ft/sec
3. Polar bear	58 ft/sec
4. House cat	45 ft/sec
5. Elephant	36 ft/sec
6. Fast human	30 ft/sec
7. Fourth grader	20 ft/sec
8. Squirrel	18 ft/sec

TEACHING MASTER

✦ *Math Masters,* p. 192

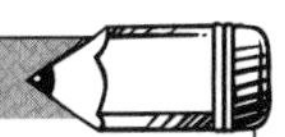

Mammal Speeds (cont.)

According to the figures in the Mammal Speeds Table, how would the 300-foot race among an elephant, a cheetah, and a fourth grader turn out?

First cheetah Second elephant Third fourth grader

About how long does the winner of the race take to run 300 feet?

About 3 seconds

About how far do the second-place and third-place mammals run in the time it takes the winner to run 300 feet?

Second-place mammal About 108 feet

Third-place mammal About 60 feet

Would it be a close race? no

Draw a diagram of your findings. On the line below, show which mammal will win the race and where the second-place and third-place mammals will be when the fastest mammal crosses the finish line.

How good was your prediction? Answers vary.

Further Explorations

1. About how many times faster is the first-place mammal
   a. than the second-place mammal? About 3 times
   b. than the third-place mammal? About 5 times

2. According to the Mammal Speeds Table, a fourth grader can run faster than a squirrel. Does this mean that you could catch a squirrel by running after it? Why or why not?
   Sample answer: No, you could not. A squirrel can change direction more quickly, run up a tree, or hide in small areas that fourth graders cannot get into.

TEACHING MASTER

✦ *Math Masters,* p. 193

12.3 Converting between Rates

OBJECTIVE **To check the validity of data by converting them to more accessible rates.**

summaries	materials
1 Teaching the Lesson	
Students examine data on the estimated number of times an "average" person does something in his or her lifetime. They convert the rates to rates for smaller units of time that can be more easily understood. [Data and Chance; Operations and Computation; Patterns, Functions, and Algebra]	□ *Math Journal 2,* p. 330 □ Study Link 12.2 □ calculator
2 Ongoing Learning & Practice	
Students collect unit-price information from a grocery store. [Data and Chance; Operations and Computation] Students practice and maintain skills through Math Boxes and Study Link activities.	□ *Math Journal 2,* p. 331 □ Teaching Master (*Math Masters,* p. 194) □ Study Link Master (*Math Masters,* p. 379)
3 Options for Individualizing	
Enrichment Students compare their heart rates to those of other mammals. [Data and Chance; Operations and Computation] **Enrichment** Students check the validity of data by converting them to more accessible rates. [Data and Chance; Operations and Computation]	□ Teaching Masters (*Math Masters,* pp. 195–197) □ *In the Next Three Seconds* ***See* Advance Preparation**

Additional Information

Advance Preparation For the second optional Enrichment activity in Part 3, you will need a copy of *In the Next Three Seconds* by Rowland Morgan (Puffin Books, 1997).

Vocabulary • **unit-price label**

Getting Started

Mental Math and Reflexes

Draw rate tables on the board for students to complete.

Dollars	$3	$6	$7.50	$9
Hours	1	2	$2\frac{1}{2}$	3

Feet	5	10	30	40
Seconds	1	2	6	8

Math Message

Solve the problems at the top of journal page 330. Use your calculator.

Study Link 12.2 Follow-Up

Students share solution strategies. Solutions to Problems 1 and 2 require just one step each (multiplication for Problem 1 and division for Problem 2). Problems 3 and 4 involve both multiplication and division. Students may fill in a rate table to arrive at a solution. In each problem, a good strategy is to find an equivalent rate for 1 day and then multiply the per-day rate by the appropriate number of days. For example, in Problem 3, Sharon practiced the piano for a total of 4 hours over 2 days—that's equivalent to 2 hours per day. At that rate, she practiced 14 hours per week.

Teaching the Lesson

✦ Math Message Follow-Up (*Math Journal 2,* p. 330)

WHOLE-CLASS DISCUSSION

Show the following rate table on the board:

Days	365	
Years	1	75

Since there are about 365 days in 1 year (366 in leap years), there must be about 75 ∗ 365, or 27,375 days in 75 years. Each day has 24 hours, so there are about 24 ∗ 27,375, or 657,000 hours in 75 years.

Remind students that they will continue to need their calculators; the rest of the problems on journal page 330 all involve big numbers.

✦ Exploring Methods for Checking Data (*Math Journal 2,* p. 330)

PARTNER ACTIVITY 

Write the following statement on the board:

In an average lifetime, a person sleeps about 214,000 hours.

Ask students how the information might have been found.

- Is it likely that people actually keep track of how long they sleep each night of their lives? It is more likely that many people are observed for a short period of time, and then this information is used to make an estimate for a lifetime.

Do These Numbers Make Sense?

Math Message

It is estimated that the average lifetime of a person living in the United States is about 75 years.

About how many days are there in an average lifetime? About 27,375 days

About how many hours is that? About 657,000 hours

Use the data from the Math Message to help you answer the following questions:

1. It is estimated that in an average lifetime of 75 years, a person sleeps for about 214,000 hours. At that rate, about how many hours *per day* does a person sleep? 7.8, or 8 hours per day

   Does this number make sense to you? Answers vary.

2. It is estimated that in an average lifetime, a person watches TV for about 105,000 hours. At that rate, about how many hours *per day* does a person watch TV? 3.8 hours per day

   Does this number make sense to you? Answers vary.

3. It is estimated that in an average lifetime, a person laughs about 540,000 times. At that rate, about how many times *per day* does a person laugh? 20 times per day

   Does this number make sense to you? Answers vary.

4. It is estimated that in an average lifetime, a person takes about 95,000,000 breaths. Does this number make sense to you? Explain.

   Sample answer: No; 95,000,000 breaths in a lifetime is about 2 to 3 breaths per minute, and a person takes about 10–15 breaths per minute.

Source: The Compass in Your Nose and Other Astonishing Facts about Humans

STUDENT PAGE

✧ ***Math Journal 2*, p. 330**

Adjusting the Activity You might use the following routine to encourage students to answer their own questions, with little outside help. Each partner is given a Question Token—it could be a chip or an index card. If students want to ask the teacher a question, they hand in a token, but only after both partners agree on the question. When a partnership has used both its tokens, it may ask no more questions. Students will soon consider the questions very carefully before they ask them.

Explain that this information was found in a reference book, but that it is important to decide whether this number makes sense. Reference books can be misleading or wrong.

Ask for suggestions on how to check whether this number makes sense.

- Would the number be easier to understand if you calculated about how many hours a person sleeps in a year? In a night?

Divide the class into partnerships. Ask students to calculate about how many hours a person sleeps per day. They should assume a lifetime of 75 years, and assume (for now) that the stated 214,000 hours of sleep is correct. Bring the class together to share solution strategies. Possible strategies might include the following:

▹ Divide 214,000 by 75 to find the number of hours of sleep per year. About 2,853 hours Then divide the result by 365 to find the number of hours of sleep per day. 7.8 hours, rounded to the nearest tenth of an hour

▹ Divide 214,000 by 27,375—the number of days in 75 years—to find the number of hours of sleep per day. 7.8 hours, rounded to the nearest tenth of an hour

▹ Round 27,375 to 27,000. (This is OK since the 75-year life expectancy figure is itself an estimate.) Then divide 214,000 by 27,000 (or, more simply, 214 by 27, since both numbers are "thousands"). The quotient is very close to 8.

Thus, according to the lifetime data, a typical person sleeps about 8 hours per day. Does this result make sense? yes

Students record the results in Problem 1 on journal page 330.

✦ Checking whether Data Make Sense (*Math Journal 2*, p. 330)

PARTNER ACTIVITY 

Assign Problems 2–4 on journal page 330. Circulate and offer assistance when necessary.

NOTE: The data for sleep, TV watching, and laughter are from *The Compass in Your Nose and Other Astonishing Facts about Humans* by Marc McCutcheon (Tarcher Putnam, 1989). The authors made up the "data" about the number of breaths in a lifetime.

Bring the class together to share solution strategies for Problems 2–4. Discuss which of the data in these problems make sense.

Problem 2: Divide 105,000 by 27,375—the number of days in 75 years—to find the number of hours of TV watched per day. 3.8 hours per day, rounded to the nearest tenth

▷ Opinions will probably vary on whether 3.8 hours of TV seem reasonable, based on students' experience. There is no right or wrong answer; what is important is that students think about whether this number makes sense.

▷ Students should be cautioned about predicting lifetime experience based on their own personal viewing habits. The typical child ages 6 to 11 watches about half the number of hours of TV per day as the typical adult.

Problem 3: Divide 540,000 by 27,375 to find the number of laughs per day. About 20

▷ Students usually think that 20 laughs per day is too high. If you have time, the class can consider why the estimate is so high. It may be that every giggle and chuckle is counted as a laugh; including these would raise the rate per day. There are many people who laugh continuously as they converse; their frequent laughs might balance out the infrequent laughs of all others, and raise the average rate to 20 laughs per day.

Problem 4: Students may have calculated several different rates. Some of these rates are difficult to interpret because the time period is so long.

▷ Divide 95 million by 27,375 to find the number of breaths per day. 3,470 It is hard to know if 3,470 breaths per day makes sense.

▷ Divide 95 million by 657,000 to find the number of breaths per hour. About 145 This hourly rate is easier to interpret. Some students may be able to decide at this point that the rate is too small and does not make sense.

▷ Divide the hourly rate of 145 breaths per hour by 60 to find the number of breaths per minute. About 2.4 All students will realize that this minute rate is too small and does not make sense, since most people take 10 to 15 breaths per minute.

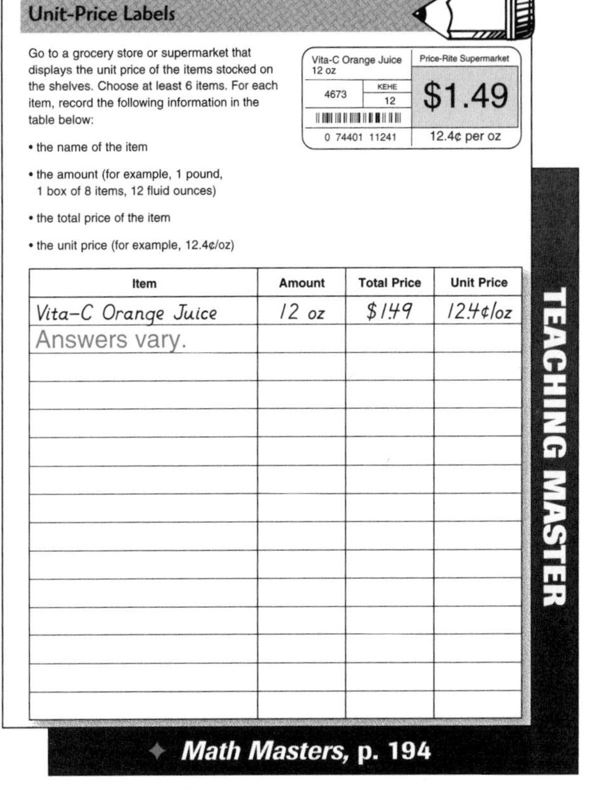

Unit-Price Labels

Go to a grocery store or supermarket that displays the unit price of the items stocked on the shelves. Choose at least 6 items. For each item, record the following information in the table below:

- the name of the item
- the amount (for example, 1 pound, 1 box of 8 items, 12 fluid ounces)
- the total price of the item
- the unit price (for example, 12.4¢/oz)

Item	Amount	Total Price	Unit Price
Vita-C Orange Juice	12 oz	$1.49	12.4¢/oz
Answers vary.			

TEACHING MASTER

✦ *Math Masters,* p. 194

The use of *Math Masters,* page 194 is described on the following page.

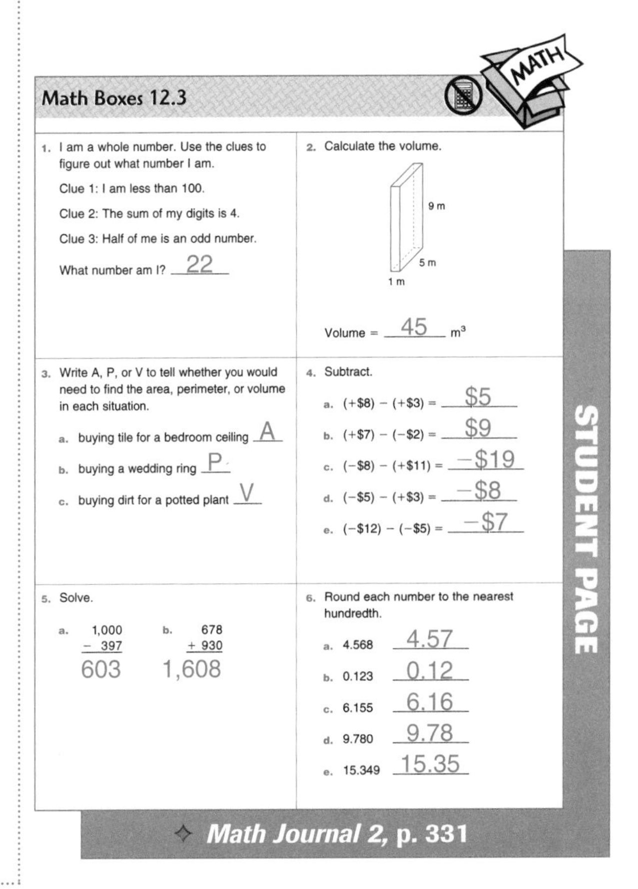

Math Boxes 12.3

1. I am a whole number. Use the clues to figure out what number I am.
   Clue 1: I am less than 100.
   Clue 2: The sum of my digits is 4.
   Clue 3: Half of me is an odd number.
   What number am I? 22

2. Calculate the volume.

   Volume = 45 m^3

3. Write A, P, or V to tell whether you would need to find the area, perimeter, or volume in each situation.
   a. buying tile for a bedroom ceiling A
   b. buying a wedding ring P
   c. buying dirt for a potted plant V

4. Subtract.
   a. (+$8) − (+$3) = $5
   b. (+$7) − (−$2) = $9
   c. (−$8) − (+$11) = −$19
   d. (−$5) − (+$3) = −$8
   e. (−$12) − (−$5) = −$7

5. Solve.
   a. 1,000 − 397 = 603
   b. 678 + 930 = 1,608

6. Round each number to the nearest hundredth.
   a. 4.568 4.57
   b. 0.123 0.12
   c. 6.155 6.16
   d. 9.780 9.78
   e. 15.349 15.35

STUDENT PAGE

✦ *Math Journal 2,* p. 331

STUDY LINK MASTER

Water Usage — Study Link 12.3

According to the American Waterworks Association, Americans each use an average of 123 gallons of water a day for their personal needs. This seems like a large amount, but you may be surprised at how much water is used for even the shortest activities. For example, people use an average of 1 to 2 gallons of water just to brush their teeth. They use about 20 gallons of water when doing dishes by hand. They may use as much as 30 gallons when taking a shower.

For each problem, complete the rate table and answer the question.

1. If you use an average of 20 gallons of water when taking a shower and you take one shower a day, about how many gallons of water do you use in 1 year?

Gallons	20	140	600	7,300
Days	1	7 (1 week)	30 (1 month)	365 (12 months)

Answer: About 7,300 gallons per year

2. The average American household uses about 2,100 gallons of water a week. About how many gallons of water does it use in 1 year?

Gallons	300	2,100	9,000	109,500
Days	1	7 (1 week)	30 (1 month)	365 (12 months)

Answer: About 109,500 gallons per year

3. Madison uses about $1\frac{1}{2}$ gallons of water each time she brushes her teeth. She brushes her teeth twice a day. About how many gallons of water does she use in 1 month for brushing teeth?

Gallons	3	21	90	1,095
Days	1	7 (1 week)	30 (1 month)	365 (12 months)

Answer: About 90 gallons per month

4. About 39,000 gallons of water are used in making 1 new car. About how many gallons of water are used to make 5 new cars? About 195,000 gallons

✦ *Math Masters,* p. 379

TEACHING MASTER

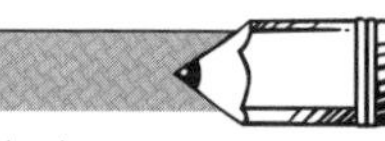

Mammal Heart Rates

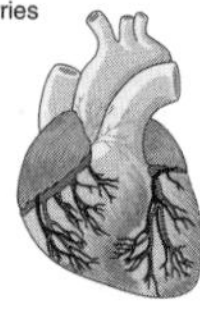

Your heart pumps blood throughout your body. The blood carries heat, nutrients, and oxygen. It also takes away waste.

The rate at which a mammal's heart pumps is determined by the size and efficiency of the heart, as well as by the mammal's need for heat, nutrients, and oxygen. These needs are affected by the mammal's size and amount of activity. A mammal's heart rate can tell you about the mammal's size and the kind of life it leads.

How fast does your heart beat?

1. If you know how, find your own heart rate; otherwise, use an estimated rate of 80 or 90 beats per minute. Record the rate below.

My heart beats about Answers vary. times per minute.

Do you think mammals smaller than you have a slower or faster heart rate? Answers vary.

Examine the chart to find out.

Mammal Heart-Rate Data

Mammal	Heartbeats per Minute	Weight in Pounds
Pygmy shrew	1,200	0.01
Mouse	650	0.25
Guinea pig	280	0.75
House cat	110	10
Human		
Newborn	110–160	7
7-year-old	90	50
Adult	60–80	160
Senior citizen	50–65	140
Tiger	40	500
African elephant	25	12,000
Gray whale	8	60,000

✦ *Math Masters,* p. 195

2 Ongoing Learning & Practice

✦ Collecting Unit-Price Information (*Math Masters,* p. 194)

INDEPENDENT ACTIVITY 

Distribute a copy of *Math Masters,* page 194 to each student (*see margin, page 857*).

Students will go to a grocery store or supermarket to collect unit-price information. Briefly discuss what a **unit-price label** looks like and set a deadline for the completion of this activity. Unit prices are discussed in Lesson 12.4, and this information on unit-price labels will be needed for Lesson 12.5.

Tell students that they need not do any calculations at this time—they should simply record the unit-price information on the master. You might also consider making this activity a field trip so that the class can collect the data at the same time.

✦ Math Boxes 12.3 (*Math Journal 2,* p. 331)

INDEPENDENT ACTIVITY 

Mixed Review Math Boxes in this lesson are paired with Math Boxes in Lesson 12.1.

✦ Study Link 12.3 (*Math Masters,* p. 379)

Home Connection Students solve rate problems involving water usage. For most problems, they complete a rate table that is then used to answer a question.

Options for Individualizing

✦ ENRICHMENT Solving Mammal Heart Rates Problems (*Math Masters,* pp. 195–197)

PARTNER ACTIVITY  **15–30 min** 

Portfolio Ideas

Science Link Students measure their heart rates and compare them to the heart rates of other mammals. They find, perhaps surprisingly, that smaller mammals have faster heart rates. Students use "times as fast" phrasing to compare smaller mammals to themselves and "fraction of" phrasing to compare larger mammals to themselves.

On *Math Masters,* page 197, students are asked to estimate the heart rates for a squirrel and a bison. You may want to provide students with typical weights (1 pound and 1,800 pounds) or you may make the problem more challenging by having students look up typical weights on their own.

✦ ENRICHMENT Analyzing Data

PARTNER ACTIVITY  **15–30 min** 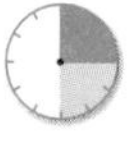

Portfolio Ideas

Literature Link The book *In the Next Three Seconds* presents statistics such as, "In the next three nights, people will sleep more than seven million years and Americans will watch more than 2,500 years of television." Challenge students to write a brief report that explains how they checked the validity of statements such as these by converting them to more accessible rates.

NOTE: In Lesson 5.4, it was recommended that students use this book as a model to write predictions from simple statistics.

Mammal Heart Rates (cont.)

2. Do heart rate and weight seem to be related? If so, how?
Sample answer: Yes; as the weight of the mammal decreases, its heart rate increases.

Answers vary for Problems 3 and 4. Answers below assume 80 heartbeats per minute for a fourth grader.

3. Compare your heart rate to the rates of smaller mammals.
   a. A mouse's heart beats about $8\frac{1}{8}$ times as fast as mine.
   b. A guinea pig's heart beats about $3\frac{1}{2}$ times as fast as mine.
   c. A house cat's heart beats about $1\frac{3}{8}$ times as fast as mine.
   d. It seems as though smaller mammals have faster (faster or slower) heart rates than I have.

4. Compare your heart rate to the rates of larger mammals.
   a. A tiger's heart rate is about $\frac{1}{2}$ (what fraction?) of mine.
   b. An African elephant's heart rate is about $\frac{1}{3}$ (what fraction?) of mine.
   c. A gray whale's heart rate is about $\frac{1}{10}$ (what fraction?) of mine.
   d. It seems as though larger mammals have slower (faster or slower) heart rates than I have.

One reason smaller mammals have faster heart rates is that they lose body heat more quickly than larger mammals. Their hearts have to pump quickly to keep a supply of warm blood constantly circulating throughout their bodies.

In order to create this heat, smaller mammals must eat a lot. They tend to be more active than larger mammals, because they are always searching for food. This makes their hearts work even harder. One result of a quicker heart rate is that smaller mammals tend to live shorter lives. The constant activity wears them out.

TEACHING MASTER

✦ *Math Masters,* p. 196

Mammal Heart Rates (cont.)

Challenge

5. Could you use what you have learned to estimate a squirrel's heart rate and a bison's heart rate? Write down your ideas and discuss them with your classmates. What other information might be helpful?
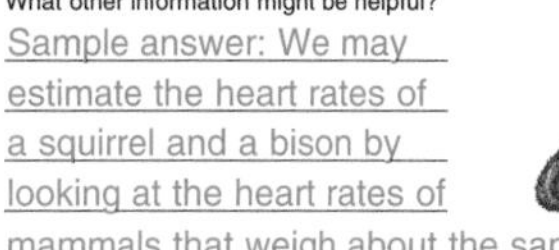
Sample answer: We may estimate the heart rates of a squirrel and a bison by looking at the heart rates of mammals that weigh about the same.

My Estimates Sample answers:

6. a. I estimate that a squirrel's heart might beat about 240 times in a minute.
   b. I think this because a squirrel weighs about 1 pound, which is much less than what a cat weighs and just a little more than what a guinea pig weighs.

7. a. I estimate that a bison's heart might beat about 35 times in a minute.
   b. I think this because a bison weighs about 1,800 pounds, which is closer to a tiger's weight than to an elephant's weight.

See if you can find data to check your predictions.

TEACHING MASTER

✦ *Math Masters,* p. 197

12.4 Comparison Shopping: Part 1

OBJECTIVES **To calculate the unit price for a product; to compare unit prices; and to identify information needed for comparison shopping.**

summaries	materials
1 Teaching the Lesson	
Students calculate the unit prices of various products. They calculate and compare the unit prices of two products to decide which is the better buy. [Patterns, Functions, and Algebra]	☐ *Math Journal 2,* pp. 332 and 333 ☐ Study Link 12.3 ☐ Teaching Master (*Math Masters,* p. 190; optional) ☐ calculator
2 Ongoing Learning & Practice	
Students solve rate problems. [Patterns, Functions, and Algebra] Students practice and maintain skills through Math Boxes and Study Link activities.	☐ *Math Journal 2,* pp. 334 and 335 ☐ Teaching Master (*Math Masters,* p. 190; optional) ☐ Study Link Master (*Math Masters,* p. 380)
3 Options for Individualizing	
Enrichment Students test products. [multiple strands]	☐ computer with Internet access ☐ *Zillions* magazine (optional) ***See* Advance Preparation**

Additional Information

Advance Preparation For the optional Enrichment activity in Part 3, you may want to have issues of *Zillions* magazine available for students to look through. *Zillions* is the child's version of *Consumer Reports.*

Vocabulary • **consumer** • **products** • **services** • **comparison shopping** • **unit price**

Getting Started

Mental Math and Reflexes

Draw rate tables on the board for students to complete.

Dollars	\$0.50	\$1.00	\$3.00	\$6.00
Packages	1	2	6	12

Dollars	\$0.30	\$1.20	\$2.40	\$4.80
Ounces	1	4	8	16

Math Message

Read and complete journal page 332.

Study Link 12.3 Follow-Up

Review answers. Ask students to think of some other ways that they and their families use water at home. Possible responses: Watering the lawn; washing the car; cooking; drinking

1 Teaching the Lesson

✦ Math Message Follow-Up
(*Math Journal 2,* p. 332)

WHOLE-CLASS DISCUSSION

Students share their definitions of the word **consumer.** Sample definition: A person who acquires **products** or uses **services**

Pose questions such as the following, and list students' responses on the board.

- What are some products and services you have used recently? Possible responses: Products: food, clothing, school supplies; Services: public transportation, school, the postal service, utilities such as the telephone or electricity
- What are some of the qualities of a smart consumer? Possible response: Makes thoughtful decisions based on the quality, price, and effect on the environment of the product or service, as well as on personal needs and taste
- What information might you want to know before choosing to attend a baseball camp? Possible responses: The number of years of experience of the counselors; the types of activities offered; the location of the camp; the cost
- How would you find the information you needed to make good decisions about which of several competing products to buy? Possible responses: Ask people who have used the products; read articles about the products in consumer magazines; compare prices. This kind of research is called **comparison shopping.**

✦ Calculating and Comparing Unit Prices
(*Math Journal 2,* p. 333)

WHOLE-CLASS ACTIVITY

Consumer Link The **unit price** is the cost of an item per unit of measure. Give several examples and write them in rate tables so that students will understand that unit prices are rates. See page 862 for suggestions.

Product Testing

Some magazines written for young people ask their readers to test many different kinds of products. The results of the tests are then published in the magazines to help readers make wise buying decisions. For example, in one issue of *Zillions*, the child's version of *Consumer Reports* magazine, 44 of the magazine's readers taste-tested several brands of potato chips. The readers considered taste, cost, and nutritional value as they tried to decide which brand was the "best buy." In another issue of *Zillions*, a team of testers compared 37 brands of peanut butter in their search for the best product.

When a reader wrote to the magazine to complain about a board game she had bought, the magazine sent board games to young people in every part of the country. Testers were asked to play each game several times and then to report on what they liked and disliked about the game.

1. If you were testing a board game, what are some of the features you would look for?
   Sample answers: Is it easy to learn? Is it fun or challenging? Does it cost a lot?

2. When readers of the magazine tested potato chips, they considered taste, cost, and nutritional value in determining the best chip. Which of these factors is the most important to you? Why?
   Answers vary.

3. What is a **consumer**? Be prepared to share your definition with the class.
   Sample answer: A person who buys products or uses services

STUDENT PAGE

✧ *Math Journal 2,* p. 332

NOTE: Although the sequence of lessons on unit pricing focuses on the arithmetic of buying products and services, it is also important to discuss the more general aspects of what it means to be a consumer.

Throughout the sequence of lessons on unit pricing, remind students that comparison shopping is not simply a matter of determining which of several comparable products or services is the cheapest. There are also other factors that enter into making wise decisions.

Unit Prices

Solve the unit price problems below. Complete the tables if it is helpful to do so.

1. A 12-ounce can of soda pop costs 60 cents. The unit price is $0.05 per ounce.

Dollars	0.05	0.15	0.30	0.60
Ounces	1	3	6	12

2. A 4-pound bunch of bananas costs $1.16. The unit price is $0.29 per pound.

Dollars	0.29	0.58	0.87	1.16
Pounds	1	2	3	4

3. A 5-pound bag of apples costs $1.90. The unit price is $0.38 per pound.

Dollars	0.38	0.76	1.14	1.52	1.90
Pounds	1	2	3	4	5

4. Three pounds of salmon cost $21.00.
   a. The unit price is $7.00 per pound.
   b. What is the cost of 7 pounds of salmon? $49.00
   c. What is the cost of $9\frac{1}{2}$ pounds of salmon? $66.50

Dollars	7.00	14.00	21.00	28.00	49.00	66.50
Pounds	1	2	3	4	7	$9\frac{1}{2}$

5. *Snickeroo* candy bars come in packages of 25 and cost $3.50 per package. *Yummy* candy bars come in packages of 30 and cost $3.60 per package. Which is the better buy? *Yummy* candy bars

Explain. *Snikeroo* candy bars have a unit price of $0.14 per bar. *Yummy* candy bars have a unit price of $0.12 per bar. *Yummy* candy bars are cheaper per bar.

STUDENT PAGE

◆ *Math Journal 2*, p. 333

Suggestions

▷ A 10-pound bag of potatoes costs $5.00. The unit price is the cost for 1 pound. $0.50

Dollars	$0.50	$5.00
Pounds	1	10

▷ A package of 6 pens costs $4.20. The unit price is the cost for 1 pen. $0.70

Dollars	$0.70	$4.20
Pens	1	6

Ask how the unit price is calculated from the cost information that is given. Divide the cost by the number of units or items. For example, $5.00 ÷ 10 = $0.50, and $4.20 ÷ 6 = $0.70. Explain that finding the unit price is like solving an equal-sharing problem: division is used to find the share of the cost attributable to 1 unit or 1 item.

Solve Problems 1–3 on journal page 333. Work together as a class and encourage students to use calculators. Continue to write the given cost information and the unit cost in a rate table.

Problem 1: A 12-ounce can of soda pop costs 60 cents. The unit price is $0.60 ÷ 12, or $0.05 per ounce.

Problem 2: A 4-pound bunch of bananas costs $1.16. The unit price is $1.16 ÷ 4, or $0.29 per pound.

Problem 3: A 5-pound bag of apples costs $1.90. The unit price is $1.90 ÷ 5, or $0.38 per pound.

Now pose several practice problems on comparison shopping. Work through these as a class and encourage students to use calculators. Calculate unit prices for similar items, and then compare these unit prices to determine which item is the better buy. Point out that unit prices are not easily compared unless they are *for the same unit*. (For example, $3.20/1 lb and $0.10/1 oz are not easily compared, but $0.20/1 oz and $0.10/1 oz are.) *Some suggested problems:*

▷ Light bulbs:

Brand A: package of 4 bulbs for $2.08

Brand B: package of 6 bulbs for $3.00

Brand A: $0.52/1 bulb; Brand B: $0.50/1 bulb; Brand B is the better buy.

▷ Crackers:

Brand A: 1-pound box for $2.40

Brand B: 24-ounce box for $3.84

Brand A: $0.15/1 oz; Brand B: $0.16/1 oz; Brand A is the better buy.

Assign the remaining problems on journal page 333 as partner or independent work.

Adjusting the Activity Tell struggling students that the unit price can always be calculated from the given cost information in a single step: Divide the cost by the number of items or units. Some students may require more assurance that this always works. Have them use blank rate tables (*Math Masters,* page 190) to solve some problems. After they have found a unit price this way and filled in the remainder of the rate table, they should use a calculator to divide each cost in the rate table by the quantity directly below it. Each division problem will result in the same answer—the unit price.

Example

Dollars				\$0.60
Ounces	1	3	6	12

Rate table used to find the unit price.

Dollars	\$0.05	\$0.15	\$0.30	\$0.60
Ounces	1	3	6	12

Completed rate table. Unit price is \$0.05 per ounce.

$0.60 \div 12 = 0.05$; $0.30 \div 6 = 0.05$; $0.15 \div 3 = 0.05$

Ongoing Learning & Practice

✦Solving Rate Problems (*Math Journal 2,* p. 334)

INDEPENDENT ACTIVITY 

Science Link Students solve rate problems involving the activities of mammals.

Adjusting the Activity If students are having difficulty solving the problems, suggest that they use rate tables (*Math Masters,* page 190) to organize the information.

Rates

1. A mole can dig a tunnel 300 feet long in one night. How far could a mole dig in one week? About 2,100 feet
2. An elephant may eat 500 pounds of hay and drink 60 gallons of water in one day.
   a. About how many pounds of hay could an elephant eat per week? About 3,500 pounds
   b. About how many gallons of water could an elephant drink per week? About 420 gallons
3. The bottle-nosed whale can dive to a depth of 3,000 feet in 2 minutes. About how many feet is that per second? About 25 feet per second
4. A good milking cow will give up to 1,500 gallons of milk in a year.
   a. About how many gallons is that in 3 months? About 375 gallons
   b. About how many *quarts* is that in 3 months? About 1,500 quarts

Challenge

5. Sloths spend up to 80 percent of their lives sleeping. Not only is a sloth extremely sleepy, it is also very slow. A sloth travels on the ground at a speed of about 7 feet per minute. In the trees, its speed is about 15 feet per minute.
   a. After one hour, how much farther would a sloth have traveled in the trees than on the ground (if it didn't stop to sleep)? About 480 feet
   b. About how long would it take a sloth to travel 1 mile on the ground? (*Hint:* There are 5,280 feet in a mile.) About 754 minutes, or $12\frac{1}{2}$ hours

STUDENT PAGE

✦ *Math Journal 2,* p. 334

STUDENT PAGE

Math Boxes 12.4

1. Write 5 names for 3.16.
   a. 1.08 + 1.04 + 1.04
   b. (41.6 ÷ 10) − 1
   c. −4 + 7.16
   d. 12.64 ÷ 4
   e. 3.20 − 0.04

   Sample answers

2. Find the solution of each open sentence.
   a. $t + 30 = -120$ $t =$ −150
   b. $75 + n = 20$ $n =$ −55
   c. $16 + b = 0$ $b =$ −16
   d. $c + (-61) = -97$ $c =$ −36

3. Complete.
   a. 7 gal = 28 qt
   b. 3 qt = 6 pt
   c. 8 pt = 16 c
   d. 16 qt = 32 pt
   e. 10 gal = 40 qt

4. a. Complete the table.

Number of Cookies	36	72	324	432	540
Number of Packages	1	2	9	12	15

   b. How many cookies are in 8 packages? 288 cookies

5. Divide.
   325.2 ÷ 4 = 81.3

6. Calculate.
   a. 10% of 520 = 52
   b. 5% of 180 = 9
   c. 60% of 20 = 12
   d. 50 % of 30 = 15
   e. 40 % of 35 = 14

✧ *Math Journal 2*, p. 335

STUDY LINK MASTER

Supermarket Ads Study Link 12.4

Look in newspapers for supermarket ads. Choose some of the items in the ads. Use the table below to record the price and quantity of each item.

Do not write anything in the Unit Price column.

Item	Quantity	Price	Unit Price
Golden Sun Raisins	24 ounces	$2.99	

✦ *Math Masters*, p. 380

✦Math Boxes 12.4 (*Math Journal 2*, p. 335)

INDEPENDENT ACTIVITY 

Mixed Review Math Boxes in this lesson are paired with Math Boxes in Lessons 12.2 and 12.6.

✦Study Link 12.4 (*Math Masters*, p. 380)

Home Connection Students look for supermarket ads in newspapers and record the information contained in some of them. In Lesson 12.5, students will calculate the unit prices of some of these items.

3 Options for Individualizing

✦ ENRICHMENT Testing Products with *Zillions* Magazine

INDEPENDENT ACTIVITY  **30+ min** 

Zillions, the child's version of *Consumer Reports,* is a bimonthly consumer magazine for children eight and up. It is published by Consumers Union, an independent, nonprofit testing and information organization.

The Web site, www.zillionsedcenter.org, provides "tools for teachers to help students evaluate products, see through ad hype, be money-smart, and think for themselves."

Some students may choose to use the Web site to become involved in product testing. For example, in the May/June 2000 issue, students compared microwave macaroni-and-cheese and the traditional stove-top version. The site contains the test protocol that was used by *Consumer Reports* and invites students to try the test on their own. Students are also encouraged to test products that will be reviewed in future issues and to send their results to *Zillions.*

PLANNING AHEAD

In Lesson 12.3, students were asked to visit a grocery store or supermarket to collect information from unit-price labels. In Study Link 12.4, they are asked to collect and record information from supermarket ads. Remind students that they must complete both of these assignments by the next math class.

12.5 Comparison Shopping: Part 2

OBJECTIVE **To calculate and compare unit prices that involve fractions of cents.**

summaries	materials
1 Teaching the Lesson	
Students share unit-price label information they collected on visits to supermarkets and use the information collected from supermarket ads to calculate unit prices. Students calculate unit prices involving fractions of cents. [Patterns, Functions, and Algebra]	☐ *Math Journal 2,* p. 336 ☐ Study Link 12.4 ☐ Teaching Master (*Math Masters,* p. 194) ☐ calculator ☐ supermarket ads ***See* Advance Preparation**
2 Ongoing Learning & Practice	
Students practice division of decimals by calculating unit prices without a calculator. [Operations and Computation] Students practice and maintain skills through Math Boxes and Study Link activities.	☐ *Math Journal 2,* pp. 337 and 338 ☐ Study Link Master (*Math Masters,* p. 381)
3 Options for Individualizing	
Extra Practice Students solve problems involving unit rates. [Patterns, Functions, and Algebra] **Enrichment** Students determine which of two items is the better buy. [Patterns, Functions, and Algebra]	☐ Teaching Masters (*Math Masters,* pp. 190 and 198) ☐ calculator ***See* Advance Preparation**

Additional Information

Advance Preparation For Part 1, have available some supermarket ads for students who did not bring them to school.

For the optional Extra Practice activity in Part 3, make a copy of *Math Masters,* page 190. On the copy, write unit-rate problems (see page 869 for suggestions). Then make sufficient copies of the completed master.

Getting Started

Mental Math and Reflexes

Pose rate problems. *Suggestions:*

- Plums are on sale at 10 for $1.20. At that rate, what is the price of 5 plums? $0.60 Of 8 plums? $0.96
- A bamboo tree can grow as much as $1\frac{1}{2}$ feet per day. About how many feet might it grow in 1 week? $10\frac{1}{2}$ feet

Math Message

Solve the five division problems at the top of journal page 336. Use your calculator.

Study Link 12.4 Follow-Up

Check that students have completed the assignment. It is discussed on page 867.

Unit Pricing

Math Message

1. Use your calculator to divide. Write down what the calculator displays for each quotient. Your teacher will tell you how to fill in the answer spaces for "cents."

 a. $9.52 ÷ 7 = $ 1 . 3 6, or 136 cents
 b. $1.38 ÷ 6 = $ 0 . 2 3, or 23 cents
 c. $0.92 ÷ 8 = $ 0 . 1 1 5, or 11.5 cents
 d. $0.98 ÷ 6 = $ 0 . 1 6 3 3 3 3 3 3 3 3, or about 16.3 cents
 e. $1.61 ÷ 9 = $ 0 . 1 7 8 8 8 8 8 8 8 9, or about 17.8 cents

2. A package of 6 candy bars costs $2.89. What is the price of 1 candy bar? 48.1, or 48.2 cents
3. A 15-ounce bottle of shampoo costs $3.89. What is the price per ounce? 25.9 cents
4. Brand A: a box of 16 crayons for 80 cents
 Brand B: a box of 32 crayons of the same kind for $1.28
 Which box is the better buy? The 32-crayon box
 Why? Sample anwer: The 32-crayon box has twice as many crayons as the 16-crayon box, but it costs less than twice as much as the 16-crayon box.

Challenge

5. A store sells a 3-pound can of coffee for $7.98 and a 2-pound can of the same brand for $5.98. You can use a coupon worth 70 cents toward the purchase of the 2-pound can. If you use the coupon, which is the better buy, the 3-pound can or the 2-pound can? Explain your answer. Sample answer: The 3-pound can costs $2.66 per pound ($7.98 / 3 = $2.66). The 2-pound can will cost $5.28 ($5.98 – $0.70 = $5.28), or $2.64 per pound ($5.28 / 2 = $2.64). The 2-pound can with coupon is the better buy.

STUDENT PAGE

✧ *Math Journal 2*, p. 336

Adjusting the Activity If you think your students can handle rounding of decimals, describe the following more precise procedure:

1. Ignore all but the first 4 digits following the decimal point.
2. If the 4th digit following the decimal point is less than 5, delete that 4th digit.
3. If the 4th digit following the decimal point is 5 or greater: increase the 3rd digit following the decimal point by 1, and then delete that 4th digit.
4. Read the 3 remaining digits following the decimal point as cents and tenths of a cent in the usual way.

Examples

▷ **Problem 1d:** $0.1633333333 → $0.1633 (4th digit is less than 5) → $0.163, or 16.3 cents

▷ **Problem 1e:** $0.1788888889 → $0.1788 (4th digit is 5 or more) → $0.179, or 17.9 cents

1 Teaching the Lesson

✦ Math Message Follow-Up
(*Math Journal 2*, p. 336)

WHOLE-CLASS ACTIVITY

Eleven-digit calculator displays will show the following amounts:

a. 1.36 **b.** 0.23 **c.** 0.115

d. 0.1633333333 **e.** 0.1788888889

ONGOING ASSESSMENT

Verify that students can enter dollars-and-cents amounts correctly on a calculator. Use Problems 1a and 1b to verify that students can *read* a 2-digit decimal as a dollars-and-cents amount.

Students may find the calculator displays for answers to Problems 1c–1e difficult to interpret as money amounts. Tell students that unit-price calculations will often result in decimals with many places. To convert them to amounts in cents, they can proceed as follows:

1. Ignore all but the first 3 digits following the decimal point.
2. Read the first two digits following the decimal point as cents.
3. Read the third digit following the decimal point as tenths of a cent.

Examples

▷ **Problem 1c:** $0.115 is 11.5 cents, or $11\frac{1}{2}$ cents.

▷ **Problem 1d:** $0.1633333333 is about 16.3 cents; the last 7 digits are ignored.

▷ **Problem 1e:** $0.1788888889 is about 17.8 cents; the last 7 digits are ignored.

Have students fill in the answer spaces for "cents" for these five division problems.

Give other examples of decimals with many places and have students read these as cents and tenths of a cent. Then reverse the procedure: Name money amounts as cents and tenths of a cent, and ask students to write these as decimals.

✦ Discussing Unit-Price Labels
(*Math Masters,* p. 194)

WHOLE-CLASS DISCUSSION

Students share some of the information they collected from unit-price labels on their visit to the supermarket. The discussion should include the following:

▷ The unit price is usually in tenths of a cent, such as in 12.4¢/oz.

▷ The unit-price information makes it possible to tell at a glance which of two or more items is the best buy as far as price is concerned (if the same unit is used).

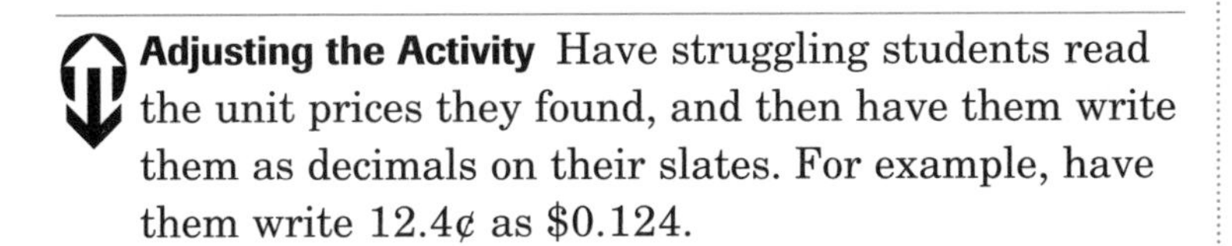

Adjusting the Activity Have struggling students read the unit prices they found, and then have them write them as decimals on their slates. For example, have them write 12.4¢ as $0.124.

✦ Solving Problems Involving Unit Pricing
(Study Link 12.4; *Math Journal 2,* p. 336)

INDEPENDENT ACTIVITY 

Consumer Link Students share some of the ad information they recorded on Study Link 12.4. Ask them to use their calculators to find the unit price of each item. Students should record each unit price as cents and tenths of a cent in column 4 of the Study Link table.

If necessary, remind students that the unit price can always be calculated from the given price information in a single step: *Divide the price (cost) by the quantity (number of items or units).*

Assign the rest of journal page 336. Students should have no trouble solving Problems 2 and 3. Watch for students who make mistakes in interpreting the results as they appear in the calculator display.

Discuss some possible solution strategies for Problems 4 and 5. Problem 5 should prove quite challenging.

Problem 4: The unit price for the 16-crayon box is 5¢; for the 32-crayon box, 4¢. Therefore, the 32-crayon box is the better buy. Some students may have reasoned this way: The 32-crayon box has twice as many crayons as the 16-crayon box, but it costs less than twice as much as the 16-crayon box. Therefore, the 32-crayon box is the better buy.

Unit-Price Labels

Go to a grocery store or supermarket that displays the unit price of the items stocked on the shelves. Choose at least 6 items. For each item, record the following information in the table below:

- the name of the item
- the amount (for example, 1 pound, 1 box of 8 items, 12 fluid ounces)
- the total price of the item
- the unit price (for example, 12.4¢/oz)

Vita-C Orange Juice 12 oz | Price-Rite Supermarket | 4673 | KEHE 12 | $1.49 | 0 74401 11241 | 12.4¢ per oz

Item	Amount	Total Price	Unit Price
Vita-C Orange Juice	12 oz	$1.49	12.4¢/oz
Answers vary.			

TEACHING MASTER

✦ *Math Masters,* p. 194

More Unit-Pricing Problems

1. A 15-ounce box of cereal costs $3.60. What is the price per ounce? 24¢
2. 20 pounds of potatoes cost $7.40. What is the price per pound? 37¢
3. One pound of sliced turkey costs $5.44. What is the price per ounce? (*Hint:* 1 pound = 16 ounces) 34¢
4. A store sells a 4-pack of AA batteries for $2.40. It sells a 6-pack of the same kind for $3.30. Which box is the better buy?
   The 6-pack
   Why? Sample answer: The unit price for the 4-pack is 60¢. At this rate, the 6-pack would cost $3.60. Since the 6-pack costs only $3.30, it must be the better buy.
5. A 6-ounce bag of potato chips costs $1.50. A 14-ounce bag costs the same amount per ounce as the 6-ounce bag.
   a. How much does the 14-ounce bag cost? $ 3.50
      Explain your answer. Sample answer: If 6 ounces cost $1.50, 1 ounce costs $0.25. So, the 14 ounce bag costs 14 * $0.25 = $3.50.
   b. Which is the better buy—the 6-ounce bag or the 14-ounce bag?
      Sample answer: Neither is the better buy, because both cost the same per ounce.

STUDENT PAGE

✦ *Math Journal 2,* p. 337

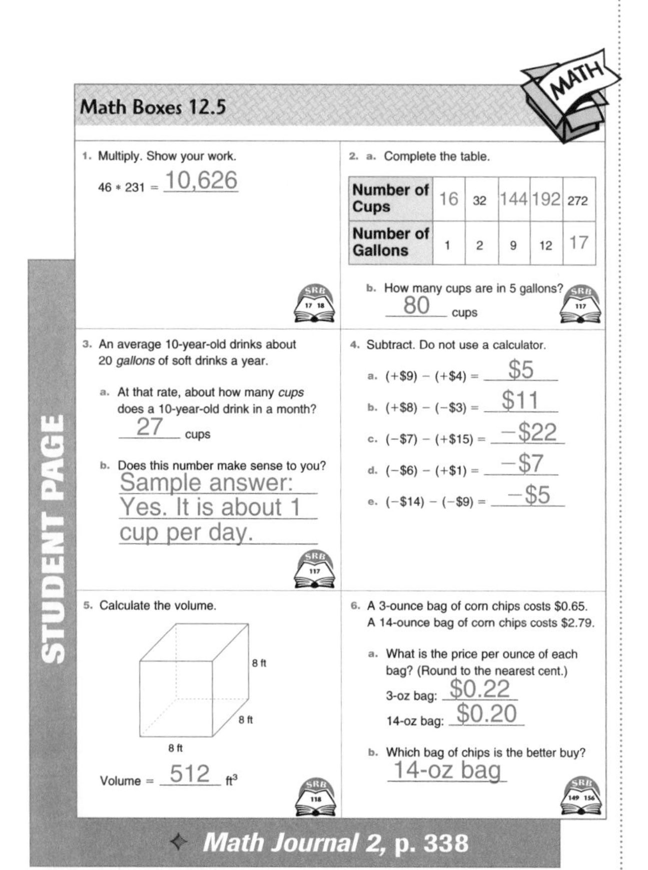
Math Boxes 12.5

1. Multiply. Show your work.
   46 * 231 = 10,626

2. a. Complete the table.

Number of Cups	16	32	144	192	272
Number of Gallons	1	2	9	12	17

   b. How many cups are in 5 gallons? 80 cups

3. An average 10-year-old drinks about 20 *gallons* of soft drinks a year.
   a. At that rate, about how many *cups* does a 10-year-old drink in a month? 27 cups
   b. Does this number make sense to you? Sample answer: Yes. It is about 1 cup per day.

4. Subtract. Do not use a calculator.
   a. (+$9) − (+$4) = $5
   b. (+$8) − (−$3) = $11
   c. (−$7) − (+$15) = −$22
   d. (−$6) − (+$1) = −$7
   e. (−$14) − (−$9) = −$5

5. Calculate the volume.
   8 ft, 8 ft, 8 ft
   Volume = 512 ft³

6. A 3-ounce bag of corn chips costs $0.65. A 14-ounce bag of corn chips costs $2.79.
   a. What is the price per ounce of each bag? (Round to the nearest cent.)
      3-oz bag: $0.22
      14-oz bag: $0.20
   b. Which bag of chips is the better buy? 14-oz bag

STUDENT PAGE

✦ *Math Journal 2,* p. 338

Problem 5: The 3-pound can costs $2.66 per pound ($7.98 / 3 = $2.66). If the 70-cent coupon is used, the 2-pound can will cost $5.28 ($5.98 – $0.70 = $5.28), or $2.64 per pound ($5.28 / 2 = $2.64). The 2-pound can, purchased with a coupon, is a better buy.

2 Ongoing Learning & Practice

✦ Calculating Unit Prices Without a Calculator
(*Math Journal 2,* p. 337)

INDEPENDENT ACTIVITY 

Students solve additional unit pricing problems. Calculators are not permitted.

ONGOING ASSESSMENT

This is an opportunity for students to practice paper-and-pencil division of decimals and for you to assess their work. (See Lesson 9.9: Division of Decimals.) None of the unit prices involves fractions of cents.

Discuss some possible solution strategies for Problems 4 and 5.

Problem 4: The unit price for the 4-pack is 60¢; for the 6-pack, 55¢. Therefore, the 6-pack is the better buy. Some students may have reasoned this way: The unit price for the 4-pack is 60¢. At this rate, the 6-pack would cost $3.60. Since the 6-pack costs only $3.30, it must be the better buy.

This problem, like Problem 4 on the previous journal page, can be solved by calculating and comparing the unit prices of the products or by mental computation. Be sure to discuss mental computation strategies, even if students don't suggest them. It is important to remind students that there is usually more than one way to solve a problem and that they should always look for creative strategies that may make a problem easy to solve.

Problem 5: If students had trouble solving this problem, you may want to display a rate table and ask students to help you complete it.

Potato chips: $1.50/6 oz

$	0.25	0.50	0.75	1.00	1.25	1.50	1.75	2.00	2.25		3.50
oz	1	2	3	4	5	6	7	8	9	...	14

✦ Math Boxes 12.5 (*Math Journal 2,* p. 338)

INDEPENDENT ACTIVITY 

Mixed Review Math Boxes in this lesson are paired with Math Boxes in Lesson 12.7.

✦ Study Link 12.5 (*Math Masters,* p. 381)

Home Connection Students solve problems involving unit pricing. None of the unit prices involves fractions of cents.

3 Options for Individualizing

✦ EXTRA PRACTICE Calculating Unit Prices (*Math Masters,* p. 190)

INDEPENDENT ACTIVITY  **5–15 min** 

Students use given cost information for an item to calculate a unit price. They use the unit price to calculate prices for other quantities of an item.

NOTE: *Math Masters,* page 190 is a blank template designed for rate problems. This template allows you to customize problems to the needs of students with a wide range of ability levels. You may want to use the Rates Museum, *Math Masters,* page 194, or Study Link 12.4 as a source for unit price ideas, or make up problems of your own.

✦ ENRICHMENT Comparing Prices (*Math Masters,* p. 198)

INDEPENDENT ACTIVITY  **30+ min** 

Portfolio Ideas

Students solve a "better buy" problem. They also go to the supermarket and find five items on sale. For each item, they decide which is the better buy—the item that is on sale or a different size of the same item that is not on sale. Have students write a brief report and share their findings with the class. Expect students to point out that the item on sale is not always the better buy.

Unit Pricing — Study Link 12.5

1. A package of 3 rolls of paper towels costs $1.89. What is the price *per roll*? $0.63
2. A 5-pound bag of rice costs $1.85. What is the price *per pound*? $0.37
3. Chewy worms are sold at $2.40 per pound. What is the price *per ounce*? $0.15
4. A 6-pack of bagels costs 90 cents. What is the price *per bagel*? $0.15
5. A 2-pound bag of frozen corn costs $1.88. What is the price *per pound*? $0.94
6. A store sells yogurt in two sizes: the 8-ounce cup costs 72 cents, and the 6-ounce cup costs 60 cents. Which is the better buy? Explain your answer.
   Sample answer: The 8-ounce cup costs $0.09 per ounce, and the 6-ounce cup costs $0.10 per ounce. So, the 8-ounce cup is the better buy.
7. Make up your own "better buy" problem. Then solve it.

STUDY LINK MASTER

✦ *Math Masters,* p. 381

Supermarket Sleuths

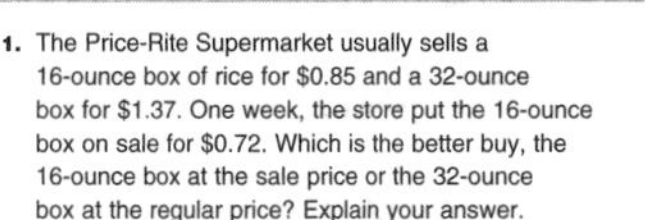

1. The Price-Rite Supermarket usually sells a 16-ounce box of rice for $0.85 and a 32-ounce box for $1.37. One week, the store put the 16-ounce box on sale for $0.72. Which is the better buy, the 16-ounce box at the sale price or the 32-ounce box at the regular price? Explain your answer.

   Sample answer: The 16-ounce box at the sale price costs 4.5 cents per ounce, and the 32-ounce box at the regular price costs 4.3 cents per ounce. So, the 32-ounce box is the better buy.

When two different sizes of the same item are sold at the regular price, the larger size is usually the better buy. Supermarkets often put the smaller size of some items on sale. However, the item on sale is not always the better buy.

2. Go to a supermarket and choose 5 items that are *on sale*. In the table below, record the information both for the item *on sale* and for another size of the same item sold at the *regular price*. Decide which is the better buy and write your choice in the last column.

Item	Size on Sale	Size at Regular Price	Better Buy
rice	72¢ for 16 oz	$1.37 for 32 oz	32-oz size
Answers	vary.		

TEACHING MASTER

✦ *Math Masters,* p. 198

12.6 World Tour Wrap-Up

OBJECTIVE **To reflect on this year's World Tour experiences.**

summaries	materials
1 Teaching the Lesson	
Students reflect on and discuss their World Tour experiences. [multiple strands]	☐ *Math Journal 2,* pp. 339 and 340 ☐ Study Link 12.5 ☐ World Tour records (*Math Journal 1,* p. 179, optional; and pp. 182–187; *Math Journal 2,* p. 345, optional; and pp. 346–355)
2 Ongoing Learning & Practice	
Students solve number stories involving rates. [Patterns, Functions, and Algebra] Students practice and maintain skills through Math Boxes and Study Link activities.	☐ *Math Journal 2,* pp. 341 and 342 ☐ Study Link Master (*Math Masters,* p. 382) ☐ Assessment Master (*Math Masters,* p. 471 or 475; optional)
3 Options for Individualizing	
Enrichment Students read books about the culture, geography, and history of countries of the world. [multiple strands]	☐ *Count Your Way through ...* books ***See* Advance Preparation**

Additional Information

Advance Preparation For the optional Enrichment activity in Part 3, you will need copies of the books in the *Count Your Way through ...* series by Jim Haskins and Kathleen Benson (Carolrhoda Books, 1987–1996). See page 873 for a complete list.

Getting Started

Mental Math and Reflexes

Pose rate problems. *Suggestions:*

- Jan was charged $515 for 5 months of car insurance. At that rate, how much will 7 months of insurance cost? $721
- Hannah bought a 6-pack of soda pop for $2.70. How much did she pay for each can of soda pop? $0.45 For 3 cans? $1.35 For 5 cans? $2.25

Math Message

Complete Problems 1–4 on journal page 339.

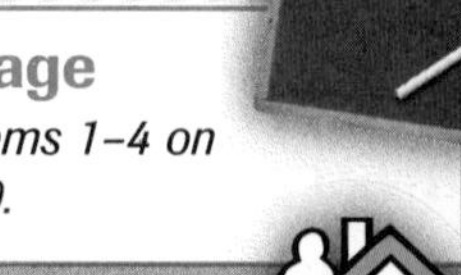

Study Link 12.5 Follow-Up

Go over the answers, as needed. Have students share the "better buy" problems they made up and solved.

1 Teaching the Lesson

Math Message Follow-Up (*Math Journal 2,* p. 339)

WHOLE-CLASS ACTIVITY

Briefly discuss the answers to Problems 2–4.

Problem 2: If students have kept the optional Route Log, they will be able to quickly calculate the total distance they have traveled. Students who did not keep a Route Log will need to use the Air Mileage Chart on the Route Map to calculate the total distance.

Problem 3: Divide the total distance by 5,000 and round the quotient to the lower number in the ones place. For example, if the calculator displays a quotient of 18.938..., this means that although you are close to having earned 19 coupons, you have flown enough miles to earn only 18 coupons.

Problem 4: Divide the number of coupons earned by 5. Again, round down to the lower number.

Adjusting the Activity If some students traveled to more countries than others, have the class find the median distance flown and the number of round-trip tickets earned for that distance.

Reflecting on the World Tour (*Math Journal 2,* pp. 339 and 340)

PARTNER ACTIVITY

Social Studies Link Students discuss their World Tour experiences with their partners and record their impressions. Students might want to refer to their Route Logs (*Math Journal 1,* page 179 and *Math Journal 2,* page 345) and their Country Notes (*Math Journal 1,* pages 182–187 and *Math Journal 2,* pages 348–355) to refresh their memories. Some students may have additional Country Notes pages to refer to if they did extended traveling. Bring the class together to share these reflections.

Adjusting the Activity Pair a student learning English with one proficient in the language for help in composing answers to questions 5–9.

Looking Back on the World Tour

Math Message

It is time to complete the World Tour. Answers vary for Problems 1–5.

1. Fly to Washington, D.C., and then travel to your hometown. Mark the final leg of the tour on the Route Map on *Math Journal 2,* pages 346 and 347.
2. What is the total distance you have traveled? _______ miles
3. The airline has given you a coupon for every 5,000 miles you have traveled. Suppose you did all your traveling by plane on the same airline. How many coupons have you earned on the World Tour? _______ coupons
4. You can trade in 5 coupons for one free round-trip ticket to fly anywhere in the continental United States. How many round-trip tickets have you earned on the World Tour? _______ round-trip tickets

Refer to "My Country Notes" in your journals (*Math Journal 1,* pages 182–187 and *Math Journal 2,* pages 348–355) as you answer the following questions.

5. If you could travel all over the world for a whole year, what information would you need in order to plan your trip?

STUDENT PAGE

Math Journal 2, p. 339

Looking Back on the World Tour (cont.)

6. To which country would you most like to travel in your lifetime? Explain your answer.
   Answers vary for Problems 6–9.
7. On your travels, you would have the opportunity to learn about many different cultures. What would you want to share with people from other countries about *your* culture?
8. What are some things about the World Tour that you did not enjoy?
9. What are some things you have enjoyed on the World Tour?

STUDENT PAGE

Math Journal 2, p. 340

STUDENT PAGE

Rates

1. According to a 1990 survey, men under 25 years old spend an average of 53 minutes a day arranging their hair and clothes. At this rate, about how much time do they spend arranging hair and clothes in a week?
   About 6 hours, 11 minutes
2. People drink an average of $2\frac{1}{2}$ quarts of water a day. At this rate, about how many quarts of water do they drink in 2 weeks?
   About 35 quarts
3. On average, Americans eat about 19 pounds of pasta per year.
   a. At this rate, about how many pounds of pasta would they eat in 23 years?
   About 437 pounds
   b. Does this number seem reasonable to you?
   Answers vary.
4. Thirty-six buses would be needed to carry the passengers and crew of three 747 jumbo jets.
   a. Fill in the rate table.

Buses	12	24	36	180	252
Jets	1	2	3	15	21

   b. How many jets would be needed to carry the passengers on 264 buses?
   22 jets
5. A man in India grew one of his thumbnails until it was 114 centimeters long. Fingernails grow about 2.5 centimeters each year. At this rate, about how many years did it take the man in India to grow his thumbnail?
   About 45.6 years
6. At Martha's Vineyard in Massachusetts, the waves are wearing away the cliffs along the coast at a rate of about 5 feet per year. About how long would it take for 10 yards to be worn away?
   About 6 years

✦ *Math Journal 2,* p. 341

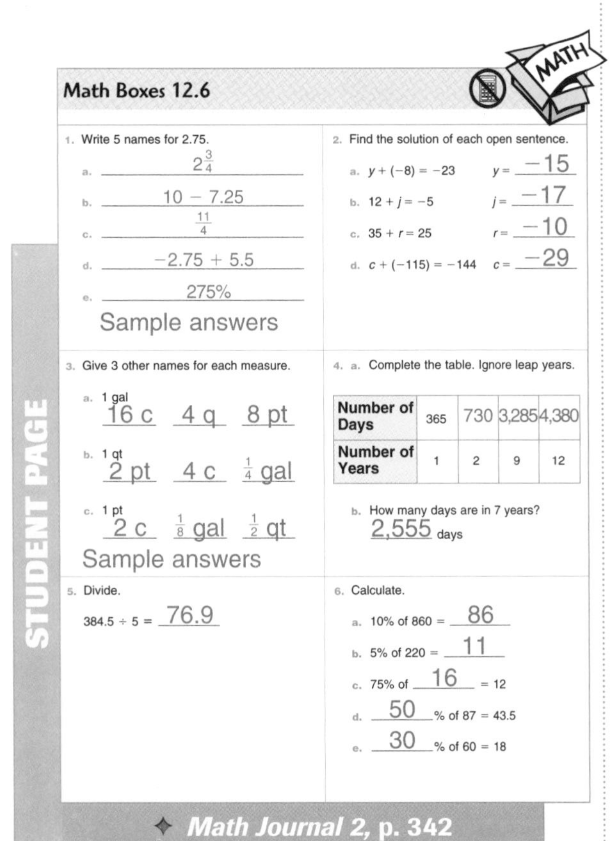
STUDENT PAGE

Math Boxes 12.6

1. Write 5 names for 2.75.
   a. $2\frac{3}{4}$
   b. 10 − 7.25
   c. $\frac{11}{4}$
   d. −2.75 + 5.5
   e. 275%
   Sample answers
2. Find the solution of each open sentence.
   a. $y + (-8) = -23$ $y = -15$
   b. $12 + j = -5$ $j = -17$
   c. $35 + r = 25$ $r = -10$
   d. $c + (-115) = -144$ $c = -29$
3. Give 3 other names for each measure.
   a. 1 gal 16 c 4 q 8 pt
   b. 1 qt 2 pt 4 c $\frac{1}{4}$ gal
   c. 1 pt 2 c $\frac{1}{8}$ gal $\frac{1}{2}$ qt
   Sample answers
4. a. Complete the table. Ignore leap years.

Number of Days	365	730	3,285	4,380
Number of Years	1	2	9	12

   b. How many days are in 7 years?
   2,555 days
5. Divide.
   384.5 ÷ 5 = 76.9
6. Calculate.
   a. 10% of 860 = 86
   b. 5% of 220 = 11
   c. 75% of 16 = 12
   d. 50 % of 87 = 43.5
   e. 30 % of 60 = 18

✦ *Math Journal 2,* p. 342

2 Ongoing Learning & Practice

✦ Solving Rate Problems (*Math Journal 2,* p. 341)

INDEPENDENT ACTIVITY 

Students solve rate problems, complete a rate table, and decide whether or not a statistic seems reasonable.

ONGOING ASSESSMENT

In a Math Log (*Math Masters,* page 471) or on an Exit Slip (*Math Masters,* page 475), ask students to explain their answer to Problem 3b.

✦ Math Boxes 12.6 (*Math Journal 2,* p. 342)

INDEPENDENT ACTIVITY 

Mixed Review Math Boxes in this lesson are paired with Math Boxes in Lessons 12.2 and 12.4.

✦ Study Link 12.6 (*Math Masters,* p. 382)

Home Connection Students solve a variety of problems involving data from different countries.

Problem 1 involves finding the difference of two numbers. Problem 2 is a "times as many" problem. Problem 3 calls for finding the percent of a number and Problem 4 for finding a fraction of a number. Problem 5 involves finding the landmarks for a data set.

✦ ENRICHMENT Exploring the Culture, Geography, and History of Countries through Numbers

INDEPENDENT ACTIVITY  **15–30 min** 

Literature Link All the books in the *Count Your Way through ...* series have a common format. The numbers 1 through 10 are related to information about the culture, geography, and history of a country. *Count Your Way through ...* books are available for each of the countries, continents, or regions listed below. Encourage students to look through the books in their spare time.

All books are published by Carolrhoda Books.

Region 1

Count Your Way through the Arab World by Jim Haskins (1987)

Count Your Way through Africa by Jim Haskins (1989)

Region 2

Count Your Way through Italy by Jim Haskins (1990)

Count Your Way through France by Jim Haskins and Kathleen Benson (1996)

Count Your Way through Greece by Jim Haskins and Kathleen Benson (1996)

Count Your Way through Ireland by Jim Haskins and Kathleen Benson (1996)

Region 3

Count Your Way through Brazil by Jim Haskins and Kathleen Benson (1996)

Region 4

Count Your Way through the Arab World by Jim Haskins (1987)

Count Your Way through China by Jim Haskins (1987)

Count Your Way through Japan by Jim Haskins (1987)

Count Your Way through Russia by Jim Haskins (1987)

Count Your Way through India by Jim Haskins (1990)

Count Your Way through Israel by Jim Haskins (1990)

Region 5

Count Your Way through Canada by Jim Haskins (1989)

Count Your Way through Mexico by Jim Haskins (1989)

Country Statistics — Study Link 12.6 — STUDY LINK MASTER

SRB 149 150

1. China has the longest border in the world—13,759 miles. Russia has the second longest border in the world—12,514 miles. How much shorter is Russia's border than China's border? 1,245 miles

2. The area of Russia is about 1,818,629 square miles. The area of Spain, including offshore islands, is about 194,897 square miles. About how many times larger is Russia than Spain? About 9 times larger

3. Students in China attend school about 251 days per year. Students in the United States attend school about 180 days per year.
   a. About what percent of the year do Chinese students spend in school? About 70 %
   b. About what percent of the year do American students spend in school? About 50 %

4. English is officially spoken in 54 countries. Portuguese is officially spoken in 8 countries. Portuguese is spoken in about what fraction of the number of English-speaking countries? About $\frac{1}{7}$

5. The table to the right shows the countries in the world with the most neighboring countries.

Country	Number of Neighbors
Brazil	10
China	15
Dem. Rep. of Congo	9
Germany	9
Russia	14
Sudan	9

Use the data in the table to answer the following questions.

a. Which country has the maximum number of neighbors? China

b. Which countries have the minimum number of neighbors? Dem. Rep. of Congo, Germany, and Sudan

c. What is the range? 6

d. What is the median? $9\frac{1}{2}$

e. What is the mode? 9

✦ *Math Masters,* p. 382

12.7 Unit 12 Review and Assessment

OBJECTIVE **To review and assess students' progress on the material covered in Unit 12.**

1 Assess Progress

	learning goals	activities
12a	**Developing Goal** Find unit rates. **(Lessons 12.2–12.5)**	❑ Slate Assessment, Problems 1 and 2 ❑ Written Assessment, Problem 2a ❑ Alternative Assessment Option
12b	**Developing Goal** Calculate unit prices to determine which product is the "better buy." **(Lessons 12.4 and 12.5)**	❑ Written Assessment, Problems 4 and 5 ❑ Alternative Assessment Option
12c	**Developing Goal** Evaluate reasonableness of rate data. **(Lesson 12.3)**	❑ Oral Assessment, Problem 1 ❑ Written Assessment, Problem 1
12d	**Developing Goal** Collect and compare rate data. **(Lessons 12.1 and 12.3–12.5)**	❑ Written Assessment, Problems 4 and 5
12e	**Secure Goal** Use rate tables, if necessary, to solve rate problems. **(Lessons 12.2–12.4 and 12.6)**	❑ Slate Assessment, Problems 1 and 2 ❑ Written Assessment, Problems 2b, 3, and 6

materials

- ☐ *Math Journal 2,* p. 343
- ☐ Study Link 12.6
- ☐ Teaching Masters (*Math Masters,* pp. 199 and 200)
- ☐ Assessment Masters (*Math Masters,* pp. 413, 414, and 419–425)
- ☐ slate
- ☐ calculator

2 Build Background for Grade 5

summaries	materials
Students practice and maintain skills through Math Boxes and Study Link Activities.	☐ *Math Journal 2,* p. 344 ☐ Study Link Masters (*Math Masters,* pp. 383–386)

Each **learning goal** listed above indicates a level of performance that might be expected at this point in the *Everyday Mathematics* K–6 curriculum. For a variety of reasons, the levels indicated may not accurately portray your class's performance.

Additional Information

Advance Preparation For additional information on assessment for Unit 12, see the *Assessment Handbook,* pages 72–74. For assessment checklists, see *Math Masters,* pages 448, 449, and 465–467.

Getting Started

Math Message

Complete the Time to Reflect *questions on journal page 343.*

Study Link 12.6 Follow-Up

Review answers. Challenge students to name the countries that are neighbors of each of the countries listed in Problem 5.

1 Assess Progress

Math Message Follow-Up (*Math Journal 2,* p. 343)

WHOLE-CLASS DISCUSSION

Students share their answers. Problem 1 provides students with an opportunity to reflect on the process of data collection. Problem 2 allows students to evaluate their own style of learning and the tools that work best for them. In Problem 3, students demonstrate an understanding of the term *consumer.* In Problem 4, students demonstrate an awareness of the uses of rates in everyday life.

Oral and Slate Assessments

WHOLE-CLASS ACTIVITY

If the suggested problems below are not appropriate for your class's level of performance, adjust the numbers or the problems themselves to better assess your students' abilities.

Oral Assessment Suggestions

1. Pose the following problem. Have students explain their solution strategies. **Goal 12c**

   On average, most people sleep about 8 hours a day. If you estimate about how many hours you have slept in your lifetime so far, will the answer be in the thousands? Ten-thousands? Hundred-thousands? Millions? There are 365 days in a year, so the number of hours slept in 1 year is about 8 * 365. This product is in the thousands. Multiply this by your age; the answer is in the ten-thousands for fourth graders.

STUDENT PAGE

Time to Reflect

1. Answer one of the following questions about your role in the eye-blinking experiment.
   a. If you were in the group that collected the eye-blinking data, which part of your job did you find the most difficult? Which part was the easiest?
   b. If you were in the group that was watched, what did you think your partner was doing? Did you guess what kind of data he or she was collecting?
2. Do you find that a rate table helps you solve rate problems? Why or why not?
3. What do you think is required in order to be considered a "smart" consumer?
4. Give five examples of rates.

Math Journal 2, p. 343

NOTE: Some of the slate assessment suggestions relate to learning goals that have been addressed in previous units. Now is a good time to evaluate students' progress toward those goals.

Slate Assessment Suggestions

1. Students solve simple rate problems. Encourage them to use rate tables if necessary. **Goals 12a and 12e**

Suggestions

- If 1 pound of apples costs 40 cents, what is the cost of 5 pounds? $2.00
- Roberto earns $3 per hour babysitting. How much does he earn in 4 hours? $12 In $2\frac{1}{2}$ hours? $7.50
- The Hole-in-One shop sells doughnuts for $2.40 per dozen. What is the cost of 1 doughnut? $0.20 Of 4 doughnuts? $0.80 Of half-a-dozen doughnuts? $1.20
- Mitchell walks at the rate of about 3 miles per hour. At that rate, what distance will he walk in 20 minutes? About 1 mile In half an hour? About $1\frac{1}{2}$ miles In 10 minutes? About $\frac{1}{2}$ mile In 3 hours? About 9 miles In $1\frac{1}{3}$ hours? About 4 miles

2. Students use calculators to find unit prices. Encourage them to use rate tables if necessary. They round to the nearest tenth of a cent. **Goals 12a and 12e**

Suggestions

- A 6-pack of cola costs $2.40. What is the price per can? 40 cents
- A box of 8 pieces of chalk costs 64 cents. What is the cost of 1 piece of chalk? 8 cents
- A 46-ounce can of pineapple juice costs $1.75. What is the price per ounce? 3.8 cents
- A 6-ounce can of tomato paste costs 34 cents. What is the price per ounce? 5.7 cents

3. Students add and subtract positive and negative integers.

Suggestions

- $6 + (-8)$ -2
- $15 - (-12)$ 27
- $20 + (-15)$ 5
- $-10 - (12)$ -22
- $-7 - (-9)$ 2
- $-12 + (-18)$ -30
- $-20 - (+14)$ -34

4. Name objects and weights. Students indicate whether the given weight is too small (S), reasonable (OK), or too large (L).

Suggestions

- A paper clip weighs about 5 kilograms. L
- A baby weighs about 8 pounds. OK
- An elephant weighs about 1,000 grams. S

✦ Written Assessment
(*Math Masters,* pp. 413 and 414)

INDEPENDENT ACTIVITY 

Depending on the needs of students, you may want to work through an example together, reading a problem aloud, discussing it, and providing additional examples as necessary before your students work the problem independently.

Each of the problems is listed below and paired with one or more of this unit's learning goals.

- Determine the reasonableness of a statistic. (Problem 1) **Goal 12c**
- Solve simple rate problems. (Problems 2 and 3) **Goals 12a and 12e**
- Determine which box of cereal is the better buy. (Problem 4) **Goals 12b and 12d**
- Make informed consumer decisions. (Problem 5) **Goals 12b and 12d**
- Make up and solve a rate number story. (Problem 6) **Goal 12e**

✦ ALTERNATIVE ASSESSMENT OPTION
Solve Multi-Step Problems Involving Rates
(*Math Masters,* pp. 199 and 200)

SMALL-GROUP ACTIVITY 

Portfolio Ideas

Students work in small groups to solve the problems. Point out that part of the assignment is to describe solution strategies in writing. If students in a group disagree on a strategy, they may write alternate strategies on the back of the page.

Part A: Here are three strategies that were submitted by students in one of the *Everyday Mathematics* field-test classes:

▷ We need to buy cookies for 27 people, and each person is to get 5 cookies. Therefore, we need to buy 5 ∗ 27 = 135 cookies. Each package has 3 rows with 15 cookies in each row: 3 ∗ 15 = 45 cookies per package. There are 45 cookies in 1 package, so there are 90 cookies in 2 packages and 135 cookies in 3 packages. We need to buy 3 packages.

Unit 12 Checking Progress

ASSESSMENT MASTER

1. It was reported that on New Year's Day, 1907, Theodore Roosevelt shook hands with 8,513 people. Does this seem reasonable? Explain your answer.
Sample answer: This seems reasonable. At a rate of 10 handshakes per minute, that would yield 10 ∗ 60 ∗ 14 = 8,400 handshakes in a 14-hour period.

2. Tina works 7 hours a day, 5 days a week. She earns $56.00 per day.
   a. How much does she earn per hour? $8.00
   b. How much does she earn per week? $280.00

3. The Davis family drove 280 miles to visit relatives. It took 5 hours. At that rate, how many miles had the Davises driven in 3 hours? 168 miles

Fill in the rate table, if needed.

Hours	1	2	3	4	5
Miles	56	112	168	224	280

4. A store charges $1.49 for a 20-ounce box of Puff Flakes cereal and $1.72 for a 24-ounce box of the same cereal. Which is the better buy? The 24-ounce box
Explain why.
Sample answer: The 20-ounce box costs 7.5¢ per ounce, and the 24-ounce box costs only 7.2¢ per ounce.

✦ *Math Masters,* p. 413

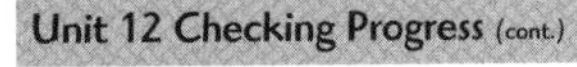
Unit 12 Checking Progress (cont.)

ASSESSMENT MASTER

5. Use the sign at the right to help you make good decisions. Solve the problems. Explain how you found your answers.

45 cents each
6 for $2.50
$4.80 a dozen
DOUGHNUTS

   a. Joey goes to Doreen's Delicious Doughnuts to buy doughnuts for the class party. What is the least amount of money he will have to pay for 30 doughnuts? $12.10
   Explain.
   Sample answer: If Joey buys two dozen at $4.80 per dozen and 6 for $2.50, the total cost will be (2 ∗ $4.80) + $2.50 = $12.10.

   b. Pretend that your mother sent you to buy 11 doughnuts. If you had enough money, would you buy a dozen doughnuts instead? Explain.
   Sample answer: Yes. 11 doughnuts would cost $2.50 + (5 ∗ $0.45) = $4.75. For 5 cents more, I could buy a dozen doughnuts. Buying one extra doughnut for only 5 cents is a good deal.

6. Make up a rate number story. Then solve it.
Sample answer: Jeanine can ride her bike 8 miles per hour. At that rate, how long would it take her to ride to her grandmother's house, 6 miles away?
Answer: 45 min (unit)

✦ *Math Masters,* p. 414

TEACHING MASTER

Cookie Problems

You may use a calculator to solve the problems.

Part A: Cynthia and Fred volunteered to buy cookies for the class party. They needed to buy enough cookies for 26 students and 1 teacher. They found a 1-pound see-through package of butter cookies and counted the cookies in the package—there were 3 rows with 15 cookies per row. They thought that they should buy enough so that each person could have 5 cookies.

1. How many packages of butter cookies would they need to buy? 3 packages

Explain how you found your answer.
Sample answer: They need 5 cookies for each of 27 people, which is 135 cookies; each package has 3 * 15 = 45 cookies; 135 cookies divided by 45 cookies per package is 3 packages.

Part B: After thinking it over, Cynthia and Fred decided that they did not want to buy butter cookies. Instead, they would buy 4 different kinds of cookies and would try to spend as little money as possible. They wanted to buy a total of 3 pounds of cookies. They walked down the cookie aisle and copied the price and weight on the package of each different kind of cookie on the shelves. Here are their data:

mint creams	$2.79/lb	chocolate chip	$2.39/12 oz
fudge marshmallow	$1.69/12 oz	oatmeal	$2.03/17 oz
sugar wafers	$2.99/8 oz	windmill	$2.59/lb
vanilla wafers	$1.39/11 oz	ginger snaps	60¢/8 oz
toffee bars	$1.79/9 oz	vanilla cream	$3.19/20 oz

✦ Math Masters, p. 199

TEACHING MASTER

Cookie Problems (cont.)

2. Study the data Cynthia and Fred collected. Which 4 kinds of cookies should they buy? Remember that the cookies should weigh about 3 pounds in all and that they should cost as little as possible.

Kind of Cookie	Number of Packages	Cost of Packages	Number of Ounces
Vanilla wafers	1	$1.39	11
Oatmeal	1	$2.03	17
Fudge marshmallow	1	$1.69	12
Ginger snaps	1	$0.60	8

Explain how you figured out the answer.
Sample answer: I divided the price of each type of cookie by the number of ounces in the package; I compared the prices per ounce and chose the cookies for the best buy whose total weight was at least 3 pounds.

3. What is the total weight of the cookies you selected? 48 oz

4. What is their total cost? $ 5.71

5. What is the cost per ounce of all the cookies you selected? 11.9 ¢ per oz

✦ Math Masters, p. 200

▷ There are 45 cookies per package. That's enough cookies for 9 people: 45 / 5 = 9. So 2 packages will have enough for 18 people, and 3 packages will feed 27 people.

▷ If we bought 5 packages, we would have 225 cookies (5 * 45 = 225). Too much. There are 180 cookies in 4 packages—still too much. But 3 packages give just the right number (3 * 45 = 135).

Students who solve the problem in Part A and are able to describe a sensible solution strategy show a good understanding of rates.

Part B: The most economical combination of cookies consists of one package each of vanilla wafers, oatmeal, fudge marshmallow, and ginger snaps. These weigh a total of 48 ounces, or 3 pounds, and cost $5.71.

Students might select these solution strategies:

▷ Find the price per ounce for each kind of cookie. For example, mint creams cost 17.4¢/oz (using a calculator, $2.79 / 16 = $0.174375). Then choose the four kinds that cost the least per ounce. This is a reasonable, methodical approach.

▷ A more creative approach is to reduce the list by a process of elimination using estimation. For example, 60¢/8 oz is $1.20/lb. That seems inexpensive, so I'll keep this one; $2.39/12 oz is more than $3/lb. That's too much, so I'll discard this one.

▷ Use trial and error to find the cost and weight of various combinations of cookies.

Students who use one or a combination of strategies and are able to give a clear explanation show a good understanding of the problem.

Watch for students who simply choose the 4 packages of cookies with the lowest price tags; that is, ginger snaps, vanilla wafers, fudge marshmallow, and toffee bars. This approach shows a poor understanding of the problem, because it does not take the *weight* of the packages into account.

NOTE: 1 package of each of these cookies together weighs a total of 40 ounces and costs a total of $5.47; but this is not a solution since the total weight is less than 3 pounds. Another package of ginger snaps will bring the total weight to 3 pounds, but the total cost will be $6.07, which is more than $5.71.

The answers to Problems 3, 4, and 5 depend on the answer to Problem 2. However, you can use the answers to these problems to evaluate students' progress, even if they did not get the correct answer in Problem 2.

✦ End-of-Year Assessment
(*Math Masters,* pp. 419–425)

INDEPENDENT ACTIVITY 

The End-of-Year Assessment (*Math Masters,* pages 419–425) provides an additional assessment opportunity that you may want to use as part of your balanced assessment plan. This test covers many of the important concepts and skills presented in *Fourth Grade Everyday Mathematics.* It should be used along with ongoing, product, and periodic assessments. Please see the *Assessment Handbook* for further information.

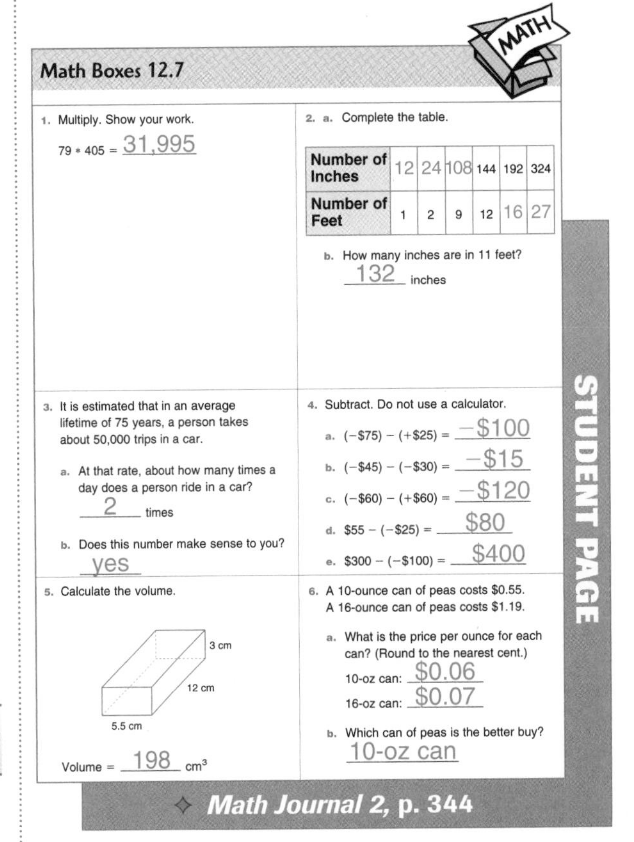

Math Boxes 12.7

1. Multiply. Show your work.

$79 * 405 =$ 31,995

2. a. Complete the table.

Number of Inches	12	24	108	144	192	324
Number of Feet	1	2	9	12	16	27

b. How many inches are in 11 feet? 132 inches

3. It is estimated that in an average lifetime of 75 years, a person takes about 50,000 trips in a car.

a. At that rate, about how many times a day does a person ride in a car? 2 times

b. Does this number make sense to you? yes

4. Subtract. Do not use a calculator.

a. (−\$75) − (+\$25) = −\$100

b. (−\$45) − (−\$30) = −\$15

c. (−\$60) − (+\$60) = −\$120

d. \$55 − (−\$25) = \$80

e. \$300 − (−\$100) = \$400

5. Calculate the volume.

3 cm
12 cm
5.5 cm

Volume = 198 cm^3

6. A 10-ounce can of peas costs \$0.55. A 16-ounce can of peas costs \$1.19.

a. What is the price per ounce for each can? (Round to the nearest cent.)

10-oz can: \$0.06

16-oz can: \$0.07

b. Which can of peas is the better buy? 10-oz can

STUDENT PAGE

✧ *Math Journal 2,* p. 344

2 Build Background for Grade 5

✦ Math Boxes 12.7 (*Math Journal 2,* p. 344)

INDEPENDENT ACTIVITY 

Mixed Review Math Boxes in this lesson are paired with Math Boxes in Lesson 12.5.

✦ Study Link 12.7: Family Letter
(*Math Masters,* pp. 383–386)

Home Connection This Study Link thanks family members for their participation in *Fourth Grade Everyday Mathematics,* suggests activities that can be done at home during the vacation, and provides a "sneak preview" of *Fifth Grade Everyday Mathematics.*

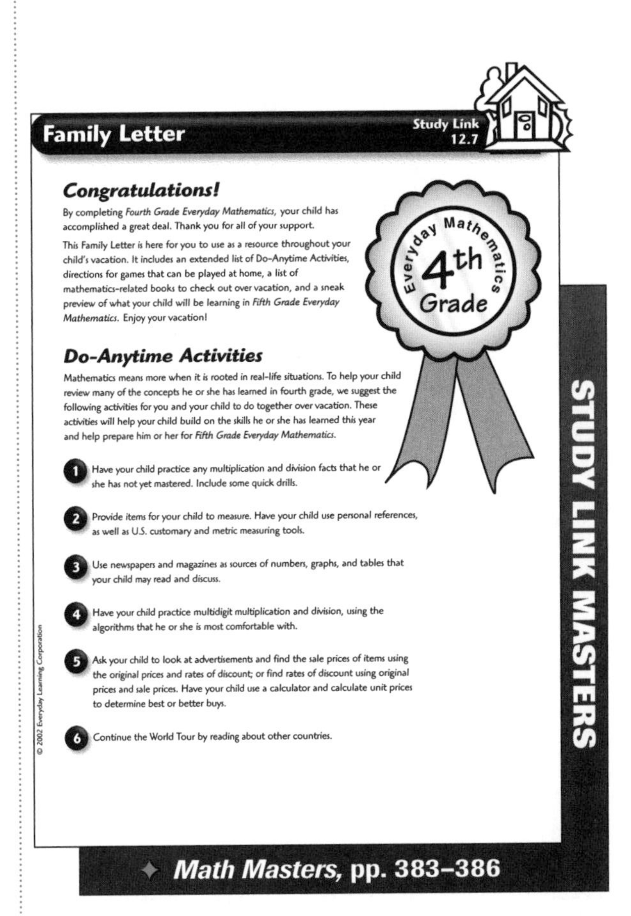

Family Letter Study Link 12.7

Congratulations!

By completing *Fourth Grade Everyday Mathematics,* your child has accomplished a great deal. Thank you for all of your support.

This Family Letter is here for you to use as a resource throughout your child's vacation. It includes an extended list of Do-Anytime Activities, directions for games that can be played at home, a list of mathematics-related books to check out over vacation, and a sneak preview of what your child will be learning in *Fifth Grade Everyday Mathematics.* Enjoy your vacation!

Do-Anytime Activities

Mathematics means more when it is rooted in real-life situations. To help your child review many of the concepts he or she has learned in fourth grade, we suggest the following activities for you and your child to do together over vacation. These activities will help your child build on the skills he or she has learned this year and help prepare him or her for *Fifth Grade Everyday Mathematics.*

1. Have your child practice any multiplication and division facts that he or she has not yet mastered. Include some quick drills.
2. Provide items for your child to measure. Have your child use personal references, as well as U.S. customary and metric measuring tools.
3. Use newspapers and magazines as sources of numbers, graphs, and tables that your child may read and discuss.
4. Have your child practice multidigit multiplication and division, using the algorithms that he or she is most comfortable with.
5. Ask your child to look at advertisements and find the sale prices of items using the original prices and rates of discount; or find rates of discount using original prices and sale prices. Have your child use a calculator and calculate unit prices to determine best or better buys.
6. Continue the World Tour by reading about other countries.

STUDY LINK MASTERS

✧ *Math Masters,* pp. 383–386

Appendices

contents

Title	Page
Projects	882
Fourth Grade Key Vocabulary	915
Scope and Sequence	927
Index	947

PROJECT

1 Making a Cutaway Globe

OBJECTIVE **To reinforce work with latitude and longitude.**

background information

Recommended Use: After Unit 6

See the discussion of Projects in the Management Guide section of the *Teacher's Reference Manual.*

materials

- ☐ *Math Masters,* p. 201 (on poster board or similar)
- ☐ *Math Masters,* p. 202 (one per partnership)
- ☐ transparent tape
- ☐ scissors
- ☐ straightedge
- ☐ two or three standard-size paper clips

***See* Advance Preparation**

Project Information

Students work with a partner to construct a cutaway version of a globe. They then find the location of various places on their globe, using latitude and longitude. They note that degrees of latitude and longitude are measures of angles whose vertices are at the center of Earth.

Advance Preparation In order for the cutaway globe to work properly, *Math Masters,* page 201 must be copied on poster board or similar paper. Before beginning the project, you may want to cut apart *Math Masters,* page 201 and follow the instructions below to construct a cutaway globe.

You will need a globe. You will also need to know the approximate latitude and longitude of your school; or use the area where it is located, or a nearby city's latitude and longitude. If not already known from work in Lesson 6.10, these can be estimated from the globe or a map in the *Student Reference Book.* They can also be found at several Internet sites; see the end of this project.

It will be helpful if you recruit one or two parents or students to help as students construct their models.

1 Doing the Project

✦ Constructing a Cutaway Globe
(*Math Masters,* pp. 201 and 202)

PARTNER ACTIVITY 

Divide the class into partnerships and distribute *Math Masters,* page 201. There are two sets of circles and semicircles on the sheet. Students will use them to construct models of two hemispheres and then assemble them to form a full globe. The directions for making the cutaway globe are on *Math Masters,* page 202. You may want to have students read and follow the directions on their own while you and your helpers circulate. Or you may prefer to demonstrate the construction while students follow along and construct their models.

Directions:

1. Carefully cut out one of the circles A along the dashed lines.
2. Cut out one of the semicircles B. Cut the slit marked at 90° on the semicircle.
3. Lay semicircle B on circle A so that the base of the semicircle aligns with the 0° to 180° diameter shown on circle A. Tape the pieces together on both sides of the semicircle. Move semicircle B so that it is perpendicular to circle A.

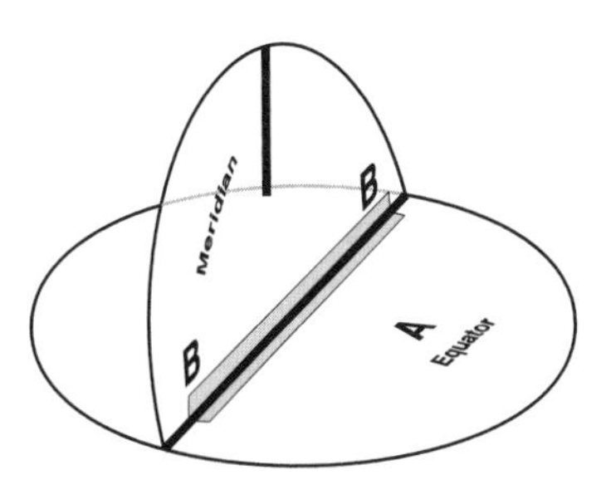

4. Cut out one of the semicircles C. Cut the slit marked at the bottom of the 90° line. Fold the semicircle in half along the 90° line. Fold it back and forth several times to make a good crease. Set semicircle C aside for later use.

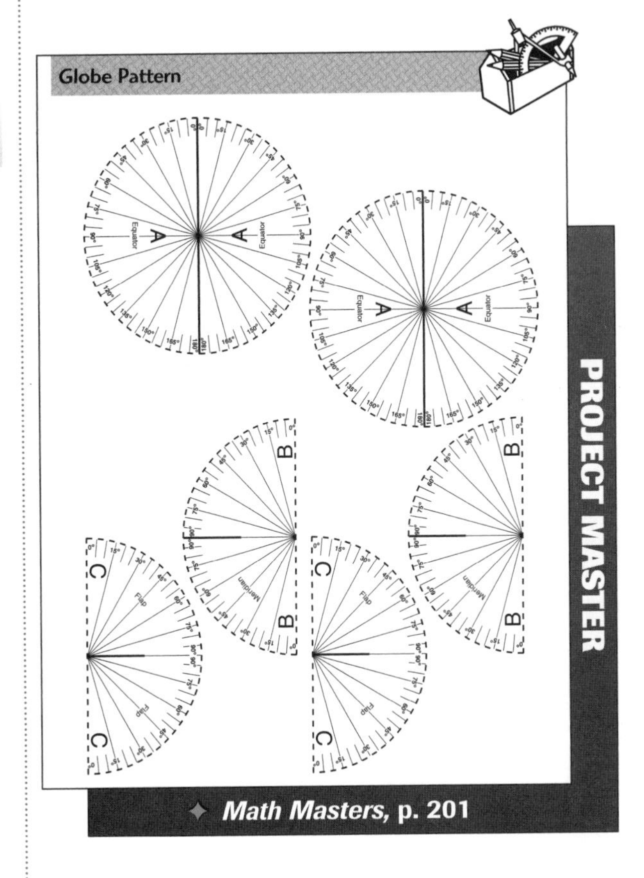

✦ *Math Masters,* p. 201

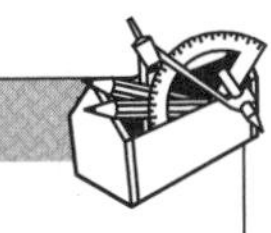

How to Make a Cutaway Globe

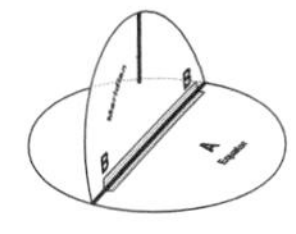

Figure 1

Figure 2

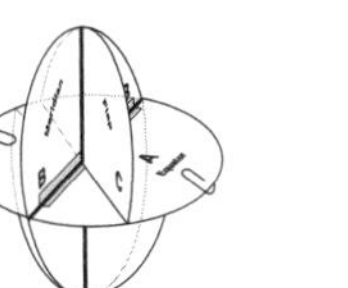

Figure 3

Directions:

Step 1: Carefully cut out one of the circles A along the dashed lines.

Step 2: Cut out one of the semicircles B; cut the thin slit on the semicircle.

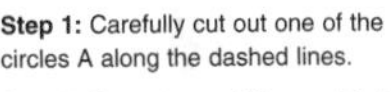

Step 3: Lay semicircle B on circle A so that the base of the semicircle aligns with the 0° to 180° diameter shown on circle A. Tape the pieces together on both sides of the semicircle. Adjust the semicircle so that it stands straight up. See Figure 1.

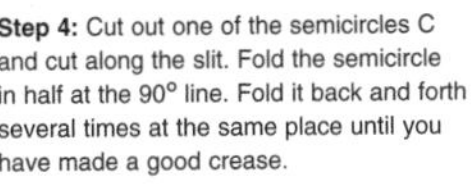

Step 4: Cut out one of the semicircles C and cut along the slit. Fold the semicircle in half at the 90° line. Fold it back and forth several times at the same place until you have made a good crease.

Step 5: Slide the slit of semicircle C through the slit of semicircle B. See Figure 2.

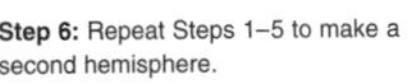

Step 6: Repeat Steps 1–5 to make a second hemisphere.

Step 7: Put the two hemispheres together with paper clips to make a full globe. Put the 0° labels on circles A together. See Figure 3.

PROJECT MASTER

✦ *Math Masters,* p. 202

Tell students that they have made a cutaway model of the Northern Hemisphere. The circumference of circle A corresponds to the equator. Ask them to point out the North Pole and the prime meridian. (Note that semicircle B shows only the northern half of the prime meridian. The rest of the semicircle is the northern half of the 180° longitude semicircle.)

Ask: *What part of the globe is at the center of circle A?* The center of the globe

Call attention to the degree labels on circle A. The labels from 0° to 180° on each side of the prime meridian correspond to the degree labels along the equator of the globe.

On semicircle B, degree labels from 0° to 90° start at each end of the base. They represent degrees of latitude north of the equator.

Now ask students to take semicircle C, which they had set aside, and slide the slit of this semicircle through the slit of semicircle B. (See Figure 1.) If necessary for a good fit, the slits should be lengthened.

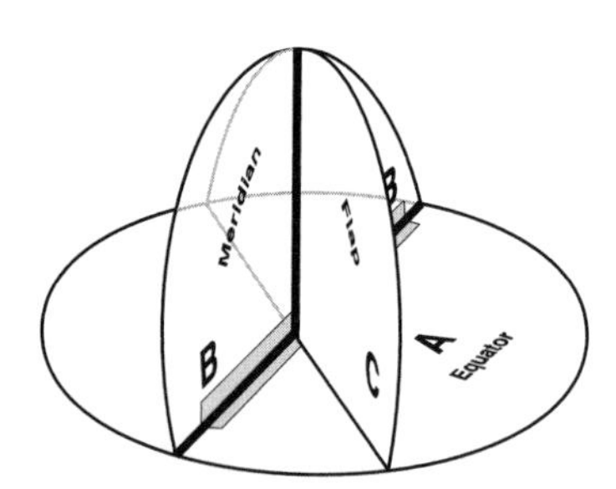

Figure 1

Demonstrate how this movable semicircle can be used to show any combination of latitude and longitude. For example, to find 50° North, 30° East, follow these steps:

1. With the prime meridian facing the class, find the 30° East mark on circle A. Rotate the right flap of the movable semicircle to that position.
2. Without moving flap C, point to the 50° North mark on it.

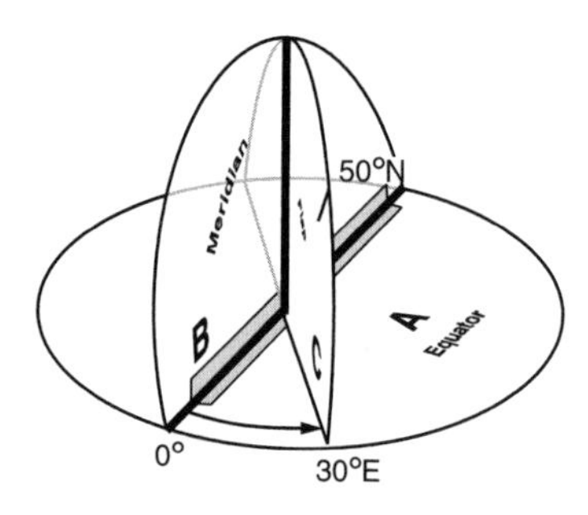

Figure 2

The model now shows the location of 50° North, 30° East. Find this location on the globe and compare it with the location on the model (Figure 2).

Ask a volunteer to give the approximate latitude and longitude of an important place—preferably the school, hometown, or nearby city. If not already known, these can be estimated from the globe or maps in the *Student Reference Book*. Write them on the board.

To mark this location on their models, direct students to do the following (See Figure 3.)

1. Move Flap C to show the longitude (east or west on the equator). Then draw a line along the base of the flap.

   This hand-drawn line, along with the base of the prime meridian flap (Flap B) and the center of the cutaway model, forms an angle on circle A.

   Ask: *What does the degree measure of the angle represent?* The number of degrees of longitude

2. Make a dot on the edge of the flap to show the latitude of the location identified on the chalkboard. Draw a line from the center of the model to the dot. This line, along with the base of the flap and the center of the model, forms a second angle.

Ask: *What does the degree measure of the angle represent?* The number of degrees of latitude north from the equator

NOTE: At this point, it is not necessary for students to be able to state that degrees of latitude and longitude are measures of angles whose vertices are at the center of Earth. It is enough that by drawing the angles, students become aware of this fact.

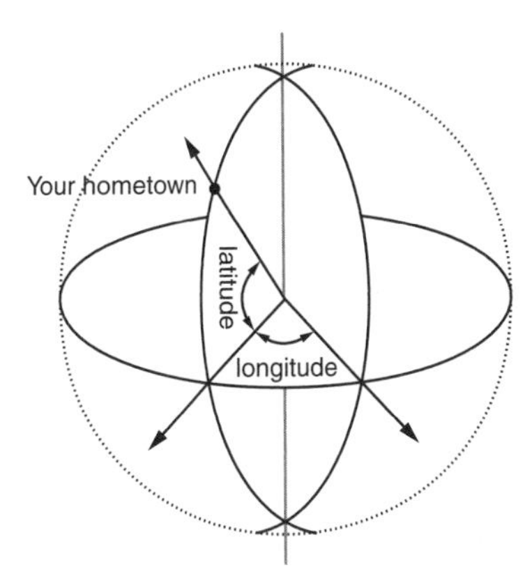

Figure 3

✦ Making a Full Cutaway Globe

PARTNER ACTIVITY

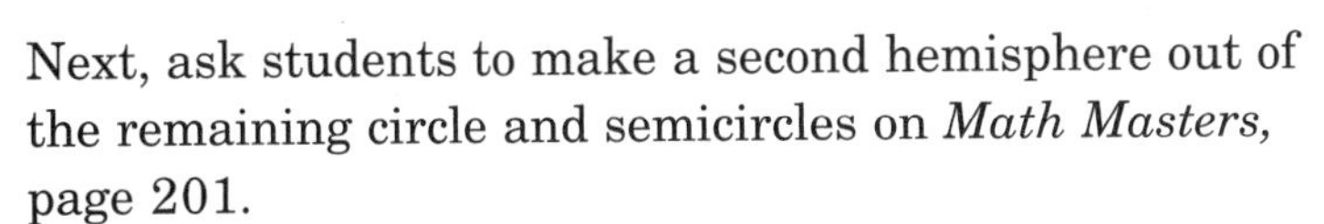

Next, ask students to make a second hemisphere out of the remaining circle and semicircles on *Math Masters*, page 201.

Then show them how to make a complete cutaway globe—that is, one that shows both the Northern and Southern Hemispheres. (See Figure 4.) Partners use paper clips to fasten the two bases of their models together, making sure to align the 0° longitude marks on both hemispheres. With this full globe, they can practice finding locations in both hemispheres.

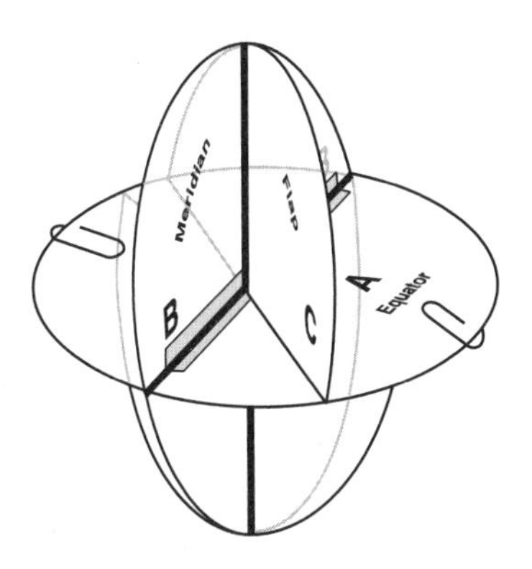

Figure 4

On the board, write other latitude/longitude pairs in the Northern Hemisphere. Ask students to move the flaps on their models to find these locations. Then have them guess on what continent these are located. Check on the globe.

Examples

20°N,	20°E	Africa
15°N,	105°E	Southeast Asia
45°N,	100°W	North America
50°N,	5°E	Northern Europe
0°S,	60°W	South America

Extending the Project

✦Digging a Tunnel

INDEPENDENT ACTIVITY 

Ask students to imagine digging a straight tunnel from their hometown through the center of Earth to the surface on the opposite side. Ask them to show the opposite point on their models and to name its latitude and longitude. Have them share strategies. Suggest other examples.

✦Looking Up Latitudes and Longitudes

INDEPENDENT ACTIVITY 

Invite students to look up latitudes and longitudes on the Internet. When this book went to press, the following sites were available:

http://kids.earth.nasa.gov/trmm/locator.html Locations in the U.S.

http://www.indo.com/cgi-bin/dist Locations in the U.S. and elsewhere; also calculates distances between locations

PROJECT

Using a Magnetic Compass

OBJECTIVE **To read a magnetic compass and find directions.**

background information

Recommended Use: After Unit 6

See the discussion of Projects in the Management Guide section of the *Teacher's Reference Manual.*

materials

- □ *Math Masters,* p. 203 (one per group); and p. 204 (optional)
- □ magnetic compass (one per group)
- □ 10-foot string (one per group)
- □ tape
- □ steel sewing needle, bar magnet, piece of cork, dish of water (optional)

***See* Advance Preparation**

Project Information

Students learn how to orient and read a magnetic compass. Then, working in small groups, they use a magnetic compass to practice finding the direction of objects in relation to north.

In an Extending the Project activity, students make a floating compass with a steel sewing needle, a bar magnet, a piece of cork, and a dish of water.

Advance Preparation You will need a magnetic compass and a copy of *Math Masters,* page 203 for a classroom demonstration. Try to obtain additional compasses for the group activity. Each group of four will need a 10-foot length of string.

Vocabulary • **compass bearing** • **magnetic north**

1 Doing the Project

✦Introducing the Magnetic Compass

WHOLE-CLASS DISCUSSION 

Gather the class around an open space in the classroom. If you have more than one magnetic compass, distribute them for students to examine.

Prompt discussion along the following lines:

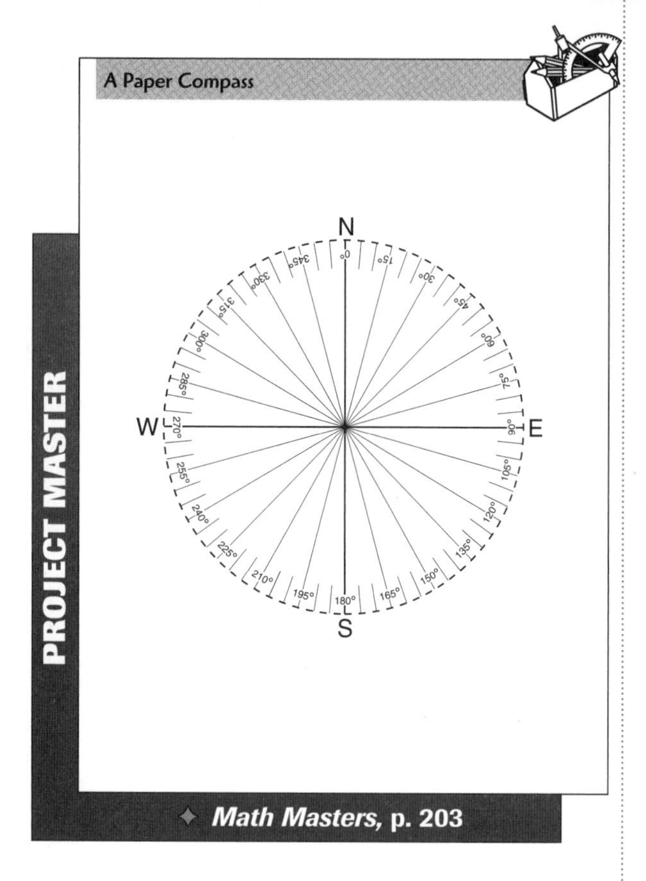

✦ *Math Masters,* p. 203

NOTE: Depending on one's location, a compass may not show "true" north. Tables that contain corrections are available. Students will notice that the magnetic compass is marked in degrees from 0° to 360° in a clockwise direction, starting at north, and that the paper compass is marked in the same way. Point out that it is easier to make accurate degree readings on the paper compass than on most magnetic compasses.

- Does anyone know how a magnetic compass works? The Earth behaves like a huge magnet. The compass needle is a tiny magnet. Earth's magnetic field exerts a force or pull on the compass needle so that the needle points north.
- How do you use a magnetic compass? Lay the compass flat on a surface or hold it level to the ground. Make sure that there are no metal objects or magnets near the compass. The compass needle will "settle down" and point north.

✦ Using a Magnetic Compass
(*Math Masters,* p. 203)

WHOLE-CLASS ACTIVITY

Show students a method for describing the direction of an object from a given point.

▷ A "paper compass" (*Math Masters,* page 203) is laid on a flat surface so that the 0° mark points north.

▷ A string is stretched from the center of the paper compass toward the object, making it possible to describe the direction of the object in relation to north.

You will need a magnetic compass to orient the paper compass so that it points north. Here is one way to do it:

1. Lay the paper compass flat on the floor.
2. Place the magnetic compass on the paper compass so that the center of the magnetic compass is over the center of the paper compass. Make sure the letter N on the paper compass points in the same direction as the letter N on the magnetic compass.
3. Gently rotate the paper with the compass on it until the needle on the magnetic compass points north. Tape the paper compass in place.

Now select a location in the classroom—for example, the class globe. Demonstrate how to find the direction of the globe from the compass, using north as a reference.

1. Have a student hold down one end of a piece of string on the center of the paper compass.

   Ask another student to pull the string as far as possible in the direction of the object you selected, keeping the string at floor level.

2. Read the number of degrees at the mark where the string crosses the edge of the paper compass. This gives the direction of the object, using north as a reference. For example: "The globe is 120° clockwise from north" or "The globe has a **compass bearing** of 120°."

Emphasize that this method measures the amount of *clockwise* rotation from **magnetic north.**

Choose other objects or locations in the classroom. Ask pairs of students to find the objects' direction from north, using the method just described.

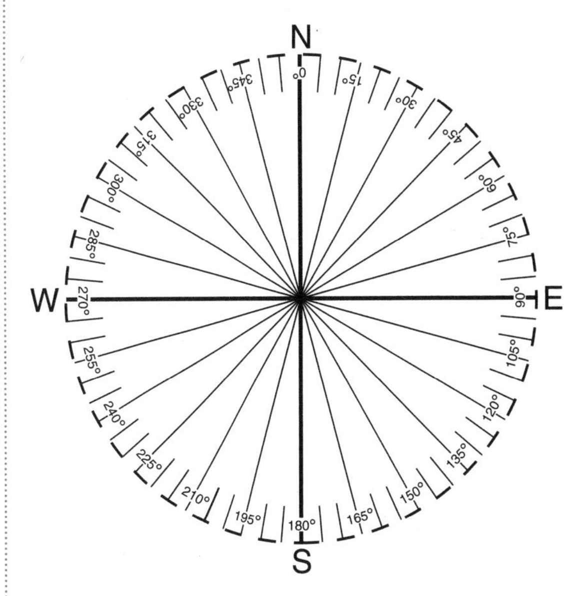

Using a paper compass to determine compass bearings of objects in the classroom

✦ Measuring Direction
(*Math Masters,* p. 203)

SMALL-GROUP ACTIVITY

Divide the class into groups of four. Pass out a length of string to each group and a magnetic compass to as many groups as possible. If there are not enough compasses to go around, groups can share.

Ask each group to lay its copy of *Math Masters,* page 203 flat on the desktop and orient it toward north, as described earlier. (Align the magnetic compass over the paper compass. Rotate the paper and compass until the needle on the magnetic compass points north.) Then tape the paper compass to the desktop.

Each group now uses its string to find the direction of each corner of the room on its taped paper compass. Students indicate the direction of each corner by drawing a line segment along the string from the center of the paper compass to the edge. Have students record next to each line segment the number of degrees from north. Circulate and assist.

Bring the class together to share results. Ask: *Why do the results differ from group to group?* The direction of any particular location depends on the point from which the direction is measured. For example, the direction of the classroom globe will vary, depending on where one is standing in the classroom.

Making a Compass

In ancient times, sailors had only the sun, moon, and stars to aid them in navigation. The most important navigational instrument was the **compass.** The compass was invented more than 1,000 years ago. The first compass was a small bar of magnetized iron that floated on a reed in a bowl of water. The magnet in the iron would make the reed point to the magnetically charged North Pole. Using a compass, sailors could tell in which direction they were traveling.

You, too, can make a floating compass.

First, magnetize a steel sewing needle by stroking it with one pole of a strong bar magnet. Slowly stroke the needle from end to end **in one direction only.** Be sure to lift your hand up in the air before coming down for another stroke.

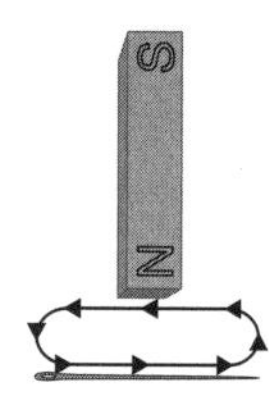

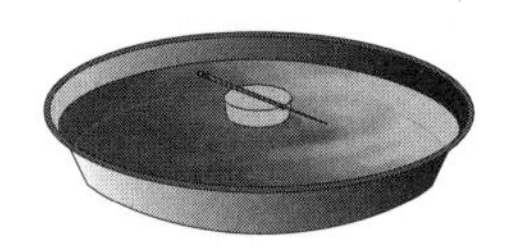

Slice a round ($\frac{1}{2}$-inch-thick) piece from a cork stopper. Cut a groove across the center of the top of the cork. Put the needle in the groove. Place the cork into a glass, china, or aluminum dish filled with water. Add a teaspoon of detergent to the water. The detergent will lower the surface tension of the water and prevent the cork from moving to one side of the dish and staying there.

The needle will behave like a compass needle. It will assume a North-South position because of Earth's magnetic field.

Source: Science for the Elementary School. New York: Macmillan, 1993.

PROJECT MASTER

✦ *Math Masters,* p. 204

2 Extending the Project

✦ Making a Compass
(*Math Masters,* p. 204)

INDEPENDENT ACTIVITY 

Math Masters, page 204 provides a brief history of compasses and directions for making a floating compass with a steel sewing needle, bar magnet, piece of cork, and dish of water.

✦ Finding Out about Compasses and Orienteering

INDEPENDENT ACTIVITY 

Invite students to learn more about the history and uses of compasses by looking in encyclopedias and books such as *Basic Essentials: Map and Compass* by Cliff Jacobson (Old Saybrook, CT: Globe Pequot, 1999).

Through scouting or camping, some students may be familiar with using a compass to follow a course and might be interested in describing their experiences to the class.

The competitive sport of orienteering involves using a detailed map and a compass to navigate around a course with designated control points. The winner of the competition is the participant who visits the control points in order and in the shortest amount of time. The International Orienteering Federation has an Internet site at http://www.orienteering.org/.

PROJECT

3

A Carnival Game

OBJECTIVES **To analyze a cube-tossing game; and to invent a profitable variation.**

background information

Recommended Use: After Unit 7

See the discussion of Projects in the Management Guide section of the *Teacher's Reference Manual.*

materials

- ☐ *Math Journal 2,* p. 225; optional
- ☐ *Math Masters,* pp. 112 and 114 (as completed by the student, if available); and pp. 205 and 206
- ☐ calculator
- ☐ cm cube
- ☐ scissors
- ☐ transparent tape

***See* Advance Preparation**

Project Information

Students make a "quilt" out of the 100-grids they colored in Lesson 7.12. They use their quilt as a target mat for a cube-tossing game. They analyze the game, based on their understanding of what results to expect.

Then students work in small groups to invent a variation in which they must decide what to charge for a ticket and what amounts to pay in prizes. Their goal is to invent a game that will show a profit.

Advance Preparation You will need the data for 1,000 cube drops collected in Lesson 7.12 on *Math Masters,* page 114. If this was not done, combine 20 students' results on 50 drops as described in Part 3 of Lesson 7.12, or generate the data with the students from their results on *Math Journal 2,* page 225. Write this information, including percents for each color, on the board.

Students will need their completed copies of *Math Masters,* page 112. If these are not available, copy the master and have students color it as described in the project.

1 Doing the Project

✦ Introducing a Carnival Game

(*Math Journal 2,* p. 225; *Math Masters,* pp. 112 and 205)

SMALL-GROUP ACTIVITY

1. Constructing a Class "Quilt" Mat

Have students take out the grid they colored on *Math Masters,* page 112. If this is not available, have students color the grid on a blank copy of the master according to the specifications shown on the table. (*See margin.*) They may color the squares in any way they want. The colors may form a pattern or a picture, or they may be arranged randomly.

How to Color the Grid

Color	Number of Squares
yellow	1
red	4
green	10
blue	35
white	50
Total	**100**

If there are fewer than 20 students in your class, divide the class into groups of four. If there are 20 or more, divide the class into groups of five. (Any "leftover" students form their own group.) Ask students in each group to cut out their 100-grids and tape them together to form one row of 100-grids. (For example, a group of four will make a row of four grids.)

NOTE: If you want the taped rows to form a rectangle or square, you may have to ask students to color additional grids. For example, with 28 students, you would need two extra grids to form a rectangular quilt with six rows of five grids each.

Bring the groups together. Have them tape their rows together to form a rectangular (or near rectangular) "quilt." For example, a class of 20 would form a quilt with four rows, each row with five grids.

2. Becoming Familiar with the Game

Introduce the Carnival Game on *Math Masters,* page 205. A player pays 10¢ for each cube the player tosses onto the class "quilt" mat. The player may win a prize, depending upon the color on which the cube lands.

Ask students to complete Part 1. Circulate and assist as needed. Then bring the class together to compare results.

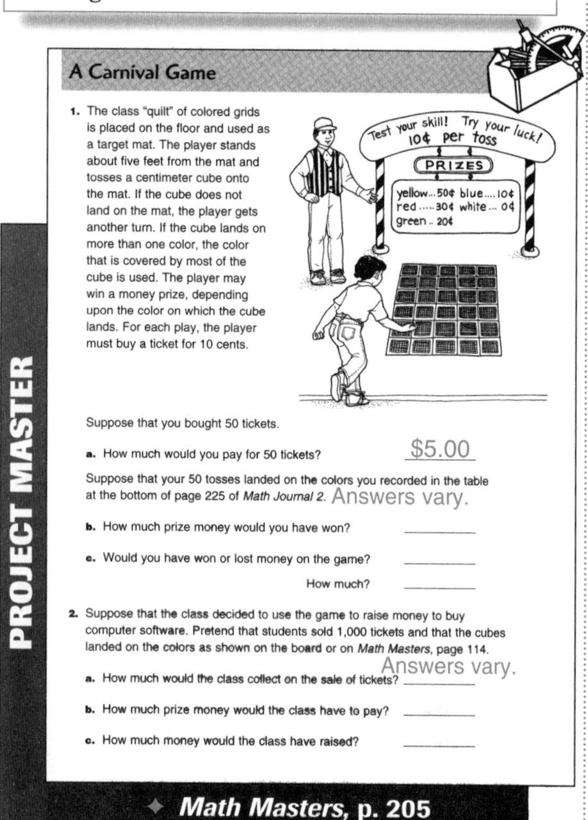
PROJECT MASTER

A Carnival Game

1. The class "quilt" of colored grids is placed on the floor and used as a target mat. The player stands about five feet from the mat and tosses a centimeter cube onto the mat. If the cube does not land on the mat, the player gets another turn. If the cube lands on more than one color, the color that is covered by most of the cube is used. The player may win a money prize, depending upon the color on which the cube lands. For each play, the player must buy a ticket for 10 cents.

Suppose that you bought 50 tickets.

a. How much would you pay for 50 tickets? $5.00

Suppose that your 50 tosses landed on the colors you recorded in the table at the bottom of page 225 of *Math Journal 2.* Answers vary.

b. How much prize money would you have won? ________

c. Would you have won or lost money on the game? ________

How much? ________

2. Suppose that the class decided to use the game to raise money to buy computer software. Pretend that students sold 1,000 tickets and that the cubes landed on the colors as shown on the board or on *Math Masters,* page 114. Answers vary.

a. How much would the class collect on the sale of tickets? ________

b. How much prize money would the class have to pay? ________

c. How much money would the class have raised? ________

✦ *Math Masters,* p. 205

Tell the class that the table on the board contains the combined results of 50 cube drops by 20 students in Lesson 7.12. Since 20 * 50 = 1,000, the table shows the number of times, and percent of total times, that a cube landed on each color out of 1,000 drops.

Suggest that the Carnival Game could be run at a school fair or similar event to raise money for the class—for a party, equipment, or other purposes. Have students complete Part 2 to find out how much money the class could earn if students sold 1,000 tickets and the results were the same as those on the board.

If you wish, have students actually play the game.

✦ Inventing a Variation on the Carnival Game (*Math Masters,* p. 206)

SMALL-GROUP ACTIVITY

By now, students should have a fairly good understanding of the rules of the Carnival Game and the factors that affect the game's profitability. Tell them that each group is to invent its own version of the game. Spend a few minutes discussing things students need to take into consideration, such as the following:

▷ How much should they charge for a ticket?

▷ Which colors should they reward with prizes?

▷ What should the prizes be?

▷ How will their decisions affect the number of tickets they sell?

▷ Will they make more money if they charge a lot for a ticket and offer large prizes? Or will a high ticket price discourage people from buying tickets?

A Carnival Game (cont.)

3. Work with your group to make up your own version of the Carnival Game.

   a. Record how much you would charge for a ticket and what the prizes would be for each color.

Ticket Price
_____ per toss

Prizes	
yellow	_____
red	_____
green	_____
blue	_____
white	_____

   b. Use the results for 1,000 cube drops shown on the board or on *Math Masters*, page 114 to answer the following questions: Answers vary.

   Would the class have won or lost money? _____

   How much? _____

4. Suppose that the class ran your game on Parents' Night. Answers vary.

   a. How many tickets do you estimate the class would sell? _____

   b. How much money would the class get from ticket sales? _____

   c. About how much money should you expect to pay in prizes? _____

   d. About how much money should the class expect to earn? _____

PROJECT MASTER

✦ *Math Masters,* p. 206

Students can complete this project over the next few days. Groups can post their ticket prices and prizes near the mat and play each other's games in their free time. To find the total amount of money the class would earn, follow this procedure: Multiply the number of times a cube lands on each color by the amount of the prize for that color. Then add the amounts won for each color. For example, suppose the cube lands on the following colors:

Cube lands on:		**Prizes:**
yellow:	1 time	1 * 50¢ = $0.50
red:	2 times	2 * 30¢ = $0.60
green:	6 times	6 * 20¢ = $1.20
blue:	11 times	11 * 10¢ = $1.10
white:	30 times	30 * 0¢ = $0.00
Total:		$3.40

The 50 tickets would cost $5.00 (50 * 10¢). The players won only $3.40. The class would earn $1.60 ($5.00 − $3.40).

Have students complete *Math Masters,* page 206.

2 Extending the Project

✦ Creating Other Games

INDEPENDENT ACTIVITY 

Invite students to make up their own games, establish prices and prizes, and use expected results to calculate prizes paid and profits.

PROJECT

4

Making a Quilt

OBJECTIVE **To explore and apply ideas of pattern, symmetry, rotation, and reflection in the context of quilts.**

background information

Recommended Use: After Unit 10

See the discussion of Projects in the Management Guide section of the *Teacher's Reference Manual.*

materials

- ☐ *Math Masters,* pp. 207–215 (one per student); and p. 216 (at least three copies per student)
- ☐ markers, crayons, or coloring pencils; or paper of various colors
- ☐ one-hole punch
- ☐ paste or glue
- ☐ scissors
- ☐ straightedge
- ☐ yarn
- ☐ crepe paper (optional)

See **Advance Preparation**

Project Information

Students apply their knowledge of symmetry and rotations to making a paper quilt. Plan to spend about four days on this project.

During the first two days, students learn about traditional quilting patterns, examine the symmetry in such patterns, and practice creating patterns of their own. During the last two days, they work in groups of three to design a quilting pattern, and each group makes nine colorful copies, or "patches," of its pattern. The class assembles all the patches into a quilt. Then each group describes its work to the class. In addition to your observations of students at work, the group reports will help you assess students' understanding of line symmetry, rotations, and reflections.

Advance Preparation Students will need yarn to assemble their quilts. If you wish, collect colored paper or wrapping paper to be cut up for "patches." You may want to make overhead transparencies of *Math Masters,* pages 208 and 212. If you can laminate the patches, the quilt will last longer and look more finished.

Vocabulary • **9-Patch Pattern** • **patchwork quilt** • **quilting bee**

PROJECT MASTER

Patchwork Quilts

Throughout American history, women have worked together to make **patchwork quilts.** Because cloth was expensive and scarce, quilts were often made out of pieces of worn-out clothing or leftovers from another project. The quilters began by sewing together pieces of different colors, shapes, and textures to create a square pattern. Then they made more "patchwork" squares with the same pattern. When they had enough squares, they sewed them together to form the top of the quilt. Next they added a layer of wool fleece or cotton, called *batting,* and a cloth backing. They made a "sandwich" of the three layers—the backing on the bottom, the batting in the middle, and the patchwork on the top. They stretched the "sandwich" on a wooden frame and sewed the three layers together with tiny stitches.

The quilt was put together at a party, called a **quilting bee.** While cutting and sewing, the women would tell stories and share what went on in their lives. When the quilt was finished, the men joined the women for supper and dancing.

Many patchwork patterns have become traditions. Their names and designs have come from the everyday lives of the people who created them. For example, the "Buggy Wheel" pattern was probably inspired by a trip in a buggy. Along with walking and riding horses, buggies were a popular form of transportation in early America.

Buggy Wheel

Although early quilters may not have studied geometry in school, we can see geometry in many of their designs. Patchwork quilting involves the cutting of fabric into various geometric shapes and sewing them together into patterns. The pattern may be repeated over and over to form a quilt, or it may be rotated or reflected as the patches are assembled. Many patchwork patterns, such as the "Buggy Wheel" and "Does and Darts" patterns, are symmetric. Others, such as the "Crazy Quilt," seem to have been created at random.

Does and Darts

The beauty of a quilt lies in its uniqueness. No two patches need ever be the same because there are many possible arrangements of fabrics and colors.

Crazy Quilt

✦ *Math Masters,* p. 207

PROJECT MASTER

Symmetric Patterns

Each pattern to the right of the "Pinwheel" pattern below has been colored in a different way. Notice how each color arrangement changes the number of lines of symmetry.

Pinwheel Pattern

lines of symmetry: 4 2 1 0

For each pattern below, draw all the lines of symmetry and record the number of lines of symmetry.

1. Bow-Tie Pattern

lines of symmetry: 4 1 2 2

2. Ohio Star Pattern

lines of symmetry: 4 4 0 0

3. Pineapple Log Cabin Pattern

lines of symmetry: 4 4 4 0

✦ *Math Masters,* p. 208

1 Doing the Project

✦ Learning about Quilts
(*Math Masters,* p. 207)

WHOLE-CLASS DISCUSSION 

Have students read the article about quilts on *Math Masters,* page 207. Then ask them to discuss it. The discussion should include the following points:

▷ Quilting patterns often reflect the lives of the people who create them.

▷ Quilting patterns display some of the geometric transformations that students have been studying, such as reflections and rotations, and the symmetries based on these transformations.

▷ **Patchwork quilts** were made from available scraps sewn into a square pattern.

Tell students that during this project, they will learn more about quilting patterns, and they will use this knowledge to make their own paper quilts.

DAYS 1 AND 2

✦ Examining Lines of Symmetry in Quilting Patterns (*Math Masters,* p. 208)

PARTNER ACTIVITY 

Introduce the activity with a discussion of the Pinwheel Pattern at the top of *Math Masters,* page 208. Students should notice the following details:

▷ The original, uncolored pattern has four lines of symmetry.

▷ This pattern may be colored in many different ways.

▷ The number of lines of symmetry varies, depending on the coloring scheme.

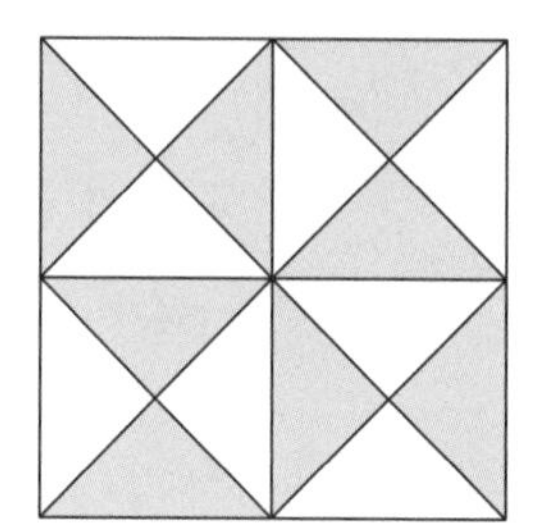

Working with a partner, students examine three other basic patterns and various coloring schemes based on these patterns. Then students draw all the lines of symmetry for each. Circulate and assist as needed.

After a few minutes, bring the class together and go over the answers. It may be helpful to refer to an overhead transparency of *Math Masters,* page 208.

✦ Designing 9-Patch Patterns
(*Math Masters,* pp. 209–211)

INDEPENDENT ACTIVITY 

If there is time left today, introduce this activity so that students can start to work on it at home. They can complete the activity the next day.

Tell the class that there is a special kind of quilting pattern called the **9-Patch Pattern.** Students will design such patterns of colored squares, triangles, and rectangles.

To make the various pieces, students follow the directions on *Math Masters,* page 209 for coloring the squares on *Math Masters,* page 210. Then they cut the squares into triangles and rectangles as directed on *Math Masters,* page 209.

To assemble a 9-Patch Pattern, students use the 3-by-3 grid on *Math Masters,* page 211. They experiment with different ways to arrange the triangles and rectangles they cut out.

When students have completed a pattern, have them copy it onto a grid on *Math Masters,* page 209. Students should make at least one pattern with four lines of symmetry, one with two lines of symmetry, and one with no lines of symmetry. Circulate and assist students who are having difficulties.

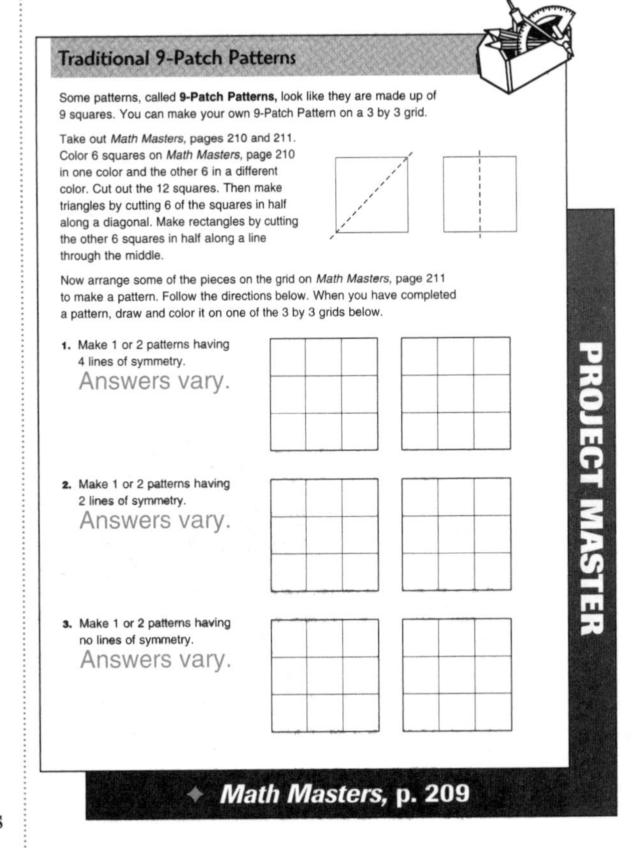

Traditional 9-Patch Patterns

Some patterns, called **9-Patch Patterns,** look like they are made up of 9 squares. You can make your own 9-Patch Pattern on a 3 by 3 grid.

Take out *Math Masters,* pages 210 and 211. Color 6 squares on *Math Masters,* page 210 in one color and the other 6 in a different color. Cut out the 12 squares. Then make triangles by cutting 6 of the squares in half along a diagonal. Make rectangles by cutting the other 6 squares in half along a line through the middle.

Now arrange some of the pieces on the grid on *Math Masters,* page 211 to make a pattern. Follow the directions below. When you have completed a pattern, draw and color it on one of the 3 by 3 grids below.

1. Make 1 or 2 patterns having 4 lines of symmetry.
   Answers vary.
2. Make 1 or 2 patterns having 2 lines of symmetry.
   Answers vary.
3. Make 1 or 2 patterns having no lines of symmetry.
   Answers vary.

PROJECT MASTER

✦ *Math Masters,* p. 209

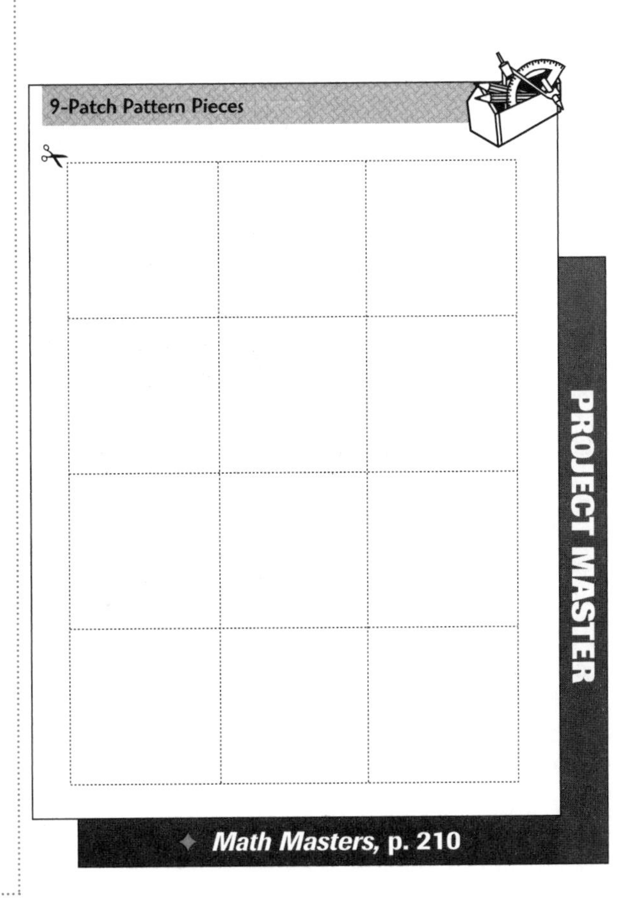

9-Patch Pattern Pieces

PROJECT MASTER

✦ *Math Masters,* p. 210

9-Patch Grid

PROJECT MASTER

Math Masters, p. 211

Looking at Rotations of Patterns
(*Math Masters,* p. 212)

WHOLE-CLASS ACTIVITY

Briefly review rotations. Ask students to place a closed journal or other book on their desks. Then have them rotate it through various turns, for example:

- ▷ clockwise $\frac{1}{2}$ turn,
- ▷ counterclockwise $\frac{1}{2}$ turn,
- ▷ clockwise $\frac{1}{4}$ turn, and so on, as needed.

Finally, go over *Math Masters,* page 212 with the class. You may want to use an overhead transparency of the master.

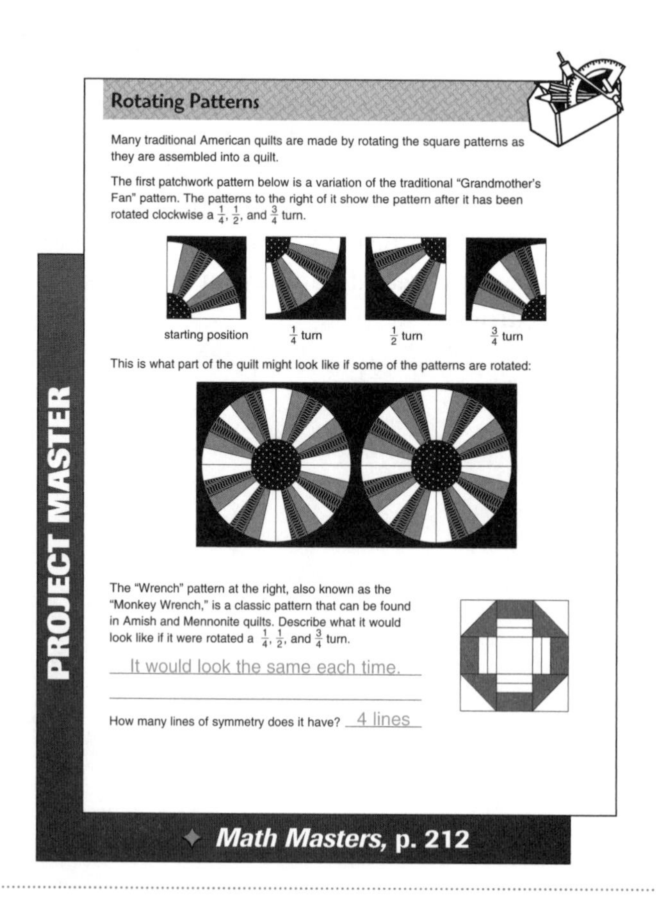
Rotating Patterns

Many traditional American quilts are made by rotating the square patterns as they are assembled into a quilt.

The first patchwork pattern below is a variation of the traditional "Grandmother's Fan" pattern. The patterns to the right of it show the pattern after it has been rotated clockwise a $\frac{1}{4}$, $\frac{1}{2}$, and $\frac{3}{4}$ turn.

starting position | $\frac{1}{4}$ turn | $\frac{1}{2}$ turn | $\frac{3}{4}$ turn

This is what part of the quilt might look like if some of the patterns are rotated:

The "Wrench" pattern at the right, also known as the "Monkey Wrench," is a classic pattern that can be found in Amish and Mennonite quilts. Describe what it would look like if it were rotated a $\frac{1}{4}$, $\frac{1}{2}$, and $\frac{3}{4}$ turn.

It would look the same each time.

How many lines of symmetry does it have? 4 lines

PROJECT MASTER

Math Masters, p. 212

DAYS 3 AND 4

✦ Making a Paper Patchwork Quilt
(*Math Masters,* pp. 213–216)

SMALL-GROUP ACTIVITY

Ask students to examine the traditional 9-Patch Patterns on *Math Masters,* page 213. Like the patterns students created previously, each of these patterns is based on a grid of nine squares. Ask students to speculate about the origin of some of the names, to comment on similarities and differences between the patterns, and to identify the lines of symmetry in each pattern.

Divide the class into groups of three and tell students that they are going to make a patchwork quilt out of paper. Go over the directions for making the quilt on *Math Masters,* page 214. Emphasize these requirements:

▷ The pattern a group chooses may not have more than two lines of symmetry.

▷ When the group assembles the quilt, at least one of the patches must have been rotated through a $\frac{1}{4}$, $\frac{1}{2}$, or $\frac{3}{4}$ turn.

Then students proceed as follows:

1. Each student cuts out the 3-by-3 grid of squares, including the border with the dots, from three copies of *Math Masters,* page 216.

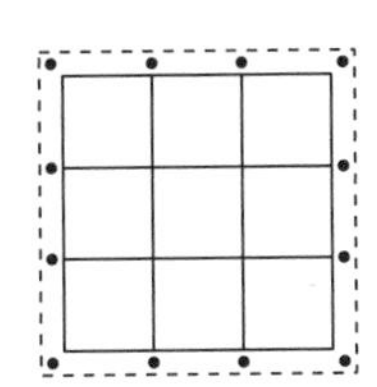

2. Each student cuts out the pieces on *Math Masters,* page 215.
3. Each group chooses one of the patterns on *Math Masters,* page 213. They decide on a coloring scheme.

Making a Quilt

As you study the traditional 9-Patch Patterns on this page, think about the following questions:

- Do you see where some of the patterns might have gotten their names?
- What are some similarities and differences among the patterns?
- How many lines of symmetry does each pattern have?

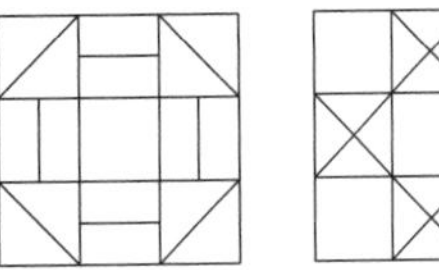
Churn Dash

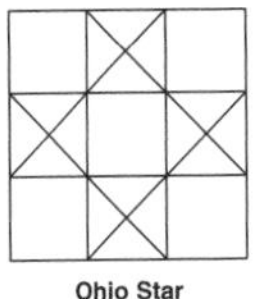
Ohio Star

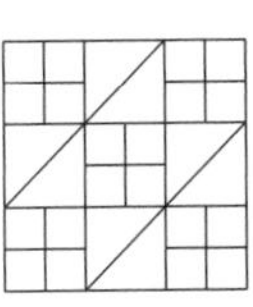
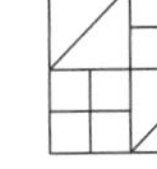
Jacob's Ladder

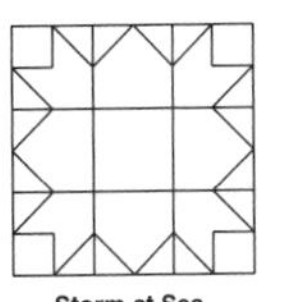
Storm at Sea

Weather Vane

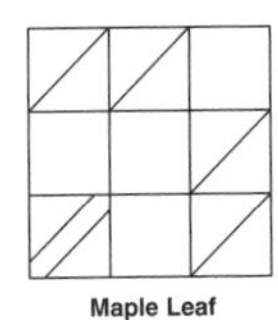
Maple Leaf

PROJECT MASTER

✦ *Math Masters,* p. 213

Making a Quilt (cont.)

Work with two partners to make a quilt.

1. Each of you needs three copies of *Math Masters,* page 216. Cut out the 3 by 3 grid on each sheet. **Make sure you include the border with the dots!**

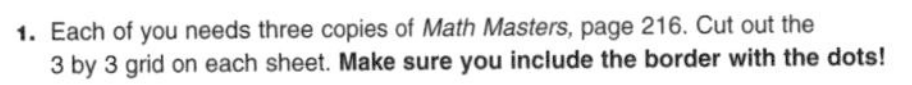

2. Cut out the quilting pattern shapes on *Math Masters,* page 215.
3. With your partners, choose one of the patterns on *Math Masters,* page 213. Decide on a way to color it. The colored pattern your group chooses **should not have more than two lines of symmetry.** Each group member should then copy this design onto three 3 by 3 grids. Use the pieces you cut out of *Math Masters,* page 215 to trace the pattern onto the 3 by 3 grids. Then color the pattern. Or you can trace the pieces onto colored paper, cut out the tracings, and paste them onto the 3 by 3 grids. Your group should end up with nine square "patches" that **look exactly alike.**
4. Punch holes through the dots along the border of the patches.
5. Lay all nine square patches on the floor and arrange them so that some of the square patterns are rotated. When your group has agreed on an arrangement, line up the holes on the edges of the squares. Then fasten the pieces together by weaving yarn in and out of the holes. If you wish, make a ruffle for your quilt out of a strip of crepe paper. Pleat and glue the ruffle around the outer edges of the quilt.

Here is an example of a quilt with the "Maple Leaf" pattern:

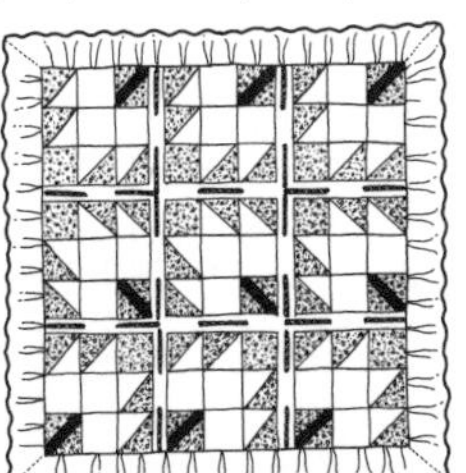

PROJECT MASTER

✦ *Math Masters,* p. 214

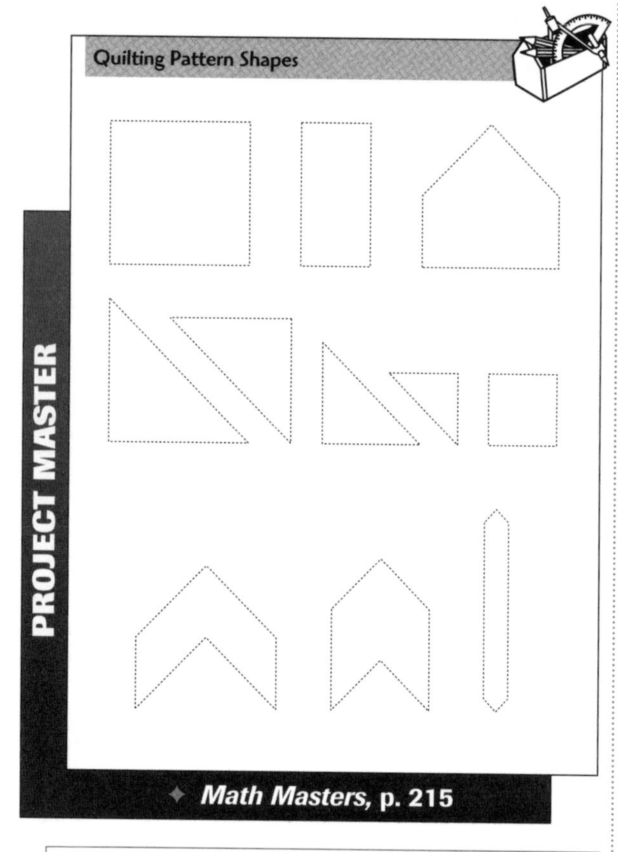

NOTE: Students are making a 9-Patch Pattern quilt, but this is by no means the only method of quilting. In the spirit of the traditional **quilting bee,** you may wish to serve refreshments after students have completed their quilts.

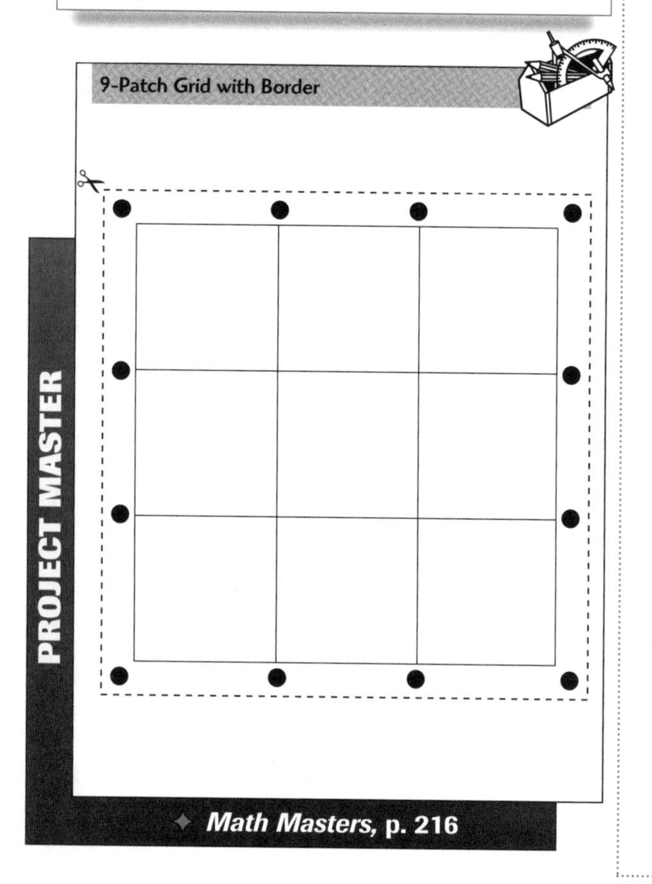

4. Each student then copies the agreed-upon pattern onto each of the 3-by-3 grids he or she cut out. The pieces cut out from *Math Masters,* page 215 can be used as templates to help in drawing the pattern.
5. Students color each pattern according to the agreed-upon coloring scheme. Alternatively, the pieces cut out from *Math Masters,* page 215 can be traced onto colored paper or wrapping paper. The tracings can be cut out and glued onto the 3-by-3 grid.
6. The students punch holes through each dot on the borders of the 3-by-3 grids. If you have access to a laminating machine, laminate the squares before students punch the holes. The quilts will look more finished and will last longer.

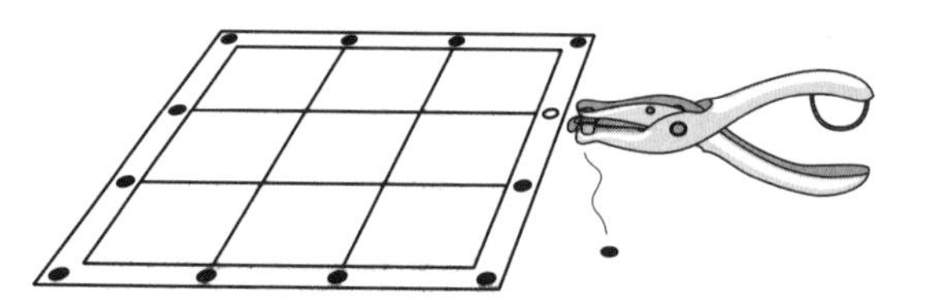

7. When all 3-by-3 "patches" have been completed, students in each group assemble them into a patchwork quilt. They lay the patterns on the floor and arrange them so that the borders of the squares overlap and the holes line up. Students use yarn to fasten the square patterns together by weaving the yarn in and out of the holes.
8. The quilt may be decorated with a ruffle made out of crepe paper. The crepe paper should be pleated and glued around the edges of the quilt.

Summarizing the Project

WHOLE-CLASS ACTIVITY

Ask each group to present its finished quilt to the class and describe how it was designed and put together. Students should point out lines of symmetry, reflections, and rotations in the pattern.

2 Extending the Project

Finding Out about Quilts

INDEPENDENT ACTIVITY 

Invite students to learn more about quilts by looking in encyclopedias and books such as *Eight Hands Round: A Patchwork Alphabet* by Ann Whitford Paul (New York: HarperCollins, 1996). This informative book speculates on the origins of the names of early American patchwork patterns for each letter in the alphabet.

PROJECT

5

Which Soft Drink Is the Best Buy?

OBJECTIVE **To calculate the unit price of various soft drinks and decide which is the best buy.**

background information

Recommended Use: During or after Unit 12

See the discussion of Projects in the Management Guide section of the *Teacher's Reference Manual.*

materials

- ☐ *Math Masters,* pp. 217 and 218
- ☐ labeled soft-drink cups
- ☐ measuring cup (fluid ounces)
- ☐ about 2 quarts or 2 liters of water or other pourable substance
- ☐ labels (optional)
- ☐ calculator

***See* Advance Preparation**

Project Information

Students collect soft-drink cups from local businesses and record the prices charged for the various sizes of soft drinks. They work in groups to determine which place offers the best soft-drink value. You may want to use this activity to assess how well students work in groups.

Advance Preparation A week or so before beginning the project, divide the class into groups of four or five. Each group is responsible for collecting soft-drink cups of various sizes (small, medium, large) from local businesses (restaurants, fast-food franchises, movie theaters, sports events, concerts, carnivals, and so on)—preferably three different sizes from each of three different places, per group. Students should rinse out each cup and label it with its source and price. You might want to collect cups yourself, for students who need additional cups. Since it is difficult to write on the waxed surface of some cups, you might want to give each group a set of stick-on labels on which to write the information.

Gather enough measuring cups so that each group has a cup. Each group will also need about 2 liters or 2 quarts of water or other pourable substance, such as sand, navy or lima beans, or unpopped popcorn.

Vocabulary • **capacity**

1 Doing the Project

✦ Introducing the Soft-Drink Project

WHOLE-CLASS DISCUSSION

Ask students to share the experiences they had buying soft drinks in various sizes at fast-food restaurants, movie theaters, sports events, concerts, carnivals, and so on.

Then ask students for suggestions for deciding which places and which sizes of soft-drink cups offer the best value.

- How can you use the information you have recorded to make this determination?
- What other information do you need?
- How would you gather this information?

✦ Carrying Out the Project (*Math Masters,* pp. 217 and 218)

SMALL-GROUP ACTIVITY 

These groups can be the same as those that collected the cups. Give each group a measuring cup and enough water or other pourable substance to carry out the investigation. (If possible, each group should work with three sets of three different-sized cups, each set from a different business.)

Students find out how much each container conveniently holds (not filled to the brim). They should round the **capacity** to the nearest fluid ounce. When calculating the price per ounce, ask them to round the answer to the nearest tenth of a cent. Then have students record all information on *Math Masters,* page 217.

After students have finished collecting the data and calculating the unit prices, have each group use *Math Masters,* page 218 to prepare a report describing the data collected and the conclusions drawn from the data. The report might include tables and pictorial representations of the data (for example, bar graphs).

ONGOING ASSESSMENT

You might want to use this project to assess students' ability to work in groups.

▷ **Do all students take part in group discussions?**

▷ **What is the level of the mathematics language used by students (for example, unit price, rate)?**

▷ **Do students stop after arriving at a simple answer, or do they investigate other possibilities?**

NOTE:

1 cup = 8 fluid ounces (fl oz)

1 pint = 2 cups = 16 fl oz

1 quart = 2 pints = 32 fl oz

1 gallon = 4 quarts = 128 fl oz

Which Soft Drink Would You Buy?

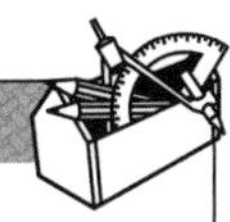

For each set of soft-drink cups, record the following information:

- The name of the place from which the cups come
- The size of the cup (small, medium, or large)
- The price
- The capacity in fluid ounces

Then calculate each unit price in cents per fluid ounce, rounded to the nearest tenth of a cent. Answers vary.

Soft-Drink Cups from

Size	Price	Capacity (fl oz)	Unit Price (¢/fl oz)

Soft-Drink Cups from

Size	Price	Capacity (fl oz)	Unit Price (¢/fl oz)

Soft-Drink Cups from

Size	Price	Capacity (fl oz)	Unit Price (¢/fl oz)

PROJECT MASTER

✦ *Math Masters,* **p. 217**

PROJECT MASTER

Consumer Report: Best Soft-Drink Prices

Imagine that you have been assigned by *Kids' Consumer Reports* to investigate and report on the prices of soft drinks. Use the information your group recorded on *Math Masters*, page 217 to prepare a group report for the magazine. Your report might contain graphs, tables, and pictures. Try to answer some of the following questions in your report:

- Do small (or medium or large) cups at different places contain the same amount?
- Are prices similar for similar sizes? (For example, are the small-size drinks about the same price at different places?)
- Which places have the least expensive soft drinks? The most expensive soft drinks?
- Is the largest size always the best value?
- Which types of businesses offer better values? (For example, do restaurants generally offer better values than movie theaters?)
- What would you recommend to consumers? Do some places offer free refills? If so, how would this affect your recommendation?

Answers vary.

(Continue on the back.)

✦ *Math Masters*, p. 218

✦ Discussing the Results
(*Math Masters*, pp. 217 and 218)

WHOLE-CLASS DISCUSSION 

Bring the groups together to present their reports. After all the reports have been heard, ask students what conclusions they can draw from their consumer survey. For example, ask: *Is getting the best value the only reason for choosing a particular size?*

ONGOING ASSESSMENT

If you use the group report as an assessment, you may want to develop a scoring rubric. Some things to look for are the clarity of the report, the use of graphs and tables, and the soundness of students' recommendations.

2 Extending the Project

✦ Looking at Consumer Magazines

INDEPENDENT ACTIVITY 

Invite students to look at *Zillions, Consumer Reports,* or other consumer magazines that may be available in the school or local library. Students might report on how measurements of various items are reported—such as dimensions, weight, capacity, and so on—and whether measurements or unit prices are used in determining best buys.

PROJECT

6

Building and Viewing Structures

OBJECTIVES **To build structures with cubes, given "blueprints" or side views of the structures; and to represent structures with diagrams.**

background information

Recommended Use: During or after Unit 11

See the discussion of Projects in the Management Guide section of the *Teacher's Reference Manual.*

materials

- ☐ *Math Masters,* pp. 219–221
- ☐ at least 25 cm cubes (or other size cubes)
- ☐ scissors

***See* Advance Preparation**

Project Information

Students build structures with cm cubes on a 4-by-4 grid. Each square in the grid can have 0, 1, or 2 cubes on it. The number of cubes to be placed on each grid square is specified by a number in the square. The numbered grid is called the "blueprint" for the structure. When students have built such a structure, they record what they see at eye level for two or more sides of the structure.

Students discover that each blueprint yields a unique structure and that the views of two *opposite* sides are reflections of each other.

Students then discover that the views of two *adjacent* sides may yield more than one structure, and they conclude that it is possible to build more than one structure from the same four views.

Advance Preparation This project can be done with cubes of any size, as long as students use cubes that are all the same size. If students use cubes other than cm cubes, you will need to make and distribute copies of a Blueprint Mat like the one on *Math Masters,* page 219. It should show squares that are the size of one face of the cubes being used.

Prepare four direction signs for a class demonstration and label them as follows:

↑BACK↑ ↑FRONT↑ ↑LEFT SIDE↑ ↑RIGHT SIDE↑

Arrange a table so that one student can sit at each of the four sides. There should be space on all sides of the table so that the rest of the class can gather around it. Place the direction signs and a copy of *Math Masters,* page 219 on the table.

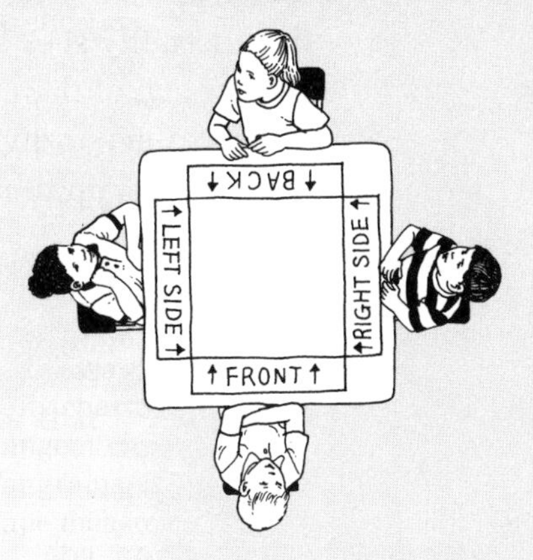

Vocabulary • **blueprint**

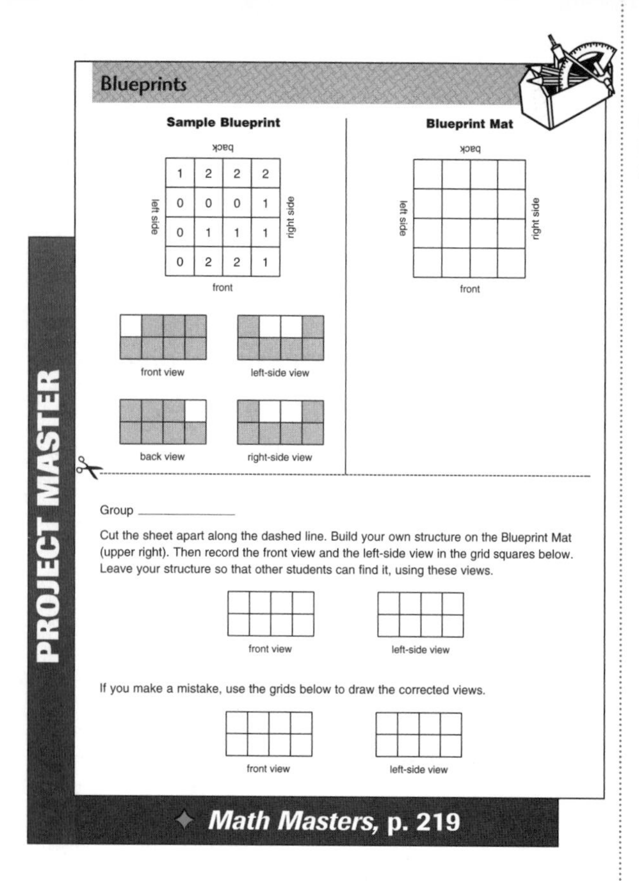
Blueprints

Sample Blueprint

back

1	2	2	2
0	0	0	1
0	1	1	1
0	2	2	1

left side / right side / front

front view; left-side view; back view; right-side view

Blueprint Mat

back; left side; right side; front

Group ________

Cut the sheet apart along the dashed line. Build your own structure on the Blueprint Mat (upper right). Then record the front view and the left-side view in the grid squares below. Leave your structure so that other students can find it, using these views.

front view; left-side view

If you make a mistake, use the grids below to draw the corrected views.

front view; left-side view

PROJECT MASTER

✦ *Math Masters,* p. 219

back

1	2	2	2
0	0	0	1
0	1	1	1
0	2	2	1

left side / right side / front

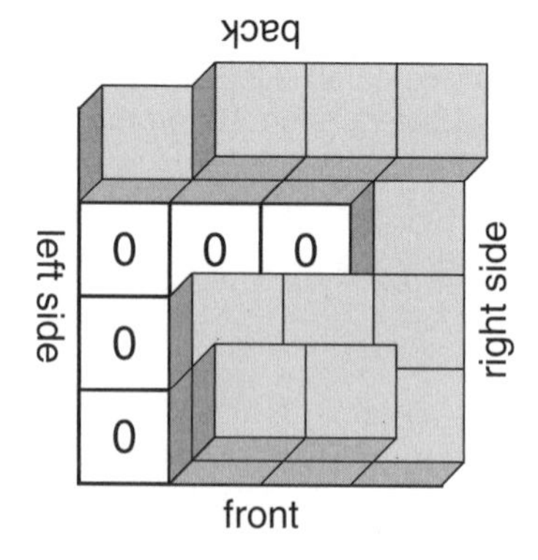

Building a structure on the blueprint

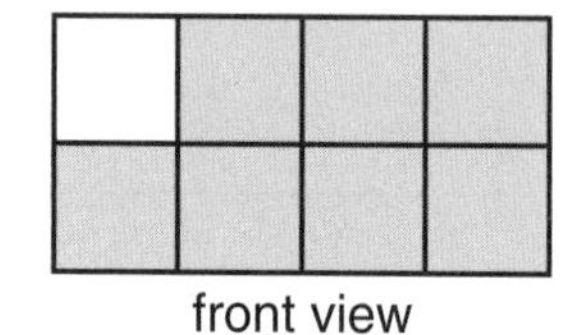

1 Doing the Project

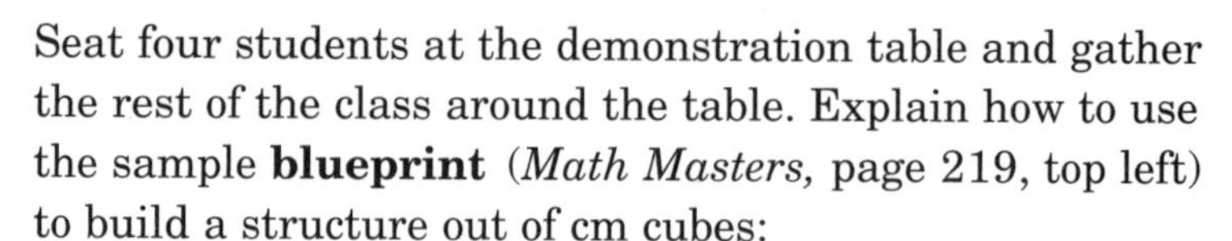

✦ Building a Structure and Recording Four Views of It (*Math Masters,* p. 219)

WHOLE-CLASS ACTIVITY

Seat four students at the demonstration table and gather the rest of the class around the table. Explain how to use the sample **blueprint** (*Math Masters,* page 219, top left) to build a structure out of cm cubes:

> The number in each square tells how many cubes to stack on the square: Stack 2 cubes on each 2-square, 1 cube on each 1-square, and no cubes on each 0-square.

After students have built the structure, have the student who is seated on the FRONT side of the blueprint stoop down so that the structure is at eye level. The student will then see the front view of the structure.

Ask the student to verify that this view of the structure looks like the shaded grid below the blueprint labeled "front view" (on *Math Masters,* page 219). Be sure to mention that the shaded squares do not show *only* what is in the *front* row of the structure. For example, the *front* row has *no* cubes in the first square on the left. Yet, since the last row has *one* cube in that position, the viewer sees *one* cube, not zero cubes. Similarly, the front row has one cube in the last square on the right. But since the back row has two cubes in that position, the viewer sees two cubes, not one cube.

Ask the other three students at the demonstration table to verify that the appropriate shaded grid below the blueprint (on *Math Masters,* page 219) represents what they actually see. Then ask them to change seats and verify each of the other three views. Let other students do the same, or divide the class into groups of four and ask each group to replicate the structure and verify the views.

✦Relating the Views of Opposite Sides
(*Math Masters,* pp. 219 and 220)

PARTNER ACTIVITY

Have partners share cubes. Students work on the tasks on *Math Masters,* page 220 independently and then compare each other's work. Have students follow the blueprint on *Math Masters,* page 220 but build it on the Blueprint Mat on *Math Masters,* page 219. Circulate and assist as needed.

Bring the class together to discuss the results. Ask questions like the following:

- Is it possible to build two different structures from the same blueprint? no
- How are the views of opposite sides alike? They have the same number of shaded squares.
- How do they differ? The shading pattern is reversed.

✦Building Structures Based on Two Views
(*Math Masters,* p. 219)

WHOLE-CLASS ACTIVITY

In this activity, each student builds a structure on the Blueprint Mat on *Math Masters,* page 219 (upper-right section of the page) and then draws the front and left-side views on two grids at the bottom of the page. Then students cut off the lower portion of the master and give it to you. Redistribute these sheets so that no student gets his or her own sheet. Students then walk around and try to find the structures recorded on their sheets.

There are a number of ways to organize this activity. Here is a suggested procedure:

1. Ask students to cut *Math Masters,* page 219 into two parts along the dashed line.
2. Divide the class in two groups—Group A and Group B. Ask students to write their group letter on the lower portion of the master.

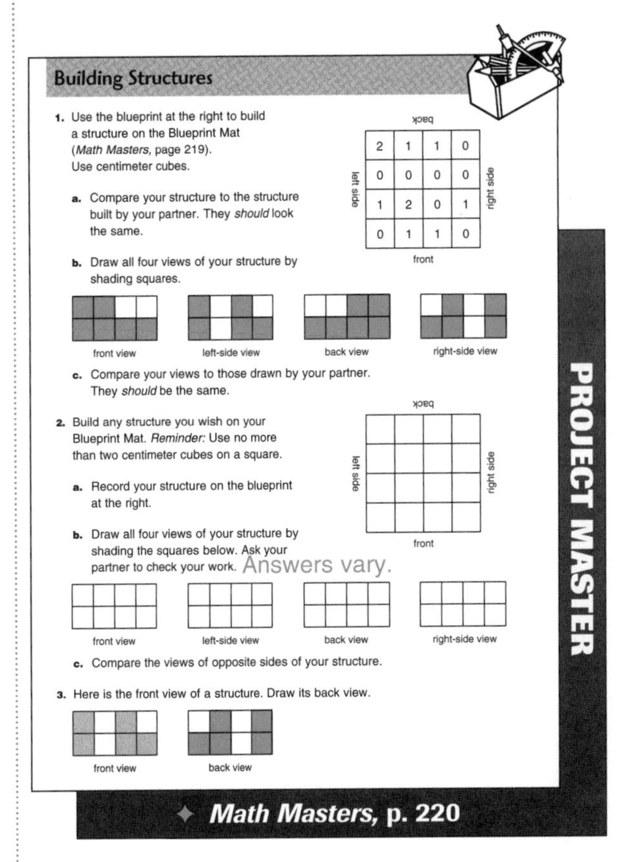

Building Structures

1. Use the blueprint at the right to build a structure on the Blueprint Mat (*Math Masters,* page 219). Use centimeter cubes.

back

2	1	1	0
0	0	0	0
1	2	0	1
0	1	1	0

left side / right side

front

a. Compare your structure to the structure built by your partner. They *should* look the same.

b. Draw all four views of your structure by shading squares.

front view / left-side view / back view / right-side view

c. Compare your views to those drawn by your partner. They *should* be the same.

2. Build any structure you wish on your Blueprint Mat. *Reminder:* Use no more than two centimeter cubes on a square.

back / left side / right side / front

a. Record your structure on the blueprint at the right.

b. Draw all four views of your structure by shading the squares below. Ask your partner to check your work. Answers vary.

front view / left-side view / back view / right-side view

c. Compare the views of opposite sides of your structure.

3. Here is the front view of a structure. Draw its back view.

front view / back view

PROJECT MASTER

✦ *Math Masters,* p. 220

3. Each student designs and builds a structure on the Blueprint Mat and draws the front and left-side views on the lower portion of *Math Masters,* page 219.
4. When students have completed Step 3, they raise their hands to signal that they are ready to have you check their work. (You may want to have more skilled students who finish early help you check.) If students made a mistake, have them correct their work on the second set of grids. Remind students that if there are drawings in the bottom grids, these are the correct ones.
5. After everyone's work has been checked, students hand in the lower portion of the master.
6. Pass out these sheets randomly—Group A's sheets to students in Group B and Group B's sheets to students in Group A. Students then walk about the classroom and try to identify the structures that match their sheets.

✦ Drawing a Structure (*Math Masters,* p. 221)

INDEPENDENT ACTIVITY 

Ask students to solve Problem 1 on *Math Masters,* page 221. Tell them to build the structure with their cubes if it will help.

Go over the answers. Remind students that the shading patterns for views of opposite sides are reversed. The back view should be the reverse of the front view, and the left-side view should be the reverse of the right-side view.

✦ Building Structures Specified by Views of Two Adjacent Sides (*Math Masters,* pp. 219 and 221)

PARTNER ACTIVITY 

In Problems 2 and 3 on *Math Masters,* page 221, students are given a front view and a left-side view of a structure. They build structures based on these views and make a blueprint for each structure.

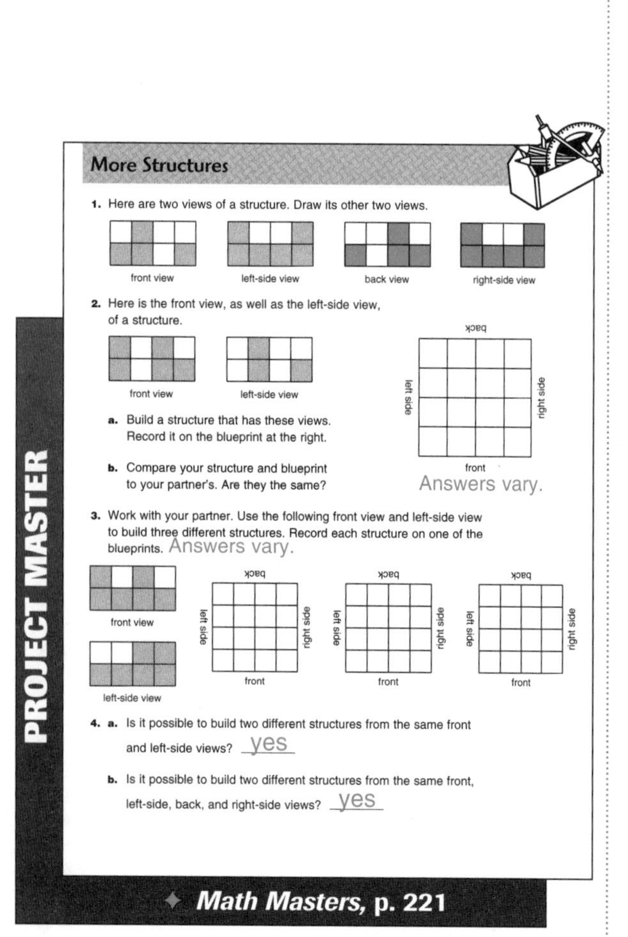

PROJECT MASTER

More Structures

1. Here are two views of a structure. Draw its other two views.

front view | left-side view | back view | right-side view

2. Here is the front view, as well as the left-side view, of a structure.

front view | left-side view

back | left side | right side | front

a. Build a structure that has these views. Record it on the blueprint at the right.

b. Compare your structure and blueprint to your partner's. Are they the same? Answers vary.

3. Work with your partner. Use the following front view and left-side view to build three different structures. Record each structure on one of the blueprints. Answers vary.

front view | left-side view

back | left side | right side | front

4. a. Is it possible to build two different structures from the same front and left-side views? yes

b. Is it possible to build two different structures from the same front, left-side, back, and right-side views? yes

✦ *Math Masters,* p. 221

From these activities, students should conclude that it is possible to build different structures from the same two adjacent views (Problem 4a). Furthermore, if students know two adjacent views, they can draw the other two views (see *Math Masters,* page 219). Therefore, it is usually possible to build different structures from the same four views (Problem 4b).

Extending the Project

✦ Building More Structures

INDEPENDENT ACTIVITY 

It is not always possible to build two different structures from the same two adjacent views, as shown in the following example:

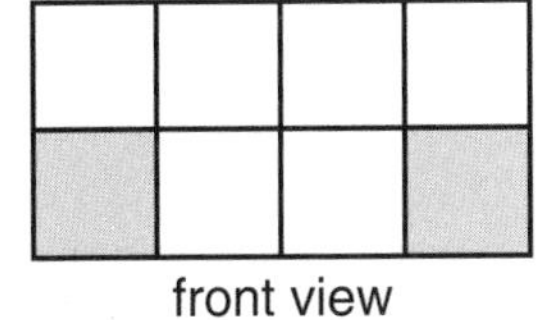

front view

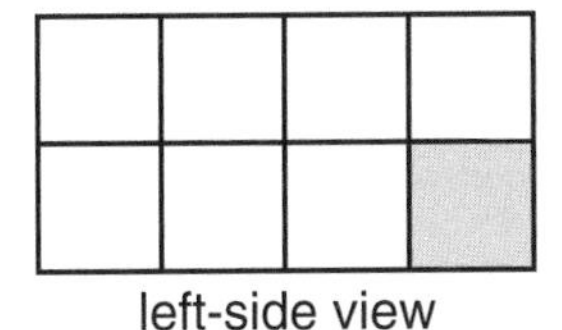

left-side view

Ask students to build the structure above and to try to find another, different structure that matches the blueprint. There is only one possible structure, shown in the following blueprint:

back (printed upside down); left side; right side

0	0	0	0
0	0	0	0
0	0	0	0
1	0	0	1

front

Answer to the optional activity:
There is only one possible structure,
as shown in this blueprint.

Invite students to build and represent structures with blueprint grids other than 4-by-4 (for example, 5-by-5, 4-by-6, and so on), and heights greater than two cubes.

PROJECT

Numbers, Maya Style

OBJECTIVES **To learn about the Maya numeration system; and to convert between Maya numerals and base-10 numerals.**

background information

Recommended Use: During or after Unit 10

See the discussion of Projects in the Management Guide section of the *Teacher's Reference Manual.*

materials

- ☐ *Math Masters,* p. 222

Project Information

Students learn about the Maya numeration system and how it compares to our place-value system. They work with partners to convert between Maya numerals and base-10 numerals.

PROJECT MASTER

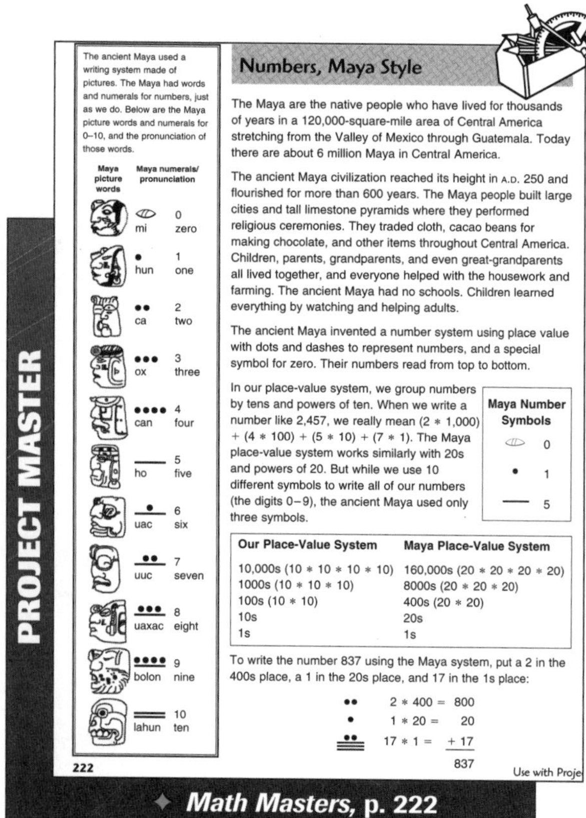

The ancient Maya used a writing system made of pictures. The Maya had words and numerals for numbers, just as we do. Below are the Maya picture words and numerals for 0–10, and the pronunciation of those words.

Maya picture words	Maya numerals/ pronunciation	
	mi	0 zero
	hun	1 one
	ca	2 two
	ox	3 three
	can	4 four
	ho	5 five
	uac	6 six
	uuc	7 seven
	uaxac	8 eight
	bolon	9 nine
	lahun	10 ten

Numbers, Maya Style

The Maya are the native people who have lived for thousands of years in a 120,000-square-mile area of Central America stretching from the Valley of Mexico through Guatemala. Today there are about 6 million Maya in Central America.

The ancient Maya civilization reached its height in A.D. 250 and flourished for more than 600 years. The Maya people built large cities and tall limestone pyramids where they performed religious ceremonies. They traded cloth, cacao beans for making chocolate, and other items throughout Central America. Children, parents, grandparents, and even great-grandparents all lived together, and everyone helped with the housework and farming. The ancient Maya had no schools. Children learned everything by watching and helping adults.

The ancient Maya invented a number system using place value with dots and dashes to represent numbers, and a special symbol for zero. Their numbers read from top to bottom.

In our place-value system, we group numbers by tens and powers of ten. When we write a number like 2,457, we really mean (2 * 1,000) + (4 * 100) + (5 * 10) + (7 * 1). The Maya place-value system works similarly with 20s and powers of 20. But while we use 10 different symbols to write all of our numbers (the digits 0–9), the ancient Maya used only three symbols.

Maya Number Symbols

Symbol	Value
(shell)	0
•	1
—	5

Our Place-Value System	Maya Place-Value System
10,000s (10 * 10 * 10 * 10)	160,000s (20 * 20 * 20 * 20)
1000s (10 * 10 * 10)	8000s (20 * 20 * 20)
100s (10 * 10)	400s (20 * 20)
10s	20s
1s	1s

To write the number 837 using the Maya system, put a 2 in the 400s place, a 1 in the 20s place, and 17 in the 1s place:

••	2 * 400 =	800
•	1 * 20 =	20
•• (3 bars)	17 * 1 =	+ 17
		837

222 Use with Proje

✦ *Math Masters,* p. 222

1 Doing the Project

✦Comparing the Maya Place-Value System to Our Place-Value System
(*Math Masters,* p. 222)

WHOLE-CLASS DISCUSSION

Have students read the article "Numbers, Maya Style" on *Math Masters,* page 222. Ask a volunteer to locate where the Maya lived on a classroom map or on page 237 of the World Tour section of the *Student Reference Book.*

Review our base-10 place-value numeration system. For example, in the numeral 2,457, the digit 2 stands for 2 [1,000s], the digit 4 for 4 [100s], and so on.

2 [1,000s] =	2,000
4 [100s] =	400
5 [10s] =	50
7 [1s] =	+ 7
	2,457

If necessary, try a few additional examples to make sure that students understand how our place-value system works before comparing it to the Maya system.

Next, discuss the Maya place-value system.

- How many symbols did the Maya use in their numerals? 3 What are the three symbols? How many symbols are used in our place-value system? 10

Refer to the example of the Maya numeral for 837 on *Math Masters,* page 222. Point out each of the "places." Remind students that Maya numerals read from top to bottom. Students should notice the space that is left between each place. If this space is not shown clearly, it is easy to mistake the place a symbol is in.

- Can there be more than one symbol in a place in the Maya system? Yes. In the Maya system, a single dot is one symbol. So two dots are two symbols in one place.
- Can there be more than one symbol in a place in our place-value system? no
- In a Maya numeral, how is the value of the symbols in a place determined? By adding the values of all the symbols in the place

Remind students that in our place-value system, the value of a place is 10 times the value of the preceding place. Thus the values of the first three places in a numeral for a whole number, from right to left, are 1, 10, and 10 * 10 (or 100). In the Maya system, the value of a place is 20 times the value of the preceding place. Thus the values of the first three places, from bottom to top, are 1, 20, and 20 * 20 (or 400).

- What is the value of the next (fourth) place in the Maya system? 20 * 20 * 20 = 8,000

Write each Maya numeral with digits. Then add.

1. 2,106

= 5 [400s] = 2000

= 5 [20s] = 100

= 6 [1s] = 6

2. 2,476

= 6 [400s] = 2400

= 3 [20s] = 60

= 16 [1s] = 16

3. 20,023

= 2 [8000s] = 16,000

= 10 [400s] = 4000

= 1 [20] = 20

= 3 [1s] = 3

Challenge

4. Write each base-10 numeral as a Maya numeral.

a. 153

b. 1,594

✦ Converting between Maya and Base-10 Numerals

WHOLE-CLASS ACTIVITY

Write the problem below on the board. Discuss how the Maya numeral in this problem is converted to a base-10 numeral. Then convert several more Maya numerals as a class. *For example:*

●●●	3 [400s] =	1,200
●●	2 [20s] =	40
●●●● (one bar)	9 [1s] =	+ 9
		1,249
●●●● (one bar)	9 [20s] =	180
●●●● (three bars)	19 [1s] =	+ 19
		199

You might also have students make up Maya numerals for the class to convert.

On the board, write Problems 1–4 shown in the margin. For Problems 1–3, have students write each Maya numeral with digits and then add. Go over the answers with the class.

For Problem 4, students will write each base-10 numeral as a Maya numeral. Conversions of base-10 numerals to Maya numerals involve division. Following are answers for Problem 4.

a. 153

How many [20s] are in 153?

$20\overline{)153}$, -140, 13 → 7

7 [20s] in 153

The remainder is 13.

13 [1s]

b. 1,594

How many [400s] are in 1,594?

$400\overline{)1594}$, -1200, 394 → 3

3 [400s] in 1594

How many [20s] are in 394?

$20\overline{)394}$, -380, 14 → 19

19 [20s] in 394

The remainder is 14.

14 [1s]

2 Extending the Project

✦ Learning More about the Maya

INDEPENDENT ACTIVITY 

Invite students to find out more about the Maya in encyclopedias and in books such as *Gods and Goddesses of the Ancient Maya* by Leonard Everett Fisher (Holiday House, 1999) and *Ancient Civilizations of the Aztecs and Maya: Chronicles from National Geographic,* edited by Arthur M. Schlesinger and Fred L. Israel (Chelsea, 1999).

NOTE: This would be a good opportunity to have students use the Internet to research and compare the Mayan numeral system with other numeral systems, e.g., the Roman or Babylonian numeral system (which uses a base of 60).

Hindu-Arabic	0	1	2	3	4	5	6	7	8	9	10
Babylonian		▾	▾▾	▾▾▾	▾▾▾▾	▾▾▾ ▾▾	▾▾▾ ▾▾▾	▾▾▾▾ ▾▾▾	▾▾▾▾ ▾▾▾▾	▾▾▾▾▾ ▾▾▾▾	<
Egyptian		|	||	|||	||||	||| ||	||| |||	|||| |||	|||| ||||	||| ||| |||	∩
Mayan	𝋠	•	••	•••	••••	—	• over —	•• over —	••• over —	•••• over —	=
Greek		α	β	Υ	δ	ϵ	ϕ	ζ	η	θ	ι
Roman		I	II	III	IV	V	VI	VII	VIII	IX	X

Students may also want to explore other base systems, such as base 5, which is used by people in Kenya. The chart below describes this "one-hand system."

Base-five Symbol	Base-five Grouping	One-hand System
0_{five}		0 fingers
1_{five}	x	1 finger
2_{five}	xx	2 fingers
3_{five}	xxx	3 fingers
4_{five}	xxxx	4 fingers
10_{five}	(xxxxx)	1 hand and 0 fingers
11_{five}	(xxxxx) x	1 hand and 1 finger
12_{five}	(xxxxx) xx	1 hand and 2 fingers
13_{five}	(xxxxx) xxx	1 hand and 3 fingers
14_{five}	(xxxxx) xxxx	1 hand and 4 fingers
20_{five}	(xxxxx)(xxxxx)	2 hands and 0 fingers

Fourth Grade Key Vocabulary

acute angle An angle with a measure greater than 0° and less than 90°. See *angle*.

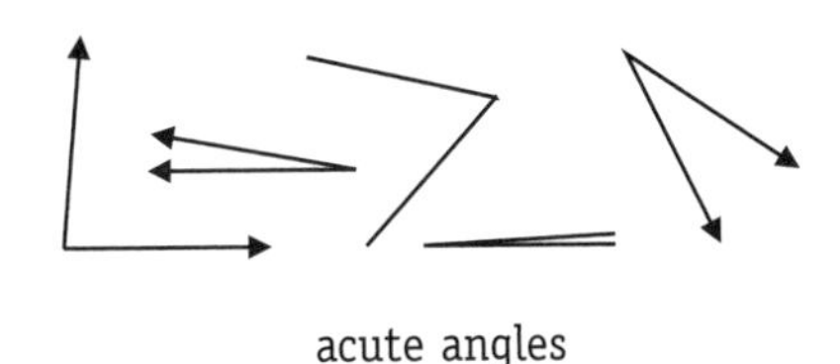

acute angles

algorithm A set of step-by-step instructions for doing something, such as carrying out a computation or solving a problem. The most common algorithms are those for carrying out basic arithmetic computations, but there are many others. Some mathematicians and many computer scientists spend much of their time trying to find more efficient algorithms for solving problems.

angle A figure that is formed by two rays or two line segments with a common endpoint. The common endpoint is called the *vertex* of the angle. The rays or segments are called the sides of the angle. An angle is measured by a number of degrees between 0 and 360, which can be thought of as the amount of rotation around the vertex from one side to the other. Angles can be represented by rotating one side while the other is kept stationary. Angles are named either by a single capital letter naming the vertex or by three letters, two naming points on the sides with the vertex letter between them.

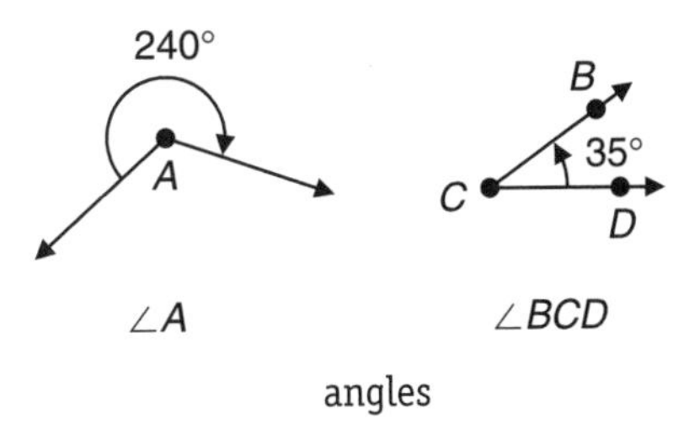

angles

area A measure of a bounded surface. The boundary might be a triangle or rectangle in a plane or the boundaries of a state or country on Earth's surface. Area is expressed in square units such as square miles, square inches, or square centimeters, and can be thought of as the approximate number of non-overlapping squares that will "tile" or "cover" the surface within the boundary.

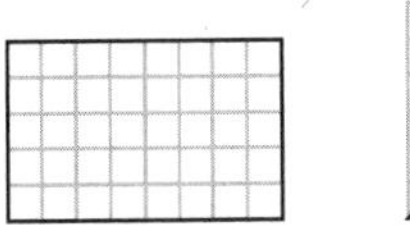
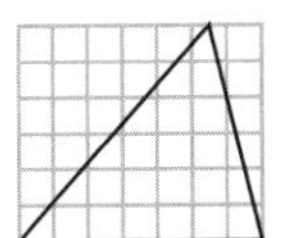

40 square units 21 square units

axis (1) Either of the two number lines used to form a coordinate grid. Plural *axes*.

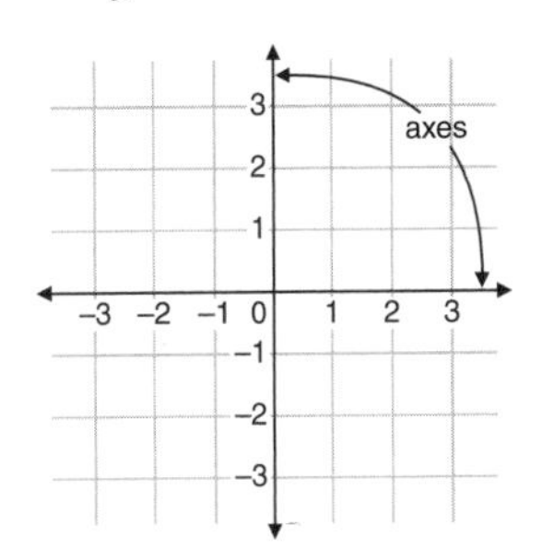

(2) A line about which a solid figure rotates.

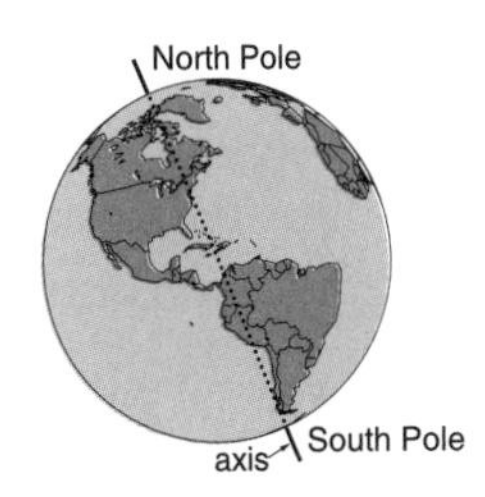

bar graph A graph that shows relationships in data by the use of bars to represent quantities.

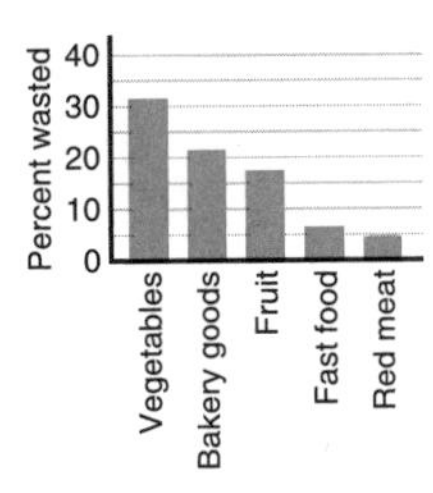

Source: *The Garbage Product*

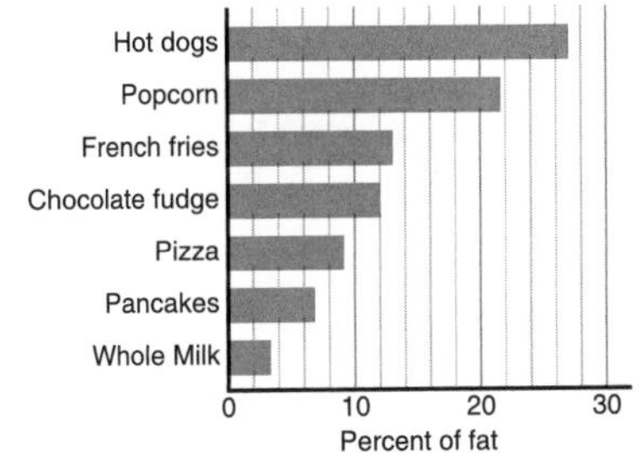

Source: *The New York Public Library Desk Reference*

base (1) Geometry: A side of a polygon usually used for area computations along with the "altitude," or height, perpendicular to it.

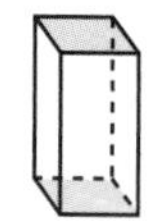 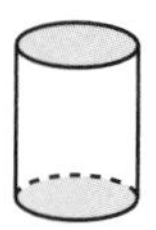  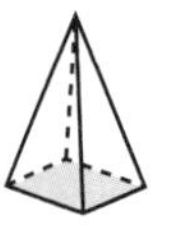

Bases are shown in blue, altitudes in grey.

(2) Geometry: Either of two parallel and congruent faces that define the shape of a prism or cylinder, or the face that defines the shape of a cone or pyramid.

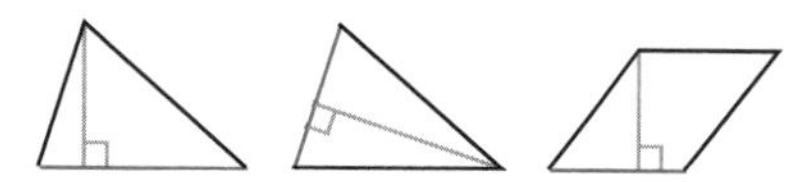

Bases are shown in blue.

(3) Arithmetic: See *exponential notation*.
(4) Arithmetic: The foundation number for a numeration system. For example, our ordinary system for writing numbers is a base-ten place-value system, with 1, 10, 100, 1,000 and other powers of 10 as the values of the places in whole numbers. In computers, bases of two, eight, or sixteen are usual, instead of base ten.

$$356 = 300 + 50 + 6$$

expanded notation for a base-ten number

baseline A set of data used for comparison with subsequent data. Baseline data can be used to judge whether an experimental intervention is successful.

billion In American usage, 1 billion is 1,000,000,000 or 10^9. In British, French, and German usage, 1 billion is 1,000,000,000,000 or 10^{12}.

center of a circle The point in the plane of a circle equally distant from all points on the circle.

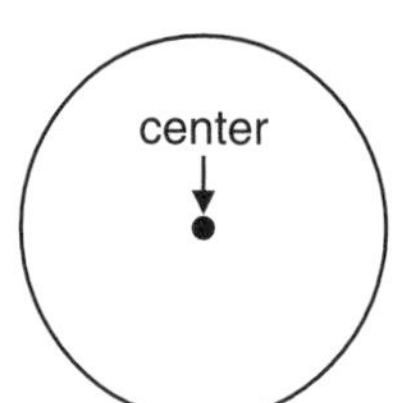

centimeter (cm) In the metric system, a unit of length equivalent to 10 millimeters, $\frac{1}{10}$ of a decimeter, and $\frac{1}{100}$ of a meter.

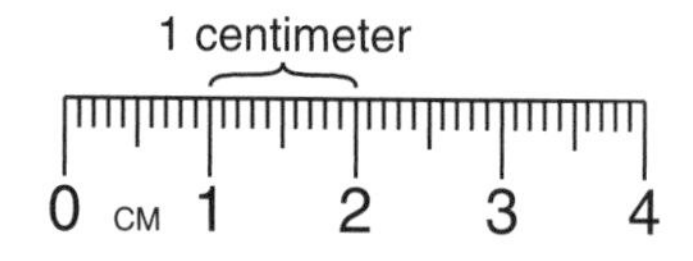

circle The set of all points in a plane that are equally distant from a given point in the plane called the *center* of the circle. The distance from the center to the circle is the *radius*. The circle is the boundary only. A circle together with its interior is called a *disk* or a *circular region*.

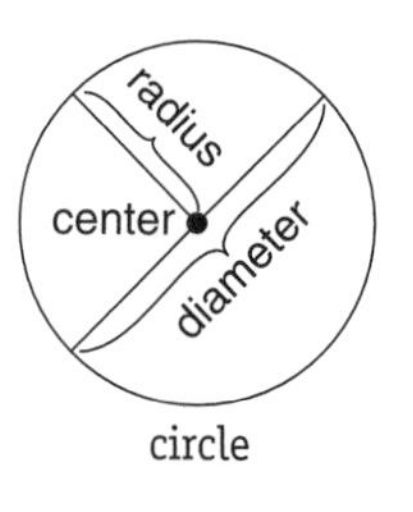

circle

circular region

clockwise A rotation in the same direction that the hands of a standard analog clock move; turning to the right.

column-addition method An addition procedure in which the addends' digits are first added in each place-value column separately, and then 10-for-1 trades are made until each column has only one digit. Lines may be drawn to separate the place-value columns.

compass (1) A tool used to draw circles and arcs and copy line segments. Certain geometric figures can be drawn using only a compass and a straightedge.
(2) A tool used to determine geographic direction.

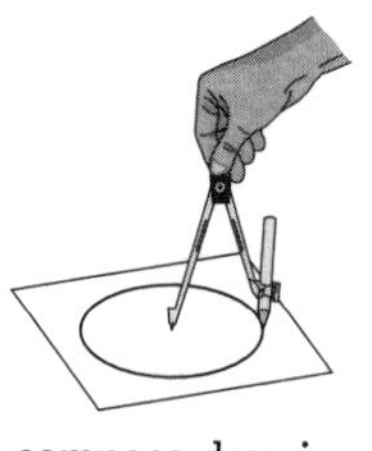

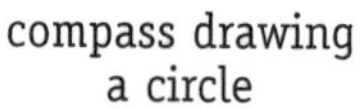

compass drawing a circle

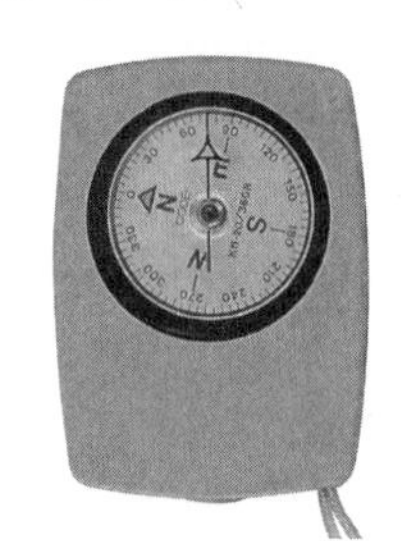

directional compass

concentric circles Circles that have the same center but radii of different lengths.

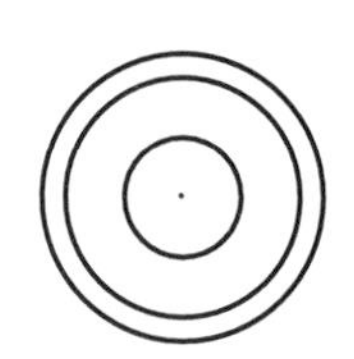

convex polygon A polygon in which all vertices are "pushed outward." A line segment connecting any two points on different sides of a convex polygon lies entirely within the polygon.

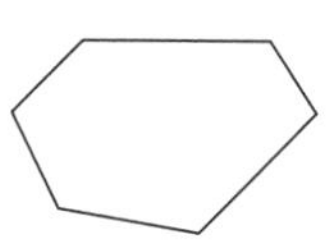

convex polyhedron A polyhedron that is everywhere "pushed out." Any line segment connecting any two points on different faces of a convex polyhedron is contained completely inside the polyhedron.

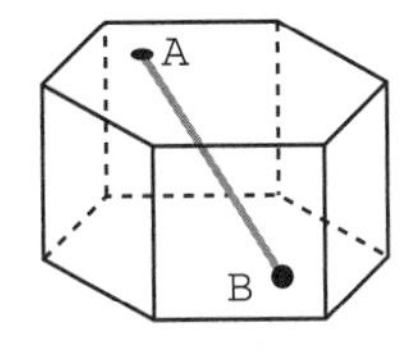

convex polyhedron

counterclockwise A rotation in the opposite direction as that of the hands of a standard analog clock; turning to the left.

counting numbers The numbers used to count things. The set of counting numbers is {1, 2, 3, 4, ...}. Sometimes 0 is included. Counting numbers are also in the set of whole numbers, the set of integers, the set of rational numbers, and the set of real numbers, but those sets also include numbers that are not counting numbers.

decimeter (dm) In the metric system, a unit of length equivalent to $\frac{1}{10}$ meter or 10 centimeters.

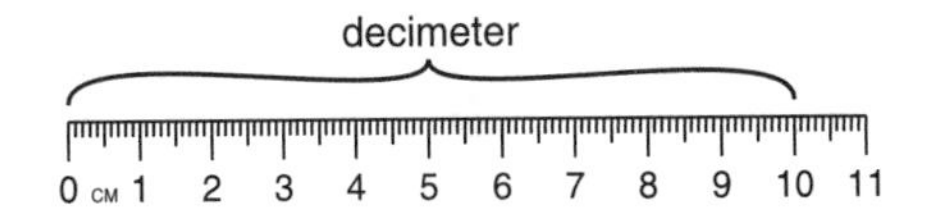

shown at 50% of actual size

degree (°) (1) A unit of measure for angles based on dividing one complete circle (rotation) into 360 equal parts.
(2) A unit for temperature on either the Celsius or Fahrenheit scale. The small, raised symbol ° is called the degree symbol.

denominator In a fraction, the number written below the line or to the right of the slash. In the fraction $\frac{a}{b}$ or *a*/*b*, *b* is the denominator. In a part-whole fraction, the denominator is the number of equal parts into which the whole (or ONE) has been divided. Compare to *numerator*.

dividend In division, the number that is being divided. For example, in 35 ÷ 5 = 7, the dividend is 35.

divisor
dividend → 35/5 = 7 ← quotient

quotient → 3
divisor → 12)36 ← dividend

divisor In division, the number that divides another number (the dividend). For example, in 35 ÷ 5 = 7, the divisor is 5.

divisor
dividend → 35/5 = 7 ← quotient

quotient → 3
divisor → 12)36 ← dividend

endpoint A point at the end of a line segment or ray. A line segment is named using the letter labels of its endpoints. "Segment *LT* or "segment *TL*" is the line segment between *L* and *T*. See *ray* and *line*.

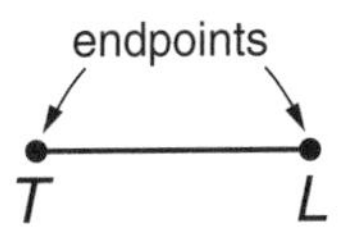

equal chance When none of the possible outcomes of an event is more likely to occur than any other, it is an equal-chance situation.

equal-groups notation A way to denote a number of equal-sized groups. The size of the groups is shown inside square brackets and the number of groups is written in front of the brackets. So, for example, 3 [6s] means 3 groups with 6 in each group. More generally, *n* [*b*s] means *n* groups with *b* in each group.

equator An imaginary circle around Earth halfway between the North Pole and the South Pole. The equator is the 0° line for latitude.
See *latitude*.

equilateral triangle A triangle in which all three sides are the same length and all three angles are the same measure. See *triangle*.

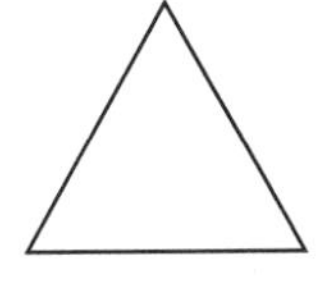
equilateral triangle

equivalent fractions Fractions that have different denominators but represent the same number.

equivalent names Different ways of naming the same number. For example: 2 + 6, 12 – 4, 100 – 92, 5 + 1 + 2, eight, VIII, and ~~////~~ /// are equivalent names for 8. See *name-collection box*.

estimate (1) A close, rather than exact, answer; an approximate answer to a computation; a number close to another number. (2) To make an estimate.

expected outcome The average outcome over a large number of repetitions of a random experiment. For example, the expected outcome of rolling one die is the average number of spots showing over a large number of rolls. Since each face of a fair die has equal probability, the expected outcome will be $(1 + 2 + 3 + 4 + 5 + 6) / 6 = 21 / 6 = 3\frac{1}{2}$. This means that the average of many rolls of a fair die will be about $3\frac{1}{2}$. (More formally, the expected outcome is defined as an average over infinitely many repetitions.)

exponent See *exponential notation*.

exponential notation A way of representing repeated multiplication by the same factor. For example, 2^3 is exponential notation for $2 * 2 * 2$. The small, raised 3, called the *exponent*, indicates how many times the number 2, called the *base*, is used as a *factor*.

$$2^3 = 2 * 2 * 2 = 8$$

$$4^5 = 4 * 4 * 4 * 4 * 4 = 1{,}024$$

extended fact A variation of a basic arithmetic fact involving multiples of 10, 100, and so on. For example, $30 + 70 = 100$, $40 \times 5 = 200$, and $560 \div 7 = 80$ are extended facts.

fact family A collection of related addition and subtraction facts, or multiplication and division facts, made from the same numbers.

For 5, 6, and 11, the addition/subtraction family consists of $5 + 6 = 11$, $6 + 5 = 11$, $11 - 5 = 6$, and $11 - 6 = 5$.

For 5, 7, and 35, the multiplication/division family consists of $5 \times 7 = 35$, $7 \times 5 = 35$, $35 \div 7 = 5$, and $35 \div 5 = 7$.

factor (1) A number being multiplied in a multiplication number model. In the number model $6 * 0.5 = 3$, 6 and 0.5 are factors and 3 is the product. (2) A whole number that can divide another whole number without a remainder. For example, 4 and 7 are both factors of 28 because 28 is divisible by both 4 and 7. (3) To represent a number as a product of factors. To factor 21, for example, is to write it as $7 * 3$.

fair Free from bias. Each of the six sides of a fair die should come up about equally often. Each section of a fair spinner should come up in proportion to its area. On a fair coin, heads and tails should come up about equally often.

formula A general rule for finding the value of something. A formula is often written symbolically using letters, called variables, to stand for the quantities involved. For example, a formula for distance traveled can be written as $d = s \times t$, where d stands for distance, s for speed, and t for time.

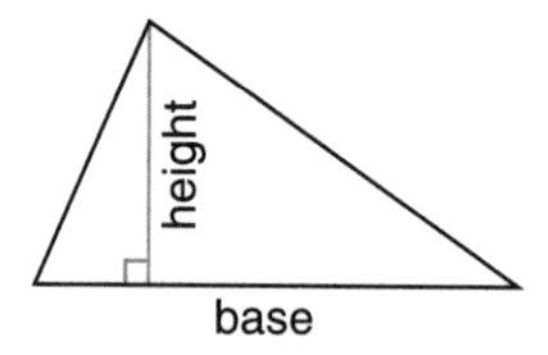

Area of triangle = 1/2 base × height

$A = 1/2\ b \times h$

grouping symbols Symbols such as parentheses ( ), brackets [ ], or braces { } that indicate the order in which operations in an expression are to be done. For example, in the expression $(3 + 4) \times [(8 + 2)/5]$, the operations within the grouping symbols are to be done first, beginning with the innermost grouping symbols and proceeding outward. Thus, the expression above first becomes $(3 + 4) \times [10/5]$, then 7×2, and then 14.

height A measure of how tall something is.

heptagon A 7-sided polygon.

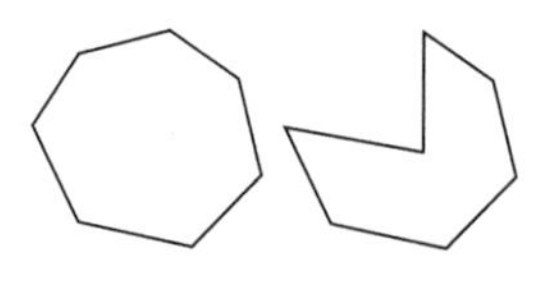

heptagons

hexagon A 6-sided polygon.

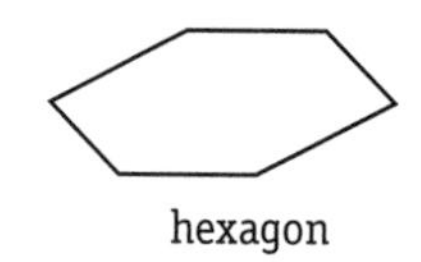

hexagon

index of locations A list of places together with a system for locating them on a map. For example, "Billings, D3," indicates that Billings can be found in the rectangle to the right of the letter D and above the number 3 on the borders of the map on page 919 .

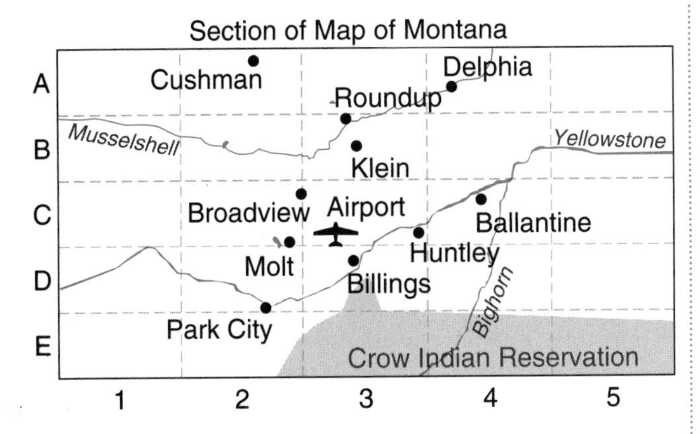

inscribed polygon A polygon all of whose vertices are points on a circle.

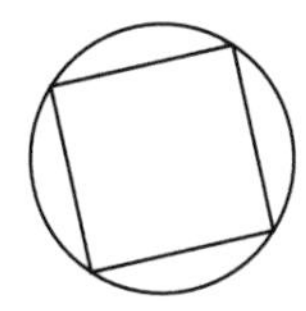

inscribed square

interest Money paid for the use of someone else's money. Interest is usually a percentage of the amount borrowed.

interior The set of all points in a plane "inside" a closed 2-dimensional figure, such as a polygon or circle. Also, the set of all points in space "inside" a closed 3-dimensional figure, such as a polyhedron or sphere. The interior is usually not considered to be part of the figure.

interior

intersect To share a common point or points.

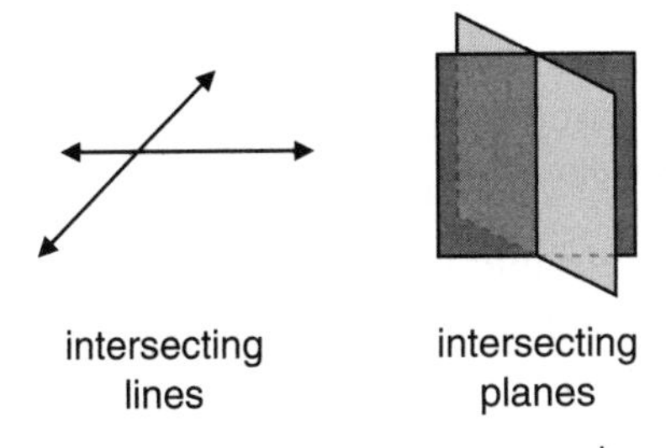

isosceles triangle A triangle with at least two sides that are the same length and at least two angles that are the same measure. See *triangle*.

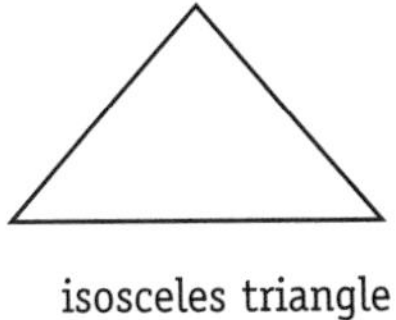

isosceles triangle

kite A quadrilateral with exactly two pairs of adjacent sides that are the same length. (A rhombus is not a kite.) Compare to *rhombus*.

landmark A notable feature of a data set. Landmarks include *median*, *mode*, *maximum*, *minimum*, and *range*.

latitude The angular distance of a point on Earth's surface, north or south from the equator, measured on the meridian of the point. See *latitude lines*. Compare to *longitude*.

latitude lines Lines of constant latitude drawn on a map or globe. Lines of latitude are used to indicate the location of a place with reference to the equator. Latitude is measured in degrees, from 0° to 90°, north or south of the equator. Lines of latitude are also called "parallels," because they are parallel to the equator and to each other. See *latitude*. Compare to *longitude lines*.

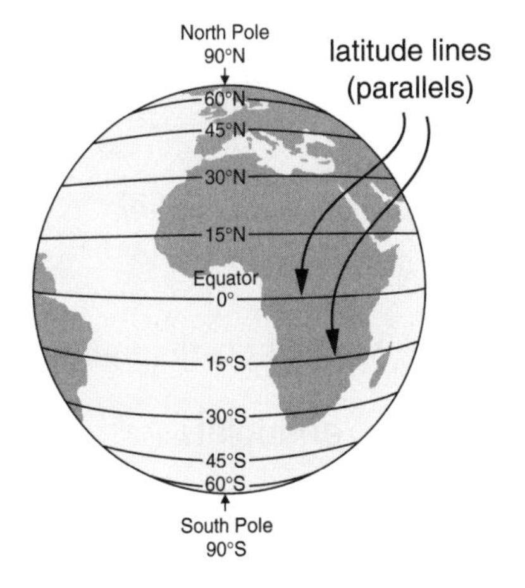

lattice method An algorithm for multiplying multidigit numbers. Lattice multiplication is a very old method, requiring little more than a knowledge of basic multiplication facts and the ability to add strings of 1-digit numbers. Once the lattice is drawn, the method is highly efficient and can be used to multiply very large numbers, including numbers too large to enter into most calculators. See lattice method example on page 920.

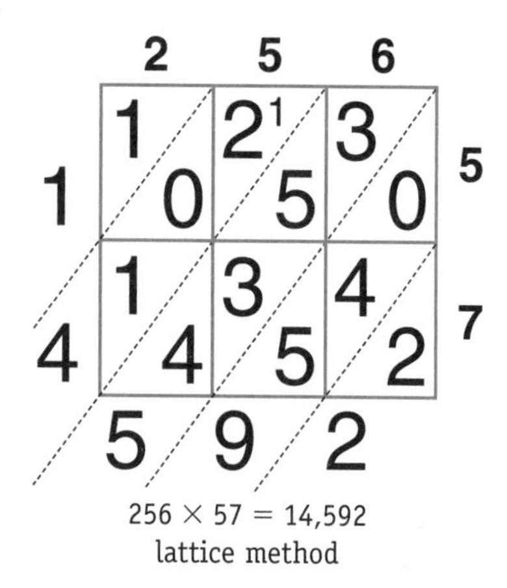

256 × 57 = 14,592
lattice method

length of a rectangle Usually, but not necessarily, the longer dimension of a rectangle or a rectangular object.

letter-number pair An ordered pair in which one of the coordinates is a letter. See *ordered pair*.

line A straight path that extends infinitely in opposite directions.

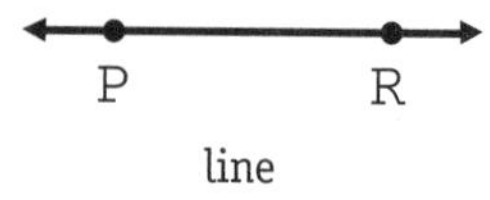

line

line plot A sketch of data in which check marks, Xs, or other symbols above a labeled line show the frequency of each value.

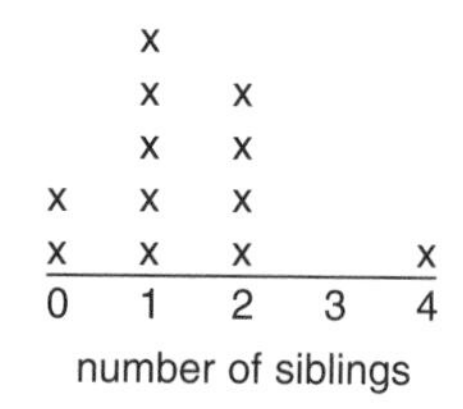

number of siblings

line segment A straight path joining two points,

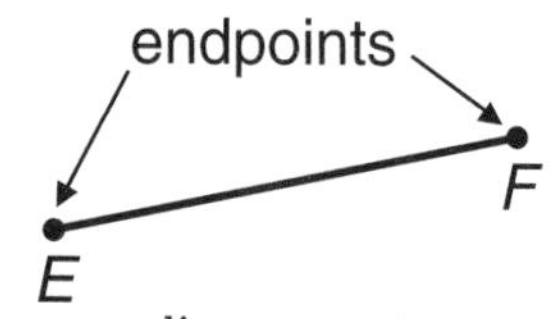

line segment

called the *endpoints* of the line segment.

logic grid A grid of rows and columns used to organize information in a problem.

	1	2	3
Sam	X	✓	X
Jon	✓	X	X
Sara	X	X	✓

logic grid

longitude A measure of how far east or west of the prime meridian a location on Earth is. Longitude is the measure, usually in degrees, of the angle formed by the plane containing the meridian of a particular place and the plane containing the *prime meridian*. Compare to *latitude*. See *longitude lines*.

longitude lines Lines of constant longitude; semicircles connecting the North and South Poles. Longitude lines are used to locate places with reference to the *prime meridian*. Lines of longitude are also called meridians. See *longitude*. Compare to *latitude lines*.

magnitude estimate A rough estimate of the size of a numerical result—whether it is in the 1s, 10s, 100s, 1,000s, and so on. In *Everyday Mathematics*, students are often asked to give magnitude estimates for problems like "How many dimes in $200?" or "How many halves are in 30?"

map scale A device for relating distances on a map to corresponding distances in the real world. One inch on a map, for example, might correspond to 1 mile in the real world. A map scale is often represented by a labeled line segment, similar to a ruler; by a ratio of distances (for example, $\frac{1}{63,360}$, when an inch represents a mile); or by an incorrect use of the = symbol (as in "1 inch = 1 mile").

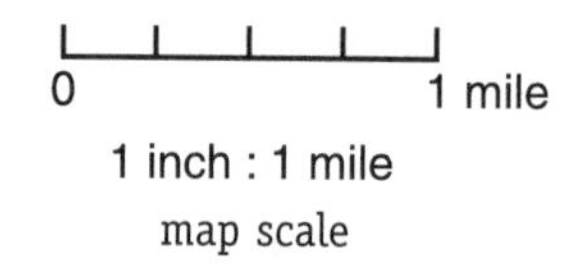

map scale

maximum The largest amount; the greatest number in a set of data. Compare to *minimum*.

mean A measure of central tendency. It is found by adding the numbers in the set and dividing the sum by the number of numbers. It is often referred to as the average. Compare to *median* and *mode*.

median The middle value in a set of data when the data are listed in order from least to greatest (or greatest to least). If there is an even number of data points, the median is the mean of the two middle values. The median is also known as the *middle value*. Compare to *mean* and *mode*.

meridian bar A device on a globe that shows degrees north and south of the equator.

meter (m) In the metric system, the fundamental unit of length from which other metric units of length are derived. Originally, the meter was defined as $\frac{1}{10,000,000}$ of the distance from the North Pole to the equator along a meridian passing through Paris. Today the meter is defined as the distance light travels in a vacuum in $\frac{1}{299,792,458}$ second. One meter is equal to 10 decimeters, 100 centimeters, and 1,000 millimeters.

millimeter (mm) In the metric system, a unit of length equivalent to $\frac{1}{10}$ of a centimeter or $\frac{1}{1,000}$ of a meter.

minimum The smallest amount; the smallest number in a set of data. Compare to *maximum*.

minuend The number that is reduced in subtraction. For example, in $19 - 5 = 14$, the minuend is 19.

mixed number A number that is written using both a whole number and a fraction. For example, $2\frac{1}{4}$ is a mixed number equal to $2 + \frac{1}{4}$.

mode The value or values that occur most often in a set of data. Compare to *mean* and *median*. In the data set 3, 4, 4, 4, 5, 5, 6, the mode is 4.

multiplication diagram A diagram used to represent numbers in which several equal groups are being considered together. The diagram has three parts: a number of groups, a number in each group, and a total number. Also called "multiplication/division diagram."

multiplication fact The product of two 1-digit numbers, such as $6 \times 7 = 42$.

***n*-gon** A polygon with n sides. For example, a 5-gon is a pentagon and an 8-gon is an octagon. Polygons with large numbers of sides are usually named only as n-gons such as 13-gon and 100-gon, and so on.

name-collection box In *Everyday Mathematics*, a box-like diagram tagged with a given number and used for collecting equivalent names for that number.

16
4^2
$\sqrt{256}$
$(4 + 6) * 6 - 4 * 11$
XVI

A typical name-collection box for 16—there are infinitely many possibilities

nonagon A 9-sided polygon.

number sentence A sentence made up of at least two numbers or expressions and a single relation symbol ($=, <, >, \neq, \leq$, or $\geq$). Number sentences usually contain at least one operation symbol. They may also have grouping symbols, such as parentheses. If a number sentence contains one or more variables, it is called an open sentence. See *open number sentence*.

$$5 + 5 = 10 \qquad a \times b \geq 16$$
$$(x + y)/2 - 4 < 20$$

number sentences

numerator In a fraction, the number written above the line or to the left of the slash. In a part-whole fraction, where the whole is divided into a number of equal parts, the numerator names the number of equal parts being considered. In the fraction $\frac{a}{b}$ or a/b, a is the numerator. Compare to *denominator*.

obtuse angle An angle measuring more than 90° and less than 180°. See *angle*.

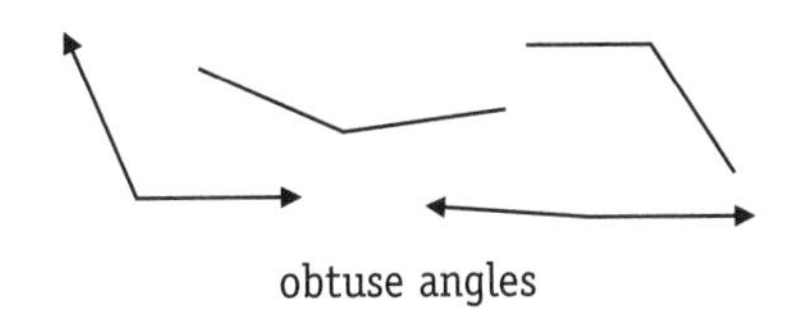

obtuse angles

octagon An 8-sided polygon.

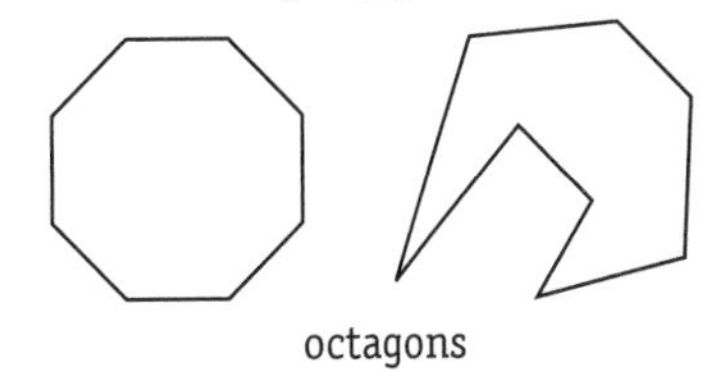

octagons

ONE In *Everyday Mathematics*, a way of denoting the unit whole in part-whole fractions and other similar situations. Same as *whole*.

open number sentence A number sentence which is neither true nor false because one or more variables hold the place of missing numbers. For example, the number sentences 9 + __ = 15 and __ − 24 $<$ 10 are open. As an introduction to algebra, *Everyday Mathematics* regards a ?, blank, or frame as a variable or "place holder."

9 + ? = 15   5 − __ ≥ 3

9 + ☐ = 15 $5 - x \geq 3$

open sentences

ordered pair 1) A pair of numbers used to locate a point on a coordinate grid. The first number corresponds to a position along the horizontal axis, and the second number corresponds to a position along the vertical axis. 2) Any pair of objects or numbers in a particular order.

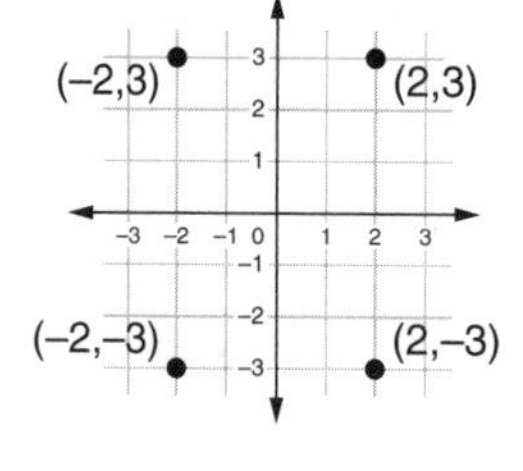

ordered pairs

parallel Lines, rays, line segments, and planes that are equidistant at all points, no matter how far extended.

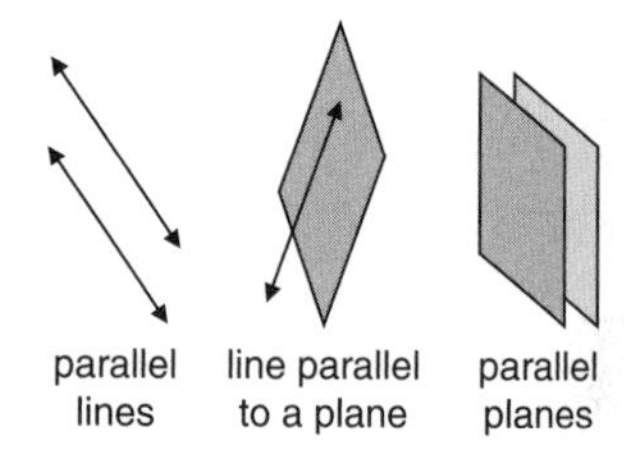

parallelogram A quadrilateral that has two pairs of parallel sides. All rectangles are parallelograms, but not all parallelograms are rectangles because parallelograms do not need to have right angles. See *rectangle.*

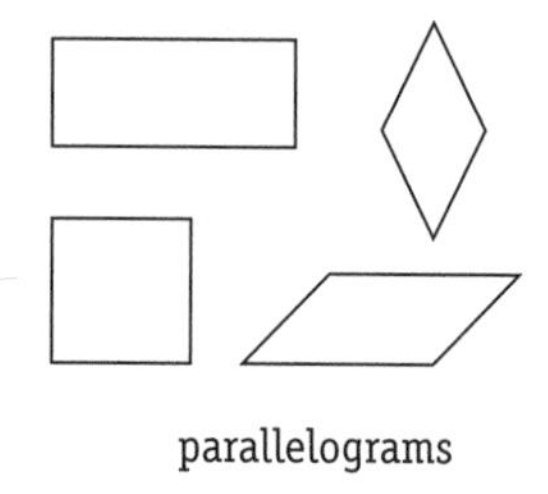
parallelograms

parentheses See *grouping symbols.*

partial-differences method A subtraction procedure in which differences are computed for each place separately and then added to yield the final answer.

	932
	– 356
Subtract 100s: 900 – 300 →	600
Subtract 10s: 30 – 50 →	– 20
Subtract 1s: 2 – 6 →	– 4
Add the partial differences → (600 – 20 – 4, done mentally)	576

partial-products method A way to multiply in which the value of each digit in one factor is multiplied by the value of each digit in the other factor.

	67
	× 53
50 × 60 →	3000
50 × 7 →	350
3 × 60 →	180
3 × 7 →	+ 21
	3551

partial-quotients method A division procedure in which the quotient is found in several steps. In each step, a partial quotient is found. The partial quotients are then added to find the final quotient.

22)400		
– 220	10	(10 [22s] in 400)
180		
– 110	5	(5 [22s] in 180)
70		
– 44	2	(2 [22s] in 70)
26		
– 22	1	(1 [22] in 26)
4	18	

400/22 → 18 R4

partial-sums method An addition procedure in which sums are computed for each place separately and then added to yield a final sum.

	268
	+ 483
1. Add 100s. 200 + 400 →	600
2. Adds 10s. 60 + 80 →	140
3. Add 1s. 8 + 3 →	+ 11
4. Add the partial sums. → (600 + 140 + 11)	751

pentagon A 5-sided polygon.

percent (%) Per hundred, or out of a hundred. 1% means $\frac{1}{100}$ or 0.01. For example, "48% of the students in the school are boys" means that out of every 100 students in the school, 48 are boys.

perimeter The distance around a closed plane figure or region. *Peri-* comes from the Greek word for "around," and *meter* comes from the Greek word for "measure"; perimeter means "around measure."

perpendicular Rays, lines, line segments, or planes that form right angles are perpendicular to each other.

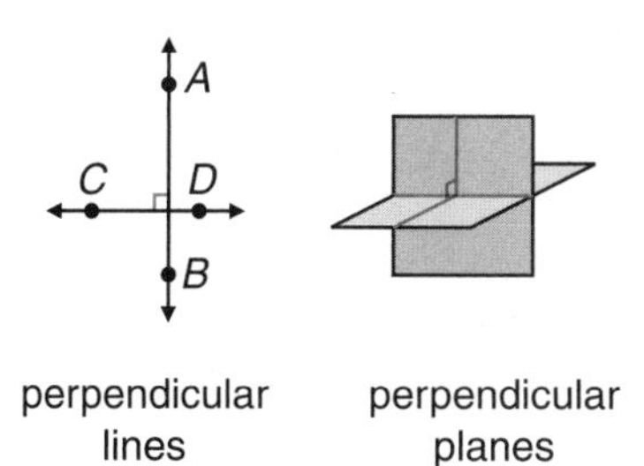

perpendicular lines   perpendicular planes

place value The relative worth of each digit in a number, which is determined by its position. Each place has a value ten times that of the place to its right and one-tenth of the value of the place to its left.

thousands	hundreds	tens	ones	tenths	hundredths

a place-value chart

point An exact location in space. Points are usually labeled with capital letters.

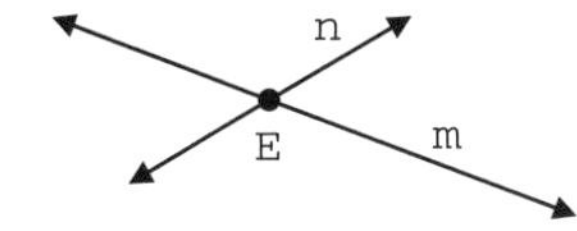

Lines *m* and *n* intersect at point *E*.

polygon A closed plane figure formed by three or more line segments that meet only at their endpoints. Exactly two segments meet at each corner of a polygon.

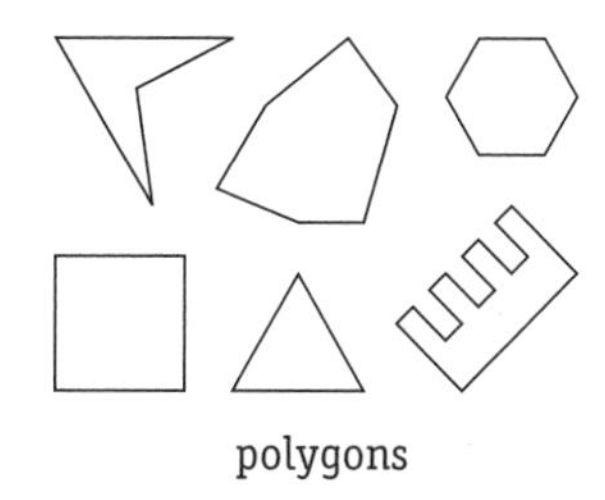

polygons

power of 10 (1) A whole number that can be written as a product using only 10 as a factor; also called a positive power of 10. For example, 100 is equal to $10 * 10$, or 10^2. 100 can also be called ten squared, the second power of 10, or 10 to the second power. (2) More generally, any number that can be written as a product using only 10s or $\frac{1}{10}$s as factors. For example, 0.01 is equal to $0.1 * 0.1$, or 10^{-2}. Other powers of 10 include $10^1 = 10$ and $10^0 = 1$.

prime meridian An imaginary semicircle on Earth, connecting the North Pole and South Pole through Greenwich, England. See *longitude* and *longitude lines.*

product The result of a multiplication. In the number model $4 \times 3 = 12$, the product is 12.

protractor A tool used for measuring or drawing angles. When measuring an angle, the vertex of the angle should be at the center of the protractor and one side aligned with the 0° mark. A half-circle protractor can be used to measure or draw angles up to 180°, a full-circle protractor to measure or draw angles up to 360°.

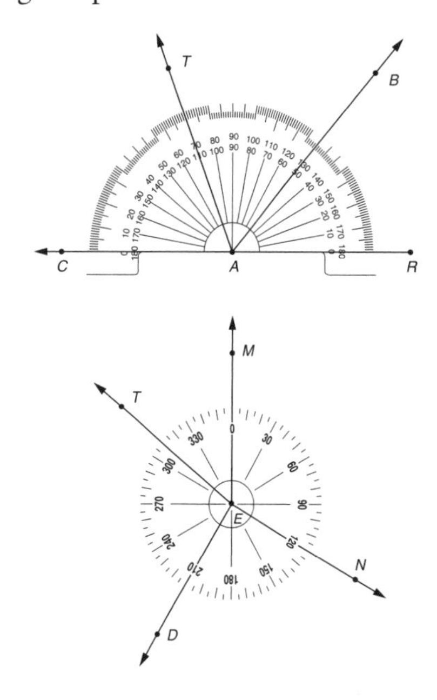

protractors

quadrangle Same as *quadrilateral.*

quadrilateral A 4-sided polygon. Same as *quadrangle.*

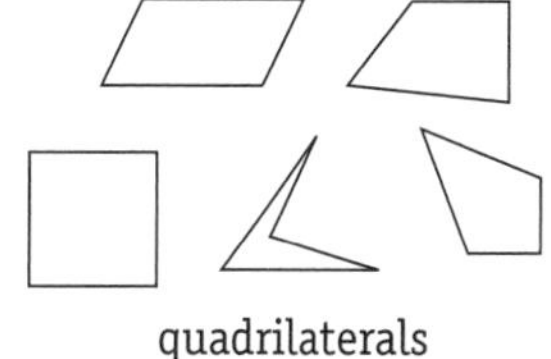

quadrilaterals

quotient The result of dividing one number by another number. In the division model $10 \div 5 = 2$, the quotient is 2.

divisor

dividend → $10 \div 5 = 2$ ← quotient

quotient → 3

divisor → $12\overline{)36}$ ← dividend

radius A line segment from the center of a circle (or sphere) to any point on the circle (or sphere); also, the length of such a line segment.

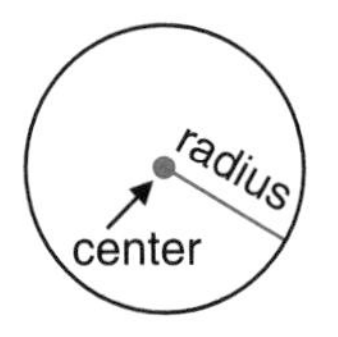

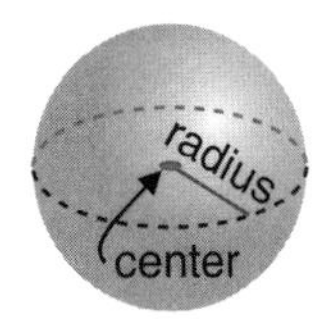

range The difference between the greatest and least values in a set of data.

ray A straight path that extends infinitely from a point, called its *endpoint*.

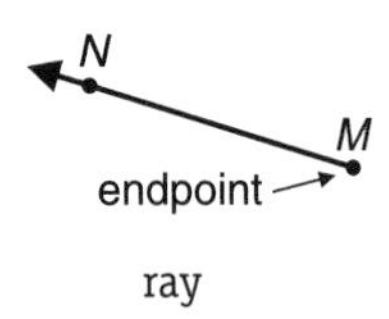

ray

rectangle A parallelogram whose angles are all right angles. See *parallelogram*.

reflex angle An angle with a measure between 180° and 360°. See *angle*.

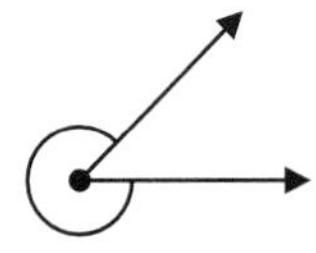

regular polygon A polygon whose sides are the same length and whose angles are all equal.

remainder An amount left over when one number is divided by another number. In the division number model $16 \div 3 \rightarrow 5$ R1, the remainder is 1.

rhombus A parallelogram with all sides the same length. The angles may be right angles, in which case the rhombus is a square.

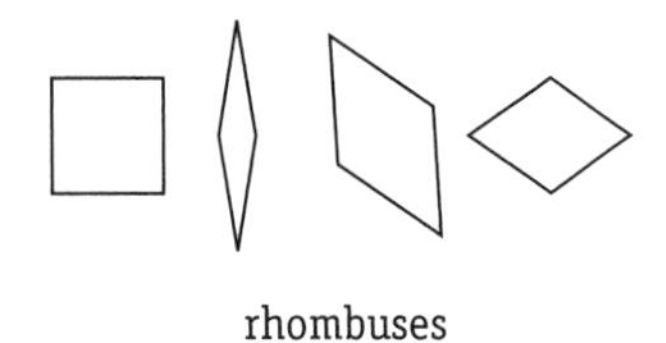
rhombuses

right angle An angle whose measure is 90°. See *angle*.

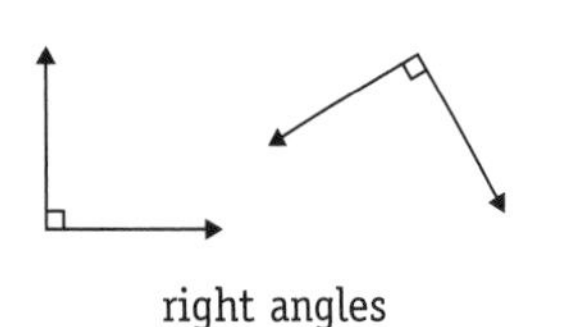
right angles

rotation A transformation that "turns" an object around a fixed point or axis. The point or axis, called the *center* or *axis of rotation*, can be inside or outside of the original image. Same as *turn*.

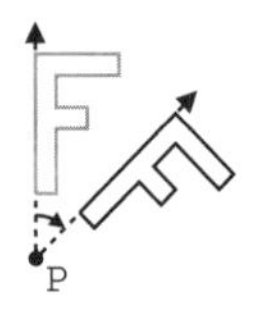

rotation

round (1) Arithmetic: To express a number in a simplified way. Examples of rounding include expressing a measure of weight to the nearest pound and expressing an amount of money to the nearest dollar. (2) Geometry: Circular in shape.

scale (1) The ratio of the distance on a map, globe, or drawing to the actual distance.

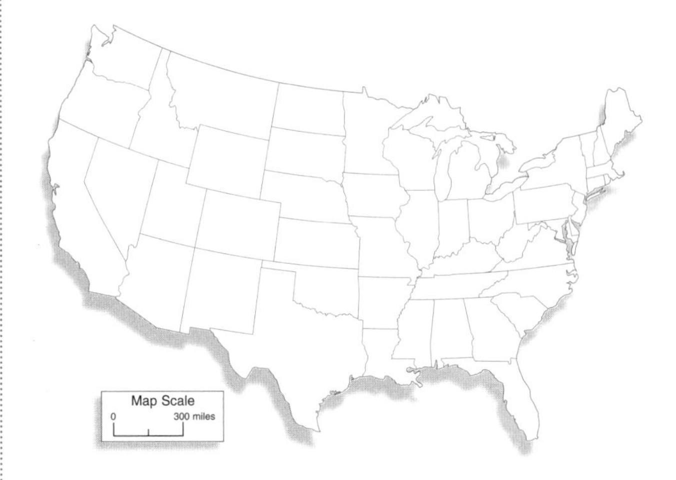

(2) A number line on a thermometer used for measuring temperature. (3) An instrument for measuring weight.

scale drawing A drawing that represents an object or area in fixed proportion to its actual size. The proportion is called the scale factor. For example, if an actual object measures 33 yards by 22 yards, a scale drawing of it might measure 33 centimeters by 22 centimeters, with all of the proportions between the drawing and the actual object being the same. A map is a scale drawing of a geographical region.

woodpecker (8 in.) shown in $\frac{1}{4}$ scale

scalene triangle A triangle with sides of three different lengths and angles of three different sizes. See *triangle*.

scientific notation A system for representing numbers in which a number is written as the product of a power of 10 and a number that is at least 1 and less than 10. Scientific notation allows writing big and small numbers with only a few symbols. For example, 4,300,000 in scientific notation is 4.3×10^6, and 0.00001 in scientific notation is 1×10^{-5}.

side Any of the line segments that make up a polygon. Sometimes a face of a 3-dimensional figure is called a side.

solution (1) Of an open sentence: A value or values for the variable(s) which make the sentence true. For example, the open sentence 4 + __ = 10 has the solution 6. See *open number sentence*. (2) Of a problem: The answer or the method by which the answer was obtained.

speed A rate that compares a distance traveled with the time taken to travel that distance.

sphere A 3-dimensional shape whose curved surface is, at all points, a given distance from its center point. A ball is shaped like a sphere. A sphere is hollow; it does not include the points in its interior.

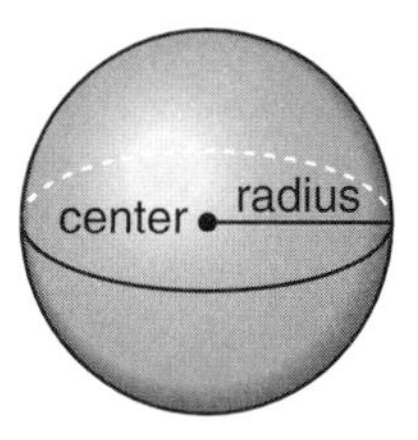

sphere

square A rectangle whose sides are all the same length.

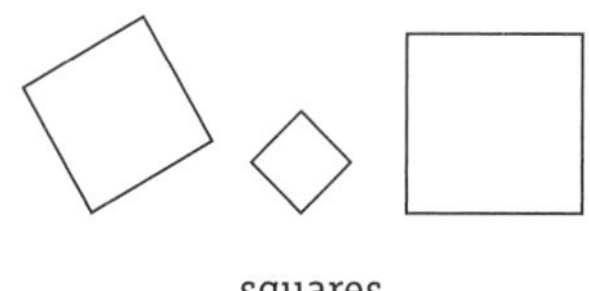
squares

square number A number that is the product of a whole number and itself; a whole number to the second power. For example, 25 is a square number, because 25 = 5 * 5. A square number can be represented by a square array.

square unit A unit used to measure area. A square unit represents a square with the measure of each side being a related unit of length. For example, a square inch is the area of a square that measures one inch on each side.

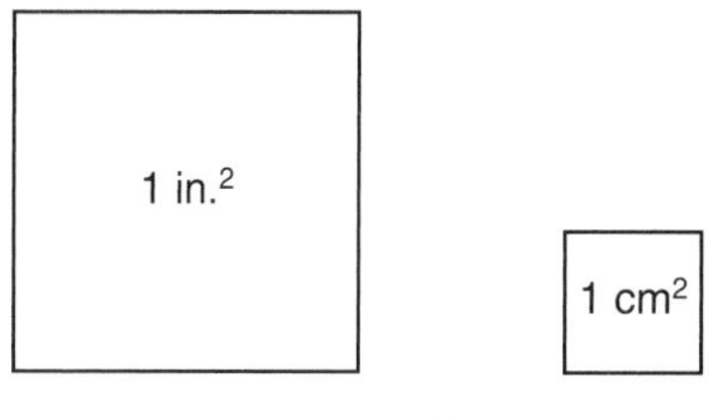

square units

straight angle An angle measuring 180°. See *angle*.

straight angle

subtrahend In subtraction, the number that is being taken away from another. For example, in 15 – 5 = 10, the subtrahend is 5.

tally chart A method for organizing data in a table in which tallies are made next to each value to show the frequency of that value in the data set.

trade-first method A subtraction procedure in which all necessary trades are done before any subtractions are carried out. Doing so simplifies the algorithm since the user can concentrate on one thing at a time.

	100s	10s	1s
	1	14	
	~~2~~	~~4~~	7
–		8	6
	1	6	1

trade-first method

trapezoid A quadrilateral that has exactly one pair of parallel sides. No two sides need be the same length.

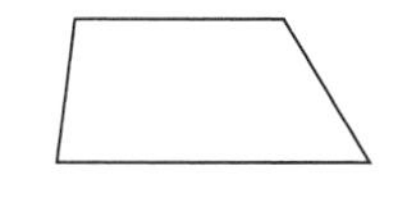

triangle A polygon with three sides and three angles. See *equilateral triangle*, *isosceles triangle* and *scalene triangle*.

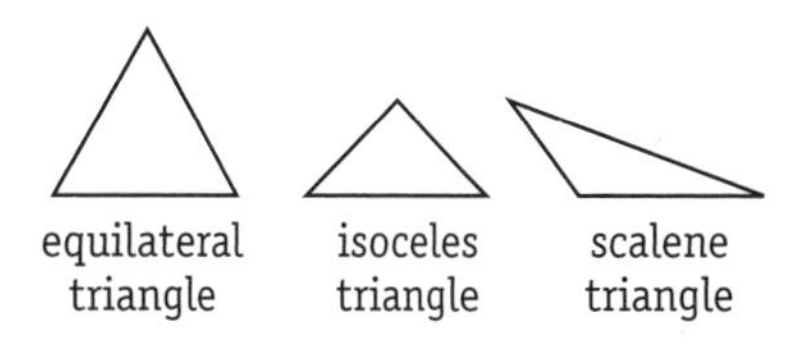
equilateral triangle   isoceles triangle   scalene triangle

turn An informal name for a rotation transformation. See *rotation.*

turn-around facts A pair of addition or multiplication (but not subtraction or division) facts in which the order of the addends or the factors is reversed. For example, $3 + 5 = 8$ and $5 + 3 = 8$ or $3 \times 9 = 27$ and $9 \times 3 = 27$. Turn-around facts illustrate the commutative properties of addition and multiplication. If a fact is known, its turn-around is also known.

unit A label, descriptive word, or unit of measure used to put a number in context. Using units with numbers reinforces the idea that numbers refer to something. Fingers, snowballs, miles, and cents are examples of units.

unit fraction A fraction whose numerator is 1. For example, $\frac{1}{2}$, $\frac{1}{3}$, $\frac{1}{8}$, $\frac{1}{12}$, and $\frac{1}{20}$ are all unit fractions.

variable A letter or other symbol that represents a number. A variable need not represent one specific number; it can stand for many different values. For example, in the expression $2x + 3y$, x and y are variables, and in the equation $a + 12 = 2b + 6$, a and b are variables.

vertex The point at which the rays or line segments of an angle, the sides of a polygon, or the edges of a polyhedron meet.

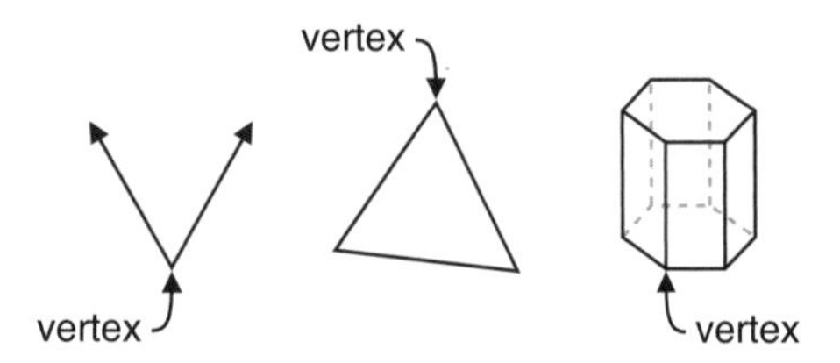

"What's My Rule?" In *Everyday Mathematics*, a routine that involves a set of number pairs in which the numbers in each pair are related to each other according to the same rule. "What's My Rule?" problems are usually displayed in table form in which two of the three parts (input, output, and rule) are known and the goal is to find the unknown part.

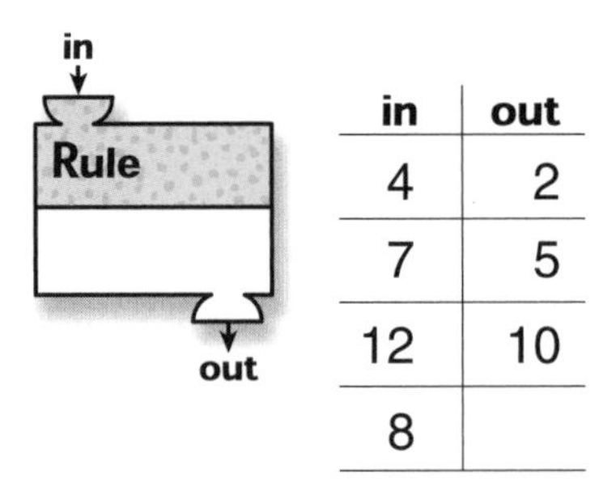

in	out
4	2
7	5
12	10
8	

"What's My Rule?" problem

whole The entire object, collection of objects, or quantity being considered; the unit, 100%. Same as the *ONE.*

whole number Any of the numbers 0, 1, 2, 3, 4, and so on.

width of a rectangle Length of one side of a rectangle or rectangular object, often the shorter side.

Scope and Sequence Chart

Throughout *Everyday Mathematics,* students repeatedly experience concepts and skills in each of the mathematical strands. Each exposure builds on and extends students' understanding. They study important concepts over consecutive years through a variety of formats. The Scope and Sequence Chart shows the units in which exposures occur and the developmental level of the skill or concept. The three levels of skill and concept development used in the chart are Beginning, Developing, and Secure. These levels refer here to unit content within the *K–6 Everyday Mathematics* curriculum rather than performance expectations for students.

The skills and concepts are divided according to the mathematical strands below.

Mathematical Strands

Mathematical Strands	Pages
Numeration	928–930
Operations and Computation	931–934
Patterns, Functions, and Algebra	935 and 936
Geometry	937–939
Measurement and Reference Frames: Measurement	940–943
Measurement and Reference Frames: Reference Frames	944
Data and Chance	945 and 946

How to Read the Scope and Sequence Chart

Each section of the chart includes a mathematical strand title, three grade level columns divided by units, and a list of specific skills and concepts grouped by major concepts.

Numeration

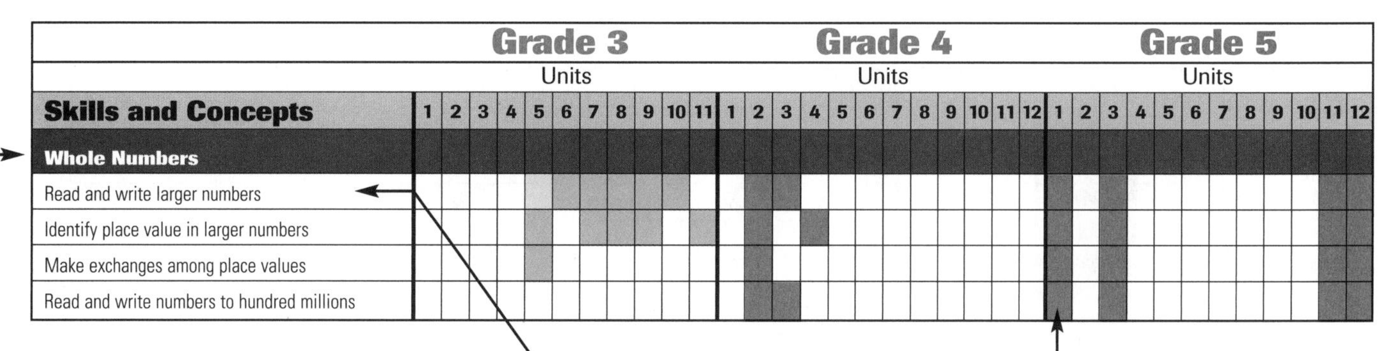

Major mathematical concepts within each strand. A list of related skills and concepts appears below this head.

Find specific skills and concepts in this list and then follow across the row for units in which they appear at each grade level.

The shading in the cells indicates the skill and concept development level for a particular exposure. The lightest shading shows beginning or beginning/developing exposures, the medium shading designates developing or developing/secure exposures, and the darkest shading indicates secure exposures.

Numeration

	Grade 3											Grade 4												Grade 5											
	Units											Units												Units											
Skills and Concepts	1	2	3	4	5	6	7	8	9	10	11	1	2	3	4	5	6	7	8	9	10	11	12	1	2	3	4	5	6	7	8	9	10	11	12
Whole Numbers																																			
Read and write numbers to millions																																			
Read and write numbers to hundred millions																																			
Read and write numbers to billions																																			
Explore numbers to trillions																																			
Identify place value in numbers to millions																																			
Identify place value in numbers to hundred millions																																			
Identify place value in numbers to billions																																			
Name the values of digits in numbers to hundred millions																																			
Name the values of digits in numbers to billions																																			
Make exchanges among place values																																			
Round whole numbers to a given place																																			
Compare larger numbers																																			
Find equivalent names for numbers																																			
Identify prime and composite numbers																																			
Find factors of numbers																																			
Find the prime factorization of numbers																																			
Find the least common multiple of two numbers																																			
Find the greatest common factor of two numbers																																			
Understand and apply powers of 10																																			
Use exponential notation to represent powers of 10																																			
Rename numbers written in exponential notation																																			

Whole Numbers (cont.)
Understand and apply scientific notation
Identify or investigate square numbers
Identify even and odd numbers
Money and Decimals
Use dollars-and-cents notation
Compare money amounts
Explore uses of decimals
Identify and name decimal numbers
Identify place value in decimals to hundredths or thousandths
Read and write decimals to thousandths
Model decimals with base-10 materials
Compare and order decimals
Relate decimals to metric measurement
Round decimals to a given place
Fractions
Identify fractional parts of a region
Identify fractional parts of a set
Find equivalent fractions
Compare and order fractions
Explore uses of fractions
Identify fractions on a number line
Identify and name mixed numbers
Convert between fractions and mixed numbers
Find common denominators
Rename fractions and mixed numbers in simplest form
Identify the whole for fractions

Beginning **Developing** **Secure**

Numeration (cont.)

	Grade 3 (Units)											Grade 4 (Units)												Grade 5 (Units)											
Skills and Concepts	1	2	3	4	5	6	7	8	9	10	11	1	2	3	4	5	6	7	8	9	10	11	12	1	2	3	4	5	6	7	8	9	10	11	12
Fractions (cont.)																																			
Find a fraction of a number																																			
Relate fractions and decimals																																			
Rename fractions as decimals																																			
Convert between fractions and decimals																																			
Convert between fractions, decimals, and percents																																			
Use a calculator to rename any fraction as a decimal or percent																																			
Positive and Negative Numbers (Integers)																																			
Explore uses for positive and negative numbers (integers)																																			
Compare and order positive and negative numbers																																			
Explore reference points for zero																																			
Ratio, Proportion, and Percent																																			
Use percents to describe real-life situations																																			
Find a percent of a number																																			
Estimate and calculate percent																																			
Find the whole, given a percent of the whole																																			
Convert between fractions, decimals, mixed numbers, and percents																																			

Operations and Computation

Skills and Concepts	Grade 3 Units											Grade 4 Units												Grade 5 Units											
	1	2	3	4	5	6	7	8	9	10	11	1	2	3	4	5	6	7	8	9	10	11	12	1	2	3	4	5	6	7	8	9	10	11	12
Addition and Subtraction																																			
Solve addition/subtraction number stories		S											S	S	S					S	S				S	S			S						
Add/subtract using a calculator	S	S								S			S		S															S					
Practice basic facts	S	S	S	S							S	S	S												S	S	S								
Practice extensions of basic facts		B	B									S	S												S	S	S								
Use mental arithmetic to add/subtract	S									S		S	S		S	S																			
Add/subtract multiples of 10		S										S	S			S																			
Add/subtract multiples of 100		D										S	S																						
Add/subtract 2-digit numbers	S	S											S	S											S										
Add 3 or more 2-digit numbers		D	D	D									S												S										
Add/subtract 3- and 4-digit numbers		S	S										S			S					S				S										
Add/subtract multidigit numbers													S			S				S			S		S	S									
Use column addition			D	D	D								D			D									S										
Use estimation to add/subtract	D	D	D			S					S			S	S	S		S								S									
Use addition/subtraction algorithms		D											S		S	S									S	S									
Add/subtract positive and negative numbers									B												B	B	B							D					
Addition and Subtraction with Decimals																																			
Add/subtract money amounts	D		D	D			D								D			D							D										
Add/subtract 1- or 2-digit decimals	D		D	D			D								D										S										
Add/subtract multidigit whole numbers and decimals															D										S										
Solve decimal addition/subtraction number stories															D										S										

Beginning (B) Developing (D) Secure (S)

Operations and Computation (cont.)

	Grade 3											Grade 4												Grade 5											
	Units											Units												Units											
Skills and Concepts	1	2	3	4	5	6	7	8	9	10	11	1	2	3	4	5	6	7	8	9	10	11	12	1	2	3	4	5	6	7	8	9	10	11	12
Addition and Subtraction with Fractions																																			
Add/subtract fractions with like denominators																																			
Find common denominators																																			
Add/subtract fractions with unlike denominators																																			
Solve fraction addition/subtraction number stories																																			
Use an algorithm to add/subtract mixed numbers with like denominators																																			
Estimate sums/differences of fractions																																			
Use an algorithm to add/subtract mixed numbers with unlike denominators																																			
Multiplication and Division																																			
Solve multiplication/division number stories																																			
Interpret a remainder in division problems																																			
Investigate properties of multiplication/division																																			
Practice multiplication/division facts																																			
Practice extended multiplication/division facts																																			
Model multiplication problems with arrays																																			
Investigate relationships between multiplication and division																																			
Multiply/divide with 2-digit numbers																																			
Use estimation to multiply/divide																																			
Make magnitude estimates for products																																			
Find the product of multidigit whole numbers																																			
Solve multiplication/division problems involving multiples of 10, 100, and 1,000																																			

Multiplication and Division (cont.)
Solve multidigit multiplication/division problems
Use the lattice method for multiplication
Use a calculator to multiply/divide
Use a Multiplication/Division Facts Table
Use mental arithmetic to multiply/divide
Multiply/divide multiples of 10, 100, and 1,000 by 1-digit numbers
Multiply/divide money amounts
Use multiplication/division algorithms
Use divisibility tests
Express remainders as fractions or decimals
Express quotients as mixed numbers or decimals
Divide by 1-digit numbers
Divide by 2-digit numbers
Solve open number sentences
Use parentheses in number sentences
Understand and apply the order of operations to evaluate expressions and solve number sentences
Multiplication and Division with Decimals
Use an estimation strategy to multiply/divide decimals by whole numbers
Multiply decimals by whole numbers
Divide decimals by whole numbers
Estimate products and multiply decimals
Make magnitude estimates for quotients of whole and decimal numbers

Beginning   Developing   Secure

Operations and Computation (cont.)

	Grade 3											Grade 4												Grade 5											
	Units											Units												Units											
Skills and Concepts	1	2	3	4	5	6	7	8	9	10	11	1	2	3	4	5	6	7	8	9	10	11	12	1	2	3	4	5	6	7	8	9	10	11	12
Multiplication and Division with Fractions																																			
Relate fractions and division																																			
Use an algorithm to multiply fractions																																			
Use an algorithm to multiply mixed numbers																																			
Use a common denominator to divide fractions																																			
Ratio, Proportion, and Percent																																			
Find unit rates																																			
Calculate unit prices																																			
Collect and compare rate data																																			
Evaluate reasonableness of rate data																																			
Use rate tables to solve problems																																			
Represent rates with formulas, tables, and graphs																																			
Solve rate and ratio number stories																																			
Explore uses of ratios and ways of expressing ratios																																			

Notes on Scope and Sequence

Patterns, Functions, and Algebra

	Grade 3											Grade 4												Grade 5											
	Units											Units												Units											
Skills and Concepts	1	2	3	4	5	6	7	8	9	10	11	1	2	3	4	5	6	7	8	9	10	11	12	1	2	3	4	5	6	7	8	9	10	11	12
Visual Patterns																																			
Create patterns with 2-dimensional shapes																																			
Explore and extend visual patterns																																			
Define and create tessellations/frieze patterns																																			
Number Patterns																																			
Find patterns in addition and subtraction facts																																			
Find patterns in multiplication and division facts																																			
Find equivalent names for numbers																																			
Investigate square numbers																																			
Plot points on a coordinate grid																																			
Find locations on a map or globe																																			
Find number patterns in data																																			
Find and extend numerical patterns																																			
Sequences																																			
Make/complete a number line																																			
Count by tenths and hundredths																																			
Functions																																			
Solve "What's My Rule?" (function machine) problems																																			
Complete a table of values																																			
Collect and compare rate data																																			
Solve rate number stories																																			

Beginning **Developing** **Secure**

Patterns, Functions, and Algebra (cont.)

	Grade 3											Grade 4												Grade 5											
	Units											Units												Units											
Skills and Concepts	1	2	3	4	5	6	7	8	9	10	11	1	2	3	4	5	6	7	8	9	10	11	12	1	2	3	4	5	6	7	8	9	10	11	12
Number Sentences and Equations																																			
Write/solve addition and subtraction number sentences																																			
Write/solve multiplication number sentences																																			
Write/solve number sentences with missing factors																																			
Write/solve division number sentences																																			
Make up/solve number sentences with parentheses																																			
Apply the use of parentheses in number sentences																																			
Solve open sentences																																			
Determine if number sentences are true or false																																			
Understand and apply the order of operations to evaluate expressions and solve number sentences																																			
Translate number stories into expressions																																			
Write and solve number sentences with variables																																			
Determine the value of a variable																																			
Solve equations with a variable																																			
Inequalities and Expressions																																			
Compare numbers using < and > symbols																																			
Evaluate expressions using <, >, and = symbols																																			
Write algebraic expressions to describe situations																																			
Positive/Negative Numbers (Integers)																																			
Compare and order integers																																			
Add and subtract integers																																			
Use properties of positive and negative numbers																																			
Compute with positive and negative numbers																																			

Geometry

	Grade 3											Grade 4												Grade 5											
	Units											Units												Units											
Skills and Concepts	1	2	3	4	5	6	7	8	9	10	11	1	2	3	4	5	6	7	8	9	10	11	12	1	2	3	4	5	6	7	8	9	10	11	12
2-Dimensional Shapes (Polygons)																																			
Identify 2-dimensional shapes																																			
Create/extend designs with 2-dimensional shapes																																			
Explore shape relationships																																			
Explore the relationship between diameter and circumference																																			
Identify characteristics of 2-dimensional shapes																																			
Construct/draw 2-dimensional shapes																																			
Solve problems involving 2-dimensional shapes																																			
Record designs with 2-dimensional shapes																																			
Explore similarities and differences among quadrilaterals																																			
Form shapes by combining polygons																																			
Classify and name polygons																																			
Identify properties of polygons																																			
Use a compass and a straightedge to construct geometric figures																																			
Classify quadrilaterals according to side and angle properties																																			
Name, draw, and label angles, triangles, and quadrilaterals																																			
Identify types of triangles																																			
Define and create tessellations/frieze patterns																																			

Beginning Developing Secure

Geometry (cont.)

	Grade 3											Grade 4												Grade 5											
	Units											Units												Units											
Skills and Concepts	1	2	3	4	5	6	7	8	9	10	11	1	2	3	4	5	6	7	8	9	10	11	12	1	2	3	4	5	6	7	8	9	10	11	12
3-Dimensional Shapes																																			
Identify 3-dimensional shapes																																			
Identify characteristics of 3-dimensional shapes																																			
Construct 3-dimensional shapes																																			
Identify faces, edges, vertices, and bases of prisms and pyramids																																			
Identify the shapes of faces																																			
Describe properties of geometric solids																																			
Symmetry																																			
Identify symmetrical figures																																			
Identify lines of symmetry																																			
Rotate figures																																			
Translate figures on a coordinate grid																																			
Identify lines of reflection, reflected figures, and figures with line symmetry																																			
Congruence and Similarity																																			
Identify congruent figures																																			
Identify similar figures																																			
Draw or form a figure congruent to a given figure																																			
Points, Lines, and Angles																																			
Draw line segments to a specified length																																			
Identify parallel and nonparallel line segments																																			
Identify and name points																																			
Identify and name line segments																																			
Identify and name lines																																			

Points, Lines, and Angles (cont.)
Identify and name intersecting lines
Identify and name rays
Draw lines and rays
Name, draw, and label line segments, lines, and rays
Identify and describe right angles, parallel lines, and line segments
Identify and name angles
Model clockwise/counterclockwise turns/rotations
Measure angles with degree units
Solve degree problems
Identify acute, obtuse, straight, and reflex angles
Make turns and fractions of turns; relate turns to angles
Use full-circle and half-circle protractors to measure and draw angles
Determine angle measures based on relationships among angles
Estimate the measure of an angle
Find angle sums for geometric shapes
Use a compass to draw a circle and angles formed by intersecting lines
Measure angles formed by intersecting lines
Solve construction problems

Beginning Developing Secure

Measurement and Reference Frames: Measurement

	Grade 3											Grade 4												Grade 5											
	Units											Units												Units											
Skills and Concepts	1	2	3	4	5	6	7	8	9	10	11	1	2	3	4	5	6	7	8	9	10	11	12	1	2	3	4	5	6	7	8	9	10	11	12
Length																																			
Estimate and compare distances																																			
Estimate and compare lengths/heights of objects																																			
Measure to the nearest foot																																			
Measure to the nearest inch																																			
Measure to the nearest centimeter																																			
Investigate the meter																																			
Solve length/height number stories																																			
Measure to the nearest $\frac{1}{2}$ inch																																			
Measure to the nearest $\frac{1}{2}$ centimeter																																			
Measure to the nearest yard																																			
Identify equivalent customary units of length																																			
Identify equivalent metric units of length																																			
Measure to the nearest decimeter																																			
Investigate the mile																																			
Solve distance number stories																																			
Use a map scale																																			
Use a mileage map																																			
Use a scale drawing																																			
Identify locations for given latitudes and longitudes																																			
Find latitude and longitude for given locations																																			
Measure to the nearest $\frac{1}{4}$ inch																																			
Measure to the nearest $\frac{1}{8}$ inch																																			

Length (cont.)
Measure to the nearest millimeter
Measure diameter and circumference
Express metric measures with decimals
Convert between metric measures
Establish personal references for metric units of length
Establish personal references for customary units of length
Capacity and Volume
Understand the concept of capacity
Identify customary units of capacity
Identify equivalent customary units of capacity
Identify metric units of capacity
Identify equivalent metric units of capacity
Calculate capacity
Solve capacity number stories
Understand the concept of volume of a figure
Understand the relationships between the volumes of pyramids and prisms, and the volumes of cones and cylinders
Find volume
Estimate volume
Use formulas to calculate volumes of 3-dimensional shapes
Examine the relationships among the liter, milliliter, and cubic centimeter

Beginning **Developing** **Secure**

Measurement and Reference Frames: Measurement (cont.)

	Grade 3											Grade 4												Grade 5											
	Units											Units												Units											
Skills and Concepts	1	2	3	4	5	6	7	8	9	10	11	1	2	3	4	5	6	7	8	9	10	11	12	1	2	3	4	5	6	7	8	9	10	11	12
Weight																																			
Use a pan balance/spring scale																																			
Solve pan-balance problems																																			
Solve weight number stories																																			
Identify customary units of weight																																			
Identify metric units of weight																																			
Estimate and compare weights																																			
Identify equivalent customary units of weight																																			
Identify equivalent metric units of weight																																			
Estimate/weigh objects in ounces or grams																																			
Perimeter and Area																																			
Investigate area																																			
Estimate area																																			
Find the perimeters of irregular shapes																																			
Find the perimeters of regular shapes																																			
Find the areas of regular shapes																																			
Estimate perimeter																																			
Compare perimeter and area																																			
Find the areas of irregular shapes																																			
Find the area of a figure by counting unit squares																																			
Use formulas to find areas of rectangles, parallelograms, and triangles																																			
Estimate surface area																																			
Identify the bases and heights of triangles and parallelograms																																			

Perimeter and Area (cont.)
Use formulas to find circumference and area of a circle
Distinguish between circumference and area in circle problems
Find the surface areas of prisms, cylinders, and pyramids
Find an approximate value for π (pi)
Use personal references for common units of area
Money
Use dollars-and-cents notation
Solve money number stories
Make change
Add/subtract money amounts
Estimate costs
Divide money amounts
Calculate unit price
Determine the better buy
Multiply money amounts
Identify/find fractional parts of units of money

Beginning **Developing** **Secure**

Notes on Scope and Sequence

Measurement and Reference Frames: Reference Frames

	Grade 3											Grade 4												Grade 5											
	Units											Units												Units											
Skills and Concepts	1	2	3	4	5	6	7	8	9	10	11	1	2	3	4	5	6	7	8	9	10	11	12	1	2	3	4	5	6	7	8	9	10	11	12
Time																																			
Solve time number stories																																			
Investigate 1-minute intervals																																			
Calculate elapsed time																																			
Tell time to the nearest minute																																			
Convert units of time																																			
Temperature																																			
Use the Fahrenheit temperature scale																																			
Solve temperature number stories																																			
Use the Celsius temperature scale																																			

Notes on Scope and Sequence

Data and Chance

	Grade 3											Grade 4												Grade 5											
	Units											Units												Units											
Skills and Concepts	1	2	3	4	5	6	7	8	9	10	11	1	2	3	4	5	6	7	8	9	10	11	12	1	2	3	4	5	6	7	8	9	10	11	12
Collecting Data																																			
Collect data by counting/interviewing	B												D			D							D					D	D						
Collect data from print sources	B		D				D						D	D		D		D	D	D	D	D	D										D		
Collect data from a map					D								D	D		D	D														D				
Make predictions about data	B										D					D				D													D		
Explore random sampling			B																	D									D						
Conduct a survey											B									D									D						
Record/compare numerical data														B		D		D	D	D	D	D	D		D										D
Organize and tabulate survey data																B				D			D						D						
Collect and compare rate data																							D												D
Recording/Displaying Data																																			
Make a tally chart	S										S		S																S						
Make a bar graph	S									S			S															S	S				S		
Record data in a table/chart	B	D	D										D	D	D				D				D										D		D
Record data on a map		B																		D									D						
Make a line plot					D		D						D		D														D						
Draw a circle graph																												D	D						
Construct a stem-and-leaf plot																													B						

Beginning **Developing** **Secure**

Data and Chance (cont.)

	Grade 3											Grade 4												Grade 5											
	Units											Units												Units											
Skills and Concepts	1	2	3	4	5	6	7	8	9	10	11	1	2	3	4	5	6	7	8	9	10	11	12	1	2	3	4	5	6	7	8	9	10	11	12
Evaluating Data																																			
Find/use the range																																			
Find/use the mode																																			
Find/use the median																																			
Find/use the mean																																			
Compare two sets of data																																			
Find/use the minimum/maximum																																			
Interpret tables, graphs, and maps																																			
Use data in problem solving																																			
Summarize and interpret data																																			
Interpret stem-and-leaf plots																																			
Probability and Chance																																			
Explore equal-chance events																																			
Predict outcomes																																			
Record outcomes																																			
Use fractions to record probabilities of events																																			
Conduct experiments																																			
Explore *fair* and *unfair* games																																			
Solve problems involving chance outcomes																																			
Understand and use tree diagrams to solve problems																																			
Compute the probability of equally-likely outcomes																																			
Calculate the probability of simple events																																			

Index

A

A Carnival Game project, 433–436, 891–894
Account balance, 233, 814–815
Acute angle, 403, 457, 915
Addition
  algorithms, 72–73, 109–114
    column-addition method, 112–113
    partial-sums method (focus), 110–112, 114, 292
  on a clock face, 537–539
  decimal, 227–231, 234–235, 247
  facts, 14, 16, 25, 61, 76, 93
  fraction, 508, 528–534, 541, 554, 580
  of multidigit numbers, 109–114, 118, 303, 315, 341
  multiples of 10, 290
  number stories, 114, 194, 217
  of positive and negative numbers, 727–729, 757–762, 820, 843
  situation diagrams, 141–142
  strategy, 130
  whole numbers, 231
Addition Top-It, 69, 101
Algebra
  definition, 143
  function machines, 178
  inequalities, 143
  number
    patterns, 162
    sentences, 179–183, 184–188
  open sentences, 189–193, 214
  order of operations, 185
  variables, 190
Algorithms, 110, 457, 915
  addition, 72–73, 229
    column-addition method, 112–113
    partial-sums method (focus), 110–112, 114, 292
  division, 358–360
    partial-quotients method (focus), 358–360, 372–376
  multiplication, 274–275, 332
    lattice, 274–275, 315–321
    partial-products method (focus), 274–275, 303–314
  subtraction, 72–73, 229
    counting-up method, 125, 152
    partial-differences method, 123–124
    trade-first method (focus), 121–123
Angle measurer, 399
Angles, 24–29, 37, 392–396, 398, 457, 915
  acute, 403
  classifying, 24–29
  comparing, 401
  constructing, 26
  definition, 26
  drawing, 28, 399–400
  of given measures, 395
  measures of, 362, 404–405, 420
  modeling, 406
  naming, 26, 28
  obtuse, 403
  reflex, 403
  right, 26, 394, 403
  straight, 403
Area, 582–643, 915
  comparing, 457, 631
  definition, 608
  formulas, 593–594, 616–631
  geoboard, 610
  geographical measurements, 632–636
  of irregular figures, 615, 635, 641–642
  of parallelogram, 621–626, 635
  of polygons, 608, 630
  of rectangle, 594, 616–620, 635
  square units, 590, 608
  of triangle, 594, 627–631, 635
  versus perimeter, 590–592
Array, 165
Art link, 6, 46, 50, 55, 502, 517, 563, 720, 740, 754, 756, 772, 799
Art and literature link, 6, 29
Assessment, 5, 15, 65, 135, 205, 269, 353, 501, 585, 647, 719, 771, 833
  end-of-year, 879
  midyear, 421
  oral, 58–59, 128, 199, 262, 346, 418, 577–578, 638, 711–712, 764, 826–827, 875
  slate, 59–60, 128–129, 199–200, 262–263, 346–347, 419, 578, 639, 712, 765, 827, 876
  written, 60, 129–130, 200, 263–264, 347–348, 419, 579, 640–641, 712–713, 765, 827–828, 877
Average. *See* Mean
Axis, 408, 457, 915

B

Bar graph, 115–119, 457, 691, 915
Base, 458, 618, 623, 628, 916
Baseball Multiplication, 139, 155–156, 160, 173–174, 187, 209, 221
Base-10 blocks, 68, 120, 214, 219, 237, 280, 303, 309, 550–551, 656, 801
  creating designs, 553, 661
  modeling
    decimals, 215–217, 238–239
    fractions, 216
    multiplication with, 307–308, 312–313
    partial-sums method, 114
    trade-first method, 126
  representing numbers, 216
  value of, 218, 241
Beat the Calculator, 139, 144, 161, 187, 209, 221, 273, 283, 290
Billions, 324–325, 458, 916
Broken Calculator, 139, 144, 191–193, 209, 259, 357, 370–371
Building and Viewing Structures project, 447–451, 905–909

C

Calculator, 14
  division on, 668–673
  fraction-decimal conversions, 668–673
  fraction-percent conversions, 674–679, 685
  games, 143, 161, 192–193, 221, 259, 283, 290, 370–371
  multiplication on, 154, 161
  place-value with, 93–97
  TI-15, 95, 211, 229, 257, 258, 283
  uses, 144
Calendar, 79
Capacity, 819–824
  units of, 780–781
Centimeters (cm), 243, 458, 916
  measuring in, 245
  and meters, converting between, 246
  personal references for, 249
Central tendency, 74, 100–101, 103–108, 146
Chance, 510, 564–569
  events, 569

Change diagrams, 142, 178
Charts and tables
  calculators, 192
  drawing base-10 blocks, 239
  "easy" fractions, 665
  logic grid, 195–196
  metric units, 783
  multiplication and division table, 147, 164
  place-value, 89, 94, 210, 258, 324
  powers of 10, 330
  rate tables, 849–851
  U.S. customary units, 783
Circle, 48, 458, 916
  center, 44, 458, 916
  concentric, 49
  constructions, 47–51
  drawing, 42–46
  tangent, 51
Circle designs, creating, 46, 50
Circle graph, 678
Circular protractor, 397–401, 420
Circumference, 116
Clock, 182, 392, 842
  facts, 151
  fractions, 535–540
Clockwise, 394, 458, 916
Column-addition method, 112, 458, 916
Common denominator, 577
Commutative property. *See* Turn-around facts
Comparison diagrams, 142–143, 178
Comparison shopping, 840, 860–869
Compass, 13, 19, 42, 47, 52, 57, 387, 458, 621, 916
  constructions with a, 53–55, 626
  designing a, 45–46
  drawing circles, 42–46
Computer Science link, 270, 296
Computer software. *See* Graphing software
Concave, 37
Concentric circles, 49, 458, 916
Cone, 777, 790, 796, 803
Congruent figures, 725
Consumer link, 66, 119, 206, 226, 648, 676, 834, 861–863, 867–868
Conversions among fractions, decimals, and percents, 652, 680–685
Convex, 37
Coordinate grids
  plotting and naming points on a, 400
  rectangular, 387–391
Counterclockwise, 398, 459, 917
Counters, 518, 559
  to solve equal-grouping problems, 371
  to solve equal-sharing problems, 381
  using to find ONE, 561
Counting
  decimal amounts, 228
  numbers, 89, 459, 917
  by tens, 281
Counting-up strategy, 88, 99, 110, 125, 152
Credits, 759–760, 814–816
Credits/Debits Game, 723, 760–761, 775, 798, 810–811
Credits/Debits Game (Advanced Version), 775, 816, 837, 852
Cross-curricular links, 6, 66, 136, 206, 270, 354, 502, 586, 648, 720, 772, 834
Cube, 215, 791, 796
  drawing a, 799
Cube-drop experiment, 570–575
Cube-stacking problems, 808–809
Cubic units, metric, 802–804
Cups, 819–821
Curved surface, 790
Cylinder, 779, 790

D

Dart Game, 723, 737
Data. *See* Graphing software
  analyzing, 100–101, 105, 859
  checking, 854–859
  collecting, 74, 99–100
  comparing marathon, 339
  describing, 74
  displaying, 98–102, 115–119
  eye-blinking, 843–845, 846
  food-survey, 299–300
  landmarks, 217
  literacy, 697
  organizing, 98–108, 115–119
  population, 692–697
  predictions from, 301
  reviewing, 104–105
  table, 739
Debits, 759–760, 814–816
Decimals, 202–265
  addition, 227–231, 234–235, 247
  comparing, 219–222
  concepts, 210–211, 214–218
  converting to fractions and percents, 652, 656–661, 668–679, 680–685
  division of, 654, 704–709, 732, 755
  division strategy, 714
  equivalent, 570
  estimating products of, 699–700
  estimating with, 223–226
  fraction-decimal conversions, 549–553, 668–673
  modeling with base-10 blocks, 215–217, 238–240
  multiplication, 654, 698–703, 732, 755
  multiplication strategy, 715
  notation, 210–213, 216
  ordering, 219–222
  percents, 652, 656–661, 673, 680–685
  place value, 256–260, 289
  quotient of, 705–707
  reading and writing, 239, 242, 259
  repeating, 670
  representing on grids, 230
  subtraction, 227–231, 247
  terminating, 670
Decimeter, 244, 459, 917
Degrees, 394, 459, 917
Denominator, 459, 917
  common, 556, 577
  definition, 514
  like/unlike, 556, 577
Deposit, 233
Diagrams
  change, 142–143, 178
  comparison, 142–143, 178
  parts-and-total, 142, 178
  situation, 142, 178
  Venn, 28
Diameter, 116
Digits, 89
Dimensions, 804
Discount, 679
Distances
  air, 171–174, 177
  finding, 81
  map, 179, 389–390
Dividend, 163, 373, 459, 917
Divisibility, 148, 151, 153
Division, 162–165, 366–371
  algorithm
    partial-quotients method (focus), 358–360, 372–376
  arrays, 165
  of decimals, 653, 704–709, 732, 755
  facts, 147–148, 164, 167, 170, 187
  Fact Triangles, 164, 170
  fractions and, 551–552
  and multiplication, 163
  number stories, 360, 377–381, 385, 387, 392, 402, 420, 709
  remainders, 163, 361, 374, 382–386
  strategy, 420
  symbol (/), 147
  of whole numbers, 690, 709
Division Arrays, 139, 165
Division Dash, 357, 376
Divisor, 163, 373, 459, 917
Dodecahedron, 796

E

Edge, 791
Efficiency of a kitchen, 597–598
Elapsed time, 396
  in degrees, 395
Endpoints, 21, 459, 917
Enlargements, 642
Equal chance, 459, 565, 917
Equal-grouping problems, 371
Equal-groups notation, 367, 459, 917
Equally-likely outcomes, 567

Equal-sharing problems, 381
Equator, 408, 459, 917
Equilateral triangle, 43, 459, 517, 628, 917
inscribing in a circle, 56
Equivalent fractions, 459, 508–509, 541–549, 917
Equivalent Fractions Rule, 546
Equivalent Names for Fractions Table, 542, 580, 683
Equivalent names for numbers, 83, 86, 459, 917
Estimates, 79, 99–100, 291–302, 460, 918
area, 608–609, 612, 615
averages, 300
with decimals, 223–226
distances, 389–390
lengths, 250, 306
magnitude, 276, 299–300
products, 297–302, 310, 699–700
rounding, 276, 632
rough, 299
sums, 291–296, 315, 341
weights, 785, 787
Exit slip, 28
Expected outcomes, 460, 567, 918
Experiments
comparing actual and expected results, 573, 575
cube-drop, 570–575
predicting results, 571–572
spinner, 566–567
Exponent, 330
Exponential notation, 328–333, 460, 918
Extended multiplication facts, 282, 287, 290, 460, 918
Eye-blinking data, 843–846

F

Face, 791
Fact family, 163, 171, 184, 460, 918
Factor Bingo, 139, 151
Factors, 147, 460, 918
Facts
addition, 14, 16, 25, 61, 76, 93
clock, 151
division, 147–148, 164, 167, 170, 187
5s, 151
multiplication, 140, 146–161, 167, 170, 187, 221, 280–285
subtraction, 14, 16, 25, 61, 76, 93, 110
Fact Triangles, 140, 147, 149–150, 163
division, 164, 170
multiplication, 170
sort activity, 149–150
Fair die, 565
False number sentence, 181
Family Letter, 18, 61, 131, 201, 265, 349, 421, 581, 643, 715, 767, 829, 879
Flat, 215
Flat surfaces, 791
Flip. *See* Reflection
Focus algorithms
partial-products multiplication method, 274–275, 303–308, 309–314
partial-quotients division method, 358–360, 372–376
partial-sums addition method, 110–112, 114, 292
trade-first subtraction method, 121–123
Formulas, 460, 918
area of a rectangle, 594, 616–620, 635
volume of a cylinder, 779
volume of a rectangular prism, 807–812
Fraction/Percent Concentration, 651, 671, 677, 701
Fractions
addition, 508, 528–534, 541, 554, 580
cards, 533, 541, 554
clocks for modeling, 535–540
comparisons, 554–558
concepts, 215, 506–507, 512–517
converting to decimals and percents, 652, 656–661, 662–679, 680–685
and decimals, 509
denominator, 514, 577
with denominators of 10 or 100, 559
and division, 551–552
"easy", 662–667, 669, 687
equivalent, 508–509, 541–549
"fraction of" problems, 519–520, 522, 523, 535, 547, 713–714, 730, 752
mixed numbers, 515, 611
modeling with base-10 blocks, 216
multiplication, 162–165
name-collection boxes, 552
notation, 506–507, 513–514
on number lines, 568
numerator, 514
the ONE for, 559–563
ordering, 555–557, 565
pattern-block, 523–527
remainders as, 383–384, 391
renaming as decimals, 549–553
of sets, 518–522, 574
and spinners, 564–569
subtraction, 508, 528–534, 541, 554, 580
using digits to create, 558
of wholes, 574
Fraction Top-It, 505, 562
Frieze patterns, 726–727, 752–756
Function machines. *See* Rate tables

G

Gallon, 780, 819–824
Games
Addition Top-It, 69, 101
Baseball Multiplication, 139, 155–156, 160, 173–174, 187, 209, 221
Beat the Calculator, 139, 144, 161, 187, 209, 221, 273, 283, 290
Broken Calculator, 139, 144, 191–193, 209, 259, 357, 370–371
Credits/Debits Game, 723, 760–761, 775, 798, 810–811
Credits/Debits Game (Advanced Version), 775, 816, 837, 852
Dart Game, 723, 737
Division Arrays, 139, 165
Division Dash, 357, 376
Factor Bingo, 139, 151
Fraction/Percent Concentration, 651, 671, 677, 701
Fraction Top-It, 505, 562
Geometry 5 Questions, 9, 35
Getting to One, 651, 673
Grid Search, 357, 391
High-Number Toss, 69, 95–96, 113, 273, 344
Multiplication Top-It, 139, 161, 209, 221
Multiplication Wrestling, 273, 286–290, 300, 314
Musical Name-Collection Boxes, 505, 548
Name That Number, 69, 84, 86, 113, 131, 139, 188, 505, 544
Name That Polygon, 9, 41
Number Top-It, 69, 97, 209, 222, 241, 273, 344
Pocket-Billiards Game, 723, 737
Robot, 357, 396
Subtraction Target Practice, 69, 125
Subtraction Top–It, 69, 107
Touch and Match It Quadrangles, 9, 29
What's My Weight?, 775, 786
Geoboard, 35, 600, 610, 620
Geography link, 354, 388
Geometric figures, 2–61
constructions, 24–29
Geometric solids, 776–777, 788–793
Geometry, 10, 11–13
angles, 24–29, 37, 392–406
circles, 42–51
congruent figures, 725
constructions, 794–800
geometric solids, 776–777, 788–793
lines/line segments, 19–23
moving geometric figures, 730–745
polygons, 36–41
Template, 19, 57, 559, 730, 735
Geometry 5 Questions, 9, 35
Getting to One, 651, 673
Global grid system, 407–411

Gram & Ounce Museum, 784, 817
Graphing software, 100, 105, 117
Graphs
  bar, 115–119, 691
  circle, 678
  function machine, 178
  labels, 115
  line, 105
Greater than (>), 183
Grid Search, 357, 391
Grids
  coordinate, 387–391
  global system, 407–411
  plotting points on, 230
Guess, 100

H

Half-circle protractor, 402–406, 407, 420
  drawing angles with, 409–410
Height, 460, 618, 623, 628, 918
Hemispheres, 409
Heptagon, 38, 460, 918
Hexagon, 38, 460, 918
  constructing, 52–56
  dividing, 55
High-Number Toss, 69, 95–96, 113, 273, 344
Hundreds
  multiples of, 370, 375
Hundredths, 217, 240
  comparing and ordering decimals in, 219–222
  fractions, 698
  reading, 217

I

Image, 732, 736, 740, 742–743
Index of locations, 388, 460, 918
Industrial Arts link, 586, 597–598
Inequality, 143, 183
Inscribed square, 44, 461, 919
  constructing, 44
Integers, 757–762
Internet, 455, 913
Interest, 233, 461, 919
Interior, 39, 461, 919
Intersect, 32, 49, 461, 919
Isosceles triangle, 461, 628, 919

K

Kilograms, 183
Kitchen
  arrangements, 598
  efficiency, 597–598
  layouts and perimeter, 596–600
Kite, 27, 28, 34, 461, 919
  constructing a, 61
  properties of, 41

L

Landmarks, 74, 100, 461, 919
  maximum, 100, 146
  median, 103–108, 146
  minimum, 100, 146
  mode, 100, 146
  range, 100, 146
Language Arts link, 6, 17, 136, 163, 188, 206, 224–225, 354, 396, 522, 569, 648, 658, 720, 732, 772, 799, 824
Language link, 6, 38–39
Large numbers, 91–92, 322–327, 329–330
  place value in, 93, 115, 277, 323–324
  reading, 92, 158, 324
  rounding and reporting, 334–339
  writing, 324
Latitude, 412–416, 461, 919
  lines, 409, 461, 919
Lattice multiplication method, 275, 315–321, 461, 919
  for decimals, 700, 702–703
  for 1-digit multipliers, 316–318
  for 2-digit multipliers, 318–319
  versus partial-products methods, 321
Learning goals, 4, 64, 134, 204, 268, 352, 500, 584, 646, 718, 770, 832
Length, 264, 462, 618, 920
  estimating with personal references, 250, 306
  measuring in millimeters and centimeters, 252–255
  metric units of, 242–246
  personal references for customary units of, 284
  personal references for metric units, 247–251
Less than (<), 183
Letter-number pair, 388, 462, 920
Life expectancy, 694
Like denominators, 577
Likelihood of events, 567–568, 569
Line plot, 105, 462, 920
Line of reflection, 740, 742
Line segments, 20–22, 462, 740
  comparing, 534
  copying a, 54
  drawing, 22, 534
  exploring with geoboard, 35
  naming, 20–21
Line symmetry, 746–751
Lines, 20–22
  drawing, 22
Lines of reflection, 735–740
Liter, 781
Literacy, percent of, 697
Literature link, 6, 18, 41, 66, 86, 91–92, 136, 150, 197, 206, 222, 270, 301, 326, 354, 386, 516, 527, 569, 648, 672, 691, 720, 734, 762, 772, 787, 824, 834, 847, 859, 873
Logic grid, 195–196, 462, 920
Logic problems, 194–197, 295
Long, 215
Longitude, 412–416, 462, 920
  lines, 409, 462, 920

M

Magnitude estimates, 276, 299–300, 462, 920
Making a Cutaway Globe project, 424–428, 882–886
Making a Quilt project, 437–443, 895–901
Mammal heart rates problems, 859
Map
  grids, 363–364, 387–391
  interpreting, 695–696
  literacy and standard of living, 697
  population, 694–695
  regional, 415
  scale, 81, 196, 389–390, 462, 920
  world, 414
Marathon data, comparing, 339
Mass, 776, 783
Mathematical expressions, 83
Mathematical puzzles, 197
Math tools, 20
Maximum, 74, 100, 146, 462, 920
Mayan numeral system, 455, 913
Mean, 300, 462, 920
Measurements
  abbreviations, 244
  angles, 362, 404–405, 420
  area, 582–643
  capacity, 780–781, 819–824
  conversions, 244, 255
  cubic units, 802–804
  distances, 340–344
  length, 242–246, 250, 253–254, 264, 284, 306, 618
  metric system, 119, 242–246, 252–255
  perimeter, 582–643
  personal references, 248
  protractors, 397–406, 407, 420
  scale drawings, 601–606
  square units, 590, 608
  temperatures, 761
  U.S. customary system, 783, 806, 819–824
  volume, 592, 779–781, 801–812
  weight, 776, 782–787, 819–824
Median, 74, 103–108, 146, 462, 920
Mental arithmetic, 233–234
Meters, 244, 251, 463, 921
  and centimeters, converting between, 246
  personal references for, 247–251
Metric system, 251, 802–804
  centimeters, 243, 245–246, 249
  converting, 244

cubic units, 802–804
decimeters, 244
equivalents, 255
liters, 781
meters, 244, 246, 249
millimeters, 243, 252–255
personal references for, 247–251
Mileage, 226
Millimeters, 243, 463, 921
measuring in, 252–255
Millions, 324–325
Minimum, 74, 100, 146, 463, 921
Minuend, 124, 463, 921
Minus, 728
Mixed numbers, 463, 515, 611, 921
Mode, 74, 100, 146, 463, 921
Money
decimals in, 232–236
using to find totals and make change, 236
Multidigit numbers
addition of, 109–114, 118
subtraction of, 120–126
Multiples of 100, 370, 375
Multiples of 1,000, 370, 375
Multiples of 10
adding, 290
strategy for division, 366–371, 372
Multiplication, 162–165
algorithms, 274–275, 332
lattice method, 275, 315–321, 700, 702–703
partial-products method (focus), 274, 303–314
basic facts, 140, 146–161, 167, 170, 187, 221, 280–285, 463, 921
of decimals, 654, 698–703, 732, 755
extended facts, 282–285, 287, 290
Fact Triangles, 140, 149, 170
factors, 149, 170
memorization, 148
modeling with base-10 blocks, 307–308, 312–313
number stories, 285, 308, 360, 377–381, 385, 387, 402, 420
problems, 232
relationship with division, 163
shortcuts, 148, 151
skills, 274
symbol (*), 147
Multiplication/Division Diagram, 378, 402, 463, 847, 921
Multiplication/Division Fact Triangle, 149
Multiplication/Division Facts Table, 140, 147–148, 163–164
Multiplication/division puzzles, 285
Multiplication Top-It, 139, 161, 209, 221
Multiplication Wrestling, 273, 286–290, 300, 314
Musical Name-Collection Boxes, 505, 548

N

N-gons, 38, 463, 921
Name-collection boxes, 83–84, 86, 463, 921
fraction, 552
Name That Number, 69, 84, 86, 113, 131, 139, 188, 505, 544
Name That Polygon, 9, 41
NCTM Standards 2000, 9, 69, 139, 209, 273, 357, 505, 589, 651, 723, 775, 837
Negative, 728
Negative numbers, 727
addition of, 757–762
confusing notation, 728–729
subtraction of, 777–778, 813–818
Nonagon, 38, 463, 921
Nonconvex, 37
North Pole, 408
Number
patterns, 148, 151, 162
puzzles, 296
Number lines
fractional parts of, 515
fractions on, 568
using to add positive and negative numbers, 762, 818
Number sentences, 143, 179–183, 220, 463, 921
open, 143, 189–193
parentheses in, 184–188
solving, 191
true or false, 179–183, 186, 190
Number stories
addition, 114, 194, 217
discount, 676, 678
division, 360, 377–381, 385, 387, 392, 402, 420, 709
elapsed time, 182
"fraction-of", 519–520, 522, 523, 535, 547, 730, 752
multiplication, 285, 308, 360, 377–381, 385, 387, 402, 420
"percent-of", 667, 680, 730, 752
solving, 175–178, 201, 264
subtraction, 126, 194, 217
temperature, 761
writing, 174, 231, 264
Number Top-It, 69, 97, 209, 222, 241, 273, 344
Numbers
equivalent names for, 70, 82–86
large, 91–92, 115, 158, 277, 322–327, 329–330, 332–333, 334–339
missing, 245
mixed, 515, 611
multidigit, 109–114, 118, 120–126
negative, 727–729, 757–762, 777–778, 813–818, 820, 843
place value, 87–92, 258–259, 277, 320, 465, 923
positive, 727–729, 757–762, 777–778, 813–818, 820, 843
reading, 90
reading and writing on a calculator, 92
representing with base-10 blocks, 216
square, 147
using, 62–131
whole, 87–92, 231, 258–259, 302, 320, 690, 703, 709
writing, 90–91
Numbers, Maya Style project, 452–455
Numerator, 463, 514, 921

O

Obtuse angle, 403, 463, 921
Octagon, 38, 463, 921
Odometer, 224
ONE, 215, 463, 513, 921
for fractions, 559–563
using counters to find, 561
using pattern blocks to find, 560
100% box, 658
Open number sentence, 143, 189–193, 214, 463, 921
Opposite of a number, 758
Ordered number pairs, 388–389, 464, 922
Order of operations, 185
Ounce, 780, 819–824

P

Paper folding
reflected images, 743–744
Parallel lines, 32–33
Parallel line segments, 32–33, 35
Parallelogram, 27, 28, 30–35, 464, 627, 922
area formula, 594, 621–626, 635
exploring, 33–34
properties of, 33–34, 622–623
Parallel rays, 32–33
Parallels, 409
Parentheses, 184–188, 464, 922
Partial-differences subtraction method, 123–124, 464, 922
Partial product, 274, 305
Partial-products multiplication method, 274, 303–308, 309–314, 464, 922
for 1-digit multipliers, 305–306
for 2-digit multipliers, 311
Partial quotient, 374
Partial-quotients division method, 358–360, 372–376, 464, 922
Partial-sums addition method, 110–112, 114, 292, 464, 922
Parts-and-total diagram, 142, 178
Pattern-block fractions, 523–527

Pattern blocks, 512, 514, 524–525, 528–532, 545, 559, 560, 616
Patterns
in base-ten place-value system, 71
in base-five place-value system, 455, 913
frieze, 726–727, 752–756
number, 162
Pentagon, 37, 464, 922
Per, 845
"Percent of"
a design, 713–714
number stories, 667, 680, 730, 752
Percent of discount, 679
Percent of literacy, 697
Percents, 464, 644–715, 922
decimal-percent conversions, 652, 656–661, 673, 680–685
equivalent names for, 658–659
fraction-percent conversions, 652, 656–661, 673, 680–685
solving problems involving, 653
Perimeter, 464, 582–643, 922
of figures, 604, 641
kitchen layouts, 596–600
Perpendicular, 465, 623, 923
Personal measurement references, 248
for customary units of length, 284
estimating lengths with, 250, 306
for metric length, 247–251
Per-unit rate, 845, 850
Pie graph. *See* Circle graph
Pint, 780, 802, 819–824
Place, 89
Place value, 465, 923
base-ten, 72
with a calculator, 93–97
decimal, 256–260, 289
flip book, 260
in large numbers, 93, 276
puzzles, 260
in whole numbers, 87–92, 258–259, 320
Pocket-Billiards Game, 723, 737
Points, 20–22, 465, 923
Polygons, 36–41, 465, 734, 923
area of, 608
concave (nonconvex), 37–39
convex, 37–39, 458, 916
lines of symmetry of, 749
perimeter of, 604, 641
properties of, 39, 50
regular, 43
Polyhedrons, 795
Population data, 692–697
Portfolio ideas, 40, 41, 45, 46, 50, 51, 56, 61, 86, 114, 126, 130, 131, 174, 178, 193, 197, 201, 222, 231, 246, 251, 260, 264, 265, 285, 296, 308, 314, 327, 348, 381, 420, 517, 522, 534, 563, 575, 580, 606, 626, 631, 636, 641, 642, 661, 667, 678, 691, 697, 713, 714, 715, 740, 750, 756, 767, 787, 799, 811, 812, 823, 828, 852, 853, 859, 869, 877
Positive numbers, 727
addition of, 757–762
confusing notation, 728–729
subtraction of, 777–778, 813–818
Powers of 10, 278, 465, 923
definition, 330–331
exponents, 328–333
multiplication, 280–285, 287, 298
notation, 328–333
Predictions
from data, 301
making, 102, 687
Preimage, 732, 736, 740, 742–743
Prices, comparing, 869
Prime meridian, 408, 465, 923
Prisms, 776–777
building, 811
rectangular, 789, 804, 807–812, 848
Probability, 510, 564–569, 609
cube-dropping experiments, 570–575
equal (greater, smaller) chance, 565
equally (more, less) likely, 567–568, 569
spinners and, 564–569, 609
Problem solving
diagram, 143, 178
estimation for, 79, 100, 291–302
by lesson chart, 6, 66, 136, 206, 270, 354, 502, 586, 648, 720, 772, 834
solution guide, 175–178
Products, 147, 297–302, 304–305, 310, 465, 861, 923
Projects
A Carnival Game, 433–436, 891–894
Building and Viewing Structures, 447–451, 905–909
Making a Cutaway Globe, 424–428, 882–886
Making a Quilt, 437–443, 895–901
Numbers, Maya Style, 452–455, 910–913
Using a Magnetic Compass, 429–432, 887–890
Which Soft Drink Is the Best Buy?, 444–446, 902–904
Protractor, 362, 402, 407, 453, 923
circular, 397–401, 420
half-circle, 402–406, 407, 420
Pyramid, 777, 789, 800

Q

Quadrangles, 24–29
Quadrilateral, 26, 465, 923
Quadrillions, 330
Quart, 802, 819–824
Quintillions, 330
Quotient, 163, 374, 465, 923

R

Radius, 49, 466, 924
Range, 74, 100, 146, 466, 924
Rate, 845
Rate problems, 865, 870
solving, 838, 848–853, 863
units analysis in, 839–840, 854–859
using multiplication/division diagrams to solve, 847
Rates, 830–879
converting between, 854–859
listing examples of, 845
multistep problems involving, 877–878
unit, 850
Rate tables, 849–850, 860
Ratios, 559–563
Rays, 20–22, 466, 924
Rectangle, 27, 466, 924
area, 594, 616–620, 635
base of, 618
drawing to scale, 619
as parallelogram, 33, 618
Rectangular coordinate grids, 387–391
Rectangular prism, volume of, 804, 848
formula, 807–812
Reference frames, 79
Reflections (flips), 725, 735–740, 753–754
creating with pattern blocks or centimeter cubes, 766
properties of, 741–745
Reflex angle, 403, 466, 924
Regular polygons, 43, 466, 924
Remainders, 163, 361, 374, 382–386, 466, 924
as fractions, 383–384, 391
Renaming
decimals, 549–553, 652, 680–685
fractions, 549–553, 652, 680–685
mixed numbers, 611
percents, 652, 680–685
Repeating decimal, 670
Review and assessment, 57–61, 127–131, 198–201, 261–265, 345–349, 417–421, 576–581, 637–643, 710–715, 763–767, 825–829, 874–879
Rhombus, 27, 33, 466, 924
Right angle, 26, 394, 403, 466, 924
Rigid motions, 725
Robot, 357, 396
Roman numeral system, 83, 455, 913
Rotations (turns), 392–396, 398, 466, 725, 754, 924
clockwise, 398
counterclockwise, 398
and degree measures, 393–394

measures of, 362
Rough estimates, 299
Rough floor plan, 602
Rounding, 276, 466, 632, 924
large numbers, 334–339
whole numbers, 302
Ruler, 19, 68, 79, 115, 247, 280, 303, 601, 735, 741
centimeter, 47, 252, 621, 627
Rural, 694

S

Sale price, 679
Sample, 102
Savings account, 234
Scale, 466, 604, 782, 788, 924
Scale drawings, 466, 601–606, 924
of rectangles, 619
Science link, 66, 77, 136, 182, 206, 254, 270, 285, 586, 636, 648, 678, 720, 761, 772, 787, 834, 853, 859, 863
Scientific notation, 278, 329–330, 467, 925
Sets, fractions of, 518–522, 574
Sextillions, 330
Side, 37, 39, 398, 467, 925
Situation diagrams, 142–143, 178
6-point designs, 55
Slides. *See* Translations
Social Studies link, 66, 77–78, 136, 167–168, 178, 196, 206, 240, 270, 293–294, 341–342, 343, 344, 354, 396, 411, 413–414, 502, 520–521, 586, 614, 633–635, 648, 682–684, 693–694, 720, 739, 744, 745, 772, 785–786, 834, 845, 871
Software. *See* Graphing software
Solids, 776–777, 788–800
Solution, 143, 190, 467, 925
Solve, 190
South Pole, 408
Speed, 467, 853, 925
mammal, 853
Speedometer, 224
Sphere, 408, 467, 797, 925
Spinners, 564–569
experiments, 566–567
Square, 27, 467, 925
inscribed, 44
as parallelogram, 33
as rhombus, 33
Square feet
converting to square inches, 615
Square inches
converting to square feet, 615
Square numbers, 147, 467, 925
Square units, 467, 590, 608, 925
Straight angle, 403, 467, 925
Straightedge, 13, 20, 24, 42, 47, 52, 57, 397, 402, 512, 523, 564, 596, 601, 621, 627, 752
constructions with a, 53–55, 626
Straw constructions
angles, 26
cubes, 791
polygons, 27, 37, 622
polyhedrons, 797
prisms, 797
regular tetrahedron, 797
Student Reference Book, 11, 16–18
Subtraction
algorithms, 72–73, 229
counting-up method, 125, 152
partial-differences method, 123–124
trade-first method (focus), 121–123
decimal, 227–231, 247
facts, 14, 16, 25, 61, 76, 93, 110
fraction, 508, 528–534, 541, 554, 580
fraction, on a clock face, 538–539
of multidigit numbers, 120–126
number stories, 126, 194, 217
of positive and negative numbers, 777–778, 813–818, 820, 843
situation diagrams, 141–142
strategy, 130
whole numbers, 231
Subtraction Target Practice, 69, 125
Subtraction Top-It, 69, 107
Subtrahend, 123, 467, 925
Sums, estimating, 291–296, 315
Survey
comparing results of, 686–691
graphing results, 691
making predictions, 687
tabulating results, 688
Symbols
division (/), 147
greater than (>), 183
less than (<), 183
multiplication (*), 147
Symmetric pictures, 747–748
Symmetry, 725, 802
line, 735–738, 753, 802
reflection, 725, 735–740, 753
rotation, 725, 754
translation, 725, 753
turn, 750–751

T

Tables and charts. *See* Charts and tables
Take away, 728
Tally chart, 100, 467, 925
Tangent circles, 51
Tangrams, 527
Tape measure, 68, 115, 116, 247, 280, 303, 601
Technology. *See* Graphing software, Internet
Technology link, 136, 170, 502, 527
Temperature, 761
Ten
multiples of, 86, 290, 366–371, 372, 375
powers of, 278, 328–333
Tens
making, 83
multiplying by, 291, 298
Tenths, 217, 240
comparing and ordering decimals in, 219–222
reading decimals for, 217
Terminating decimal, 670
Tetrahedron, 796, 800
Thermometers, 79
Thousands, 325
multiples of, 370
Thousandths, 237–241
3-dimensional figures, 793
reflections of, 745
Time-and-motion studies, 597
Timed inventory test, 40
Touch and Match It Quadrangles, 9, 29
Trade-first subtraction method, 121–123, 467, 925
modeling with base-10 blocks, 126
Transformation geometry, 724
Transformations, 725
reflections (flips), 725, 735–745, 753
rotations (turns), 392–396, 398, 725, 754
translations (slides), 725, 753–754
Translations (slides), 725, 753–754
Transparent mirror, 725, 730–734
Trapezoid, 27, 467, 925
Tree diagrams, 31
Triangles, 24–29, 467, 925
area formula, 594, 627–631, 635
constructing, 26–27, 52–56
equilateral, 43, 628
isosceles, 628
measuring angles in, 405
Triangular prism, 789, 797
Triangular pyramid, 796
Trillions, 330
Trip meter, 224
True number sentence, 181
Turn. *See* Rotations
Turn-around facts, 148, 468, 926
Turn symmetry, 750–751
2-dimensional shapes, 29, 730–734, 793

U

Unit-price label, 858, 867
Unit prices
calculating and comparing, 861–863, 865–869
calculating without a calculator, 868
solving problems, 867–868

Unit-rate strategy, 839
Unit rate, 839, 850–851
Unit squares, 610
Units, 215, 428, 513, 926
analysis in rate problems, 839–840
area, 590, 608
cubic, 802–804
personal references, 248
square, 590–608
Unlike denominator, 556
U.S. customary system, 783, 806
Using a Magnetic Compass project, 429–432, 887–890

V

Variable, 143, 190, 468, 618, 926
Venn diagram, 28
Vertex, *plural:* vertices, 26, 37, 39, 398, 468, 791, 926
Volume, 592, 779–780, 801–806
definitions, 806
of rectangular prism, 807–812
units of, 780–781

W

Weight, 776, 782–787, 819–824
comparing mammals', 787
converting between metric and customary, 785
"What's My Rule?" problems, 170, 178, 468, 838, 849–850, 926
What's My Weight?, 775, 786
Which Soft Drink Is the Best Buy? project, 444–446, 902–904
Whole, 215, 513
fractions of, 574
"Whole" box, 514
Whole numbers, 89, 468, 926
adding and subtracting, 231
dividing, 690, 709
multiplying, 314, 665, 703
place value in, 87–92, 258–259, 320
reading, 90
rounding, 302
Width, 468, 618, 926
Work triangle, 597, 599
World globe, 408–409
making model of, 411
World map
locating places on a, 414
World Tour Project, 70, 76–81, 140–141, 166–174, 212, 240, 340–344, 405, 507, 520–521, 614, 684, 744, 781, 785–786, 840, 870–873

Y

Yardstick, 138, 171

Z

Zero
as a counting number, 260
as a placeholder, 229
decimals with, 229
in operations, 283
Zillions magazine, 864